97.00

HUMAN ECOLOGY

Collected Readings

JACK B. BRESLER

Editor

ADDISON-WESLEY · READING, MASSACHUSETTS
ADDISON-WESLEY (CANADA) LIMITED, DON MILLS, ONTARIO

This book is in the
**ADDISON-WESLEY SERIES IN
THE LIFE SCIENCES**

ADDISON-WESLEY PUBLISHING COMPANY, INC.
READING, MASSACHUSETTS · Palo Alto · London
NEW YORK · DALLAS · ATLANTA · BARRINGTON, ILLINOIS

ADDISON-WESLEY (CANADA) LIMITED
DON MILLS, ONTARIO

This book is dedicated to Beulah

Acknowledgments

We wish to thank the following for permission to reprint the papers in this volume.

American Anthropologist	(Nos. 6, 7)
American Journal of Physical Anthropology	(No. 19)
American Journal of Public Health	(Nos. 14, 16)
American Scientist	(Nos. 1, 21, 23, 27, 28)
The American Journal of Human Genetics	(No. 15)
The American Naturalist	(No. 3)
Bulletin of the Atomic Scientists	(No. 22)
California Medicine	(No. 18)
Evolution	(Nos. 8, 9, 10, 11, 12)
Fertility and Sterility (Hoeber Medical Division Harper and Row)	(No. 13)
National Academy of Sciences	(No. 17)
Nature	(No. 30)
Science	(Nos. 2, 4, 5, 20, 24, 25, 26, 29)
The Yale Review	(No. 21)

Contents

This table of contents is also a bibliography of the collected papers.

Introduction

Part I

SOME NATURAL ENVIRONMENTS OF MAN

Temperature and the Evolution of Man

Temperature and Human Reproduction

The Land and Disease Patterns

Altitude

Cycles in Man

Part II

SOME ENVIRONMENTAL FACTORS
DEVELOPED BY MAN

Man in Space

Introduction

Human life exists in many environments. Some natural environments bring benefit to man; others may kill him. Some man-made environments, in the same way, may be beneficial to human life; others may be lethal.

This book is a collection of papers dealing with environments of human beings and their subsequent adaptation or lack of adaptation to those environments. The first of the major divisions consists of papers which are concerned with the natural environments of man. These represent long-term or historical problems. Human life has been determined (although it is somewhat unfashionable to use the word "determinism" nowadays) by the position of the continents and the seas, the water supplies, temperature, light, soil, oxygen pressure, and even the uterine environment.

The second division contains papers on man-made environmental factors. In general these represent the newer problems. There are references to the consequences of large population numbers, nuclear bomb developments, medical use of x-rays, cigarette smoking, automobile exhaust, and, finally, the space capsule.

Sometimes it was difficult to decide in which category a paper belonged, according to the classification used in this collection. Obviously they were placed in the position which in my judgment was most suitable.

These papers will be most useful to the student who is seeking a broad orientation to the multidisciplinary area called *human ecology*. There are many interpretations of human ecology and some readers may feel I should have included more material from economics, anthropology, nutrition, or other fields. However, I believe that virtually all will agree that the themes in this book have an important place in any overall scheme of human ecology. It will become apparent that I have tended to follow a biological or animal ecological orientation in the selection of the papers. It will also be apparent that I have tended to select those studies showing the effects of the environment upon man, rather than man's effects on his environment.

A few of the papers are highly controversial but by their publication they have helped to focus attention on an area which needed investigation. Whenever possible, literature citations of critics and supporters are listed in the Supplementary Readings.

Since these readings have an historical progression, let us start at the beginning.

J. B. B.

Boston, Massachusetts
November 1965

Part 1

SOME NATURAL ENVIRONMENTS OF MAN

CLIMATES
OF THE EARTH:
An Historical Review

It is important to recognize that climatic conditions on earth have changed in the past and are continuing to change today. The reports in this section will give an historical perspective as background for the other readings in the collection.

One question may be asked in connection with the paper by Dorf: "From the standpoint of environmental temperatures and other salient climatic conditions, could man have lived on earth at an earlier time?" The answer is a tentative yes.

SUPPLEMENTARY READINGS

BIEL, E. R., Microclimate, Bioclimatology, and Notes on Comparative Dynamic Climatology. 1961, *American Scientist,* **49:** 325–357.

DONN, WILLIAM L., and DAVID M. SHAW, Sea Level and Climate of the Past Century. 1963, *Science,* **142:** 1166–1167.

EWING, MAURICE, and WILLIAM L. DONN, A Theory of Ice Ages. 1956, *Science,* **123:** 1061–1066.

SHEPARD, FRANCIS P., Sea Level Changes in the Past 6000 Years: Possible Archeological Significance. 1964, *Science,* **143:** 574–576.

Climatic Changes
of the Past
and Present*

ERLING DORF

Inhabitants of the so-called temperate zone are quite familiar with both unusual weather and rapidly changing weather conditions. Lately, however, even the climate—that is, the composite weather conditions over a period of years—has seemed somewhat unusual and the "reality" of changing climatic conditions has become not only apparent, but even newsworthy. Some people may be old enough to have recollections of the "good old days" when the climate was different: the winters at least seemed to have been much colder and the snows much deeper than they are today. Although reliable meteorological records do not go back very far, they do seem to show that major climatic changes rather than minor fluctuations are taking place. Present conditions are warmer than they were in the latter half of the 19th century.

In terms of the remote geologic past, however, today's climate is actually unusually cold. In fact, we are still living in a "glacial age" compared to the much warmer conditions of 35 to 40 million years ago. An examination of Figure 1 will show that, since the beginning of the Cambrian Period, 500 million years ago, the earth's climate has been considerably warmer than at present about two-thirds of the time. The evidence indicates that major climatic changes from this warmer "non-glacial" to much colder "glacial" climate have occurred several times during geologic history. The world today is in one of these glacial episodes, which only a few thousand years ago was frigid enough to support an ice sheet over most of Canada and as far south as the northern United States.

* Based on the 1957 Ermine Cowles Case Memorial Lecture delivered before the Society of Sigma Xi, University of Michigan, November 13, 1957. Published in Contributions from the Museum of Paleontology, University of Michigan, Vol. XIII, No. 8, pp. 181–210, April 17, 1959. This article was also the subject of a distinguished lectureship series given under the auspices of the American Association of Petroleum Geologists in 1960.

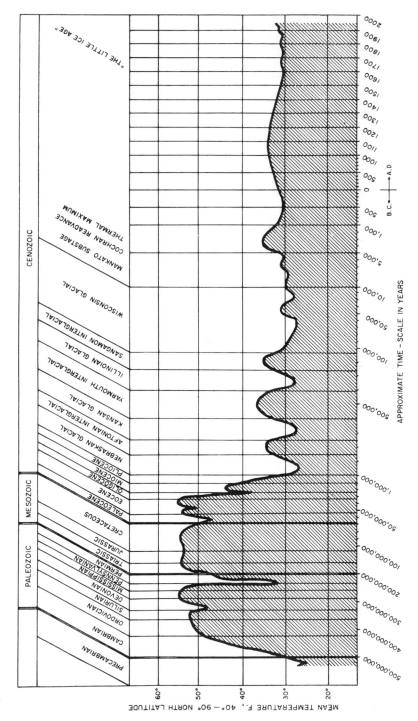

FIG. 1. Generalized temperature variations during the geologic past. After Brooks, 1951.

Furthermore, it may be noted (Fig. 1) that the cooling trend which culminated in the most recent glacial episode really started back in the Oligocene Epoch and not, as some people still believe, in the Late Pliocene.

In the present paper three major topics are discussed: (1) the climatic changes of the remote geologic past from about 50 million to about 12,000 years ago, that is, from about the beginning of the Eocene Epoch to the end of the Pleistocene "Ice Age"; (2) the climatic changes of the immediate past, from the end of the "Ice Age" to the present; and (3) a prediction of the possible climatic changes of the near future and of the next few thousand years.

Climatic changes of the geologic past

Methods of Study: One may ask how is it possible for geologists to reconstruct climates of thousands or even millions of years ago? Since climates are conditions and not, therefore, subject to fossilization, the evidence for depicting ancient climates must come entirely by inference from whatever clues are available in the geologic record. Throughout their work geologists rely at the outset on the doctrine that the present is the key to the past. It is supposed that fossil plants and animals lived under approximately the same climatic conditions as their most closely related living relatives. In this respect assemblages of fossils rather than individuals have proved to be the more reliable. Certain morphological features such as shape, size, and marginal character of fossil dicot leaves are useful. They confirm the inferences obtained through other methods. Even the rocks possess certain features which indicate that they originated under a particular kind of climate.

Fossil plant remains have, in general, proved to be the most widespread and dependable indicators of ancient climates of the earth's land areas available. This is true in large part because plants are more sensitive than animals to their environment. A comparison of any map of the world's vegetation zones with one of the world's climatic zones will show how nearly the two coincide. Plants, moreover, are stationary and they can, therefore, not migrate nor burrow underground to escape the rigors of an unfavorable season. No palms or breadfruit trees, for instance, will live in the parks of New York, Chicago, or Ann Arbor, simply because the climate is too cold or, more specifically, the winter season is too cold. Such plants represent types which can be used as climatic indicators of the past. A specimen of a palm and one of a cycad were collected from the Eocene rocks in Kupreanof Island in southeastern Alaska. These leaves were associated with the remains of laurels, magnolias, acacias, peppers, and other forms which clearly indicate conditions much warmer than exist in that region today; in fact, they were subtropical. A collection of poplars, maples, elms, and oaks would, on the contrary, indicate temperate conditions of growth; and a fossil occurrence of northern spruce, larch, alpine fir, and birch would point to subarctic (boreal) conditions.

Although the above is true, it must be emphasized that not all plants are equally valuable as climatic indicators. Some forms are too cosmopolitan; that is, they are too tolerant in their requirements. For example, pines occur in modern forests from sea level to the mountain tops and from the subtropics to the subarctic. The common brake, or bracken fern, is equally at home whether in the tropics or in temperate regions. Clearly neither fossil pines nor fossil bracken ferns would be reliable indicators of particular climates of the past. The best climatic indicators of the past are obviously those forms whose nearest living relatives have the narrowest climatic requirements in modern forests.

Generally, conclusions based on a few climatic indicators should be confirmed, whenever possible, by inferences based on the study of an entire assemblage of fossil plants. This eliminates the possibility of a few unrepresentative forms giving erroneous conclusions regarding past climates. A number of tropical families have temperate relatives which appear to be "foreigners," climatically speaking, in the temperate forests. Magnolia, for instance, which belongs to a tropical family, extends into the temperate forests as far north as Massachusetts and southern Ontario, and the persimmon and the sassafras, both members of tropical families, extend as far north as southern New England. Along the Pacific Coast the pepperwood (*Umbellularia*) is another typical temperate representative of a normally tropical family. If such forms as these were found in a fossil plant assemblage whose composition was predominantly temperate, they would be regarded as foreigners and eliminated from the list of valid climatic indicators.

In spite of the appearance of a few anomalous plants in a collection, the general facies of the total assemblage gives the only safe and reliable basis for reconstructing ancient climates. It is useful, however, to apply another, quite independent, method of determining past climatic conditions by means of certain anatomical features of plants. The majority of the deciduous leaves in forests in the humid subtropics and tropics are relatively large and smooth-margined, whereas those in temperate forests are dominantly smaller and variously lobed or toothed along their borders (Bailey and Sinnott, 1915). The arrangement and number of stomata on leaves are also helpful in determining the conditions under which the leaves developed. Since these morphological features can usually be observed in fossil leaves, their use in making paleoclimatic inferences is of great value.

Among animals used in the study of ancient climates, the marine corals, especially the reef corals, are the most reliable. Contemporary reef corals live only in the warm, clear seas of the subtropics and tropics. It is, therefore a fair assumption that closely related reef corals, when found as fossils, likewise indicate warm, clear seas at the time they lived. The fossilized remains of alligators and crocodiles, manatees, and tapirs are generally regarded as proof of subtropical to tropical conditions, whereas the recovery of fossil bones or skeletons of reindeer, musk oxen, walrus, or the boreal lemming points to cold, subarctic conditions. The discovery that the proportion of oxygen isotopes in the shells of marine shellfish depends upon the temperature of the sea water in which the animal built its shell has been found of value in reconstructing the changing oceanic temperatures of the past (Piggot and Urry, 1942). This last has been a particularly welcome method, because it is completely independent of the actual species, genus, or family to which the shells may belong.

Geologists have also found it possible to confirm climatic inferences by means of certain characters of associated sedimentary rocks. Lowland glacial deposits, for example, which are not too difficult to recognize, clearly indicate a past episode sufficiently cold to allow for the development of lowland ice sheets. On the other hand, reddish sedimentary rocks, generally owing their origin to the red soils called laterites, are known to form mainly under conditions having an annual temperature of at least 60°F. and 40 inches of annual rainfall (Krynine, 1949). Evaporite deposits, including salt and gypsum, usually indicate that conditions were semiarid to arid during their formation. Extensive coal deposits, even from such unlikely places as Antarctica and Spitsbergen, are generally interpreted as having accumulated during a humid, temperate to subtropical period.

The known physical conditions of a particular period of the geologic past have also been used to reconstruct ancient climates. Inferences derived from this source are based on the relative heights of continents, the relative amount of land *versus* water, the inferred direction and temperature of ocean currents, and the amount of volcanic activity. Climatic curves based on such studies approximate very closely those derived from the study of fossil organisms (Brooks, 1951, p. 1016).

In the present discussion the reconstruction of past climatic conditions is limited to those of the Cenozoic Era, which began about 70 million years ago. The record of this portion of geologic time is more complete than that of more ancient periods. Furthermore, Cenozoic fossils show closer relationships to living plants and animals than is true of older fossils; hence, comparisons of the climatic requirements of Cenozoic with living assemblages are considered more reliable.

Tertiary climates of North America

Late Eocene-Early Oligocene: The inferred climatic zones* of the Late Eocene to Early Oligocene epochs, beginning about 40 million years ago and lasting until

---

* The terminology for the climatic zones here and on the remaining figures is a slight modification of that used by climatologists and geographers: the term "temperate" is used as a general term for the zone of the middle latitude continental climates, including both the humid, warm summer and cool summer phases, the semi-arid steppe, the arid desert, and the marine, cool summer phase (during most of the Tertiary Period only the warm and cool temperate phases can be distinguished); the term "subtropical" includes the climate which many botanists refer to as "warm temperate"; for example, southeastern United States, which the majority of geographers and climatologists call "humid, subtropical" (Köppen and Geiger, 1936; Lackey, 1944).

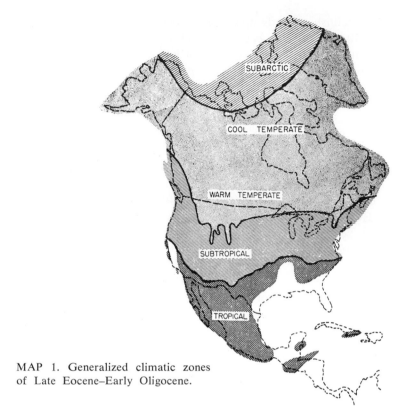

MAP 1. Generalized climatic zones
of Late Eocene–Early Oligocene.

about 30 million years ago, are illustrated in Map 1. The climatic zones of the
preceding Paleocene Epoch, though not yet as well-established, indicate somewhat cooler conditions. In both Europe and North America a general warming
trend began before the end of the Paleocene Epoch and continued into the
Eocene. As a consequence, by the end of the Eocene and continuing into the
Oligocene, the temperate forest belt in North America had shifted about 20
degrees of latitude farther north than its present position and, at the same time,
the tropical forest belt extended about 10 to 12 degrees farther north than at
present. In the Gulf Coast states, for example, there are numerous fossil remains of both Late Eocene and Early Oligocene forests whose nearest living
relatives live in the tropical lowlands of northern South America and coastal
Mexico. Fossil remains of these forests occur in widespread coastal plain
deposits as far north as Tennessee and Missouri. Both mangrove swamp and
beach jungle associations are represented. Some of the notable members of
these floras include the date palm and the East Indian Nipa palm (Berry, 1937;
Arnold, 1952). In the Cordilleran region, fossils of subtropical vegetation are
found in northern California, Oregon, Washington, and northern Wyoming. In
western Oregon, for example, Dr. Ralph W. Chaney and his students collected

a great many well-preserved leaves of Eocene age, including figs, laurels, cinnamons, avocados, and magnolias. These forms are typical of a forest dominated by large, smooth-margined dicot leaves whose nearest living equivalents are found in the lowlands of Central America (Chaney and Sanborn, 1933). Remains of this same forest occur also in the Eocene rocks of the John Day Basin of eastern Oregon, where the living desert vegetation presents a striking contrast to the lush, subtropical forest recorded in the rocks. Fossilized remains of marine faunas along the Pacific Coast confirm the northward extension of warmer tropical climate during the Eocene (Durham, 1950).

Numerous fossil remains of a forest transitional between subtropical and warm temperate are found in Late Eocene–Early Oligocene deposits of British Columbia as well as on Kupreanof Island in southeastern Alaska. Modern equivalents of this transitional forest, which included palms and cycads, lie more than 20° in latitude south of their Eocene occurrences. Farther east among the spruces, firs, and quaking aspens of the present-day boreal forest of Yellowstone Park, Wyoming, my own field parties have collected many Middle Eocene fossils of lowland, warmth-loving forms, such as breadfruit, laurels, figs, and magnolias in association with more temperate elements, such as true redwoods, hickories, maples, and oaks. Southeast of Yellowstone Park, a Late Eocene flora is closely related to the subtropical forests of the same age in Oregon and California (Dorf, 1953). Fossil bones of subtropical alligators have also been found in rocks of this age as far north as central Wyoming. In the eastern states the Brandon fossil flora of Vermont—largely made up of seeds, fruits, and pollens—is interpreted as transitional between the warm temperate and subtropical forests of this age (Traverse, 1955, pp. 21–34). Further south along the Atlantic coast, the bryozoans of the Eocene deposits of New Jersey indicate subtropical marine waters. Truly warm temperate forests, dominated by such forms as dawn redwoods, maples, beeches, oaks, sycamores, and basswoods, are widely recorded in rocks of this age in the belt extending from central Alaska to west-central Greenland and eastward to Spitsbergen and Siberia (Chaney, 1947). In Greenland the fossil-leaf beds occur on the bleak Arctic wastes of Disco Island, almost within sight of the glacial mantle of ice covering the mainland. Today the stunted vegetation, with prostrate willows and dwarf birches, is striking witness to the hardships of the polar climate and contrasts vividly with the cool temperate aspect of the fossil forests. Fossil remains of subarctic boreal forests, including spruces, pines, willows, hazels, and birches, have been found in the rocks of Late Eocene age as far north as Grinnell Land, only 8.5° from the North Pole (Berry, 1930, p. 10). There is no evidence of either a polar ice cap or a continental ice sheet on Greenland during this portion of geologic time. On the other hand, neither is there any evidence to support the view, unfortunately still often expressed, that the polar regions above the Arctic Circle supported subtropical or tropical forests during this time, or at any time, for that matter.

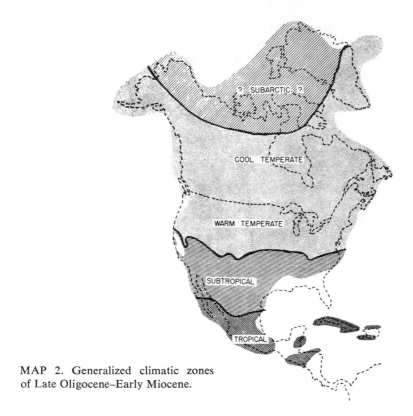

MAP 2. Generalized climatic zones
of Late Oligocene–Early Miocene.

Late Oligocene–Early Miocene: By the end of the Oligocene and the beginning of the Miocene Epoch, about 25 million years ago, the older subtropical
forests of the Pacific Northwest had been replaced by warm temperate equivalents of the redwood forest association of the California Coast Ranges (Map 2).
In eastern Oregon, for example, the Late Oligocene Bridge Creek flora from the
John Day Basin contains numerous remains of a forest which included dawn redwoods, alders, maples, pepperwoods, dogwoods, tan oaks, hazels, and sycamores.
This assemblage is essentially similar in its generic composition to the Late
Eocene forest of central Alaska (Chaney, 1947). Its gradual southward shift
in position during the course of 12 to 15 million years had apparently been
accomplished without any major changes in its characteristic physiognomy.
Eastward as far as the Dakotas the older subtropical forests appear to have
moved to the south, with their places taken by warm temperate forests. This
replacement was already under way earlier in the Oligocene Epoch, as is illustrated by the Middle Oligocene Ruby Basin flora of southwestern Montana
which records a warm temperate forest dominated by dawn redwoods, oaks,
beeches, maples, alders, and ash (Becker, 1916). Farther south in central
Colorado the Florissant flora of the same age is an association of true red-

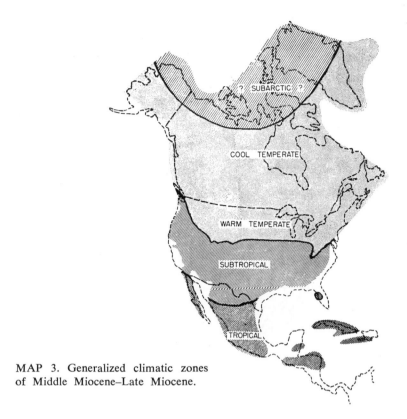

MAP 3. Generalized climatic zones
of Middle Miocene–Late Miocene.

woods and warm temperate hardwoods, in which there was a small lingering
subtropical element as well as a few xeric forms (MacGinitie, 1953, pp. 36–
42). Fossil records indicate that it was at this time that open woodland scrub
and grasslands were beginning to develop in the lowland areas of the eastern
Rockies and the Great Plains. In the southeastern United States the Oligocene
Vicksburg flora, though small, is interpreted as a subtropical strand-line association (Berry, 1937). In marine deposits of Oligocene age, reef corals are
known from as far north as 51.5° N. Lat. (at present their northern limit is
about 32° N. Lat.).

Middle Miocene–Late Miocene.   By the Middle to Late Miocene Epoch, about
18 to 12 million years ago, the fossil plant record of western North America
indicates a slight reversal of forest migrations (Map 3). A small subtropical
element, which included palmettos, avocados, mahogany, and lancewood, returned north at least as far as Oregon and Washington (shown in the Mascall
and Latah floras; Chaney, 1938, p. 387). Other members of these two floras
were of typically warm temperature aspect. From northern Mexico an element
of hardy drought-resistant shrubs and chaparral moved north into southern

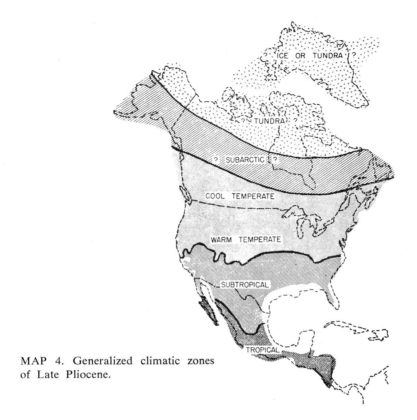

MAP 4. Generalized climatic zones
of Late Pliocene.

California and the Great Basin regions, where there was a marked development
of semiarid steppes (Axelrod, 1940). Fossil fish remains from the Miocene of
southern California point to subtropical marine conditions that lasted well into
the Late Miocene (David, 1943, pp. 47, 87, 96, 113, 174). Some time before
the close of the Miocene Epoch, or early in the Pliocene, the climate began to
change again and the cooling trend was resumed. In the Great Plains area the
Miocene fossil record indicates a gradual development and spread of open
grasslands and savannahs at the expense of true forests (Elias, 1942, pp. 15–18).
Farther east the Miocene forests of the Virginia area were similar to the South
Atlantic and Gulf Coast swamp forests of the present day. The Mid-Miocene
deposits of Virginia have yielded bones of the southern manatee and crocodiles;
neither of these warm-water animals occur north of Florida today. In the
southern states the Miocene forests show a continuing replacement of tropical
elements by subtropical and warm temperate forms (Berry, 1937).

Late Pliocene. Near the end of the Pliocene Epoch, about 2 million years
ago, the fossil records of forest distribution indicate an approach toward present
climatic conditions (Map 4). Along the west coast of the United States, as
a result of the cooling trend, the southward shifting of forest belts had con-

tinued since the Late Miocene trend. Major topographic changes brought about by the Cascadian mountain-building revolution produced a great variety of habitats and exerted a stronger influence than previously on the distribution of floral associations. Desert vegetation developed in the Great Basin and the interior of northern Mexico because of lower rainfall and greater seasonal temperature ranges (Chaney, 1944; Axelrod, 1944). Grasslands in the Great Plains appear to have reached essentially their modern aspect and distribution. In the southeastern states, Pliocene floras were wholly modern in general facies and were made up of species whose living forms are mostly native to the same region today (Berry, 1937).

Corroborative evidence

The inferred trend from warmer conditions in the Eocene Epoch to much cooler conditions in the Pliocene has been amply substantiated by certain characters of the fossil leaves. In the Eocene floras of North American middle latitudes the dominantly large, smooth-margined leaves with elongate tips indicate humid subtropical to tropical conditions. But such leaf forms are gradually replaced in the succeeding Oligocene, Miocene, and Pliocene Epochs by the smaller, toothed, or lobed leaves characteristic of more temperate conditions. This gradual cooling off has been further confirmed by study of the sequence of Tertiary marine faunas of the Pacific states (Durham, 1950). A drop in oceanic temperatures during the Tertiary has also been inferred from the gradual equatorward shifts of the northern limits of coral reefs and a gradual change in oxygen isotope ratios in shells of bottom-dwelling foraminifera from the mid-Pacific (Emiliani, 1954). On land, the record of the Tertiary mammals of western North America shows essentially the same general cooling of the climate (Colbert, 1953, pp. 266–70).

Tertiary climates of Western Europe

In western Europe, for comparison, the fossil record of both plants and animals indicates the same climatic trend from essentially tropical conditions in the Eocene to progressively cooler and cooler conditions to the end of the Pliocene (Reid and Chandler, 1933, pp. 50–59) and, as in North America, the episode of maximum warmth occurred in the Eocene Epoch. Both fossil plants and invertebrates reveal that the preceding Paleocene Epoch started with a somewhat cooler climate. A gradually warming trend began before the middle Paleocene and continued into the Eocene. The Eocene episode of maximum warmth is well illustrated by the tropical flora of the Eocene London Clay. This fossil flora, obtained from a region lying at about 50° N. Lat., finds its nearest living counterpart at about 10° N. Lat. in the lowland tropical rainforest of the Indo-Malayan region. The remains of alligators, crocodiles, the pearly nautilus, and large warm-water volutes in Eocene marine deposits of western Europe indicate subtropical-to-tropical marine waters far north of their present limits. Plant remains of the Eocene forests of Spitsbergen, collected about 11 to 13 degrees from the North Pole, include species of beech, sycamore, linden, oak, and water lilies—an assemblage whose modern equivalents are among the dominants of the temperate forests and lakes that now live 15 to 20 degrees farther south on the Continent (Heer, 1868, pp. 60–62). The fossil plant record of western Europe shows that a gradual change from the tropical conditions of the Eocene to subtropical in the Oligocene and warm temperate in the Miocene took place. This cooling trend apparently continued into the succeeding Pliocene Epoch, which ended with a climate believed to have been quite similar to the cool temperate conditions of western Europe at the present time. The annual mean temperature of the region is estimated to have dropped about 15°C. from the Eocene to the end of the Pliocene.

The gradual cooling off of western Europe during the Tertiary Period is further confirmed by the relative proportions of woody to herbaceous plants in the geologic sequence. The proportion of woody species shows a downward progression from 97 percent in the Eocene London Clay to 57 in the Oligocene, and to 22 in the Late Pliocene. Twenty-two percent compares closely with the figure of 17 percent for the woody species now in the region (Reid and Chandler, 1933, p. 53). This reduction in the course of time parallels the geographical reduction noted in living forests, from about 88 percent woody species in the tropical lowlands of the Amazon Basin to about 10 percent in the subarctic vegetation of Iceland.

Independent studies of Tertiary marine invertebrates and fishes, and of terrestrial insects, corroborate the climatic inferences based on fossil plants (Davies, 1934; Theobald, 1952; Schwarzbach, 1950). Evidence from the rocks themselves, the Tertiary laterites of Europe, has led to the same general conclusions regarding climatic changes as have the studies based on the fossil record (Harassowitz, 1926, pp. 544–88).

Quaternary climates

Glacial: In the Pleistocene, or "Glacial," Epoch the cooling trend, which had begun in the Oligocene Epoch, led to the formation and slow spread of lowland ice sheets in higher latitudes. Beneath the ice all plant and animal life was obviously obliterated. As the ice sheets spread southward from central Canada the extreme glacial climate caused a farther and more rapid southward shift of the forests south of the ice margins. Just how far south the forests were driven is a matter of debate. For many years both paleobotanists and botanists have believed that forest belts shifted only slightly (Berry, 1956, p. 99; Braun, 1950, pp. 458–72), but evidence for major forest migrations over wide distances has

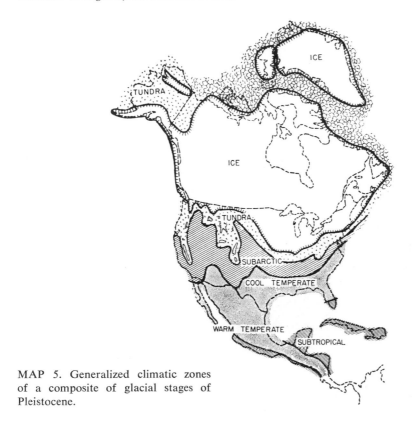

MAP 5. Generalized climatic zones
of a composite of glacial stages of
Pleistocene.

been accumulating during the past decade (Deevey, 1949, pp. 1360–66, 1375;
Frey, 1953; Martin, 1958). The latter view is that supported here (*cf.* Map 5).

There are numerous Pleistocene records of both subarctic plants and animals
far to the south in North America. Occurrences of northern spruce and fir are
found in the lowlands of northern and central Florida, southcentral Texas,
northern Oklahoma, and southern Kansas (Deevey, 1949, pp. 1360–61; Davis,
1946; Potzger and Tharp, 1947). Cones of white spruce and Canadian larch,
twigs of the northern arbor vitae, and the delicate remains of two species of
northern mosses have been recorded in southeastern Louisiana, up to 1000 miles
south of their present southern limits (Fisk, Richards, Brown, and Steere, 1938).
Fir and northern pines occur on the coastal plain of North Carolina and larch in
southeastern Georgia (Buell, 1945). Cold-temperate diatoms, whose living
forms are characteristic of New England and eastern Canada, are abundant in
northern and central Florida (Hanna, 1933). In southern California there is a
Pleistocene record of a kind of vegetation now found growing between 8 and 10
degrees farther north along the coast. A possible indirect effect of the shifting
of temperate forests as far south as shown on Map 5 is the presence today in the

MAP 6. Generalized climatic zones
of a composite of interglacial stages of
Pleistocene.

mountains and high plateaus of Mexico and Central America of remnants of the
typical warm temperature to subtropical association normal to the lowlands
farther north in the United States.

Among the vertebrates, the records of musk oxen as far south as Mississippi,
Texas, Oklahoma, and southern California indicate a considerable southward
shift, as does the record of reindeer in southeastern Kentucky, Iowa, and central
Nevada. Wooly mammoth remains are known from as far south as west-central
Florida and southern Texas. Walrus bones have been found along the Atlantic
coast as far as South Carolina and Georgia, over 1000 miles south of the
southern limit of the modern walrus (Hay, 1923). Fossils of the northern
moose are recorded from Oklahoma, Kentucky, and South Carolina. Conies,
which live above timberline in the Rocky Mountains at the present time, occur
as fossils in the Pleistocene deposits of Pennsylvania and Maryland. Fossils
of western marmots are found from 2500 to 4500 feet below their present
lower limit in central New Mexico (Deevey, 1949, pp. 1374–75; Stearns, 1942).

Among the invertebrates there is a record of a cold-water assemblage in
southern California and of subarctic Foraminifera as far south as the Sigsbee
Deep in the middle of the Gulf of Mexico (Trask, Phleger, and Stetson, 1947).

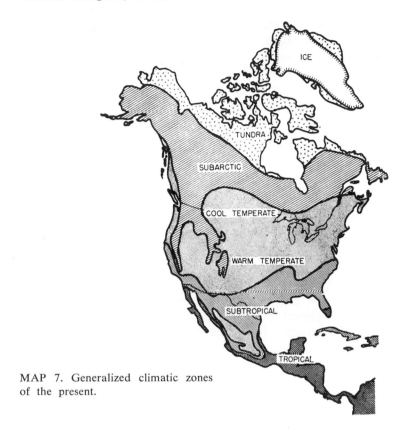

MAP 7. Generalized climatic zones
of the present.

In western Europe extensive records of both faunas and floras of glacial age
show that subarctic (boreal) conditions extended south as far as the shores and
adjacent lowlands of the Mediterranean.

Interglacial: Alternating with the glacial stages were the interglacial. During
several of these the climates appear to have been somewhat warmer than today
(Maps 6 and 7); as the ice sheets melted away, a rapid northward shift of the
forests took place, extending them into the newly exposed glaciated wastelands
of the north. At Toronto, for example, both the plants and invertebrates of the
late interglacial age indicate conditions about 2 to 3°C. higher than today
(Flint, 1957, p. 340); the plant remains include the pawpaw, red cedar, and
osage orange, whose northern limits are now several hundred miles south of
Toronto. On the Seward Peninsula of Alaska occurrence of fossil plants of an
early interglacial age indicate a climate both warmer and more humid than in
the same region today (Hopkins and Benninghoff, 1953). Cape Cod has a
record of an interglacial forest similar to that of present-day Virginia and North
Carolina. On Long Island an interglacial shellfish fauna points to water
temperatures higher than now in the region, and in New Jersey the record of a

manatee indicates conditions like those off the present coastline of Florida. In Pennsylvania there are interglacial records of tapirs of Central American aspect and of peccaries whose nearest living relatives range only as far north as Arizona, New Mexico, and Texas. Farther west, in southwestern Kansas, interglacial records of a Gulf Coast box turtle and the rice rat point to conditions warmer than at present (Hibbard, 1955, p. 202). Sediment cores from the bottom of the Atlantic Ocean show layers of interglacial deposits with the remains of Foraminifera of warmer waters than those of the region today (Bradley, 1940).

Climatic changes of the near past and present

The knowledge of climatic changes since the last of the ice sheets (the Cochran readvance) depends in part upon the fossil record and in part on archeological and historical records. On the basis of the pollen record there was a period of somewhat higher temperatures than today (the so-called Thermal Maximum or Hypsithermal), which lasted from about 5000 to 2000 B.C. (Fig. 1). This was apparently followed by a general cooling, which reached a minimum in about 500 B.C., and a subsequent rise in temperature. Archeological records indicate that the last major warm episode before the present occurred about 1000 to 1300 A.D. During this time a colony of about 3000 Norsemen grew crops and raised both cattle and sheep in southwestern Greenland (Ahlmann, 1949, p. 165) and vineyards were productive as far north as southern England. Beginning in about 1600, however, the climate began to change toward cooler conditions. Glaciers in the northern hemisphere began to readvance; in the Alps several valley settlements were completely overrun by advancing valley glaciers. This cooling episode led to the so-called "Little Ice Age," which lasted from about 1650 to about 1850. Since 1850 the general climatic trend has been toward warmer conditions.

In broad retrospect, then, where do we find ourselves today, near the middle of the twentieth century, in the everchanging pattern of climatic cycles? In the first place, it is quite clear that for the past million years or so (up to and including the present time) the earth has been subjected, geologically speaking, to an abnormally cold climate (see Fig. 1). The greater part of at least the last 500 million years, however, has had a warmer, nonglacial climate rather than the colder glacial climate of the past million years. In the second place, it is evident that the earth is not in one of the truly frigid glacial stages, but is rather in one of the slightly warmer interglacial stages, that it is perhaps about two-thirds of the way out of the last glacial stage, so to speak. By comparison with the long duration of past interglacial and glacial episodes in earth history, it is generally believed that we shall return to another glacial stage in about 10,000 to 15,000 years. Such a prospect, with its accompanying ice sheets devastating northern lands and settlements is not a happy one to contemplate in terms of physical, economic, or political consequences.

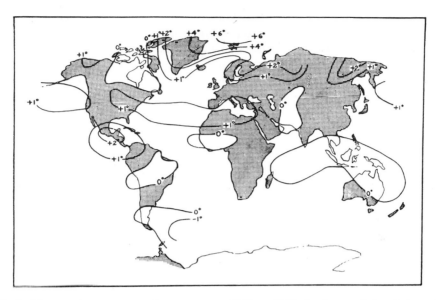

FIG. 2. Changes in mean annual temperature, 1920 to 1940, in degrees Fahrenheit. After Willett, 1950.

In the meantime we are apparently well along in a general world-wide warming trend (Fig. 2). In the United States the rise in mean annual temperature, since 1920, has been about 3.5°F., and the rise in winter temperatures has been about twice as much as that in summer temperatures (Visher, 1954, Part VII). In Boston, winter temperatures are about 3.5°F. higher than they were a hundred years ago. In Philadelphia the temperature has risen more than 3°F. since 1880, and in Montreal more than 2.5°F. since 1850. In the years between 1931 and 1952 New Jersey's mean annual temperature has been above normal 18 years, below normal 3 years, and normal only 1 year; Michigan's temperature in the same interval has been above normal 15 years and below only 7 years. The U.S. Weather Bureau (1953) reported that, during the same period, all but 8 of the 48 states had annual temperatures which were above normal the majority of the years; those which were below normal during most of the years were the three Pacific coast states (California, Oregon, and Washington), four of the western states (Arizona, Idaho, New Mexico, and Montana), and one southern state (Texas). In both the Middle West and the Great Plains, the records of cities such as St. Louis and Kansas City indicate a similar rise in temperatures: 1.9°F. for the former since 1880, and 1.4°F. for the latter since 1894 (Oltmann and Tracy, 1951, p. 17). It has been observed, however, that the greatest temperature increases during the last hundred years have been in the Arctic regions (Fig. 2). In Spitsbergen, only about 10 to 12 degrees from the North Pole, the mean winter temperatures have risen about 14°F. since 1910 (Willett, 1950). Ice-free ports there are now open to navigation about 7 months of the year as compared with only 3 months fifty years ago (Ahlmann, 1953, p. 32). If the warming trend of the north polar region should continue at its present rate, it has been estimated that the entire Arctic Ocean would be navigable all year long within about a hundred years. At the opposite end of the world, according to recent reports from the Weather Bureau (Wexler, 1958), the Antarctic region has undergone a rise of about 5°F. in average temperature in the last fifty years. There has been no appreciable rise, however, in the mean annual temperatures in the tropical regions of the world.

What have been some of the notable results of this warming trend during the last hundred years? Glaciers throughout the world have been melting away at a rapidly increasing rate. Brooks, the eminent British paleoclimatologist, stated (1949, p. 24), that "Since the beginning of the 20th Century glaciers have been wasting away rapidly, or even catastrophically." In the Juneau region of Alaska, all but one of the numerous glaciers began melting away as far back as 1765. Muir Glacier, for example, has retreated as much as two miles in 10 years. Baird and Sharp (1954, p. 143) have referred to the "alarming retreat of glaciers" in the Alaskan region; along the Pacific Coast of North America and in Europe they believe the glacial melting "appears to be progressing violently." In the north polar region, measurements of melting of the ice islands in the Arctic Sea indicate an approach toward an open polar sea (Crary, Kulp, and Marshall, 1955). In only a few regions of the world, such as the Pacific Northwest, are there any records of glaciers advancing during the past century, and these have been mostly since 1950 (Hubley, 1956). The warmer temperatures have also caused a general rise of the snow line throughout the mountainous regions of the world, even in the tropics: in northern Peru it has risen about 2700 feet during the 60 years.

Believed in large part to be the result of the melting of the world's glaciers, sea level has been rising at a rapidly increasing rate, amounting to as much as a 6-inch rise from 1930 to 1948 (Marmar, 1948). This is about four times the average rate of sea level rise during the past 9000 years, as recorded by Shepard and Suess (1956). It should be noted that more than a sixfold increase in the rate of sea level rise occured in the mid-1920's at the same time that there was a striking change in the rate of glacial melting in the north (Ahlmann, 1953, Fig. 11).

Changes in vegetation brought about by the warmer temperatures include the encroachment of trees into the subpolar tundra as recorded in Alaska, Quebec, Labrador, and Siberia. In the Canadian prairies the agricultural crop line has shifted from 50 to 100 miles northward as a result of the lengthening of the growing season by as much as ten days. In parts of northern New England and eastern Canada the birch trees have been dying off over large areas, and the spruces and balsams have begun to suffer as a result of the rise in summer temperatures. In Sweden the timberline has moved up the mountain slopes as much as 65 feet since 1930 (Ahlmann, 1953, p. 35).

In the animal world many southern types of both birds and mammals have been extending their habitat ranges northward as a result of the warming trend. The cardinal, the turkey vulture, the tufted titmouse, and the blue-winged warbler, as well as the warmth-loving opossum, have slowly moved their ranges into the northern United States. A good many central European species of animals have been shifting their limits northward into Scandinavia, Greenland, Iceland, and the Faeroe Islands. Twenty-five species of birds alone are reported to have invaded Greenland from the south since 1918 (Jensen and Fristrup, 1950). Codfish from the Atlantic have replaced the seals in the waters along the coast of Greenland. It is reported that compared to a shipment of 5 tons of codfish from Greenland in 1913, the 1946 shipment had risen to over 13,000 tons; the Greenland Eskimos have become cod fishermen instead of seal fishermen (Kimble, 1950). Farther south, tunafish have moved northward into the waters off New England, and tropical flying fishes have become increasingly common off the coast of New Jersey.

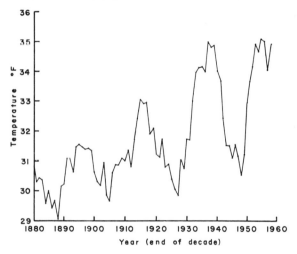

FIG. 3. January temperatures in New York City, 1871 to 1958, ten-year running means. After Spar, 1954.

In spite of its numerous and striking effects, the warming trend of the past hundred years has not been world-wide nor uniform in direction. Over most of the northern hemisphere there have been rather regular cyclic fluctuations from warmer spells to colder spells, each lasting a decade or so. Most of the eastern and central United States is at present in a decade that is somewhat colder than the one which ended in 1955. These shorter cyclic fluctuations are observable in both summer and winter temperatures. As shown in Figure 3, for example, the ten-year averages of January temperatures in New York City show colder 10- to 11-year cycles followed quite regularly by warmer 10- to

11-year cycles since at least 1880 (Spar, 1954). Even here it may be noted that the trend is upward, that is, the average temperatures of the last few decades have been warmer than those of the decades prior to 1900. Certain regions of the world, moreover, have actually experienced a cooling trend during the time that most of the rest of the world was warming up. Such regions (Fig. 2) include the Hudson Bay Region, the west coast of North America, central South America, and the East Indies (Willett, 1950).

Possible climatic changes of the near future

The usefulness of observations from the past has been demonstrated in many fields to be of real value in the forecasting of events in the future. In the words of Byron, "The best prophet of the future is the past." Unfortunately, as one is reminded much too often, the forecasting of either weather or climate on the basis of past performance is notoriously even less reliable than predicting the future actions of human beings or race horses. Several climatologists expressed the opinion, in the late 1940's, that the 1930–1940 decade marked the culmination of the trend toward higher temperatures, and that a reversal of the trend had begun. In the middle 1950's, when it had become quite obvious that the reversal had not occurred and that the rising temperatures had continued after a short colder cycle, opinions were revised to the effect that it was the 1940–1950 decade which marked the maximum of the warming trend, which was due for a reversal. Other climatologists have stated their belief that the present warming episode will continue for at least a few centuries. Brooks (1949, p. 24), in his forecast of the future, stated that the melting of the world's glaciers "may be expected to continue until either the reduced ice-cap reaches a new position of stability, or until some meteorological 'accident' reverses the trend and ushers in a new period of re-advance."

Extrapolation of the known climatic curves into the future is one of the more reasonable approaches to the prediction of posible future trends. Such extrapolation suggests (1) that the earth is at present still in an interglacial stage but heading toward another glacial stage, perhaps 10,000 to 15,000 years hence; (2) that the winters are getting slightly colder again and should continue to average colder until about 1965; and (3) that though marked by minor alternating colder and warmer cycles, the general trend of increasing warmth should continue for at least two or three hundred years over most of the lowland regions of the northern hemisphere.

REFERENCES

AHLMANN, H. W. 1949. The Present Climatic Fluctuation. *Journ. Geog.,* vol. *112,* pp. 165–93.

———, 1953. Glacier Variations and Climatic Fluctuations. Amer. Geog. Soc., Bowman Mem. Lectures. ser. 3, pp. 1–51.

ARNOLD, CHESTER A. 1952. Tertiary Plants from North America. *Palaeobotanist,* vol. *1,* pp. 73–78.

AXELROD, DANIEL I. 1940. Late Tertiary Floras of the Great Basin and Border Areas. *Bull. Torrey Bot. Club.* vol. *67,* pp. 477–87.

———, 1944. Pliocene Sequence in Central California. Chap. 8 *in:* Pliocene Floras of California, by R. W. Chaney. Carnegie Instit. Wash. Publ., No. 553, pp. 207–24.

BAILEY, I. W., and SINNOTT, E. W. 1915. A Botanical Index of Cretaceous and Tertiary Climates. *Science,* vol. *41,* pp. 831–34.

BAIRD, P. D., and SHARP, R. P. 1954. Glaciology. *Arctic,* vol. 7, nos. 3–4, pp. 141–52.

BECKER, HERMAN F. 1916. An Oligocene Flora from the Ruby River Basin in Southwestern Montana. Univ. Mich. Microfilm Publ., No. 1956. (Doctoral Dissertation.)

BERRY, E. W. 1956. Pleistocene Plants from North Carolina. U.S. Geol. Surv., Prof. Paper No. 140-C, pp. 97–120.

———, 1930. The Past Climate of the North Polar Region. *Smithsonian Misc. Coll.,* vol. *82,* no. 6, pp. 1–29.

———, 1937. Tertiary Floras of Eastern North America. *Bot. Rev.,* vol. *3,* pp. 31–46.

BRADLEY, WILMOT H. 1940. *Geology and Climatology from the Ocean Abyss. Sci. Mon.,* vol. *50,* no. 2, pp. 97–109.

BRAUN, E. LUCY. 1950. Deciduous Forests of Eastern North America. Phila.: Blakiston. 533 pp.

BROOKS, C. E. P. 1949. Post-glacial Climatic Changes in the Light of Recent Glaciological Research. *Geog. Ann.,* vol. *31,* pp. 21–24.

———, 1951. Geological and Historical Aspects of Climate Change. *In:* Compendium of Meteorology, Thomas F. Malone, ed. Boston: American Meteorological Society, pp. 1004–1018.

BUELL, MURRAY F. 1945. Late Pleistocene Forests of Southeastern North Carolina. *Torreya,* vol. *45,* pp. 117–18.

CHANEY, RALPH W. 1938. Paleoecological Interpretations of Cenozoic Plants in Western North America. *Bot. Rev.,* vol. *4,* pp. 371–96.

———, 1944. Pliocene Floras of California and Oregon. Carnegie Instit. Wash. Publ., No. 553, pp. 353–73, summary and conclusions.

———, 1947. Tertiary Centers and Migration Routes. *Ecol. Monogr.,* vol. *17,* pp. 139–48.

———, and SANBORN, ETHEL I. 1933. The Goshen Flora of West Central Oregon. Carnegie Instit. Wash. Publ., No. 439.

COLBERT, EDWIN H. 1953. The Record of Climatic Changes as Revealed by Vertebrate Paleoecology. *In:* Climatic Change, H. Shapley, ed. Cambridge: Harvard Univ. Press, pp. 249–71.

CRARY, A. P., KULP, J. L., and MARSHALL, E. W. 1955. Evidences of Climatic Change From Ice Island Studies. *Science,* vol. *122*, pp. 1171–73.

DAVID, L. R. 1943. Miocene Fishes of Southern California. Geol. Soc. Amer., Spec. Paper, No. 43. 193 pp.

DAVIES, A. MORLEY. 1934. *Tertiary Faunas,* vol. *2*. London: Murby. 252 pp.

DAVIS, JOHN H., JR. 1946. The Peat Deposits of Florida, Their Occurrence, Development and Uses. Florida Geol. Surv., Geol. Bull. No. 30, pp. 1–247.

DEEVEY, E. S., JR. 1949. Biogeography of the Pleistocene. Pt. I. Europe and North America. *Bull. Geol. Soc. Amer.,* vol. *60*, pp. 1315–1416.

DORF, ERLING. 1953. Succession of Eocene Floras in Northwestern Wyoming. *Bull. Geol. Soc. Amer.,* vol. *64*, p. 1413.

DURHAM, J. R. 1950. Cenozoic Marine Climates of the Pacific Coast. *Bull. Geol. Soc. Amer.,* vol. *61*, pp. 1243–64.

ELIAS, MAXIM K. 1942. Tertiary Prairie Grasses and Other Herbs from the High Plains. *Geol. Soc. Amer.,* Special Paper, No. 41, pp. 1–176.

EMILIANI, CESARE. 1954. Temperatures of Pacific Bottom Waters and Polar Superficial Waters during the Tertiary. *Science,* vol. *119*, pp. 853–55.

FISK, H. N., RICHARDS, H. F., BROWN, C. A., and STEERE, W. C. 1938. Contributions to the Pleistocene History of the Florida Parishes of Louisiana. Louisiana Dept. Conserv. Geol. Bull. No. 12, pp. 1–137.

FLINT, R. F. 1957. Glacial and Pleistocene Geology. New York: John Wiley & Sons. 553 pp.

FREY, DAVID G. 1953. Regional Aspects of the Late-glacial and Post-glacial Pollen Succession of Southeastern North Carolina. *Ecol. Monogr.,* vol. *23*, pp. 289–313.

HANNA, G. DALLAS. 1933. Diatoms of the Florida Peat Deposits. Florida State Geol. Surv., 23rd–24th Ann. Rept. 1930–32, pp. 68–119.

HARASSOWITZ, HERMANN. 1926. Laterit. Fortschritte der Geol. und Palæont., Bd. 4, Heft 14, pp. 253–566.

HAY, O. P. 1923. The Pleistocene of North America and Its Vertebrated Animals from the States East of the Mississippi River and from the Canadian Provinces East of Longitude 95°. Carnegie Instit. Wash. Publ., No. 322, pp. 1–499.

HEER, OSWALD. 1868. Die Fossile Flora der Polarländer. *Flora Fossiles Arctica,* vol. *1*, pp. 1–192.

HIBBARD, C. W. 1955. The Jinglebob Interglacial (Sangamon?) Fauna from Kansas and Its Climatic Significance. *Contrib. Mus. Paleontol. Univ. Mich.,* vol. *12*, No. 10, pp. 179–228.

HOPKINS, D. M., and BENNINGHOFF, W. S. 1953. Evidence of a Very Warm Pleistocene Interglacial Interval on Seward Peninsula, Alaska. Abstract *in: Bull. Geol. Soc. Amer.,* vol. *64*, pp. 1435–36.

HUBLEY, RICHARD C. 1956. Glaciers of the Washington Cascade and Olympic Mountains; their Present Activity and Its Relation to Local Climatic Trends. *Journ. Glaciol.,* vol. *2*, No. 19, pp. 669–74.

JENSEN, AD. S., and FRISTRUP, B. 1950. Den Arktiske Klimaforandring og dens Betydning, saerlig for Grönland. *Geog. Tidskr.,* vol. *50*, pp. 20–47.

KIMBLE, C. H. T. 1950. The Changing Climate, *Sci. Amer.,* vol. *182*, No. 4, pp. 48–53.

KÖPPEN, W., and GEIGER, R. 1936. *Handbuch der Klimatologie,* vol. *2*, Pt. J.

KRYNINE, PAUL. 1949. Origin of Red Beds. *New York Acad. Sci.*, ser. 2, vol. *11*, No. 3, pp. 60–68.

LACKEY, E. E. 1944. The Pattern of Climates. *In:* Global Geography, by George T. Renner and Associates. New York: Crowell. 714 pp.

MACGINITIE, HARRY D. 1953. Fossil Plants of the Florissant Beds, Colorado. Carnegie Instit. Wash. Publ. No. 599, pp. 1–188.

MARMAR, H. A. 1948. Is the Atlantic Coast Sinking? The Evidence from the Tide. *Geog. Rev.*, vol. *38*, pp. 652–57.

MARTIN, P. S. 1958. Pleistocene Ecology and Biogeography of North America. Zoogeography, Amer. Assoc. Adv. Science.

OLTMANN, R. E., and TRACY, H. J. 1951. Trends in Climate and in Precipitation— Runoff in Missouri River Basin. U.S. Geol. Surv., Circ. 98, pp. 1–113.

PIGGOT, C. S., and URRY, W. D. 1942. Time Relations in Ocean Sediments. *Bull. Geol. Soc. Amer.*, vol. *53*, pp. 1187–1210.

POTZGER, JOHN E., and THARP, B. C. 1947. Pollen Profile from a Texas Bog. *Ecology*, vol. *28*, pp. 274–80.

REID, ELEANOR M., and CHANDLER, M. E. J. 1933. The London Clay Flora. London: Brit. Mus. (Nat. Hist.). 561 pp.

SCHWARZBACH, M. 1950. Das Klima der Vorzeit. Stuttgart: Ferdinand Enke. 211 pp.

SHEPARD, F. P., and SUESS, H. E. 1956. Rate of Postglacial Rise of Sea Level. *Science*, vol. *123*, pp. 1082–83.

SPAR, JEROME. 1954. Temperature Trends in New York City. *Weatherwise*, vol. *7*, No. 6, pp. 149–51.

STEARNS, CHARLES E. 1942. A Fossil Marmot from New Mexico and Its Climatic Significance. *Amer. Journ. Sci.*, vol. *240*, pp. 867–78.

THEOBALD, NICOLAS. 1952. Les Climates de l'Europe Occidentale au cours des Temps Tertiares d'aprés l'Etude des Insectes Fossiles. *Geol. Rundschau*, Bd. 40, H. 1, pp. 89–92.

TRASK, PARKER D., PHLEGER, F. B., JR., and STETSON, H. C. 1947. Recent Changes in Sedimentation in the Gulf of Mexico. *Science*, vol. *106*, pp. 460–61.

TRAVERSE, ALFRED. 1955. Pollen Analysis of the Brandon Lignite of Vermont. U.S. Bur. Mines, Rept. of Invest. No. 5151, pp. 1–107.

TREWARTHA, GLENN T. 1954. An Introduction to Climate. New York: McGraw Hill. 395 pp.

U.S. WEATHER BUREAU. 1953. Climatological Data, National Summary. 81 pp.

VISHER, STEPHEN S. 1954. Climatic Atlas of the United States. Cambridge: Harvard Univ. Press. 403 pp.

WEXLER, HARRY. 1958. (Quoted in New York Times, Saturday, May 31.)

WILLETT, H. C. 1950. Temperature Trends of the Past Century. Centenary Proc. Royal Meteorol. Soc., pp. 195–206.

Trends in Climatology

H. E. LANDSBERG*

The aim of climatology is to abstract from the varied and rapidly changing weather phenomena the underlying patterns that characterize the atmospheric environment for regions of the earth and for the earth as a whole. In recent decades climatology has gradually evolved from a purely descriptive science to a science that is grounded in physics. But climatology is not confined to the study of large-scale climatic events alone; it is also, for example, concerned with microclimates and with the influence of climatic factors on the life processes of plants and animals. The field is so broad that it is impossible to treat more than a limited number of topics in a single article; accordingly, I have selected certain topics for discussion but at the same time have tried to present a general view of climatology.

History

The problems in this field are difficult because of the many different ingredients—in complex spatial and temporal interrelations—which make up a climate. The major factors affecting climate are the sun (the primary source of energy), the position of the earth in the solar system, and the inclination of the earth's axis with respect to its orbit. That these are the most important factors in causing differences in climate was recognized even by some early Greek scientists, probably first by Eratosthenes. The Greeks defined climate according to the

* The author is director of the Office of Climatology, U.S. Weather Bureau, Washington, D.C.

mean inclination of the sun's rays with respect to the terrestrial horizontal. Thus temperature zones according to latitude were distinguished. This gave rise to an organization of climatic facts into a causally related scheme of *torrid, temperate,* and *frigid* zones, albeit somewhat anthropocentric in scope.

Little was added to this concept for over 1800 years. But then, one by one, the complicating factors and their influence became obvious. On a large scale, these were the distribution of land and ocean on earth and the existence of larger and smaller mountains. The local influences of lakes, forests, and vegetation-covered and bare soil also became recognized. In the atmosphere itself one of the controlling factors is that *bête-noire* of the meteorologist, the water. Its presence in all states of aggregation—vapor, liquid, solid—often the three of them simultaneously, and quickly changing from one to another, complicates matters immensely. Through evaporation and condensation, cloudiness and precipitation, it governs much of the climate, as is discussed more specifically later.

Historically, significant advances in the study of climates were made after systematic measurements of atmospheric parameters began. Although such measurements started in some places in Europe in the 17th century, it was during the high surge of science in the second half of the 18th century that many learned men the world over became interested in the atmospheric environment. Physicians, astronomers, natural philosophers, and clergymen recorded the temperature, pressure, wind, precipitation, and weather conditions faithfully. There was considerable appreciation that knowledge about climate might be useful and broad speculation that climate had a notable influence on health. This last was a notion which had an early antecedent in Greece, in the theories of Hippocrates. Equipment and procedures, though primitive in the beginning, became gradually standardized.

The problem of standardization has remained with us for nearly two centuries because only with standardization can comparisons between simultaneous records at various localities or between earlier data and later readings become meaningful. Only in recent years has the World Meteorological Organization, one of the specialized agencies of the United Nations, shown a modicum of success in establishing uniform observation practices in all countries.

The interest in the atmospheric environment in the outgoing 18th century was quite universal among the well-educated. Thomas Jefferson (*1*) considered climatic observations important to "increase the progress of human knowledge." From data collected at Williamsburg, Virginia, in the years 1772 to 1777, he prepared one of the first climatic summaries for North America (Fig. 1). A cooperative venture of sizable proportions was initiated by the Societas Meteorologica Palatina with the Prince Elector Karl Theodor of the Palatinate as sponsor. Uniformly calibrated instruments and observing instructions were distributed to 35 academies and learned societies in the then readily accessible parts of the world. Data were collected and published in detail (*2*). These data became the

	Fall of rain, &c. in inches	Least and greatest daily heat by Farenheit's thermometer.	WINDS.								
			N.	N.E.	E.	S.E.	S.	SW.	W.	NW.	Total.
January.	3.192	$38\frac{1}{2}$ to 44	73	47	32	10	11	78	40	46	337
Feb.	2.049	41 $47\frac{1}{2}$	61	52	24	11	4	63	30	31	276
March.	3.95	48 $54\frac{1}{2}$	49	44	38	28	14	83	29	33	318
April.	3.68	56 $62\frac{1}{2}$	35	44	54	19	9	58	18	20	257
May.	2.871	63 $70\frac{1}{2}$	27	36	62	23	7	74	32	20	281
June.	3.751	$71\frac{1}{2}$ $78\frac{1}{4}$	22	34	43	24	13	81	25	25	267
July.	4.497	77 $82\frac{1}{2}$	41	44	75	15	7	95	32	19	328
August.	9.153	$76\frac{1}{4}$ 81	43	52	40	30	9	103	27	30	334
Sept.	4.761	$69\frac{1}{2}$ $74\frac{1}{4}$	70	60	51	18	10	81	18	37	345
Oct.	3.633	$61\frac{1}{4}$ $66\frac{1}{2}$	52	77	64	15	6	56	23	34	327
Nov.	2.617	$47\frac{3}{4}$ $53\frac{1}{2}$	74	21	20	14	9	63	35	58	294
Dec.	2.877	43 $48\frac{3}{4}$	64	37	18	16	10	91	42	56	334
Total.	47.038	8 A. M. 4 P.M	611	548	521	223	109	926	351	409	3698

FIG. 1. Climatic table for Williamsburg, Va.; from Thomas Jefferson (*1*).

raw material for the first comparative climatological studies. Twelve annual volumes appeared before this pioneering survey ceased in the turmoil of revolutions and wars of the outgoing 18th century.

However, the pattern was set. From a few score stations, climatological networks have been expanding. Including rainfall stations, there are presently probably about 150,000 land locations from which some climatological information is available. The rapid rise in stations is well marked in the United States (Fig. 2). The desirable end is not in sight because station density goes hand in hand with population density and many areas are void of settlements. Only since the start of the International Geophysical Year have we had systematic climatological information, for example, from the South Pole area. The uneven coverage of the land areas with observing posts is a handicap to climatological research. It is even worse over the oceans. There regular observations started in the 1850's. One of the principal movers to obtain weather data from the sea was the U.S. naval lieutenant Matthew F. Maury. Millions of individual readings have been gathered in the weather archives since, but they are bunched on the shipping lanes. There are vast ocean areas which are hardly ever crossed by a ship. From the Arctic sea, ice data are also scarce. We have no systematic measurement of rainfall over the ocean. Some data are accumulating from Texas Towers offshore, but a climatological survey of the oceans, perhaps by regularly spaced, anchored, automatic weather floats, is still a dream for the future (*3*).

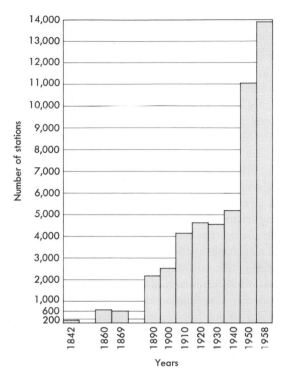

FIG. 2. Number of climatic observing stations in the United States and possessions, 1842–1958.

Thus the climatologist is still struggling with the question, "What is there?" For this reason the answers to the usual second question in science—Why is it so?—are woefully incomplete.

Climatic energetics

At the basis of all quantitative considerations in climatology are the questions of energy balance. Presently this starts with the assumption that income from solar radiation and loss of heat by the earth are equal. The income from the sun (the so-called solar constant) is known to be about 2 calories per square centimeter per minute at the boundary of the atmosphere, at the mean distance between earth and sun, normal to the incident rays. This over-all value is probably valid within 1 percent. However, in various spectral regions, especially in the short wavelengths, considerable fluctuations in intensity can occur. The total energy income and its spectral distribution are now amenable to direct measurements from satellites. This will be one of the most valuable contributions of these vehicles to climatology. Equally important will be essentially extra-atmospheric measurements of the earth's albedo, that is, the portion of the incoming energy directly lost to space by the planet through reflection from clouds, snow and ice surfaces (as primary contributors to the loss), and from land and ocean surfaces (as secondary reflectors). The over-all albedo of the earth has been estimated at 35 percent, but this value might be off by several percent either way. There are certainly considerable seasonal variations and, possibly, changes from year to year. Equally important for areal climates are the local values of albedo and the variations in different landscapes and seasons. These values govern how much heat is absorbed and becomes available for atmospheric energy transformations.

Quite unknown are the storage factors. There is certainly the possibility that heat energy beyond the yearly cycle is stored in the ocean. It may then be released again over a longer period of time, rather than be used immediately for driving the general circulation of the atmosphere. Even though this question of heat storage is open, attempts have been made to estimate the heat balance of the earth and of smaller portions of its surface. Various approaches have been used, most of them indirect. Among the direct approaches are the measurements of incoming and outgoing radiation to establish locally the radiation balance. This has been done at too few places as yet to furnish significant information for the global picture. However, net-radiometers which measure and integrate the radiation balance from day to day are becoming more common equipment at observing stations. The other components of the total heat budget—condensation-evaporation and advection—are difficult to observe directly. They are generally deduced from other climatic elements. The most comprehensive study in this connection has been carried on by Russian investigators (*4*). For the earth as a whole, and on an annual basis, they obtained the following figures (all in kilocalories per square centimeter per year): total radiation received, 129; heat available for atmospheric transactions and motions after reflection and other direct losses, 68; lost by use in evaporation, 56; lost by turbulent transport, 12. The values for continents and oceans by individual latitudes are, of course, quite different from these means. The differences between the larger subdivisions of the globe are the cause of the general atmospheric circulation and its local manifestations. They cause the tradewinds, the westerlies, the monsoons, and all the embedded eddies, such as ordinary cyclones and tropical storms. All of these currents, including the now famous atmospheric jet streams, are part of the energy-dissipating mechanism.

As already stated, the role of water in the atmosphere is of fundamental importance. It enters actively into all heat balance considerations. In a limited way this is due to the infrared absorption spectrum of water vapor. But the primary contribution comes about by evaporation (consuming heat) and condensation or freezing (liberating heat). The vapor phase is a means of transporting latent heat from one place to another. Last but not least, water plays a passive role in heat transactions because, as clouds and surface snow or ice, it reflects large amounts of incoming short-wave radiation from the sun. Next to air temperature, it is also the element which has the greater influence on plants, animals, and human activities. In the form of rain or snow it governs water supplies; in the form of hail it causes crop damage. Its lack spells desert conditions or temporary drought for afflicted areas. Even as fine droplets in clouds or fog it affects life processes and recreation or traffic on land, sea, and in the air.

The water cycle from the ocean through the air to rivers, streams, and underground storage in its relation to the general atmospheric circulation has become fairly well known in broad outline and is reflected on the climatic charts. But as a process of atmospheric energetics, understanding has barely begun. Considerable effort has been expended on the problem of evapotranspiration (5). This concerns the water losses from land surfaces. Evaporation from open water surfaces in terms of the atmospheric environment has at least yielded to empirical approaches, but the water losses from bare and plant-covered soil can as yet be ascertained only in rough approximation. Locally it can be calculated as a function of the heat flux and the turbulent transfer of mass. Such losses, together with the gains by rainfall, can be entered into a bookkeeping system which indicates an approximation of available soil moisture. This factor is important in farm management and irrigation planning. The climatology of the moisture balance has become one of the most important factors in agricultural land utilization. It is likely to stay in the foreground of interest because of the world food problems engendered by population pressures.

It is fortunate that theoretical schemes whch underlie much of present-day procedures for ascertaining the water cycle can now be supplemented by tracer techniques. These make use of isotope determinations. Both deuterium and tritium have recently been employed for this purpose (6). Interesting new facts have been added to our knowledge by these procedures. For example, the storage time of water in vapor form in the air ranges, on an average, from 3 to 10 days. In the central United States it also appears that the storage time of water lost to the soil by percolation is of an order of magnitude of several years. More work needs to be done with these techniques. Also, a wide geographical coverage is desirable. This new avenue of research will certainly supply quantitative answers to many of the questions related to atmospheric water transport.

The foregoing problem is one among many that make it clear that solutions in climatology can no longer be looked for or found by reference to surface observations alone. Great strides have been made in the collection and summarization of upper air data. These have found practical application in the planning for air routes and as basic design information for rockets. They have been used as guidelines for estimating radioactive fallout from various levels (7). They also give us better insight into the three-dimensional flow patterns of global air currents. Among them are the swift, meandering jet streams. The jet streams are a dynamic consequence of momentum transport into narrow zones of confluence of various air currents produced by the general circulation. The primary seat of these fast flows is in the upper troposphere, where they not infrequently exceed speeds of 200 miles per hour. The strongest jet streams are in the

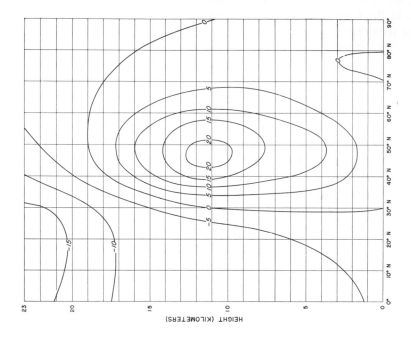

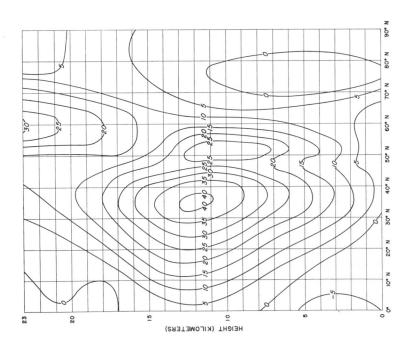

FIG. 3. Mean westerly component of the wind in meters per second in vertical section through the atmosphere along the 80th meridian west, based on ten years of observations (38). Negative values indicate prevailing easterly winds. Left section shows values for January, right section for July.

middle latitudes, but there are less pronounced and less steady currents of this type in the tropics and polar regions. It even appears that stratospheric jets are in existence. The main jet stream is quite noticeable even in atmospheric cross sections reflecting mean conditions (Fig. 3). The mean flow patterns are now reasonably well known for the Northern Hemisphere, but in the Southern Hemisphere data are still too sparse for more than local climatological analysis (8). Also, the fluctuations of the jet streams in time and space are still targets of exploration. As there are close associations between the jet streams and rainfall, studies of the more comprehensive data to be expected in the future will give better insight into the broad dynamics of global precipitation (9).

Climatic classification

For several decades the problem of climatic classification has created lively discussions. More than a score of schemes for classifying climates have been proposed (10). None of them satisfies all the requirements. The basic difficulty is inherent in the fact that there exist hardly any sharp boundaries between climatic zones. Except at the crests of high mountains (Fig. 4) and at the coast lines, various climatic regimes gradually fade into each other. Also, the shifts of the general circulation of the atmosphere from season to season and year to year bring fixed localities on the surface of the earth sometimes into one climatic zone and then into another. Hence a strict taxonomy which separates natural entities is not possible. All dividing lines are essentially arbitrary. This is the more the case when, as in most climatic classifications, the class criteria are based on mean value of climatic elements. A climatological mean value is often only a very poor representation of conditions. The width of variation of atmospheric elements harbors often decisive factors. In addition, the choice of combination of elements represented in the classification is usually dictated by a specific application rather than by inherent properties of the climate itself.

For geographical purposes, climatic classifications often have the boundaries of types essentially governed by other entities, such as plant cover associated with (or perhaps caused by) a specific combination of climatic conditions. Even that will not yield an unambiguous answer, because several combinations of climatic factors may have the same end result. The classical climatic classification schemes, which essentially arranged their limits to coincide with the major plant provinces on earth, have didactic value. They help in visualizing the global distribution within a readily comprehensible framework.

In many climatic classifications only temperature and precipitation are considered as climatic elements. Admittedly, these are most widely observed. They also generally affect human activities, particularly agriculture. However, there can be as many classifications with various combinations of elements as there are practical purposes. For air conditioning, one would choose suitable combinations of temperature, humidity, and air motion as classification elements. In

FIG. 4. Major mountains act as great climatic divides. Usually their windward and lee slopes have radically different climatic conditions. Orographic cloud formations such as those shown are frequently very spectacular. They offer a primary hope of increasing precipitation by suitable seeding techniques. [U.S. Weather Bureau, by F. Ellerman]

that case the class limits would be comfort sensations. To classify airports or air routes in a climatic sense one has to consider the flying weather. The class limits are then determined by cloud ceilings, visibilities, turbulence, wind directions and speeds, and their respective joint frequencies. Essentially, one can arrive at a classification for every activity influenced by climate. To illustrate this point further: Very recently a classification has been devised for refractivity of the atmosphere as it affects radio wave transmission (*11*). This incorporates the pertinent elements of pressure, temperature, and humidity and their normal vertical and seasonal variations.

A purely qualitative scheme of climatic classification can be designed to avoid the multiplicity and the difficulty of fixed, yet arbitrary, numerical values. This classification stems from the broad meteorological aspects of climate and the basic factors of the general circulation. It is in line with attempts in recent years to get away from the static concept represented by mean values of cli-

TABLE 1. Notation for climatic typing. Mixtures of two types are indicated in parentheses, as *(CA)*, *(AE)*. A further symbol employed is the subscript *e* to designate extreme conditions.

Feature	Symbol
Major circulation patterns (primary controls)	
Migrating cyclones	*C*
Quasi-stationary anticyclones	*A*
Equatorial convergence	*E*
Secondary or seasonal circulation features	
Typical monsoons	*S*
Predominant trade winds	*T*
Major surface influences	
Continental	*c*
Oceanic	*o*
Mountain	*m*
windward slope	*mw*
lee slope	*ml*
Glaciated	*g*

matic elements *(12)*. After all, there is nothing fixed in the atmosphere, and even such abstractions from its unending motions as the climate should reflect the dynamics of the system. The classification procedure then is nothing but a descriptive symbolism or shorthand notation of major types. Table 1 shows such a notation system. In this notation the climate of western New York State would be designated as *Cc,* that of Ireland as *Co,* and that of North Dakota as *Cc$_e$.* The coast of California would be *(CA)o;* the Sahara, *Ac$_e$;* Bermuda, *Ao;* and Oahu, *ATo.* The central Amazon valley would be labeled *Ec* and the Gilbert Islands *Eo.* Among the mountain climates, the Cascades have *Cm,* the Australian Great Dividing Range has *Am,* and the Mount Kenya area, *Em.* The various combinations of symbols cover all macroclimates. However, they do not reflect the local influences, usually labeled meso- or microclimates, such as lake breezes, slope exposures, and vegetation conditions.

Climatic changes

Another reason why classification, in fixed terms, is an ad hoc procedure, is inherent in the fluctuations of climate with respect to time. These climatic changes are among the most fascinating problems in climatology. Changes occur both in short and long intervals of time. The long intervals comprise geological

FIG. 5. Climatic changes through the millenia are particularly notable in the arid and semiarid regions of the southwestern United States. At one time heavy rainfall and run-off helped in modeling outstanding features of the landscape such as those shown in the Grand Canyon of the Colorado. [U.S. Weather Bureau, by Madison Gilbert]

epochs; the short ones, centuries and millenia (Fig. 5). There is little point in talking about *climatic* changes or fluctuations when only a few years or decades are under consideration. Usually the fluctuations in such limited intervals are difficult to distinguish from random variations, if indeed they are not such variations. Any cyclical—or better rhythmical—elements in the same decadal intervals, if any, are masked by "noise." There is some evidence of weak components of one half, one, two, and perhaps other multiples of the sunspot cycle in some series of climatic data, but their amplitude is small. Other rhythmical elements appear and then vanish again from climatic times series.

For a great many practical purposes the values in a climatic time series can be treated on probability premises as if they had occurred by chance. This makes it possible to use climatic data from the past with considerable confidence for purposes of future planning. Various risks can be assessed for engineering construction and design as well as agricultural use. The list of such applications is large and steadily growing. A few examples will suffice as illustration. Many structures have to be built with knowledge of extreme weather events to insure adequate safety: the maximum wind for a tower, hangar, or bridge; the highest snow load for a roof; the heaviest rain intensities for culvert design. The probabilities of various limits can be estimated from the observations by use of various extreme-value distributions (*13*). For heating or air conditioning plant capacity, the knowledge of normal and extreme loads is also essential. These, too, can be efficiently estimated from the statistical properties of the past climatic record. Statistical functions, such as the incomplete gamma distribution, have been successfully applied to weekly or monthly rainfall values. This approach yielded valuable planning information for agricultural purposes (*14*). Similar analyses for freeze dates have been of considerable practical value for crop practices.

Even if we can safely assume that for plans not exceeding a few decades the past climatic record can be taken as a guide to the future, this does not imply the absence of trends. As more data accumulate the evidence for measurable climatic changes multiplies. For nearly half a century a gradual warming of the Northern Hemisphere has been noted. Were we to rely on temperature readings alone, the data for many areas could be challenged. To be sure, a rise of several degrees Fahrenheit can be noted in many temperature series since 1900. Unfortunately, numerous weather observing stations have been shifted around, and their records are far from homogeneous. Moreover, many are in or near growing cities. Part of the rise of temperature must be attributed to the large number of heat-producing factors of modern industrial communities. These factors, together with air pollution, have created a new man-made climate which has developed in parallel with any natural climatic changes over the same time period. It is hard to apportion what part of the temperature rise has been artificial and what portion natural. This difficulty will be minimized in the future by establishment and maintenance of climatic stations in isolated areas where man-made environmental changes will remain minimal. These will be called climatic reference or "bench-mark" stations (*15*). Fortunately, there exist now enough rural data and other evidence to give us some clues. For the moderate latitudes, 30° to 50° N, in the area around the Atlantic, the natural rise can be estimated at about 2°F. per century. At higher latitudes the value may be about twice that amount. The rise has been particularly pronounced in the winter season (Fig. 6).

It is interesting to revert here for a moment to Jefferson's climatic table of Williamsburg. Even though we know little about the circumstances under which the observations were made, comparison with a recent time interval shows that no *radical* change of climate has taken place. Temperatures are now slightly higher than they were at the end of the 18th century. But it should be remembered that there was a marked temperature fall between the beginning and middle of the 19th century, which was followed by the rise of the 20th. Rainfall is still about the same. The winds seem to show now a few more southerly and less northerly components than in Jefferson's day.

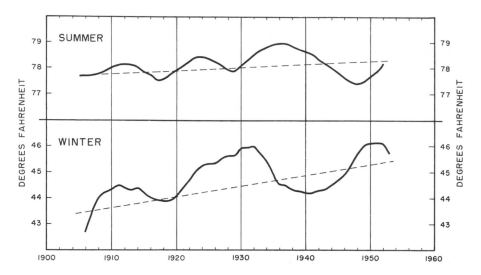

FIG. 6. Time series of seasonal mean temperatures at Winthrop College, South Carolina, one of the climatic reference stations (lat. 34°57′N, long. 81°03′W, elevation 690 ft). Summer comprises the months June–August, 1900–57; winter, December–February, 1900–58. Data have been smoothed by a normal curve smoothing function of length $2\sigma = 5$ years. Values are plotted at the midpoint of the smoothing interval (*39*). Dashed lines show the general temperature trend of the region.

FIG. 7. The recent warming of the arctic has been particularly notable at the edges of the forested regions both in North America and Eurasia. The tree line has been advancing gradually northward. In some areas which have been resurveyed, the forest has advanced 2 miles northward over the last 30 years. [U.S. Weather Bureau]

The indirect evidence for the most recent warming in higher latitudes is, however, quite impressive. There are positive trends of sea surface-water temperatures in the North Atlantic of the same order of magnitude as the long-term air temperature changes (*16*). Also, retreats of glaciers (*17*), upward migration of snow lines, lengthening of the freeze-free season, northward migration of animal species and plants (Fig. 7), and phenological data all point in the same direction. There is little doubt that the past two or three decades, taken over-all, have been among the warmest in centuries. The question as to what may be the causes immediately arises. First, let me state that periods of similar warmth have been noted in earlier historical times. Even warmer intervals have occurred since the last glaciation. The most widely held opinion ascribes the changes to variations in the solar radiation. Satisfactory proof for this relationship is still lacking (*18*).

For the latest temperature change, there is an important contender as cause: atmospheric carbon dioxide. There are some interpretations of historical and current observations pointing toward a gradual increase of this atmospheric constituent (*19*). The increased consumption of fossil fuels has brought very large quantities of carbon dioxide into the air. Isotope investigations attest to this fact. Carbon dioxide is an absorber of outgoing long-wave radiation, and hence has an influence similar to that of a glass cover. This phenomenon is therefore often referred to as the "greenhouse effect." Only since the start of the International Geophysical Year have there been sufficiently widespread and accurate observations of atmospheric carbon dioxide to enable us to gain perspective on this question. Local variations and the uncertainties in the carbon dioxide balance between ocean and atmosphere make interpretations difficult. For an answer on the role of carbon dioxide in atmospheric temperature trends, many more years of systematic observations will be necessary (*20*).

Even if one accepts the thesis that atmospheric pollutants, such as dust and carbon dioxide, or terrestrially caused changes in atmospheric water vapor content could have an influence on the decadal or perhaps century-long trends, the main question still remains: What causes the large-scale epochal changes? Much thought has been given to this problem in recent years. New techniques, such as oxygen isotope analysis of sea shells, have been applied to it (*21*). But basically no new answers have been obtained.

If anything has happened, the ingenious hypothesis of attributing major climatic changes to the periodic elements in the obliquity of the earth's axis and in the eccentricity of its path (*22*) has lost its attractiveness. These path elements of the planet seem to account for only minor changes (*23*). Some new ideas have cropped up. They link pole shifts, oceanic currents, the ice conditions of the North Polar Sea, and the land glaciations (*24*). There is, of course, a much underrated relation between the oceanic heat (or cold) reservoir and the climatic fluctuations on land. However no *quantitative* consideration has as yet demonstrated that these could account for the observed, and evidently recurring, phenomena of major ice epochs. They may perhaps be adequate to explain stages within these eras.

Sooner or later most considerations get back to the question of changes in the solar radiation. Some astrophysicists contend that there are simply none of the magnitude required for major climatic changes (25). Others equally stoutly maintain that nuclear refueling processes on the sun actually call for periodic substantial changes in solar energy output (26). A once favored idea that cosmic dust clouds might act as interceptors has not been refuted but no new supporting facts have been marshaled either.

There is no unanimity about what the effects of changes in the solar radiation would be. Some contend that an increase could lead to an ice age (27). The essential reasoning is that initially higher temperature and increased circulation would lead to more cloudiness and hence greater albedo values. It is, however, more logical to assume that increases in radiation cause warmer conditions, such as once prevailed in the Tertiary, and that decreases in radiation produce ice ages of the Pleistocene type. Both sides of this question are still being vigorously argued in current writings (28).

Climatic "control"

Of late there has been a great deal of publicity about controlling the climate. The word *control* implies that you know what to do, and when and where to do it. Some of this talk about control can be ascribed to misinterpretation of dimensions. Most of it glosses over the fact that for *major* climatic changes one would have to modify substantially the tremendous amount of solar energy received by the earth. We might note here in passing that the energy liberated from the total probable stores of fission and fusion bombs would not equal the energy of the average thunderstorm activity on earth over a few days' time. Albedo changes can presently be envisaged only on a relatively small scale. Ocean currents are hard to divert; mountains are difficult to move. And these remain the major terrestrial climatic controls.

Conceivably one could throw enough dust into the stratosphere by nuclear explosions to intercept an appreciable amount of the solar radiation. This might, again conceivably, cause some changes of the general circulation. The effect would pass off in a few years—a short time as climatic spans go. Also, the effect would be general over the globe, with unpredictable effects as far as small land segments are concerned. It could hardly be called control.

Some talk glibly about trigger effects. This means that a small amount of energy can set off a much larger, latent energy store. But where is the "loaded gun" in the atmosphere? The nearest analogy is the latent heat of the water vapor. If condensed in spots it could add heat which could be transformed into other forms of energy. Temperatures might be raised, motions increased. Here, too, in spite of the sometimes advocated spreading of hygroscopic nuclei, little in the form of "control" can be foreseen in the near future. There are also some latent electric energies available in the atmosphere. These have hardly been explored yet.

The trigger effects, the albedo effects, even the direct addition and subtraction of energy, can now only be envisaged for local modifications of climate. The microclimate is readily manipulated and much along this line has been accomplished over the last few decades. This includes many of the horticultural practices from frost protection to shelter belts, from moisture-conserving mulching to irrigation. On a somewhat larger scale, creation of artificial lakes, changing of river courses, large-scale reforestation, and artificial suppression of evaporation have small, but measurable climatic influences. Also along this line, slight local increases of orographic rainfall by cloud seeding have been made probable (*29*). Cloud modification, if systematically carried on, by coalescence of droplets or by their dissipation, is among the potential producers of local climatic effects. There is theoretically a bare possibility of operating on the latent energies of severe storms and causing measurable effects. Experimental evidence has yet to be obtained in this respect. If practical, it will have, at best, climatic influences on a meso-scale. In all these aspects, a little more humility in the face of the overwhelming powers of nature seems to be indicated for the present.

Microclimatology and bioclimatology

It has long been known that in the layers close to the ground, climatic conditions of wide variety can exist in close proximity (*30*). These conditions are often quite different from the general, or macro, climate of the region. Because they are often confined to small spaces they have been labeled microclimates. The term is, however, loosely used in the literature. Some authors restrict it to indicate differences on the smallest scale only. This might show the comparison of the climate of a furrow compared to that of level soil, or the climate on the windward versus the lee side of a small hill or hedge. It might show the climatic difference between a forest and bare soil in the same area. Generally, however, climatic differentiation of somewhat larger scale is usually included in a discussion of microclimatology. In this broader sense the scope of this field includes the contrasts of valley, slope, and crest climates in a hilly terrain, or it pertains to the climates of a settlement, town, or city as distinct from the surroundings, undisturbed by human activity.

The microclimatic differences are often startling. They develop primarily under conditions of clear sky and little wind, but some still exist with clouds, wind, and rainfall. Human interference, as can be seen from the foregoing, is important in creating and destroying microclimates (*31*). Manipulation of microclimates is, or should be, an important adjunct to planning land utilization, agricultural management, architecture, and urban development. In this connection, it may be interesting to cite a few figures on the major climatic differences between cities and their surroundings (Table 2) [40].

In many instances air pollution accumulations are direct consequences of microclimatic settings. Topography, source of pollution, and general climatic conditions combine in patterns which become a typical element of local climate. It is feasible to estimate the pollution hazards of an area from climatic records and the terrain features, if sources of contamination come into being.

TABLE 2. Climatic changes produced by cities.

Element	Comparison with rural environment
Dust and pollution	10 to 25 times more
Radiation	15 to 20 percent less
Clouds	5 to 10 percent more
Precipitation	5 to 10 percent more
Temperature (average)	1 to 2° F more
Relative humidity	3 to 10 percent less
Windspeed	20 to 30 percent less

Microclimatic principles are among the best established in climatology. The facts are usually the most readily amenable to observation. Advanced instrumentation is available (32). Quantitative theories that begin to explain the observed facts are in a better state than those of general climatology. Last but not least, experimentation with test plots, not too far removed from laboratory conditions, is feasible and is being carried on.

The microclimatic conditions play an important role in life processes. Some of these influences operate on the smallest scale. Bacterial, fungal, and insect life in plant cover are governed to a considerable extent by prevalent temperature and moisture conditions. Presence or absence of dew on leaves may determine infestations of plant pests. The microclimate in a high stand of grass, for example, may prevent extremes of heat and cold and thus enable survival of certain insects in otherwise lethal conditions. Intricate relations between climate, plant life, and low forms of animal life exist, but much remains to be learned about the microecological complex.

A mixture of both macro- and microclimatological influences operate on plants. These effects have been the target of a great many investigations because of their importance in crop ecology. In its simplest aspects, photosynthesis is, of course, a direct function of sunlight, and hence is subjected to the climatic variations of this element. But this is where simplicity ends in the plant-climate relation. The effect of temperature is fairly well understood, but when it comes to water use, the problems become really involved. In the higher plants, light, heat, and water interact in a nonlinear fashion. At various stages of development the requirements of the plant for optimal conditions change, and the interplay of climatic factors subtly shifts (*33*).

Although a modicum of order for the atmospheric environment can be obtained for plants growing in phytotrons, under field conditions it is hard to ascertain the role of each climatic influence. The only exceptions are singular, lethal events, such as a hard freeze or absolute drought. In their absence one has to ascertain the complex effect of *all* climatic elements on the development of the plant. The use of statistical techniques with multiple regressions is of some help. More commonly, investigators have tried to condense the complex climatic factors into single influence indices. This is helped somewhat by the fact that there exist fairly high correlations between some of the climatic elements. Thus temperature is correlated with sunshine, and water depletion is, to some extent, a function of saturation deficit and wind. These, in turn, vary not entirely independently of temperature and sunshine. Among the influence indices which have been used with some success are the (i) soil temperature at shallow depth; (ii) evaporation (from porous bodies or open water surfaces); (iii) heat sums (expressed in terms of temperature excess above a given threshold); (iv) potential evapotranspiration. The first two are directly measurable; the other two can be derived from simple climatic observations. These influence indices substitute, even if in an incomplete fashion, for radiation, soil moisture depletion, and transpiration from plants. They can be used as correlatives for various stages of phenological developments of plants (*34*).

Similarly complex are the climatic influences on the human and animal bodies (*35*). In the healthy organism we deal with problems of acclimatization. Some phases are well understood. As an example, we can cite the reactions of the human skin to ultraviolet solar radiation. Another one is the adaptation to reduced oxygen tension in the atmosphere, resulting in increased red blood corpuscles and thoracic capacity. Considerable evidence has also been advanced that the primary differentiation of races was caused by climatic conditions (*36*).

The influence of climate on pathological states is not well known. We find ourselves in a vast realm of speculation. Are there climates beneficial to older persons? Opinion leans toward an affirmative answer, specifying as optimal a "mild climate," without extremes of temperature and with a minimum of change. Are climates with low relative humidities beneficial to sufferers from sinus disease? Again, a poorly documented "yes" sums up the present level of knowledge, or better, ignorance.

Seasonal incidence of certain infectious diseases, or geographical distribution of endemic plagues, points toward a climatic causative factor. However, it is not known whether the influence is on the receptiveness of the human organism, on the pathogen, or on the various disease-carrying vectors. Equally ill-established is the role of climate in the air-borne allergies.

Outlook

Let me indulge now in speculating a little where we will go from here in climatological research. It is certain that the vast stores of accumulated climatic observations will be tapped for their concealed information by use of modern electronic methods of data processing. The phases of this work applied to various branches of engineering will flourish. Similarly, much progress can be expected in establishing the true climate of the upper air. From this will be derived dynamic parameters of the general atmospheric circulation which will define local and areal climates. Hand in hand with this will go research on energy transactions that determine climatic regimes (*37*). As a first step, a comprehensive radiation climatology of the globe is needed.

Better information on extraterrestrial fluctuations of radiation and deeper understanding of the atmosphere-ocean relations will throw new light on the problem of climatic trends. The tedious analysis of geological evidence is likely to leave the problem of ice ages in the state of working hypotheses.

The greatest advances of climatology are destined to lie in the border field of biology, provided an adequate cooperative research program is started. The interactions between the physical changes in the atmosphere and living organisms are too great a challenge to scientific curiosity to remain in a relatively unexplored state. We have already pointed to the special problems of agroclimatology, a solution to which population increase will demand. Similarly, climate's role in gerontology and various pathological states begs for quantitative studies.

It is further certain that some experimentation with artificial alteration will take place. One can only hope that the long-range view will prevail and that the experiments will be carefully designed with a view toward physical and statistical validation. This is a large program which probably will take years and permit of few short cuts. Man may not become master of his climatic environment, but the next decades at least promise that he will be able to understand it much better than in the past.

REFERENCES

1. T. JEFFERSON, *Notes on the State of Virginia* (Carey and Lea, Philadelphia, 1825). First published 1787.
2. Societas Meteorologica Palatina, *Ephemerides-Observationes* (Mannheim, Germany, 1784–1795), vols. 1–12.
3. P. D. LOWELL, W. HAKKARINEN, L. M. ALLISON, JR., "Final report: Ocean-Based Automatic Weather Station AN/SMT-1," *Natl. Bur. Standards U.S.* 95678 (1958).
4. M. I. BUDYKO, *The Heat Balance of the Earth Surface* (U.S. Weather Bureau translation, 1958). First published 1956.
5. C. W. THORNTHWAITE and J. R. MATHER, "The water balance," *Lab of Climatol. Publs. in Climatol.* **8,** No. 1 (1955); T. E. A. van Hylkkama, "The water balance of the earth," *ibid.* **9,** No. 2 (1956).

6. F. BEGEMAN and W. F. LIBBY, *Geochim. et Cosmochim. Acta* **12,** 257 (1957); I. Friedman, D. R. Norton, D. B. Carter, A. C. Redfield, *Limnol, and Oceanog.* **1,** 239 (1956).

7. Federal Civil Defense Administration, "Probability of Fallout Debris Deposition," *Civil Defense Tech. Bull.* 11–31 (1957).

8. J. GENTILLI, *Scope* **2,** 30 (1957).

9. H. RIEHL, M. H. ALAKA, C. L. JORDAN, R. J. RENAUD, "The jet-stream," *Meteorol. Monographs* **2,** No. 7 (1954).

10. K. KNOCH and A. SCHULZE, *Methoden der Klimaklassifikation* (Gotha, Germany, 1952).

11. B. R. BEAN and J. D. HORN, "On the climatology of the surface values of radio refractivity of the earth's atmosphere," *Natl. Bur. Standards U.S. 5559* (1958).

12. A. GIÃO, *Geofis. pura e appl.* **37,** 268 (1957).

13. E. J. GUMBEL, "Statistical theory of extreme values and some practical applications," *Natl. Bur. Standards U.S. Appl. Math. Ser. 33* (1954); H. C. S. Thom, "Frequency of maximum windspeeds," *Proc. Am. Soc. Civil Engrs.* **80,** separate No. 539 (1954).

14. G. L. BARGER and H. C. S. THOM, *Agron. J.* **41,** 519 (1949).

15. J. R. SWARTZ, *Weatherwise* **9,** 88–89, 106 (1956).

16. P. R. BROWN, *Quart. J. Roy. Meteorol. Soc.* **79,** 272 (1953).

17. H. W. AHLMANN, "Glacier variations and climatic fluctuations," *Bowman Memorial Lectures Am. Geograf. Soc. Ser.* **3,** 1 (1952).

18. H. SHAPLEY, Ed., *Climatic Change* (Harvard Univ. Press, Cambridge, Mass., 1953).

19. C. JUNGE, *Advances in Geophys.* **5,** 1 (1958).

20. G. N. PLASS, *Am. Scientist* **44,** 302 (1956).

21. C. EMILIANI, *Science* **125,** 383 (1957).

22. M. MILANKOVITCH, "Kanon der Erdbestrahlung," *Veröffentl. Serb. Akad. Wiss. Belgrade* **42,** 1 (1941).

23. E. J. ÖPIK, *Irish Astron. J.* **2,** 71, (1952).

24. M. EWING and W. L. DONN, *Science* **123,** 1061 (1956); **127,** 1159 (1958).

25. G. P. KUIPER, *The Solar System,* vol. 1, *The Sun* (Univ. of Chicago Press, Chicago, Ill., 1953).

26. E. J. ÖPIK, "A climatological and astronomical interpretation of the ice ages and of past variations of terrestrial climate," *Armagh Observatory Contrib. No. 9* (1953).

27. G. C. SIMPSON, *Quart. J. Roy. Meteorol. Soc.* **83,** 459 (1957).

28. I. I. SCHELL, "On the origin and nature of changes in climate" (unpublished manuscript, Tufts University Meteorological Studies, Ref. No. 58–1, 1958).

29. *Advisory Committee on Weather Control, Final Rept.,* vols. 1 and 3 (Government Printing Office, Washington, D.C., 1957).

30. R. GEIGER, *The Climate near the Ground* (Harvard Univ. Press, Cambridge, Mass., 1957).

31. C. W. THORNTHWAITE, "Modification of rural microclimates," in *Man's Role in Changing the Face of the Earth* (Univ. of Chicago Press. Chicago, 1956), pp. 567–583.

32. H. H. LETTAU and B. DAVIDSON, Eds., *Exploring the Atmosphere's First Mile,* vols. 1 and 2 (Pergamon Press, New York, 1957).

33. F. W. WENT, *Am. Scientist* **44,** 378 (1956).
34. M. Y. NUTTONSON, "Wheat-climate relationships and the use of phenology in ascertaining the thermal and photo-thermal requirements of wheat" (American Institute of Crop Ecology, 1955); J. Y. WANG, "Weather and canning crops," lecture at the Raw Products Conference, Wisconsin Canners, Madison (1958).
35. F. SARGENT and R. G. STONE, Eds., "Recent studies in bioclimatology," *Meteorol. Monographs* **2,** No. 8 (1954).
36. C. S. COON, "Climate and race," in *Climatic Change* (*18,* pp. 13–34).
37. M. YE. SHVETS, *A. I. Voyeykov i Sovremennyye Problemy Klimatologii* (Leningrad, 1956), pp. 205–225.
38. Data for this diagram were analyzed by my collaborator, Mr. B. Ratner, whose help is gratefully acknowledged.
39. Analysis from original data for this graph was carried out by my collaborator, Mr. J. Murray Mitchell, Jr., whose assistance is acknowledged with appreciation.
40. H. E. LANDSBERG, "The climate of towns," in *Man's Role in Changing the Face of the Earth* (Univ. of Chicago Press, Chicago, Ill., 1956), pp. 584–606.

THE ECOLOGY OF PREHISTORIC MAN

*In his early evolution man lived by means of
hunting and collecting. Unfortunately we do not have
observations on this period of time by trained investigators.
We may accept, as a reasonable substitute, the
observations by Birdsell on aboriginal populations still
alive today. The manner in which these individuals have
adapted to their environment is highly suggestive of
human adaptations to earlier environments. Other
reports by Birdsell on the Australian aboriginal tribes
should also be consulted.*

SUPPLEMENTARY READINGS

BIRDSELL, J. B., Some Population Problems Involving Pleistocene Man. 1957, *Cold Spring Harbor Symposia on Quantitative Biology,* **22:** 47–69.

BIRDSELL, J. B., On Population Structure in Generalized Hunting and Collecting Populations. 1958, *Evolution,* **12:** 189–205.

KURTEN, BJORN, Mammal Migrations, Cenozoic Stratigraphy, and the Age of Peking Man and the Australopithecines. 1957, *Journal of Paleontology,* **31:** 215–227.

Some Environmental and Cultural Factors Influencing the Structuring of Australian Aboriginal Populations

JOSEPH B. BIRDSELL*

Theory in population genetics has been so vigorously developed in recent decades that its mathematical elaboration has run far ahead of its concrete applications to natural populations. Much of the theory requires empirical checking, yet this is difficult since the parameters which determine the characteristics of populations are generally ill-defined. There is great need to isolate and quantitatively evaluate the variables influencing the structuring of natural populations.

Man is sometimes considered an intractable subject for studies in population genetics. He is warm-blooded, produces few offspring, is long lived, and most important, his culture partially shields him from the forces in the natural environment. Nevertheless, properly chosen human populations may offer unusual research advantages. The aboriginal Australians are such an example. They are unique in that only in Australia did there survive into modern times an entire continent of peoples whose economy was based exclusively upon hunting and collecting, and whose culture was broadly uniform in terms of extractive efficiency. In ecological terms the aborigines represent a latter day survival of man at an essentially paleolithic level of economy, despite the presence of pressure-chipping, microliths, and stone grinding in some regions. Hence they are important as capable of revealing some aspects of the evolutionary processes affecting man in the Pleistocene, a period in which he passed through the definitive stages of racial differentiation.

* Department of Anthropology and Sociology, The University of California at Los Angeles. Corresponding member, Institute for the Study of Human Variation, Columbia University, New York, N.Y.

Determinants of Australian aboriginal population structure fall into two broad categories: (1) cultural; and (2) environmental. Certain of the more obvious cultural determinants have been discussed in a previous paper (Birdsell, 1950). Aboriginal populations in Australia do not represent an amorphous pattern of biological family units, but are structured in terms of two larger social units, the horde and the tribe. The horde, or local group, is equivalent to an extended family, usually numbers about 40 persons, and is the primary land-owning unit. Throughout Australia the horde is exogamous, patrilineal and patrilocal; that is, a man takes his wife from outside his local unit, she lives with his horde, and their children belong to it. Thus in each generation 50 percent of the local group gene pool is introduced from other hordes outside its boundaries.

The Australian tribe consists of a group of hordes, which are united by a common dialect, by a common attributed line of descent, and by a similar culture. No form of authority exists to bind the hordes of a tribe into a single cohesive unit, but its existence as a discrete social entity is recognized both by the natives themselves and by anthropologists. The tribe owes its existence to subtle forces of internal cohesion which are operative even at the low level of social integration characteristic of Australia. Territoriality, limitations on intergroup communication and on personal mobility doubtless contribute to defining tribal limits through lower rates of social interaction between distant hordes. In terms of the concepts of genetic space and genetic distance (Birdsell, 1950) the nature of population structuring is such that tribal boundaries operate as the essential barriers to gene flow, and probably act in most regions as barriers to cultural diffusion. Tindale (1940) has listed 574 aboriginal tribes for Australia. Brown (1930) estimated that at the time of discovery the total aboriginal population numbered 251,000 as a minimum, but more probably exceeded 300,000. Using Tindale's total for the number of tribes, these estimates give 437 and 523 upwards respectively for the mean number of persons per tribe.

If a genetic isolate is defined (see Stern, 1949, among others) as a population which forms a more or less closed group, so that its members are less likely than is expected by chance to exchange genes with members of another group, then the Australian horde, with its rapid influx of genic materials in each generation, does not answer these requirements. The tribe, on the other hand, as a socially self-defining unit, fulfills the essential requirements of the isolate.* Since popu-

---

* The real determinant of rates of gene flow between groups is sanctioned sexual relations, which occur commonly between hordes and occasionally between tribes. Since it would be difficult if not impossible to measure directly, it may require indirect evaluation through differences in intergroup marriage rates. There are little published data at the level of inter-horde marriage rates. N. B. Tindale has prepared a manuscript providing the first comprehensive data on the frequency of intertribal marriages. This paper should assist in defining the rates of interisolate gene flow in Australia. There are some suggestions in the literature that the rate is higher between small tribes than between large tribes.

lation pyramids will be generally uniform from tribe to tribe, and tend to remain nearly constant through time, isolate size will be highly correlated with, but larger than, the size of the effective breeding population. A crude and preliminary analysis suggests that for Australia the size of the effective breeding population would be less than 40 percent of the tribal population. Thus, the former would approximate but 40 persons for a tribe of 100; 200 for a tribal population of 500; and 400 for tribes totalling 1,000 natives. Hence the size of the effective breeding population in aboriginal Australia is small, and random genetic drift might be expected to be operative.

In an earlier paper (Birdsell, 1950) concerned with the construction of simple gene flow models for Australia, one of the primary simplifying assumptions used was that the average aboriginal tribal population was constant and approximated 500 individuals. Clearly not true when applied to a small series of tribes, it was presumed to hold as a central statistical tendency when applied to large numbers of tribes. The present study is a result of the further investigation of this primary assumption.

Materials and methodology

The basic materials for this analysis are derived from the excellent annotated Australian tribal map published by Norman B. Tindale (1940), my collaborator in the original field work of the Harvard-Adelaide Universities Anthropological Expedition of 1938–1939. In this paper Tindale briefly discusses the physiographic and ecological controls apparent in tribal distributions. He notes a high degree of correlation between tribal boundaries and ecological and geographical limits. Thus mountain ranges, divides, rivers, general ecological and plant associational boundaries, microclimatic zone limits, straits, and peninsulas often furnish clear-cut and stable boundaries. In deserts the cluster distributions of hordes around the few permanent waters are equally clear, and waterless stretches delimit many tribal boundaries. Tindale (1940, p. 150) further stresses that "The general reverse relationship between size of tribal area and rainfall is marked." In qualitative form this important but not unexpected relationship is not an efficient predictive device.

The present investigation was begun in order to quantify the relationship between rainfall and the size of the Australian tribal area as a step in devising a method for evaluating the size of tribal populations.* First, the area was

---

* After the completion of the present analysis it was discovered that N. B. Tindale had commenced a similar type of investigation using the same basic materials. After discussing this instance of parallel invention, we have decided to exchange materials at the data level, but to work totally independently at the conceptual level. Thus, when time becomes available, Tindale will publish his independent analysis, and Birdsell will publish his investigation in a more comprehensive and refined form than presented here. Opportunities for replicative research of this type are rare in the natural sciences, and the implications of these data are of sufficient importance to provide justification in this instance.

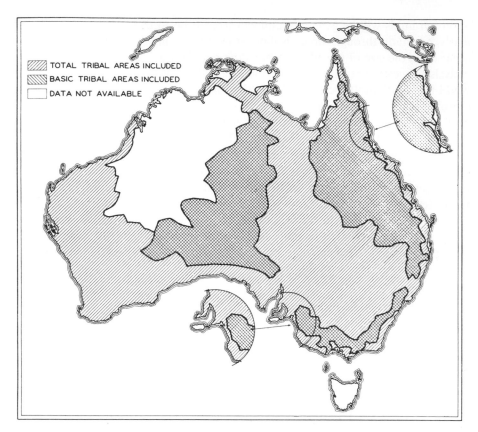

TOTAL TRIBAL AREAS INCLUDED
BASIC TRIBAL AREAS INCLUDED
DATA NOT AVAILABLE

FIG. 1. Distribution of total and basic series of tribes.

determined from Tindale's map for the 409 mainland tribes whose boundaries could be considered as reasonably established. The tribal boundaries are given as they existed just prior to the advent of white interference. This total series is shown by the combined hachured areas in Figure 1. Tindale differentiated between well established and probable boundaries, but both classes have necessarily been used in this study. For 14 tribes portions of boundaries had to be arbitrarily assumed, and where possible these were based on natural ecological limits. Thus a slight, but unknown, degree of inaccuracy has been introduced in the identification of tribal limits. Since a closed spatial system is involved, this error may be presumed to be non-systematic, but it contributes to the unexplained variance in the correlation between the primary variables.

The determination of all areas was made with a Keufel and Esser planimeter, model No. 4236. The projection used for Tindale's map could not be determined accurately, but it seemed to be a compromise between equal area and equal distance systems. Empirical planimeter tests against areas of known size (based upon 16 trials each, involving four replications of four different combinations of planimeter arm position, placement of the pole weight, and direction of tracing) gave one planimeter unit equal to 100.0 square miles ±1.0. The centers of the areas so tested ranged from 320 to 1,040 miles distant from the center of the map, and the three tests revealed no consistent system of distortion of area values proceeding toward the margins of the continent. It was therefore assumed that no error of importance would be introduced by using the above conversion value throughout Tindale's map.

The area of each tribe was determined from the average of four planimeter runs, each involving either a change in the position of the pole weight, planimeter arm, or the direction of tracing. The range of the four values was usually ±1.0 planimeter units over a range between 10 and 500 planimeter units, indicating that the relative error of estimate decreased as the size of the tribal areas increased. For very small tribes, with areas less than 10 planimeter units, the procedure was modified by extending each tracing of the boundary to five continuing replications, then dividing the resultant reading by five, and so obtaining a lower error of estimate.

In addition to the generally non-systematic errors introduced by the above operations, and which contribute to some small extent to the unexplained variance, there remains another possible source of error. This involves the definition and identification of the tribe as an entity. Tindale accomplished the enormous task of surveying the distribution of Australian aboriginal tribes with great skill, but he noted a number of difficulties encountered in the process. Much of the literature on the subject is filled with synonyms and confusing variations of tribal names. In many instances the earlier workers confused horde-like units with tribes. Tindale carefully evaluated these errors in nomenclature, and brought the data into a single, consistent system. Of the approximately 600 tribes on the continent, he obtained fresh information in the field on 400 tribal units, thus providing a sound matrix for the entire survey. Even so, other complications rendered his work difficult. He notes that tribal fragmentation seems to have occurred in three areas: (1) among the Murngin people of northeast Arnhem Land; (2) among the tribes along the Daly River in Northern Territory; and (3) in the Boulia district in central Queensland. On the other hand, consolidation among tribal groups seems to have occurred in the central interior of New South Wales, among such tribes as the Kamilaroi and Wiradjuri. This trend appears to reflect the development of a more advanced type of political organization based upon matrilineal descent. In addition to these regionally systematic variations, it is to be noted that sporadic shifts in the fortunes of individual tribes may result in their gradual differentiation into new multiple tribal units, in the case of growth in numbers, or their absorption into neighboring tribes in instances of declining population. Both tendencies alter the size of the tribal population, and hence the nature of intra-tribal and inter-tribal interactions. As pointed out in later sections, systematic regional deviations in either direction can be corrected for, but those of erratic occurrence cannot be excluded. Such cases result in increasing the unexplained variance of the size of

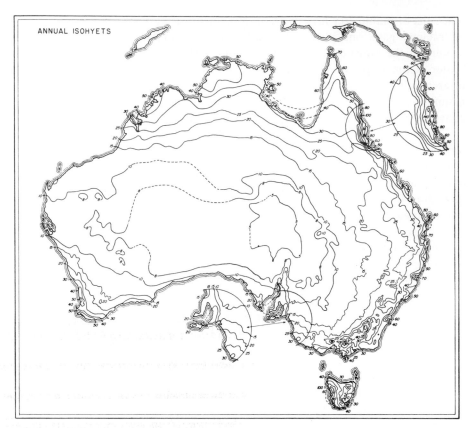

FIG. 2. Distribution of mean annual rainfall.

the tribal area. The same will be true of those occasional cases involving inadequate data in which horde-like units have been elevated to full tribal status. In
total effect these errors may have introduced a small systematic bias toward
elevating portions of tribes to full tribal status. The size of this error cannot be
estimated, but the thorough nature of Tindale's survey assures that it has been
kept at a minimum.

Mean annual rainfall, the independent variable with which size of tribal
areas is to be correlated, was obtained from a map modified after that published
in the "Climatological Atlas of Australia" (1940 ?). The map is shown in
Figure 2. The method used in estimating the rainfall values for each tribal
territory was crude but reasonably effective. It is analogous to estimating the
center of gravity of an irregularly shaped and variably loaded plane surface.
The "center of gravity" gives, through its position with respect to the isohyets
traversing the area, the average mean annual rainfall for the tribal territory.
In simple cases, as in arid regions, the estimate can be made rapidly by eye.
In more involved instances, in which several isohyets cross a single tribal area,

the latter is broken down into a number of sub-areas, and the mean annual rainfall is estimated for each. The resultant average rainfall for the entire tribal area is then calculated by a method of weighted means.

To test the error of estimate, replicative estimates of rainfall were made along three transects which covered the full range of values from four inches to 150 inches annually. Each transect originated in the territory of the Won-kanguru in the Lake Eyre Basin, an area of minimal rainfall: the first extended north to the Njangga tribe of the Gulf of Carpentaria; the second stretched northeast to terminate in the rainforest wih the Mamu tribe; and the third ran a little south of east to end in Dainggati tribal territory on the northern coast of New South Wales. Thus 33 tribes were subjected to re-estimation. In 23 cases the estimates of mean annual rainfall taken to the nearest inch were identical in the two trials. A brief analysis of the error of estimate gives approximately a mean error of ±1.0 percent distributed over the total 33 cases. The value of the error was roughly constant over the total range of rainfall values.

A further source of error in the independent variable results from the gen-eralized nature of the map used to estimate rainfall. In the few tribes where it has been possible to check against more detailed data, the error from this source was sometimes appreciable. It is hoped that in a future analysis it will be possible to obtain data giving more accurate microgeographical rainfall values than those here used from necessity. Yet another source of possible error lies in the factor of time. Current rainfall estimates are based primarily upon records of 50 years or less in duration. In the older settled area of the south and east the tribal boundaries are given as they existed a century or more ago. To the extent that slight climatic shifts may have occurred in this ill-defined time interval the esti-mate of current rainfall may be systematically in error.

Beyond Tindale's comment that a general reverse relationship exists between the size of tribal area and rainfall, and the fact that this map shows it quite clearly, there are good theoretical reasons to expect such a correlation. In mammalian ecology it is generally recognized that the density of a given type of population will be some function of the critical environmental variables. While this relationship has not previously been demonstrated quantitatively for man, it seems likely that for hunting and gathering peoples similar forms of environ-mental determinism might obtain. In aboriginal Australia, with its moderate temperatures and small altitudinal variations as compared to other continents, it might be presumed that the biotically effective quantity of rainfall would prove one of the more important of the variables of the environment.

There remains the important problem of functionally relating the size of the tribal area to density. There is no reason for rainfall directly to determine the area occupied by the Australian social unit known as the tribe. Unfortunately there are too few estimates of the population size of aboriginal tribes to work directly with density as the dependent variable. The bridging device is found in the definition of population density as the number of individuals per unit of area. It follows that an exact inverse relationship is established between tribal

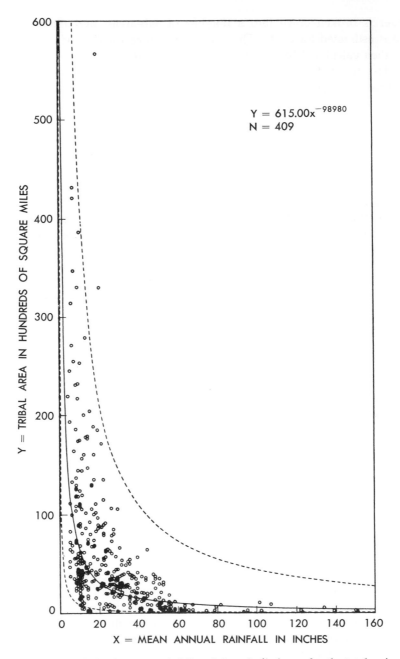

FIG. 3. Correlation between rainfall and size of tribal area for the total series.

area and tribal density if the population size of the tribes is held constant throughout this series. Thus it becomes crucial for the following analysis to make the intervening assumptions that: (1) population densities are causally and inversely related to the mean annual rainfall within the tribal territory; and (2) in a statistical sense the population size of the Australian tribe may be considered a constant, in this case approximately 500 persons. If the mean annual rainfall, which is the best simple measure available for biotically effective rainfall, does in fact show a reasonably high degree of correlation with the size of the tribal area, it will tend to validate both of the foregoing interlocked assumptions.

Since a certain rashness is apparent in the above statements, further explanations and qualifications are in order. The degree of correlation between two variables merely demonstrates the degree of association, and may or may not indicate a causal relationship. In the present instance as later evidence will show the ecology of the aborigines clearly argues that such a relationship is causal in nature. A further qualification must be added with regard to the interpretation of such a correlation. If other critical parameters vary as some systematic function of rainfall, it would not be apparent from this form of analysis. Thus if the slight regional differences in aboriginal culture were to affect efficiency in extracting energy from the environment in some fashion associated with changes in rainfall, this complicating factor could not be identified in the primary correlation. Or if for any reason the average size of the tribal population varied as a function of rainfall, the distorting influence of this factor could not be detected. Thus, for example, tribes might have consistently small sized populations in desert areas, and larger ones in regions of high rainfall without this being apparent in the original correlation. But there is little evidence to suggest that this type of variation is important.

The scattergram showing the relationship between the size of the tribal area of the 409 tribes of the total series and their mean annual rainfall is given in Figure 3. The distribution is by no means a random one, and shows a high degree of association. Several attempts at curve-fitting indicated that the data were satisfied by an exponential equation in the form:

$$Y = {}_aX^b,$$

where Y is the tribal area and X is mean annual rainfall. The coefficient of curvilinear correlation, rho, is 0.59 and σLog Y is 0.42854. Calculation of the constants gives the following equation:

$$Y = 615.00 \, X^{-0.98980}.$$

The band of error calculated to give 95 percent inclusion of the data is shown by the dotted lines in Figure 3. It will be noted that rather fewer points fall outside than might have been expected. The logarithmic curve fits the central mass of the data fairly well, but in the asymptotic regions the data conform less closely to the curve.

A curvilinear coefficient of 0.6 for the unselected total series is encouraging, but from an ecological point of view the series is a heterogeneous one. Before proceeding to interpretation it seems wise to obtain an ecologically more homogeneous series by making certain types of systematic correction. Since our method involves assumptions that: (1) the size of the tribal populations approximates a statistical constant, and (2) that the size of the tribal area is an inverse expression of the tribal density, it will be advisable to eliminate systematically from further consideration those groups of tribes which show marked deviations from either assumption. Thus the categories of tribes subject to such exclusion may be chosen by two types of criteria: (1) systematic deviations from expected densities due to variation in ecological factors; and (2) deviations in either direction from the assumed constant size of 500 persons per tribe owing to the action of cultural variables. A validation for these categorical exclusions will be presented in later sections.

Ecologically, any environmental factors which alter the relationship between the area occupied by a tribe and the density expected for its rainfall regime will be considered grounds for exclusion. To provide the broadest and most stable basis for comparison, our ecological standard will consist of those tribes whose resources are primarily terrestrial in origin, and whose territories are essentially watered by rainfall which falls within their territories. Those tribes whose domain lay wholly or partially upon islands were excluded prior to the creation of the basic series of 409 tribes. All coastally situated tribes are now further eliminated, since marine food resources would be expected to increase the population density compared to purely terrestrial tribal standards.* Just as marine food resources alter the usual density-area relationships, so will the foods provided by rivers. While much of the southern and western coasts, as well as nearly all of the interior of Australia, is characterized by intermittent or transient streams and rivers, there are coastal areas, particularly in the east and north, where permanent rivers are the rule. In such cases their waters are largely derived from small drainage areas, and the riverine food resources are considered here to be a normal manifestation of a high rainfall regime. But in the interior of the southeastern portion of the continent there exists a great and largely permanent river system, the Murray-Darling, which represents a rather different set of ecological conditions. There, in near-desert country, largely with less than 20 inches of rainfall annually, flow great rivers whose waters are derived from the western slopes of the Dividing Range. Insofar as the plains tribes of this drainage system are concerned, such rivers represent unearned surface water resources, since they are primarily nourished by rainfall from outside the plains country. Such riverine resources, like marine foods, alter the assumed relationship between the size of the tribal area and population density.

---

* In a few instances in which the tribal territory included but a very narrow coastal strip, and hence only one or two hordes were presumed to reflect increased densities owing to the availability of marine foods, this criterion for exclusion was relaxed.

For this reason, the tribes along the Murray and Darling Rivers, and their major tributaries, have been systematically excluded from the basic series.

From the cultural point of view, several factors operate so as to cause systematic deviations from the assumption that the size of the tribal population approximates a constant value of about 500 persons. Such deviations will disturb the usual relationship between size of tribal area and population density. As noted by Tindale (1940, p. 150) a group of tribes occur in the eastern interior of New South Wales in which a more advanced type of political organization, characterized by matrilineal descent, has allowed the development of especially widespread communities; that is, tribal entities in which the population size substantially exceeds 500 persons. He specifies the Kamilaroi and Wiradjuri as examples. Kryzwicki (1934) considered the Kamilaroi to have totalled betwen 6,000 and 7,000 persons and the Wiradjuri to have numbered about 3,000. His opinion was based upon rather unsatisfactory estimates by early settlers, but even though these tribal populations may have been over-estimated, they must be eliminated from our basic series as essentially representing confederacies of tribes. Data for the neighboring Wongaibon tribe are less exact, but it too can be safely excluded owing to the systematic operation of cultural factors in this region.

Allowances by exclusion must be made for a further set of cultural influences. Tindale (1940, p. 150) indicated certain areas of postulated cultural clash, in which tribal fragmentation seems to have taken place, as exceptions to the generally inverse relationship between the size of tribal territory and rainfall. He specifies northeast Arnhem Land, the Daly River district of the Northern Territory, and the region around Boulia, Queensland, as examples of this tendency. These areas seem to reveal an intensified form of tribal fragmentation, but in a less extreme form the phenomenon is more widespread. The boundaries which separate the centrally situated circumcising and subincising tribes from the marginal groups which practice neither initiatory rite are shown in Figure 7. An examination of Tindale's map reveals that the tribal areas lying just west of the eastern limits of the circumcising and subincising boundaries are notably smaller than those just to the east of the circumcising line. The Boulia district of fragmentation is just to the west of the three combined boundary lines.

Similar evidence for fragmentation associated with the spread of the initiatory rites occurs along their northern boundaries in the Northern Territory. Between the line representing the advancing front of the rite of circumcision and the less extended boundary of the subincision rite lie the two other areas of fragmentation mentioned by Tindale, the Daly River district and the Murngin region of northeast Arnhem Land. While these are focal points for the phenomenon of fragmentation, the same process seems to a lesser degree to have affected the other tribes which have recently taken over either or both of these ceremonies. Since in the case of neither the eastern nor northern limiting boundaries of the rites are there any visible ecological factors to explain the changes in tribal densities implied by the reduced size of the tribal areas, it must be presumed that the

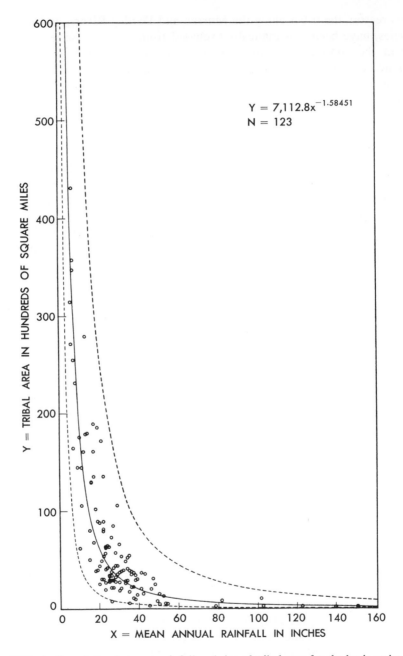

FIG. 4. Correlation between rainfall and size of tribal area for the basic series.

size of the tribal populations there is smaller than the assumed constant of 500 persons. The ethnological evidence for fragmentation tends to confirm such a conclusion.

The western boundaries of the rites of circumcision and subincision coincide. The signs of fragmentation expected to the east of the line are not visible from the map. As will be seen later, there are a number of possible explanations for this apparent difference. Nonetheless, to remove the potentially disturbing factor of fragmentation and consequently small-sized tribal populations from our analysis, a band of tribes lying just inside the limits of both the circumcising and subincising boundaries on their eastern, northern and western limits have been excluded from the basic series. While the width of the excluded band varies to some degree with the intensity of the fragmentation, in general it ranged three tribes deep inside the subincising boundary. The Boulia area, because of the extreme form of the phenomenon there, was treated more drastically.

Of the total original series of 409 tribes, 286 have been systematically eliminated from further consideration on the grounds that either ecological factors distorted the basic relationship between the size of tribal area and population density, or cultural variables produced undue deviations in the size of the tribal population as compared to the assumed constant of 500 persons per tribe. There remain 123 tribes which seem to be ecologically and culturally relatively constant in their characteristics, in so far as they effect this analysis. These 123 tribes constitute our basic series. As shown in Figure 1 in the cross-hachured area, the basic series consists of three blocks of tribes: a large series numbering about two thirds of the total centered in Queensland; and two smaller groups of about 20 tribes each, one spreading through the desert area of the interior, the other extending through the southern portion of the Dividing Range to terminate in the west in the mallee scrub just short of the mouth of the Murray River. Thus the basic series, while ranging through nearly the full variation in rainfall, from five to 151 inches, is predominantly representative of the regional ecological conditions obtaining in non-coastal Queensland. In so far as the ecological variables for this region may not be representative for the continent as a whole, a systematic error may have been introduced into the analysis.

The scattergram showing the relationship between the size of the tribal area and mean annual rainfall for each of the 123 tribes of the basic series is given in Figure 4. The distributional pattern is again that of a J-shaped curve, and these more cohesive data are likewise satisfactorily fitted by an exponential equation. Solving for the constants, the equation takes the form:

$$Y = 7,112.8 \, X^{-1.58451}.$$

Rho, the coefficient of curvilinear correlation, here reaches the very satisfactory value of 0.81. The band of error shown by the dotted lines, and calculated to give 95 percent inclusion of the data, is derived from $\sigma = 0.31495$. But 2 of the 123 tribes fall outside the band of error. This exponential curve, unlike that

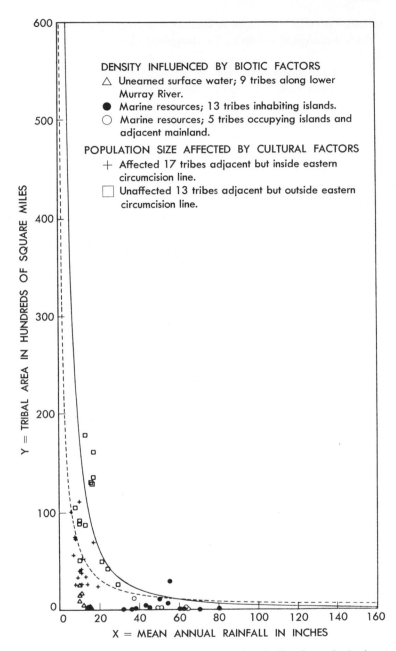

FIG. 5. Deviations of certain excluded categories of tribes from the basic curve.

fitted to the total series, shows a more satisfactory relationship with the central body of the data, and more importantly with the data along both asymptotes. This improved degree of fit suggests that the systematic exclusions practiced in defining the basic series have in fact diminished the heterogeneity of the data arising from ecological and cultural variables. The degree of displacement between the curves for the total and basic series is shown in Figure 5. It must be inferred that there exists a very high degree of association between the size of the tribal area in the basic series and the mean annual rainfall occurring within its territory.

Food resources

Now it is time to reconsider the question of whether the association between these two variables is to be interpreted as causal in nature. Ethnologically it is well established that the diet of the aborigines in Australia is characterized by its broadly omnivorous nature. They consume all the edible animal and plant food in their environment which can be economically obtained and prepared by the techniques available at their cultural level. Examples may be quoted to give emphasis to this statement. Grey (1841), one of the most accurate of the very early recorders of native life, noted the following items of diet for the groups of tribes along the southwestern coastal region of Western Australia:

A. Animal Foods

(1) 6 sorts of kangaroos.
(2) 5 marsupials somewhat smaller than rabbits.
(3) 2 species of opossums.
(4) 9 species of marsupial rats and mice.
(5) Dingoes.
(6) 1 type of whale.
(7) 2 species of seals.
(8) Birds of every kind including emus and wild turkeys.
(9) 3 types of turtles.
(10) 11 kinds of frogs.
(11) 7 types of iguanas and lizards.
(12) 8 sorts of snakes.
(13) Eggs of every species of bird and lizard.
(14) 29 kinds of fish.
(15) All saltwater shellfish except oysters.
(16) 4 kinds of freshwater shellfish.
(17) 4 kinds of grubs.

B. Plant Foods.

(1) 29 kinds of roots.
(2) 4 kinds of fruit.
(3) 2 species of cycad nuts.
(4) 2 other types of nuts.
(5) Seeds of several species of leguminous plants.
(6) 2 kinds of mesembryanthemum.
(7) 7 types of fungus.
(8) 4 sorts of gum.
(9) 2 kinds of manna.
(10) Flowers of several species of Banksia.

This exhaustive inventory suggests that very few food resources in the environment remain unexploited. Two further dietaries may be quoted for reference. The first, from Sweeney (1947), lists the foods eaten by a single desert tribe, the Walpari. The second, from Roth (1901), details the wide variety of foods eaten by the coastal and interior tribes of Queensland. Such sample dietaries serve to substantiate the claim that the aborigines exploit all, or very nearly all, of the sources of energy culturally available to them in their environment, and cover the full range of food size which can be economically utilized. In a dry continent such as Australia, ranging from tropical to temperate climate, the variations in the flora will be dependent to a large degree upon the rainfall received. It would be expected that the biomass of the flora would be correlated to a high degree and in a causal sense with the mean annual rainfall. The densities of aboriginal man, standing near the peak of the trophic pyramid and exploiting all lower levels, both animal and plant, must also respond sensitively to variations in rainfall. For these reasons it seems proper to assign a causal relationship to the high degree of correlation existing between the size of tribal territory in the basic series, and the independent variable, mean annual rainfall. The density of the aboriginal population in Australia was determined to a large measure by rainfall operating indirectly through the biota.

The excluded material

Since the basic series was created by systematic exclusion of certain groups of tribes which were considered ecologically or culturally to increase the heterogeneity of the data, it will now be profitable to reexamine the relationship of these categories to the basic series. Table 1 lists the excluded categories, and gives the mean area ratio and mean density ratio for each. The area ratio represents the measured area of the tribal territory divided by the area predicted by the basic equation for its value of rainfall. The density ratio is the reciprocal of the area ratio. In most instances it may be considered to indicate the ratio of the actual tribal density compared to the density predicted from the basic equation, based upon the assumed tribal population size of 500 persons. In a few instances, where the ecological factors remain essentially constant and the cultural factors vary, the density ratio must be interpreted as reflecting variations in the size of the tribal population rather than deviations in density. Thus an area ratio of 0.500 indicates that the tribe occupies but half the area predicted from its rainfall regime. This reduced area may either be due to ecological advantages in its territory, or to a population half the size of the expected 500 persons. The density ratio in this case would be 2.00, and might either mean the tribal density was twice that predicted, or that the size of the population was half that expected, depending upon whether the deviation is interpreted as resulting from ecological or cultural factors. In more complex instances both types of factors may be operative, but this possibility is necessarily ignored in the present analysis. While interpretations of this type cannot safely be applied to single tribes, it is considered that they may hold with some validity for systematic categories of tribes.

TABLE 1. Effects of ecological and cultural factors upon density ratios.

	Area ratios	Density ratios
1. ECOLOGICAL FACTORS CHANGING DENSITIES OF TRIBAL POPULATIONS.		
A. Unearned Surface Water:		
(1) 9 lowest tribes on Murray River:	0.058	17.33
(2) 5 lowest tribes on Murray River:	0.026	38.46
B. Marine Resources of Islands:		
(1) 27 tribes partially or completely insular:	0.402	2.49
(2) 26 tribes (omitting Tiwi) partially or completely insular:	0.326	3.07
(3) 13 tribes completely insular:	0.349	2.86
(4) 12 tribes (omitting Tiwi) completely insular:	0.179	5.58
(5) 5 tribes with 20 to 65 per cent insular domains:	0.220	4.56
(6) 8 tribes with 0.005 to 10 percent insular domains:	0.653	1.53
C. Marine Resources of Mainland Coastal Tribes:		
(1) Total available sample of 119 tribes:	0.751	1.33
(2) Southern coast: 8 tribes (Wirangu through Wardandi):	1.425	0.70
(3) Western coast: 17 tribes (Pindjarup through Ngaluma):	0.453	2.21
(4) Eighty mile Beach coast: 2 tribes (Njangamada and Karadjeri):	0.620	1.61
(5) Dampier Land coast: 7 tribes (Jauor through Ninanboro):	0.184	5.44
(6) Arnhem Land coast: 6 tribes (Wogait with 3 breaks through Gunavidji):	0.408	2.45
(7) Gulf of Carpentaria: 10 tribes (Nungubuju with 1 break through Karundi):	0.895	1.12
(8) Eastern coast Cape York Peninsula: 15 tribes (Ankamuti with 1 break through Koko-imudji):	0.586	1.71
(9) Rainforest coast of Queensland: 8 tribes (Jungkurara through Warkamai):	0.961	1.04
(10) Central coastal Queensland: 9 tribes (Bindal through Kabikabi):	1.267	0.79
(11) Southern coastal Queensland and northern New South Wales: 13 tribes (Jagara through Awabakal):	1.050	0.95
(12) Southern New South Wales and eastern Victorian coasts: 10 tribes (Kameraigal through Bratauolung):	0.671	1.49
(13) Western Victorian and eastern South Australian coasts: 14 tribes (Kurung through Nauo):	0.606	1.65
2. CULTURAL FACTORS CHANGING SIZE OF TRIBAL POPULATIONS.		
A. Advanced Type of Political Organization:		
(1) The "confederacies" of New South Wales: 3 tribes (Kamilaroi, Wiradjuri and Wongaibon):	5.200	0.192

(*cont.*)

TABLE 1. (*continued*)

	Area ratios	Density ratios
B. Fragmentation of tribes due to Recent Acquisition of Circumcision and Subincision Rites:		
(1) Eastern Circumcision boundary:		
(a) Western side: 25 tribes affected (Jokula through Kaurna):	0.467	2.14
(b) Eastern side: 21 unaffected tribes (Kalibamu through Ramindjeri):	0.728	1.37
(c) Western side: 17 affected tribes between points A-B in Fig. 7. (Workabunga through Maljangapa):	0.286	3.50
(d) Eastern side: 13 unaffected tribes between points A'-B' in Fig. 7. (Kukatji through Wiljakali):	1.002	1.00
(e) Western side: 12 affected tribes (Workabunga through Ngandanjara):	0.318	3.14
(f) Eastern side: 8 unaffected tribes (Kukatji through Wadjalang):	1.334	0.75

One of the most revealing categories of exclusion involves the ecological effect of unearned surface water upon population density. Unearned surface water in this sense refers to rivers, or freshwater lakes, which depend for their existence upon rainfall from distant regions. The Murray and Darling Rivers are the best Australian examples. Both originate on the relatively well-watered western slopes of the Dividing Range and flow through increasingly arid country. Much of their way lies through regions with but 10 to 15 inches of rainfall, and hence in their lower reaches the rivers provide locally unearned ecological resources. Tindale (1940, p. 150) indicated that the fisher-folk of the Murray River enjoyed special food advantages. A quantitative analysis strikingly extends the meaning of his statement. In Figure 5, the nine tribes of the lowest portion of the Murray have been plotted as hollow triangles in their appropriate positions. As compared to the basic curve, these riverine tribes show drastically reduced area ratios with the mean value of but 0.058. Their mean density is 17.33 times that expected from the local rainfall regimes.

Since all the tribes in the drainage of the Murray and Darling Rivers were eliminated from the basic series, it will be well to examine their position as a group. In Figure 6, the area ratios of the tribes bordering on these two rivers have been plotted against their distance from the mouth of the Murray. The trend in the unaltered data was clear, but fluctuated sufficiently so that for plotting purposes the data were smoothed out by calculating the value of the area for each tribe from a moving 3-point average. Thus treated, the data show a consistent reduction in the size of the area ratios from the Pangerang tribe near the headwaters of the Murray to the Warki at its mouth.

In a similar if less striking fashion the area ratios of the tribes along the Darling diminish from the Koamu tribe near its headwaters (in actuality, on

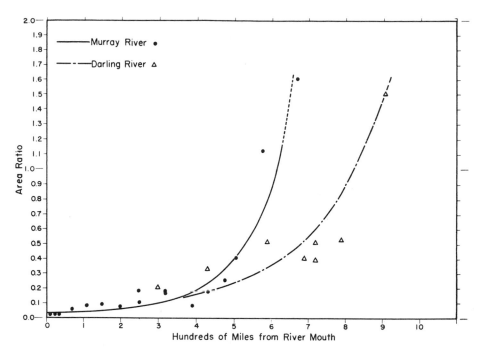

FIG. 6. Area ratios of Murray and Darling River tribes plotted against distance from Murray mouth.

the Balonna River, a major tributary of the Darling), to the Maraura tribe situated at the junction of the Darling with the Murray. The curves shown in Figure 6 were drawn freehand merely to indicate approximate trends, and a more detailed future analysis may modify their form considerably. The data show a consistent decline from the initially higher than normal values of the area ratios at the headwaters of the two rivers to the extraordinarily low values at the Murray mouth. While the data do not lend themselves to exact curve fitting, certain regularities show through. Those few tribes which include but one bank of the Murray in their territory uniformly show higher area ratios than those which include both banks. The three tribes nearest the Murray mouth show disproportionately low area ratios, perhaps as a consequence of bordering upon ecologically rich Lake Alexandrina. The five tribes nearest the mouth have an average area ratio of but 0.026, and the spectacular mean density ratio of 38.46. Since the population estimates available for these tribes, as summarized by Kryzwicki (1934) indicate that they have exceeded our assumed constant of 500 persons per tribe, it must be concluded that here the ecological effect of the unearned surface water of the Murray is responsible for aboriginal densities perhaps 40 times that to have been predicted from local rainfall values.

An ecological analysis of the Murray-Darling tribes cannot be attempted in detail at this time, but the region is obviously superior in its food resources. The waters of the river directly contribute a number of important food fish, shell-fish, and waterfowl. Indirectly the forested banks of the river increase the supply of birds and arboreal marsupials. The rich bottom lands offer a greater abundance of food plants. The ecological variables operating to increase human densities along these rivers cannot be identified in detail but it is obvious that such density ratios are not primarily determined by rainfall alone. The volume of water flow and its reliability may prove to be fair ecological indices. On the other hand, stream gradient appears to be correlated with aboriginal density and may be the primary factor. It may be postulated that the younger, steep-sided valleys of the upper water would provide less abundant food for the aborigines than would the mature, broad valley lands of the lower river. These points involve research for the future and are of no further concern here. The available evidence validates the exclusion of the Murray and Darling River tribes from the basic series on the grounds that unearned surface waters markedly alter their area ratios and hence density ratios.

Insular populations

Insular tribes represent another category in which deviations from a primarily terrestrial economy are a cause for disqualification. On *a priori* grounds all tribes residing completely or partially on islands were excluded from the total series, and hence from the basic series. This decision was based on several factors. The very configuration of islands, with a long coastline enclosing a relatively small area of land, indicates that abundant marine foods should be available. Further, unlike mainland tribes, the area of land available to a given tribal population is determined by variations in the topography of land and eustatic sea level rather than by a complex of social interactions between groups of people. Thus the area of islands bears no functional relationship to our assumed constant of 500 persons per tribe, save in the cases of islands large enough to support a greater population than this, or so close to the mainland that a single tribal population can maintain an adequate level of internal cohesion across the straits. An insular environment may operate both to increase aboriginal densities as compared to terrestrial standards, or to limit the size of a population in the case of very small islands lying well offshore. Both factors may be operative in many cases.

   Despite these complexities, it is of some interest to compare the position of the insular tribes with the basic series. In Figure 5 the positions of 13 tribes wholly insular are plotted with solid circles, and 5 tribes occupying islands and portions of the adjacent mainland are shown by half-solid circular symbols. In the latter cases the islands provide from 20 to 65 percent of their total domain. Data for nine additional tribes even less insular in nature are given in Table 1. The plotted positions for the tribes in the first two categories show the expected deviations from the basic curve in the direction of higher density ratios. A single exception, the Tiwi tribe of Melville and Bathurst Islands, has a much larger population than the assumed constant of 500 persons, and this may partially explain its position above the curve.

Table 1 presents an interesting trend in terms of insular density ratios. The total series of 27 wholly or partially insular tribes have a mean density ratio of 2.49, and if the Tiwi are omitted, the ratio rises to 3.07. For 13 completely insular tribes, the density ratio is 2.86, a value which rises to 5.58 with the exclusion of the Tiwi. Five tribes whose domain is from 65 to 20 percent insular show a mean density ratio of 4.56. Eight tribes with 10 percent or less of their territory on islands show a mean density ratio of but 1.53. Despite the small size of these samples, and the ecological variations along the different coastal regions of Australia, it is perhaps fair to infer that marine food resources do importantly alter aboriginal ecology and hence density. The detectable trend for density ratios to increase in passing from slightly to completely insular tribes is taken as confirmation, even though changes in population size may also be involved. As mentioned earlier, tribes with a foothold on the mainland have potential room for expansion to our assumed constant of 500 individuals per tribe via give and take adjustments with neighboring peoples, but totally insular groups may have their numbers limited in part by available land area. Despite their limitations the data do justify the decision to eliminate on ecological grounds both completely and partially insular tribes from the total and the basic series.

The coastal populations

The ecological position of the mainland coastal tribes is one further aspect of the problem posed by the addition of marine foods to the aboriginal diet. The available data consist of 119 tribes totally unselected, save that four gaps occur along the northern coast as shown in Figure 1. The average area ratio for the series of coastal tribes is 0.751 and the mean density ratio reaches 1.33. On a gross level access to the coast may be interpreted as increasing density by one third over the value predicted for inland tribes by the basic rainfall equation. Thus the systematic exclusion of the coastal tribes from the basic series seems justified, since there is no evidence to suggest that their tribal populations are smaller in numbers than that assumed for the whole continent.

But a regional examination of the coastal tribes indicates a complex pattern of variation which implies that much is yet to be learned of their ecology at a detailed and local level. It is convenient to survey briefly these tribes, beginning at Eyre Peninsula and going around the continent in a clockwise direction, lumping together groups of tribes which show generally consistent deviations from predicted density ratios. The 119 tribes have thus been divided into 12 subgroups which are listed in Table 1 under the subheading, I-C. The first local group, C-2, extends from the Eyre Peninsula westward across the shores of the Great Australian Bight, around Cape Leeuwin to Geographe Bay. This group is characterized by the surprisingly low density ratio of 0.70. For the tribes along the Bight this low ratio may be explained by the total lack of even transient streams, the limiting factor of very scarce surface water in the form of springs and soaks, and a lack of watercraft. But it is more difficult to account for the continuance of these low density ratios into the well-watered southwestern corner of the continent. A detailed study of the marine fauna might provide a partial answer.

The second group of tribes, C-3, extends northward from Geographe Bay around Northwest Cape to Nickol Bay and shows the inexplicably high mean density ratio of 2.21. This coast has low rainfall and intermittent streams and rivers. At first sight it would seem to offer few advantages for aboriginal life. Yet Grey (1841), traversing much of this coast on foot under forced marches, concluded that parts of this region were the most densely settled he had seen in aboriginal Australia. He noted valleys rich in yams and lagoons abundant in their marine life and waterfowl. Further, marine turtles extend as far south as Shark Bay, so that this coastal country may have been more attractive from the native point of view than rainfall values suggest.

The next group, C-4, consisting of but two tribes along the Eighty Mile Beach, shows a mean density of 1.61, which reduction may be accounted for by the poor country and lack of streams. A fourth group, C-5, consisting of tribes along the Dampier Land coast, shows a mean density ratio of 5.44, the highest value for any of the coastal regions. Unless an abundance of turtle and dugong make this an ecologically rich coast, it may be suspected that the size of the tribal populations here falls below our assumed constant, and results in an apparent increase in the density ratio. Neither aboriginal food resources nor population estimates are obtainable in detail to determine this point.

There are at present no data for the tribes of the Kimberley coast, so that the next group, C-6, consists of scattered tribes along the coast of Arnhem Land. Here the mean density ratio falls to a more normal value of 2.45 which may be more representative of the tropical coastal regions. After a short break, group C-7, lying along the lowland stretch of the southern shore of the Gulf of Carpentaria, shows a mean density ratio of 1.12, a value which needs explanation in terms of both local ecology and population sizes. After another break and beginning at the tip of Cape York Peninsula a block of 15 coastal tribes extend down to the northern margin of the rainforest. They comprise group C-8 and show a mean density ratio of 1.71. Some of these tribes are essentially marine rather than terrestrial in their mode of life, owing to the dugout canoe, a trait diffused from New Guinea, which allows increased efficiency in the exploitation of marine foods.

Group C-9 includes eight rainforest tribes with a mean density ratio of 0.96, a value slightly below that predicted for inland tribes having no access to the sea. A breakdown of this group reveals that the four northern members, all of whom use the dugout canoe, have a mean density ratio of 1.63, whereas the four southern tribes, limited to less efficient watercraft, average but 0.76 for their density ratio. It would be tempting to consider that these differences in density ratio are a measure of the ecological contribution of the dugout, but present data are insufficient to allow this conclusion. With more information it may be possible to evaluate the contribution made by this cultural factor to the ecology of a coastal people for whom turtle, dugong and other marine foods are of great importance.

The tribes of the central Queensland coast, C-10, show the inexplicably low mean density ratio of 0.79. Since this region is well watered, with permanent rivers, and both terrestrial and marine foods are abundant, one is at a loss to explain the low density ratio in ecological terms. It may be that this value reflects a systematic increase in population size; present data suggest but do not allow this as a final decision. The next group, C-11, roughly extends from Brisbane to a little north of Sydney and yields a mean density ratio of 0.95. This low value may reflect the disappearance of turtle and dugong along the coast in combination with mountains which in many places approach the sea and may reduce the exploitable terrestrial resources. Another group, C-12, stretches from just north of Sydney to a little east of Melbourne and gives a mean density ratio of 1.65. Here again mountains encroach upon the sea, but the coast is broken by numerous deep bays, estuaries and lake-like lagoons which, through their lengthened shoreline and ecological variation, probably confer advantages not to be predicted from mean annual rainfall as the sole determinant of density. On the other hand, early population estimates (Kryzwicki, 1934) suggests that here the size of the tribal population falls below the assumed value of 500 persons, and thus may cause an apparent increase in the density ratios. The relative contributions of these two factors cannot yet be determined. The final group, C-13, extending from Melbourne through to Yorke Peninsula, and including the coastal tribes at the mouth of the Murray River shows an average density ratio of 1.65. This value is of little significance because of the ecologically heterogeneous nature of the tribes which contribute to it.

The foregoing rapid survey of the regional variations in the average density ratios among Australian coastal tribes provides but few useful generalizations. As might have been anticipated from the relative contribution of marine foods, the coastal tribes have density ratios intermediate between the insular and purely terrestrial inland tribes. Beyond that, it seems safe to infer that density ratios run higher along tropical than temperate coasts. Here the sea turtle, and to a lesser extent the dugong, may contribute importantly to the difference. Evidence from the Bight indicates that a lack of free surface water may act as a limiting factor of even coastal peoples. There are hints that technological improvements, such as the dugout canoe, may measurably influence the extractive efficiency of a people in a given environment, and hence directly change their density. It is quite evident that the ecology of coastal peoples becomes sufficiently complex so that most of the observed variations cannot be explained in terms of rainfall alone.

A detailed ecological investigation of the coastal tribes cannot be undertaken at this time, but certain of the steps necessary for a solution can be predicted.

Systematic deviations in the size of tribal populations, if they occur, must be determined. The relative contributions of marine and terrestrial food resources must be evaluated, for rainfall will be of predictive use only for the latter. Further, there are some cultural hints that coastal peoples do not exploit the available terrestrial foods as intensively as do interior tribes. Along the rugged southeastern coast the encroachment of mountains will require corrective factors for differences in altitude and land gradients, for these will affect the types of land resources available and the intensity with which they can be exploited. Finally, the ecology of the marine contributions must be defined in detail. Differences between cold and warm water biota must be established. The contribution per running mile of deep water shorelines, sandy shoal water, brackish bay and lagoon, and mangrove swamp will require determination for different sections of the coastline. The task is a formidable one, but some predictive formulae, although clearly complex ones, can be derived to take the more important variables into account. Such an analysis would be facilitated if ethnologists, who have provided much useful qualitative information, would go further and obtain quantified data concerning the important foods used in a full seasonal cycle.

Populations excluded on cultural grounds

The preceding sections validated the exclusion of categories of tribes which for ecological reasons had densities deviating from those predictable from the basic rainfall equation. There remain two cultural factors to be justified as grounds for elimination. Since they operate to change the size of the tribal population, it will be convenient to use the area ratios for comparison. The first factor concerns the influence of a more advanced type of political organization characterized by matrilineal descent. The three excluded tribes, the Wiradjuri, Kamilaroi and Wongaibon, showed area ratios of 8.46, 5.03 and 2.10 respectively. The three tribes together show a mean area ratio of 5.02. It may be inferred from this that tribal populations in this region approximated 2,500 persons, as against the value of 500 assumed for the continent. The early observers quoted by Kryzwicki (1934) gave even higher estimates for the first two tribes. Thus it may be concluded that these three tribes on cultural grounds should not be included in the basic series.

A second cultural factor considered as a basis for exclusion in the basic series is involved in the spread of the initiation rites of circumcision and sub-incision. These ceremonies seem, in terms of age-area theory, to have originated in the center of the continent, and hence at the outer boundaries of their distribution they appear to be recent acquisitions among the affected tribes. The distribution of the rites are given in Figure 7, in which an eastern, a northern, and a western set of boundaries can be identified. On its eastern limits, the boundaries of the two ceremonies coincide from the Gulf of Carpentaria southwards until a point of bifurcation is reached; then the limits of circumcision pass in a

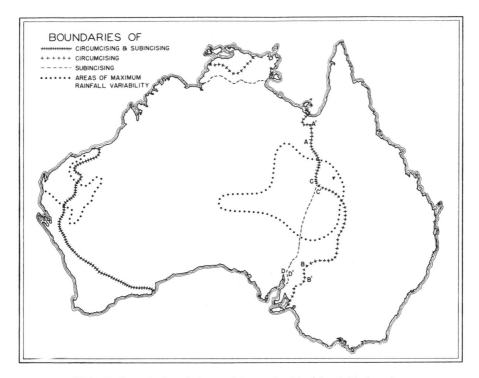

FIG. 7. Boundaries of circumcision and subincision initiation rites.

more easterly direction to ultimately reach the Gulf of St. Vincent, while the boundary for subincision proceeds in a more westerly direction to terminate at the head of Spencer's Gulf. This eastern set of boundaries shows the phenomenon of fragmentation most clearly since larger numbers of tribes are available along its limits, and coastal ecological disturbances are minimized. It is our thesis that the recent acquisition of either or both of these initiation rites operates in some as yet unknown fashion to produce tribal units with fewer than the 500 persons assumed as our continental constant. In short, the advent of these ceremonies is associated with tribal fragmentation.

This hypothesis may be tested by comparing area ratios and early population estimates. As shown in Table 1 subheading 2-B, the 25 tribes lying just west of the circumcision line have an average area ratio of 0.467, whereas the 21 tribes adjacent to the line on the east show a mean area ratio of 0.728. Thus as predicted from the basic rainfall equation, tribes lacking the circumcision ceremony have an area 1.56 times as large on the average as those tribes which have recently received the rite. The contrast would be even greater save for the fact that the coastal tribes do not follow this pattern as closely as do the interior tribes. A better basis for comparison can be obtained by eliminating the aberrant coastal tribes. When this is done, a transect of 17 non-coastal tribes lying between points A-B to the west of the circumcision line shows a mean area ratio of 0.286, whereas 13 tribes comparably situated to the east of the boundary have an average area ratio of 1.002. By this comparison, the unaffected tribes average 3.50 times the area of those which have newly taken over the rite. In Figure 5, these 13 unaffected tribes are plotted as hollow squares, and it will be seen that they are distributed rather uniformly about the basic rainfall curve. The corresponding 17 affected tribes are plotted as crosses, and they consistently fall far below area values predicted from rainfall, thus demonstrating reduced tribal areas. A further disturbing factor arises from the presence of ecologically important unearned surface water from the Darling River in the territory of nine unaffected tribes lying to the east of the line. By further eliminating the tribes thus influenced, and their partners in comparison across the line, even more striking results are obtained. Thus 12 affected tribes west of the line show a mean area ratio of 0.318, whereas eight contiguous tribes to the east of the line give an average area ratio of 1.33. Even though the smaller numbers involved diminish the validity of the comparison, it is striking that the non-circumcising tribes have areas averaging 4.19 times larger than their western neighbors who have recently acquired the ceremony. This series of comparisons suggest that, in the absence of visible ecological factors capable of producing changes in densities, the tribes just to the west of the line are characterized by much smaller population sizes than the assumed constant of 500 persons. The population estimates for this region as summarized by Kryzwicki (1934) strikingly confirm this inference. There can be little doubt that the diffusion of circumcision rites to the east has been associated with tribal fragmentation.

The above analysis was concerned with the rite of circumcision, either alone or combined with subincision. Since the most striking differences were found in a transect in which some of the affected tribes practiced subincision as well as circumcision, it will be of some interest to examine the effect of subincision alone as a differentiating trait. This can be achieved by comparing tribes just to the west of the subincision line, as shown between points C-D in Figure 7, with corresponding tribes practicing only circumcision lying just east of this boundary between points C'-D'. The six affected tribes to the west of the line have a mean area ratio of 0.185, whereas the five unaffected tribes across the line to the east show an average area ratio of 0.262. The tribes which practice only circumcision have 1.42 times as large an area on the average as those neighboring groups which perform both initiation rites. Despite the very small size of the samples involved, these data suggest that the rite of subincision when recently acquired tends to produce tribal fragmentation beyond that involved with the spread of circumcision alone. The available estimates given by Kryzwicki (1934) indicate very small tribal populations for the tribes here practicing dual initiation rites, and thus lend confirmatory evidence to the theory of fragmentation.

The evidence from the northern boundaries of circumcision and subincision is based upon very small samples, but it tends to substantiate the trends observed among the tribes along the eastern limits of the rites. Three non-coastal tribes lying just north of the circumcision boundary show an area ratio averaging 2.31. Five interior tribes positioned between the limits of circumcising and subincising show a mean area ratio of 1.56. It should be recalled that the Daly River tribes and the Murngin complex of northeastern Arnhem Land, both coastal in location and lying between these lines, were remarked by Tindale (1940, p. 150) as showing fragmentation. Three interior tribes just inside the subincision boundary average 1.01 for their area ratio. These data are scanty but consistent with the suggestion of fragmentation following the acceptance of both circumcision and subincision that was noted along the eastern limits of these ceremonies.

The western boundaries of the rites coincide throughout their length. An examination of the area ratios on either side of this line does not confirm the trends found for the eastern and northern boundaries. The 19 unaffected tribes to the west of the line show an average area ratio of 0.534, whereas the 12 tribes practicing both rites just east of the line have a mean area ratio of 0.751. There are several local factors which may explain these discordant results. Information relating to the tribal groups in this region is less detailed than for most of the rest of the area used for analysis. Thus occasionally subtribal units may have been confused with tribal entities. The boundaries of most tribes are approximate rather than fully defined by the data. As noted earlier coastal tribes do not closely follow the pattern of fragmentation established for interior tribes: of the 19 tribes outside the boundary, no less than 11 are coastal in location. Further, this coastal stretch was characterized by unexpectedly low average area ratios. Unfortunately there are virtually no population estimates for these tribes to indicate whether their populations conform reasonably to the assumed constant of 500 persons.

Finally, a further environmental factor may have some influence here. The two areas of maximum rainfall variability in Australia, occur (modified after Gentilli, 1946), as might be expected, in arid regions. The largest is found centered in the Boulia region of Queensland, as shown in Figure 7. Here the pattern of tribal fragmentation so closely follows the region affected by minimum rainfall reliability as to suggest that some causal relationship exists between the two. In these terms unreliable rainfall may increase the tendency toward fragmentation which also seems associated with the recent acquisition of circumcision and subincision. A second area of maximum rainfall variability centers in Western Australia along the Ashburton River, as indicated in Figure 7, and extends over the broken highlands of the Hammersley Range to the north and the Barlee Range to the south. Again, maximum fragmentation seems to have coincided remarkably with the pattern of minimum rainfall reliability. For these various reasons it is considered that the negative evidence from the western boundaries of the initiatory rites does not vitiate the earlier conclusion that tribes which have recently acquired circumcision and subincision rites show a tendency toward fragmentation. The affected belts of tribes have therefore been properly excluded from the basic series.

Tribal fragmentation

The question as to why such fragmentation should occur is not to be easily answered. The spread of both initiation ceremonies is known to have been a gradual and essentially undramatic process. Neighbors were known to be practicing the rites, they were witnessed by visitors, and when introduced later with ceremonial sanctions, it is difficult to comprehend why diffusion should be accompanied by social shock-effects. The problem is further complicated by the fact that both the patterning of area ratios and the population estimates of early observers for tribes deep within the affected area strongly suggest that tendency toward fragmentation was transient, that tribes which had practiced the rites for longer periods of time tended toward reintegration so that tribal populations returned to the assumed constant of about 500 persons. It is on these grounds that a block of 20 tribes in the center of the area of initiating tribes have been included in the basic series. It is perhaps enough to indicate here that the area ratio method has served to identify the phenomenon of transient tribal fragmentation in Australia, to associate it with the diffusion of circumcision and subincision, and to note that the tendency seems heightened in areas of minimum rainfall reliability. The functional explanation will certainly be found in the realm of social forces and interactions, and thus will await further research by cultural anthropologists.

Average size of tribes

Throughout the discussion the assumption has been used that the Australian tribe, in a broad statistical sense averages about 500 persons. In this assumption the existence of a marked central tendency is more important than the absolute size of the estimate. The calculations of Brown (1930), who systematically surveyed the problem, yield averages from 437 to above 523 persons per tribe. Kryzwicki (1934) comprehensively covered the available literature and reached similar values. He tabulated early estimates for 123 tribes with the following results: 70 tribes numbered less than 500 persons; 37 tribes numbered between 500 and 1,000; 12 tribes ranged between 1,000 and 2,500; and four tribes contained more than 2,500 individuals. From these figures Kryzwicki concluded that the tribe in Australia averaged about 550 persons, but he cautioned that his compilation contained inherent errors. The majority of his estimates originated from the correspondents of E. M. Curr, and Kryzwicki (1934, p. 305) provided the following evaluation of them:

> ... individuals, with but few exceptions, who were fundamentally far from any systematic scientific interest in the phenomena observed by them. In the best cases they were persons who were willing to relate what they had seen during their personal contacts with the natives. They saw, or rather encountered, a certain number of bands forming integral parts of tribes: this was usually enough for them, and more often than not they treated such bands as tribal communities. ... And so, more especially as regards tribes with a population of under

500 souls, the possibility is very great that we may have included in our list such names which are designations of portions of tribes. . . . Another difficulty to overcome is to ascertain where the limits of a tribe end and those of a nation begin. The category of tribes with over 2,500 head of population quoted in our table really embraces only nations. . . . We cannot issue any definite opinion whether these were really nations or only large tribes, on the basis of the material we have at hand. But we draw attention to this difficulty as also to the caution which is indicated and even essential when studying the data given hereunder.

Kryzwicki further warns that his list of 123 tribes represents poor regional sampling for the continent, and that Curr's informants tended to ignore the many small tribes, reporting on disproportionate numbers of large and very large tribes. He concludes cautiously that the typical population of an Australian tribe may be considered to range between 300 and 600 persons.

Of the 123 tribes listed by Kryzwicki it has been possible to identify 77 as corresponding to those defined by Tindale (1940). Most of the unidentified "tribes" are hordes by the latter's list, some cannot be equated with Tindale's nomenclature, and half a dozen required exclusion for other reasons. Although Kryzwicki was fully aware of the dubious accuracy of the estimates he quotes, the situation is further complicated by an epidemic which seems to have been smallpox, that spread through parts of eastern Australia in the early nineteenth century, and may have affected most of the continent. Depopulation clearly followed, but the magnitude of its impact cannot now be estimated. This factor may result in Kryzwicki's values, and our own, being underestimations.

Comparisons of population estimates

Despite these difficulties it seems worth testing population data against our predictions for tribal population size derived from the basic rainfall equation. The method of estimating the size of tribal populations from the area ratio determined from the basic equation requires that the size of the populations approximates a statistical constant. In this case it has been assumed to be 500 individuals, but should later more accurate data indicate a changed value, it would not affect the method. Estimated population size will vary directly with the area ratio: thus an area ratio of 1.00 indicates a tribal population estimate of 500 persons; a ratio of 2.00 gives an estimate of 1,000; and a ratio of 0.50 an estimate of 250 persons. Since the method is applicable only to those groups of tribes in which the area is a direct and constant expression of population size, the following categories in which ecological factors modify tribal densities have been eliminated: (1) coastal and insular tribes; (2) tribes affected by unearned surface water.* This leaves for comparative purposes the basic series plus those

---

* The three large "confederacies" have been excluded to keep the coordinates of the diagram shown in Fig. 8 within reasonable and convenient scale values. They should perhaps also be excluded as being probably affected by unearned surface water.

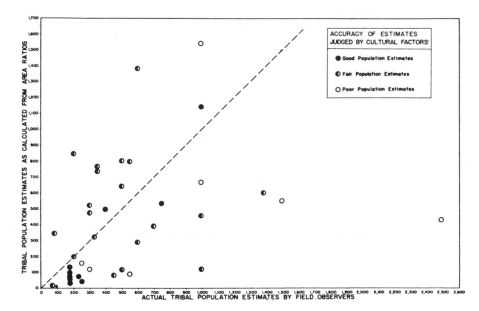

FIG. 8. Correlation between tribal population estimates from early observers and those calculated by area ratio methodology.

circumcising and subincising tribes which have not been excluded by the above criteria. From Kryzwicki's list of tribes there are 45 which fulfill the necessary conditions. Figure 8 shows the population estimates of early observers plotted against estimates calculated from area ratios. Prior to plotting, the estimates by field observers were independently graded as to their validity as judged from cultural factors involving care of observation and internal consistency. Of the 45 estimates, 11 were judged as good (largely the data of modern anthropologists), 27 were considered as fair, and 7 were classed as poor in probable accuracy. These categories are shown by appropriate symbols in Figure 8. It will be noted that the estimates considered to be poor give the greatest scattering, whereas those thought to be good give the least, thus suggesting that the independent judgments of the accuracy of these estimates was made with a basis of reason.

The relationship between the observer's estimates of population size and the values predicted by the area ratio methodology can be tested in several different ways. One involves the coefficient of linear correlation, r, and merely gives the degree of association. The value for r is 0.436 for the total series of 45 tribes, and 0.509 for the 38 tribes judged to represent good or fair estimates. In view of the scattering shown by the 7 estimates judged to be poor, it seems proper to ignore this category as representing inaccurate guesses by poorly qualified observers.

A better method of measuring the agreement between the two sets of estimates is given by r_i, the coefficient of intra-class correlation. This more exact way measures the deviation of the data from exact agreement, represented by the dotted line. Its calculation involves the duplication of the data by reflection about this axis of agreement. The value for r_i for 45 tribes is 0.400; for the 38 tribes judged to represent good to fair estimates it rises to 0.504. Although not high, the degree of agreement indicated is fairly satisfactory considering the dubious nature of the tribal estimates by early observers. With accurate estimates from modern observers and a refined predictive equation, a much closer measure of agreement should result. Even in its present form the result suggests that the assumption of 500 persons per tribe is close to a proper figure. More importantly, the result validates the area ratio methodology, and suggests that when the basic equation has been refined to include the full set of ecological variables it will become more accurate than the population estimates quoted by Kryzwicki, and hence a useful demographic instrument for aboriginal Australia.

Variation in population size

If it will be granted that the validity of the assumed average of 500 persons per tribe has been demonstrated as a statistical abstraction, it becomes feasible to investigate the variance of the size of Australian tribal populations. Estimates for the 123 tribes of the basic series were made from their area ratios and the results were seriated. Using group intervals of 100, the distribution is shown in Figure 9. It will be noted that the frequencies for the extremes of the distribution seem to show a deficiency in numbers. Thus of the 123 tribes, but 6 cases

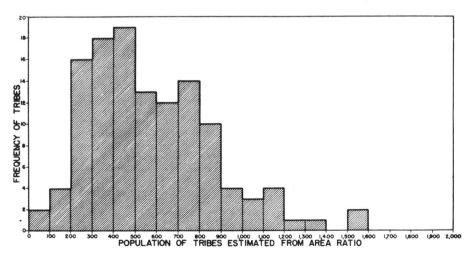

FIG. 9. Frequency distribution of tribal populations as estimated from area ratio methodology.

fall below 200 and only 15 occur in the unlimited range above 900. Consequently there appears to be a more than expected clustering tendency for tribes to average between 200 and 900 in population. It is unfortunate that the total series is too small in numbers to allow a statistical demonstration of the significance of this clumping. The mean value of the frequency distribution lies at 575, but this value is an artefact resulting from the use of arithmetic mean rather than the geometric mean. (The proper calculation was precluded by limitations of time in preparing for two years' further field work in Australia.) Thus the calculated mean is higher than the true mean, which by the nature of the area-ratio method is dependent upon the value assumed for the size of the tribal population and should have approximated 500. The mode falls between 400 and 500, giving a measure of the skewness of the distribution. The standard deviation is 300, and since it would presumably be of the same general magnitude for the proper calculation using the geometric mean, the corrected values can be estimated as a mean of 500 with a range from 200 to 800 as defined by plus and minus one standard deviation. Despite the evident inadequacies of the data, it may be claimed that Kryzwicki's earlier analysis is essentially confirmed.

The validation of 500 persons per tribe as a statistical constant of approximately correct magnitude allows the conversion of the basic equation expressing the relationship between tribal area and mean annual rainfall into a new form expressing density, D, as a function of rainfall:

$$D = \frac{0.0703037}{X^{-1.58451}}$$

where X is mean annual rainfall, (as indicated in Figure 4).

Discussion

In the early stages of this investigation it was assumed, in the absence of adequate data for the size of the Australian tribal population, that in the basic series the size of the tribal territory is an inverse measure of the density of the population, through the interlocking assumption that there tribes average about 500 persons in size. The high degree of curvilinear correlation between mean annual rainfall and the size of the tribal area confirms both of the intervening assumptions. The lack of functional validity in either case would have resulted in a low value for rho, save for the improbable instance in which one unrelated assumption somehow systematically compensated for the uncorrelated vagaries in the other. The value of 0.81 for rho is ample evidence that both of these independent assumptions hold true with a reasonable degree of validity.

A brief examination of the variance of the size of tribal populations in this correlation is revealing. With rho equal to 0.81, the explained variance of the dependent variable amounts to 65 percent of the total, the unexplained variance to but 35 percent. It is understood that the explained variance is expressed not only in terms of mean annual rainfall, but also in terms of such other variables as may prove to be partially correlated with the former. The unexplained variance must be considered to contain deviations due to the following types of errors which diminish the value of rho:

(1) *Errors of verification:* the nature of the tribe as an entity; location of tribal boundaries; instrumental errors in planimeter values for tribal areas; type of map projection; assignment of mean annual rainfall values tribally; and unrecorded microgeographical variations in rainfall.

(2) *Errors of space:* assumption that basic series ecologically represents complete regional homogeneity.

(3) *Errors of time:* assumption that no shifts in rainfall values through time have affected recorded tribal boundaries.

(4) *Errors of culture:* assumption that with broad cultural uniformity in Australia no small regional differences exist which might affect extractive efficiency.

(5) *Errors of the environment:* use of mean annual rainfall as the sole environmental variable. It must be expected that the following variables will also influence aboriginal densities; (a) rainfall reliability, (b) rainfall intensity, (c) seasonality of rainfall, (d) humidity, (e) evaporation rates, (f) temperature, (g) length of growing season, (h) altitudinal differences, (i) soil variations including trace mineral deficiencies, and (j) other unspecified factors affecting the biota.

(6) *Errors in population size:* appreciable deviations from assumption that tribal populations approximate 500 persons as a constant will occur, whether systematic or erratic in nature.

In addition to the above specified sources of error, the value of rho is dependent upon the causal relationship between mean and annual rainfall and size of the tribal population. The exact contribution to the unexplained variance can be evaluated for none of these types of errors, but each of the first four categories must have affected it slightly, while the last two must have increased it substantially. Thus it must be inferred that a very close causal relationship exists between rainfall and the size of tribal territory; that the densities of Australian aboriginal tribes are rigorously subject to environmental determinism.

Anthropologists have been so impressed with the bewildering variability of cultural expression that they have tended to deny the possible operation of environmental determinism. Historically this is understandable, for the early proponents of the latter concept claimed so much that their position was easily discredited. Our claim here is merely that on the simplest cultural levels the densities of human populations are primarily determined by the variables of the environment. Since man, like other living things, must extract his energy from the environment there are good ecological reasons for such determinism. In economies higher than the hunting and collecting level, the environmental control of densities will become less rigorous and hence less visible. The same will be true for cultures changing their form rapidly in time, especially at the technological level. But as long as man extracts his energy from the environment by crude means his population density will depend to some extent upon such determinism. For man in the Pleistocene, and much of our evolutionary interest in him centers in this period, the environment must have determined his population density as completely as it did for the Australian aborigines.

It follows as an important corollary of environmental determinism of aboriginal densities that these populations must have been in essential equilibrium with their environment. This idea will not be new to biological students of natural populations, for it is a major premise in the structure of evolutionary thinking, but it has remained foreign to most anthropological conceptualization. Although utilized in a qualitative form, either explicitly or implicitly, by Kaberry (1939), Kryzwicki (1934), Steward (1938), Tindale (1940), and Wolfe (1933) among others, it has not received widespread anthropological acceptance. It is not claiming too much to insist that studies of the population dynamics of man at a hunting and collecting level of economy whether Pleistocene or modern, must start with the premise that such groups are usually in equilibrium with their environment.* A more detailed discussion of the utility of this concept will be found in Bartholomew and Birdsell (ms.).

The present study has a number of applications to research in aboriginal Australia. The finding that the size of the tribe approximates 500 persons in a statistical sense validates one of the primary simplifying assumptions used by Birdsell (1950) for the construction of simple gene flow models used in exploring the dynamics of aboriginal populations. Even in the present tentative form of the basic equation, the area ratio method allows for the construction of considerably improved gene flow models compared to those previously published. In the latter devices such as "accelerators" were used in the Boulia region, and "inhibitors" in the region of the New South Wales "confederacies," to partially adjust for suspected deviations from the tribal norms. It is now evident that these adjustments were much too conservative and that other regions may need alteration. It is now possible to start with Tindale's tribal map and to make the corrections required for those areas in which the average size of the tribal population systematically deviates from the statistical mean of 500 persons. Sporadic deviations from this mean may also be corrected by the area-ratio method. Thus an idealized grid of genetic isolates can be created for modern aboriginal Australia which is superior for gene-flow models to the actual tribal map.

In a like way the high correlation between mean annual rainfall and the size of the tribal area will allow the construction of idealized genetic isolate grids

---

* Exceptions occur among such peoples as the salmon fishermen of the Northwest Coast and the bison hunting horsemen of the Great Plains of North America. Technically both belong with the hunting and gathering peoples but in each case these more complicated cultures are based upon special circumstances. Among culturally simple groups the concept should hold with considerable regularity.

for any time point in the Recent or terminal Pleistocene for which paleoclimato-logical estimates for approximate rainfall can be provided. Such data now are too scanty to be used, but recent strides in the natural sciences in Australia suggest that they may become available within the next decade. Then it will be possible to construct gene flow models, to determine the distribution of aboriginal densities, and to take an approximate census for a given period of prehistory. When the paleoclimatological variables can be defined for the now sunken Sahul Shelf, which formerly connected Australia with New Guinea during glacial periods of eustatic lowering of sea-level, the same techniques can be applied to that submerged land surface, an area which is of some importance in the reconstruction of population dynamics in prehistoric Australia.

The basic curve in Figure 4, which depicts the relationship between mean annual rainfall and the size of the tribal territory, suggests that the apparently simple material culture of the aborigines is in fact surprisingly adaptable. While the curve is a statistical artefact, the data show a remarkable smoothness in their distribution around the curve from one extremity to the other. This may be interpreted as indicating that, despite the relative uniformity of their material culture throughout the continent, the aborigines maintain the same high level of extractive efficiency (for a hunting and collecting people) from the most arid environment to the wettest regions in Australia. Thus no breaks occur in the distributional pattern of the data as one passes from spinifex and sandhill country at one extreme through the various types of desert scrub lands, mallee country, grassland and open forest, dense eucalyptus forest, finally to the nearly im-penetrable rainforests of the Cairns tableland region. Both the flora and fauna change drastically in abundance and in type in such a transect and the pattern of the data is witness to the constant level of cultural adaptedness of the aborigines. One qualifying statement must be made at this point. If densities were substituted for the size of tribal areas in relationship to rainfall, the picture might change slightly. This conversion is dependent upon the absence of systematic regional variations in the average size of the tribal population.*

The broad generalizations resulting from this investigation are applicable to other culturally simple hunting and collecting peoples in different places and in different times. But it must be stressed that the specific variables and the detailed constants for the Australian equation are not transferable to any other people.

---

* As stated earlier, there is little evidence for such variation save possibly in the region of the tropical rainforest. Tindale informs me that an examination of his genealogies for the tribes of this region suggests that the nuclear 11 tribes may have had considerably smaller populations than the 500 considered generally valid for the continent. If confirmed, the curve for density would deviate in form from that shown in Fig. 8, in that a point of inflec-tion would occur at about 60 inches of rainfall, and beyond this value densities would again diminish. This change would not greatly modify preceding discussions, but it would require curve fitting anew, and a different mathematical expression for the relationship between density and rainfall.

The equation relating human population densities to a given environment will depend in each instance upon three major categories of variables:

(1) The variables of the environment in terms of climatic, soil, and topographic factors;

(2) The variables influencing the phylogenetic history of the local biota;

(3) The variables in culture which determine a people's extractive efficiency.

In Australia mean annual rainfall at this preliminary level of analysis gives reasonably accurate predictions for population densities, and the same may hold true for other interior temperate and tropical populations. On the other hand, a people such as the Eskimo living in the Arctic would show densities conditioned by other variables such as temperature, length of the growing season, and the various factors which affect the marine fauna upon which they are dependent for winter survival. In general those variables which influence the local biota most importantly can be expected to be the ecologically important variables of the density equation.*

Even regions which seem environmentally to be approximately equivalent to portions of Australia will not show similar human densities or density equations for peoples at about the same level of extractive efficiency. The Shoshoni of the Great Basin in the United States, and the Bushmen of the Kalahari Desert of South Africa have been shown by Vorkapich (ms.) to have quite different densities from the Australians for the same rainfall regimes. Aschmann (ms.) shows even more striking density differences for the hunters and collectors of the middle region of Baja California. With similar environments, and extractive efficiency differing but little among these four peoples, the disparities in their densities must be attributed primarily to differences in the local biota and food chains. The Australians are dependent upon a unique flora and a marsupial fauna. The trophic levels these comprise will not be duplicated elsewhere. The Shoshoni have specialized of necessity as seed and root gatherers; game is of but little importance to them. The Bushman can depend more upon grazing animals which are more abundant in his environment than in those of the other three peoples. For Baja California human densities were markedly conditioned by the presence of a wealth of starchy plant food in the form of half a dozen species of agave. These brief examples are sufficient to indicate that the phylogenetic history of the local biota of a region is of prime importance in the formulation of the human density equation; constants derived from one region cannot be applied to another biotic province. The fact that the Indians of middle

---

* While the Australian data lent themselves to an analysis primarily based upon the size of tribal territories, it must not be presumed that the relative constancy of size of the Australian tribal population will be met with among all other peoples. In terms of cultural analogy, the assumption of similar sized population groups in the Pleistocene makes an attractive working hypothesis, but among modern peoples it seems likely that similar investigations will have to deal directly with data for densities.

Baja California with lower rainfall and no higher extractive efficiency show more than 50 times the density that Australians do in roughly equivalent climatic conditions highlights the importance of the biotic variable. Its evaluation will require detailed and quantitative ecological research upon the composition of food chains and trophic levels as they affect man.

This efficiency with which a people extract energy from their environment will vary with the content and complexity of their culture. Forms of social organization may contribute to efficiency, but for simple hunting and collecting cultures the techniques for the fabrication of primary and secondary tools will usually be of greater importance. It is unfortunate that to this late date ethnologists have provided little quantitative data on the relative efficiency of extractive devices used at this cultural level. Without such information, and there remains but little time in which to collect it, it will remain impossible for archeologists to evaluate the extractive efficiency of the various populations in the Pleistocene which are necessary to our understanding of human evolution. In view of the magnitude of the task remaining to be accomplished in this field it is perhaps fortunate that of the three categories of variables influencing the human density equation that referring to cultural variation appears to be the least important. For most simple hunting and collecting peoples, a surprisingly large proportion of the total food supply is probably obtained through the use of the unaided hands, a digging stick, and the simple spear or bow.

Summary and conclusions

(1) For the Australian aborigines a simple exponential relationship exists between mean annual rainfall and the size of the tribal territory. For the total series of 409 tribes the equation takes the form of: $Y = 615.00\ X^{-0.98980}$ where Y is the size of the tribal territory and X is the mean annual rainfall.

(2) By the systematic exclusion of categories of tribes in which ecological factors change the population density, as compared to an inland terrestrial standard, and by the elimination of tribes in which cultural factors modify the size of the population from the assumed consant of 500 persons, the equation for the basic series becomes:

$$Y = 7,112.8\ X^{-1.58451}.$$

(3) The validation of the ecologically and culturally excluded tribal categories through the area ratio method yields preliminary data toward the establishment of a quantitative human ecology in Australia. Densities are increased measurably by the marine foods available to coastal and insular tribes. Riverine foods from unearned surface water may provide the greatest increase in density. Among the cultural factors, advanced political organization may result in a marked increase in the size of the tribal population, whereas the recent acquisition of either or both circumcision and subincision ceremonies, for reasons which

have not been defined, is associated with a transient decrease in the size of tribal population.

(4) A comparison between the admittedly inaccurate early estimates for the size of tribal populations and estimates based upon the area ratio methodology confirms the assumption that statistically the size of the Australian tribe approximates 500 persons, with an effective range of variation between 200 and 800. This clustering tendency of tribal population size is apparently based upon territoriality, limited personal mobility, and absence of tribal authority as these factors operate through the forces of social cohesion to define and maintain an effective social entity.

(5) The value of 0.81 for the coefficient of curvilinear correlation of the basic equation results in an explained variance of 65 percent and an unexplained variance of but 35 percent. A listing of the categories of errors which have contributed to the unexplained variance indicates that the size of the tribal territory is causally and rigorously determined by the magnitude of the mean annual rainfall. This relationship validates the intervening, independent assumptions that for the basic inland tribes density is an inverse function of the size of the territory and that tribal populations approximate 500 persons in a statistical sense. Thus the basic equation can be rewritten in the form of an equation for density as follows:

$$D = \frac{0.0703037}{X^{-1.58451}}.$$

(6) The high degree of correlation between rainfall and density indicates that the Australian aborigines are subject to a rigorous environmental determinism of their densities. There is little reason to believe that most other Recent or Pleistocene hunting and collecting populations were not equally subject to environmental determinism of this nature. An obvious corollary is that such populations were in equilibrium with their environment, provided that culture, and hence extractive efficiency, was but slowly changing.

(7) The methodology here developed for Australia can be extended to simple hunting and collecting populations at other points of time or space, but the density equation will differ in terms of: (a) the variables of the environment critical for the biota; (b) the variables of the phylogenetic history of the local biota; and (c) the variables of culture which determine the extractive efficiency of a population.

(8) Applications of this study for Australia allow the correction of existing tribal maps to approximate an idealized distribution of genetic isolates for use in gene flow models. Similar genetic grids can be constructed for various points in prehistory when paleoclimatological estimates for mean annual rainfall in times past become available. Such instruments will allow the taking of prehistoric censuses and the determination of the pattern of distribution of prehistoric densities, even extending out onto the now submerged Sahul Shelf.

Acknowledgments

This paper is one of the results of the Harvard-Adelaide Anthropological Expedition of 1938–1939 which was generously sponsored by the Carnegie Corporation of New York. Subsequent research has been supported by the John Simon Guggenheim Memorial Foundation, the Wenner-Gren Foundation for Anthropological Research, Inc., and the Committee on Research at the University of California at Los Angeles. My indebtedness to these institutional sources of support is gratefully acknowledged. Special gratitude is due to Professor E. A. Hooton, Department of Anthropology, Harvard University, through whose foresight and initiative the original project was made possible. The success of field work was to a large measure due to the collaboration of Mr. N. B. Tindale, Ethnologist, South Australian Museum. Further indebtedness to him for the publication of the tribal map upon which this analysis has been based is gladly acknowledged. Professor William Robinson, a departmental colleague, has given much helpful advice, and assistance in the statistical analysis used in this paper.

REFERENCES

ASCHMANN, HOMER, (unpublished paper on demography of aborigines of Baja California).

BARTHOLOMEW, GEORGE A., JR., and JOSEPH B. BIRDSELL, (ms.) Ecology and the protohominids.

BIRDSELL, JOSEPH B., 1950, Some implications of the genetical concept of race in terms of spatial analysis. *Cold Spring Harbor Symposia Quant. Biol.,* 15: 259–314.

BROWN, A. R. RADCLIFFE, 1930, Former numbers and distribution of the Australian aborigines. *Off. Yrbk Commonwealth of Australia,* 23: 669–696. Melbourne, Govt. Printer.

BUREAU OF METEOROLOGY, 1940 (?), *Climatological Atlas of Australia,* Melbourne.

GENTILLI, JOSEPH, 1946, Australian climates and resources, 1–333, Melbourne, Whitcombe and Tombs, Pty., Ltd.

GREY, GEORGE, 1841, Journals of two expeditions of discovery in northwest and western Australia during the years 1837, 38 and 39. 2 vols.: 412 pp.; 482 pp. London, T. and W. Boone.

KABERRY, PHYLLIS M., 1939, Aboriginal woman. 294 pp. London, George Routledge and Sons, Ltd.

KRYZWICKI, LUDWIK, 1934, Primitive society and its vital statistics. 589 pp. London, Macmillan and Co., Ltd.

ROTH, WALTER E., 1901, Food: its search, capture and preparation. *North Queensland Ethnography, Bull.* No. 3; 1–31, Brisbane.

STERN, CURT, 1949, Principles of human genetics, San Francisco, W. H. Freaman and Co.

STEWARD, JULIAN H., 1938, Basin-plateau aboriginal socio-political groups. *Smithson. Inst., Bur. Amer. Ethn., Bull.* 120: 1–346.

SWEENEY, G., 1947, Food supplies of a desert tribe. *Oceania,* 17: 4; 289–299.

TINDALE, NORMAN B., 1940, Distribution of Australian aboriginal tribes: a field survey. *Trans. Roy. Soc. So. Aust.* 64: 1; 140–231.

VORKAPICH, MYRA, (unpublished research on population densities among Shoshoni and Bushman).

WOLFE, A. B., 1933, The fecundity and fertility of early man. *Hum. Biol.,* 5: 1; 35–60.

THE LAND
AND EARLY
FOOD PRODUCTION

*The opportunities for food production were major
factors in the formation of human settlements. Once
settlement had taken place, various environmental factors,
such as soil conditions, temperature, and other
climatic influences, had substantial effects upon the
population density, health, and culture of the settlers.
These three papers deal with food, settlements, and culture.*

SUPPLEMENTARY READINGS

BRAIDWOOD, ROBERT J., BRUCE HOWE, CHARLES A. REED, The Iranian Prehistoric Project. 1961, *Science,* **133:** 2008–2010.

REED, CHARLES A., Animal Domestication in the Prehistoric Near East. 1959, *Science,* **130:** 1629–1639.

WEDEL, WALDO R., Some Aspects of Human Ecology in the Central Plains. 1953, *American Anthropologist,* **55:** 499–514.

WEDEL, WALDO R., The High Plains and Their Utilization by the Indian. 1963, *American Antiquity,* **29:** 1–16.

Microenvironments and Mesoamerican Prehistory

MICHAEL D. COE AND
KENT V. FLANNERY*

A crucial period in the story of the pre-Columbian cultures of the New World is the transition from a hunting-and-collecting way of life to effective village farming. We are now fairly certain that Mesoamerica (*1*) is the area in which this took place, and that the time span involved is from approximately 6500 to 1000 B.C., a period during which a kind of "incipient cultivation" based on a few domesticated plants, mainly maize, gradually supplemented and eventually replaced wild foods (*2*). Beginning probably about 1500 B.C., and definitely by 1000 B.C., villages with all of the signs of the settled arts, such as pottery and loom-weaving, appear throughout Mesoamerica, and the foundations of pre-Columbian civilization may be said to have been established.

Much has been written about food-producing "revolutions" in both hemispheres. There is now good evidence both in the Near East and in Mesoamerica that food production was part of a relatively slow *evolution*, but there still remain several problems related to the process of settling down. For the New World, there are three questions which we would like to answer.

(1) What factors favored the early development of food production in Mesoamerica as compared with other regions of this hemisphere?

(2) What was the mode of life of the earlier hunting-and-collecting peoples in Mesoamerica, and in exactly what ways was it changed by the addition of cultivated plants?

(3) When, where, and how did food production make it possible for the first truly sedentary villages to be established in Mesoamerica?

* Dr. Coe is associate professor of anthropology at Yale University, New Haven, Conn. Kent Flannery is a graduate student in the department of anthropology, University of Chicago, Chicago, Ill.

The first of these questions cannot be answered until botanists determine the habits and preferred habitats of the wild ancestors of maize, beans, and the various cucurbits which were domesticated. To answer the other questions, we must reconstruct the human-ecological situations which prevailed.

Some remarkably sophisticated, multidisciplinary projects have been and still are being carried out elsewhere in the world, aimed at reconstructing prehistoric human ecology. However, for the most part they have been concerned with the adaptations of past human communities to large-scale changes in the environment over very long periods—that is, to alterations in the *macroenvironment,* generally caused by climatic fluctuations. Such alterations include the shift from tundra to boreal conditions in northern Europe. Nevertheless, there has been a growing suspicion among prehistorians that macroenvironmental changes are insufficient as an explanation of the possible causes of food production and its effects (*3*), regardless of what has been written to the contrary.

Ethnography and microenvironments

We have been impressed, in reading anthropologists' accounts of simple societies, with the fact that human communities, while in some senses limited by the macroenvironment—for instance, by deserts or by tropical forests (*4*)—usually exploit several or even a whole series of well-defined *microenvironments* in their quest for food (*5*). These microenvironments might be defined as smaller subdivisions of large ecological zones; examples are the immediate surroundings of the ancient archeological site itself, the bank of a nearby stream, or a distant patch of forest.

An interesting case is provided by the Shoshonean bands which, until the mid-19th century, occupied territories within the Great Basin of the American West (*6*). These extremely primitive peoples had a mode of life quite similar to that of the peoples of Mesoamerica of the 5th millennium B.C., who were the first to domesticate maize. The broadly limiting effects of the Great Basin (which, generally speaking, is a desert) and the lack of knowledge of irrigation precluded any effective form of agriculture, even though some bands actually sowed wild grasses and one group tried an ineffective watering of wild crops. Consequently, the Great Basin aborigines remained on a hunting and plant-collecting level, with extremely low population densities and a very simple social organization. However, Steward's study (*6*) shows that each band was not inhabiting a mere desert but moved on a strictly followed seasonal round among a vertically and horizontally differentiated set of microenvironments, from the lowest salt flats up to piñon forest, which were "niches" in a human-ecological sense.

The Great Basin environment supplied the potential for cultural development or lack of it, but the men who lived there selected this or that microenvironment. Steward clearly shows that *how* and *to what* they adapted influenced many other aspects of their culture, from their technology to their settlement pattern, which was necessarily one of restricted wandering from one seasonally occupied camp to another.

Seasonal wandering would appear to be about the only possible response of a people without animal or plant husbandry to the problem of getting enough food throughout the year. Even the relatively rich salmon-fishing cultures of the Northwest Coast (British Columbia and southern Alaska) were without permanently occupied villages. Contrariwise, it has seemed to us that only a drastic reduction of the number of niches to be exploited, and a concentration of these in space, would have permitted the establishment of full-time village life. The ethnographic data suggest that an analysis of microenvironments or niches would throw much light on the processes by which the Mesoamerican peoples settled down.

Methodology

If the environment in which an ancient people lived was radically different from any known today, and especially if it included animal and plant species which are now extinct and whose behavior is consequently unknown, then any reconstruction of the subsistence activities of the people is going to be difficult. All one could hope for would be a more-or-less sound reconstruction of general ecological conditions, while a breakdown of the environment into smaller ecological niches would be impossible. However, much if not most archeological research concerns periods so recent in comparison with the million or so years of human prehistory that in most instances local conditions have not changed greatly in the interval between the periods investigated and the present.

If we assume that there is a continuity between the ancient and the modern macroenvironment in the area of interest, there are three steps which we must take in tracing the role of microenvironments.

(1) Analysis of the present-day microecology (from the human point of view) of the archeological zone. Archeological research is often carried out in remote and little known parts of the earth, which have not been studied from the point of view of natural history. Hence, the active participation of botanists, zoologists, and other natural scientists is highly recommended.

The modern ethnology of the region should never be neglected, for all kinds of highly relevant data on the use of surrounding niches by local people often lie immediately at hand. We have found in Mesoamerica that the workmen on the "dig" are a mine of such information. There may be little need to thumb through weighty reports on the Australian aborigines or South African Bushmen when the analogous custom can be found right under one's nose (7). The end result of the analysis should be a map of the microenvironments defined (here aerial photographs are of great use), with detailed data on the seasonal possibilities each offers human communities on certain technological levels of development.

(2) Quantitative analysis of food remains in the archeological sites, and of the technical equipment (arrow or spear points, grinding stones for seeds,

baskets and other containers, and so on) related to food-getting. It is a rare site report that treats of bones and plant remains in any but the most perfunctory way. It might seem a simple thing to ship animal bones from a site to a specialist for identification, but most archeologists know that many zoologists consider identification of recent faunal remains a waste of time (*8*). Because of this, and because many museum collections do not include postcranial skeletons that could be used for identification, the archeologist must arrange to secure his own comparative collection. If this collection is assembled by a zoologist on the project, a by-product of the investigation would be a faunal study of micro-environments. Similarly, identification of floral and other specimens from the site would lead to other specialized studies.

(3) Correlation of the archeological with the microenvironmental study in an overall analysis of the ancient human ecology.

The Tehuacán Valley

An archeological project undertaken by R. S. MacNeish, with such a strategy in mind, has been located since 1961 in the dry Tehuacán Valley of southern Puebla, Mexico (*2, 9*). The valley is fringed with bone-dry caves in which the food remains of early peoples have been preserved to a remarkable degree in stratified deposits. For a number of reasons, including the results of his past archeological work in Mesoamerica, MacNeish believed that he would find here the origins of maize agriculture in the New World, and he has been proved right. It now seems certain that the wild ancestor of maize was domesticated in the Tehuacán area some time around the beginning of the 5th millennium B.C.

While the Tehuacán environment is in general a desert, the natural scientists of the project have defined within it four microenvironments (Fig. 1).

(1) *Alluvial valley floor,* a level plain sparsely covered with mesquite, grasses, and cacti, offering fairly good possibilities, especially along the Río Salado, for primitive maize agriculture dependent on rainfall.

(2) *Travertine slopes,* on the west side of the valley. This would have been a niche useful for growing maize and tomatoes and for trapping cottontail rabbits.

(3) *Coxcatlán thorn forest,* with abundant seasonal crops of wild fruits, such as various species of *Opuntia,* pitahaya, and so on. There is also a seasonal abundance of whitetail deer, cottontail rabbits, and skunks, and there are some peccaries.

(4) *Eroded canyons,* unsuitable for exploitation except for limited hunting of deer and as routes up to maguey fields for those peoples who chewed the leaves of that plant.

The correlation of this study with the analysis, by specialists, of the plant and animal remains (these include bones, maize cobs, chewed quids, and even feces) found in cave deposits has shown that the way of life of the New World's first farmers was not very different from that of the Great Basin aborigines in

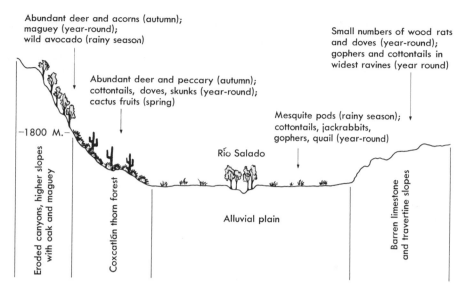

Abundant deer and acorns (autumn);
maguey (year-round);
wild avocado (rainy season)

Small numbers of wood rats
and doves (year-round);
gophers and cottontails in
widest ravines (year round)

Abundant deer and peccary (autumn);
cottontails, doves, skunks (year-round);
cactus fruits (spring)

Mesquite pods (rainy season);
cottontails, jackrabbits,
gophers, quail (year-round)

-1800 M.-

Río Salado

Eroded canyons, higher slopes
with oak and maguey

Coxcatlán thorn forest

Alluvial plain

Barren limestone
and travertine slopes

FIG. 1. An idealized east-west transection of the central part of the Tehuacán Valley, Puebla, Mexico, showing microenvironments and the seasons in which the food resources are exploited. East is to the left. The length of the area represented is about 20 kilometers.

the 19th century. Even the earliest inhabitants of the valley, prior to 6500 B.C., were more collectors of seasonally gathered wild plant foods than they were "big game hunters," and they traveled in microbands in an annual, wet-season-dry-season cycle (*10*). While slightly more sedentary macrobands appeared with the adoption of simple maize cultivation after 5000 B.C., these people neverthe-less still followed the old pattern of moving from microenvironment to micro-environment, separating into microbands during the dry season.

The invention and gradual improvement of agriculture seem to have made few profound alterations in the settlement pattern of the valley for many mil-lennia. Significantly, by the Formative period (from about 1500 B.C. to A.D. 200), when agriculture based on a hybridized maize was far more important than it had been in earlier periods as a source of food energy, the pattern was still one of part-time nomadism (*11*). In this part of the dry Mexican highlands, until the Classic period (about A.D. 200 to 900), when irrigation appears to have been introduced into Tehuacán, food production had still to be supplemented with extensive plant collecting and hunting.

Most of the peoples of the Formative period apparently lived in large villages on the alluvial valley floor during the wet season, from May through October of each year, for planting had to be done in May and June, and harvest-ing in September and October. In the dry season, from November through February, when the trees and bushes had lost their leaves and the deer were easy to see and track, some of the population must have moved to hunting camps, principally in the Coxcatlán thorn forest. By February, hunting had become less rewarding as the now-wary deer moved as far as possible from human habitation; however, in April and May the thorn forest was still ripe for exploitation, as many kinds of wild fruits matured. In May it was again time to return to the villages on the valley floor for spring planting.

Now, in some other regions of Mesoamerica there were already, during the Formative period, fully sedentary village cultures in existence. It is clear that while the Tehuacán valley was the locus of the first domestication of maize, the origins of full-blown village life lie elsewhere. Because of the constraining effects of the macroenvironment, the Tehuacán people were exploiting, until relatively late in Mesoamerican prehistory, as widely spaced and as large a number of microenvironments as the Great Basin aborigines were exploiting in the 19th century.

Coastal Guatemala

Near the modern fishing port of Ocós, only a few kilometers from the Mexican border on the alluvial plain of the Pacific coast of Guatemala, we have found evidence for some of the oldest permanently occupied villages in Mesoamerica (*12*). We have also made an extensive study of the ecology and ethnology of the Ocós area.

From this study (*13*) we have defined no less than eight distinct microenvironments (Fig. 2) within an area of only about 90 square kilometers. These are as follows:

(1) *Beach sand and low scrub.* A narrow, infertile strip from which the present-day villagers collect occasional mollusks, a beach crab called *chichimeco* and one known as *nazareño,* and the sea turtle and its eggs.

(2) *The marine estuary-and-lagoon system,* in places extending considerably inland and ultimately connecting with streams or rivers coming down from the Sierra Madre. The estuaries, with their mangrove-lined banks, make up the microenvironment richest in wild foods in the entire area. The brackish waters abound in catfish (*Arius* sp. and *Galeichthys* sp.), red snapper (*Lutjanus colorado*), several species of snook (*Centropomus* sp.), and many other kinds of fish. Within living memory, crocodiles (*Crocodylus astutus*) were common, but they have by now been hunted almost to extinction. The muddy banks of the estuaries are the habitat of many kinds of mollusks, including marsh clams (*Polymesoda radiata*), mussels (*Mytella falcata*), and oysters (*Ostrea columbiensis*), and they also support an extensive population of fiddler and mud crabs.

(3) *Mangrove forest,* consisting mainly of stilt-rooted red mangrove, which slowly gives way to white mangrove as one moves away from the estuary. We noted high populations of collared anteater (*Tamandua tetradactyla*) and arboreal porcupine (*Coendu mexicanus*). A large number of crabs (we did not determine the species) inhabit this microenvironment; these include, especially,

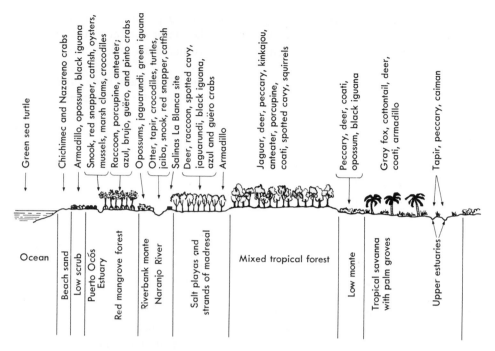

FIG. 2. Northeast-southwest transection of the Ocós area of coastal Guatemala, showing microenvironments in relation to the site of Salinas La Blanca. Northeast is to the right. The length of the area represented is about 15 kilometers.

one known locally as the *azul* (blue) crab, on which a large population of raccoons feeds.

(4) *Riverine,* comprising the channels and banks of the sluggish Suchiate and Naranjo rivers, which connect with the lagoon-estuary system not far from their mouths. Freshwater turtles, catfish, snook, red snapper, and mojarra (*Cichlasoma* sp.) are found in these waters; the most common animal along the banks is the green iguana (*Iguana iguana*).

(5) *Salt playas,* the dried remnants of ancient lagoon-and-estuary systems which are still subject to inundation during the wet season, with localized stands of a tree known as *madresal* ("mother of salt"). Here there is an abundance of game, including whitetail deer and the black iguana (*Ctenosaura similis*), as well as a rich supply of salt.

(6) *Mixed tropical forest,* found a few kilometers inland, in slightly higher and better drained situations than the salt *playas*. This forest includes mostly tropical evergreens like the ceiba, as well as various zapote and fan palms, on the fruit of which a great variety of mammals thrive—the kinkajou, the spotted cavy, the coatimundi, the raccoon, and even the gray fox. The soils here are highly suitable for maize agriculture.

(7) *Tropical savannah,* occupying poorly drained patches along the upper stream and estuary systems of the area. This is the major habitat in the area for cottontail rabbits and gray foxes. Other common mammals are the coatimundi and armadillo.

(8) *Cleared fields and second growth,* habitats which have been created by agriculturists and which are generally confined to areas that were formerly mixed tropical forest.

Among the earliest Formative cultures known thus far for the Ocós area is the Cuadros phase, dated by radio-carbon analysis at about 1000 to 850 B.C. and well represented in the site of Salinas La Blanca, which we excavated in 1962 (14). The site is on the banks of the Naranjo River among a variety of micro-environments; it consists of two flattish mounds built up from deeply stratified refuse layers representing house foundations of a succession of hamlets or small villages.

From our analysis of this refuse we have a good idea of the way in which the Cuadros people lived. Much of the refuse consists of potsherds from large, neckless jars, but very few of the clay figurines that abound in other Formative cultures of Mesoamerica were found. We discovered many plant remains; luckily these had been preserved or "fossilized" through replacement of the tissues by carbonates. From these we know that the people grew and ate a nonhybridized maize considerably more advanced than the maize which was then being grown in Tehuacán (15). The many impressions of leaves in clay floors in the site will, we hope, eventually make it possible to reconstruct the flora that immediately surrounded the village.

The identification of animal remains (Fig. 3), together with our ecological study and with the knowledge that the people had a well-developed maize agri-

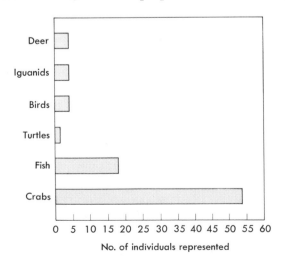

FIG. 3. Animal remains, exclusive of mollusks, found in Cuadros phase levels at Salinas La Blanca.

culture, gives a great deal of information on the subsistence activities of these early coastal villagers. First of all, we believe they had no interest whatever in hunting, a conclusion reinforced by our failure to find a single projectile point in the site. The few deer bones that have been recovered are all from immature individuals that could have been encountered by chance and clubbed to death. Most of the other remains are of animals that could have been collected in the environs of the village, specifically in the lagoon-estuary system and the flanking mangrove forest, where the people fished, dug for marsh clams, and, above all, caught crabs (primarily the *azul* crab, which is trapped at night). Entirely missing are many edible species found in other microenvironments, such as raccoon, cottontail rabbit, peccary, spotted cavy, and nine-banded armadillo.

There is no evidence at all that occupation of Salinas La Blanca was seasonal. An effective food production carried out on the rich, deep soils of the mixed tropical forest zone, together with the food resources of the lagoon-estuary system, made a permanently settled life possible. Looked at another way, developed maize agriculture had so reduced the number and spacing of the niches which had to be exploited that villages could be occupied the year round (*16*).

Conditions similar to those of the Ocós area are found all along the Pacific Coast of Guatemala and along the Gulf Coast of southern Veracruz and Tabasco in Mexico, and we suggest that the real transition to village life took place there and not in the dry Mexican highlands, where maize was domesticated initially (*17*).

Conclusion

The interpretation of archeological remains through a fine-scale analysis of small ecological zones throws new light on the move toward sedentary life in Mesoamerican prehistory. In our terms, the basic difference between peoples who subsist on wild foods, and those who dwell in permanent villages is that the former must exploit a wide variety of small ecological niches in a seasonal pattern—niches which are usually scattered over a wide range of territory—which the latter may, because of an effective food production, concentrate on one or on only a few microenvironments which lie relatively close at hand.

Fine-scale ecological analysis indicates that there never was any such thing as an "agricultural revolution" in Mesoamerica, suddenly and almost miraculously resulting in village life. The gradual addition of domesticates such as maize, beans, and squash to the diet of wild plant and animal foods hardly changed the way of life of the Tehuacán people for many thousands of years, owing to a general paucity of the environment, and seasonal nomadism persisted until the introduction of irrigation. It probably was not until maize was taken to the alluvial, lowland littoral of Mesoamerica, perhaps around 1500 B.C., that permanently occupied villages became possible, through reduction of the number of microenvironments to which men had to adapt themselves.

REFERENCES

1. Mesoamerica is the name given to that part of Mexico and Central America which was civilized in pre-Columbian times. For an excellent summary of its prehistory, see G. R. WILLEY, *Science* **131,** 73 (1960).
2. R. S. MACNEISH, *Science* **143,** 531 (1964).
3. See C. A. REED and R. J. BRAIDWOOD, "Toward the reconstruction of the environmental sequence of Northeastern Iraq," in R. J. BRAIDWOOD and B. HOWE, "Prehistoric Investigations in Iraqi Kurdistan," *Oriental Institute, University of Chicago, Studies in Ancient Oriental Civilization No. 31* (1960), p. 163. Reed and Braidwood also convincingly reject the technological-deterministic approach of V. G. Childe and his followers.
4. See B. J. MEGGERS, *Am. Anthropologist* **56,** 801 (1954), for an environmental-deterministic view of the constraining effects of tropical forests on human cultures.
5. See F. BARTH, *ibid.* **58,** 1079 (1956), for a microenvironmental approach by an ethnologist to the exceedingly complex interrelationships between sedentary agriculturists, agriculturists practicing transhumant herding, and nomadic herders in the state of Swat, Pakistan.
6. J. H. STEWARD, "Basin-Plateau Aboriginal Sociopolitical Groups," *Smithsonian Inst. Bur. Am. Ethnol. Bull. 120* (1938).
7. The pitfalls of searching for ethnological data relevant to archeological problems among cultures far-flung in time and space are stressed by J. G. D. CLARK, *Prehistoric Europe, The Economic Basis* (Philosophical Library, New York, 1952), p. 3.
8. See W. W. TAYLOR, Ed., "The Identification of non-artifactual archaeological materials," *Natl. Acad. Sci.–Natl. Res. Council Publ. 565* (1957). For a general article on the analysis of food remains in archeological deposits see R. F. HEIZER in "Application of quantitative methods in archaeology," *Viking Fund Publications in Anthropology No. 28* (1960), pp. 93–157.
9. P. C. MANGELSDORF, R. S. MACNEISH, W. C. GALLINAT, *Science* **143,** 538 (1964). We thank Dr. MacNeish for permission to use unpublished data of the Tehuacán Archaeological-Botanical Project in this article.
10. R. S. MACNEISH, *Second Annual Report of the Tehuacán Archaeological-Botanical Project* (Robert S. Peabody Foundation for Archaeology, Andover, Mass., 1962).
11. The research discussed in this and the following paragraph was carried out by Flannery as staff zoologist for the Tehuacán project during the field seasons of 1962 and 1963; see K. V. FLANNERY, "Vertebrate Fauna and Prehistoric Hunting Patterns in the Tehuacán Valley" (Robert S. Peabody Foundation for Archaeology, Andover, Mass., in press); ———, thesis, Univ. of Chicago, in preparation.
12. M. D. COE, "La Victoria, an early site on the Pacific Coast of Guatemala," *Peabody Museum, Harvard, Papers No. 53* (1961).
13. The study was carried out largely by Flannery.
14. The final report on Salinas La Blanca by Coe and Flannery is in preparation. The research was supported by the National Science Foundation under a grant to the Institute of Andean Research, as part of the program "Interrelationships of New World Cultures." The oldest culture in the area is the Ocós phase, which has complex ceramics and figurines; the paleoecology of Ocós is less well known than that of Cuadros, which directly follows it in time.

15. P. C. Mangelsdorf, who has very kindly examined these maize specimens, informs us that they are uncontaminated with *Tripsacum,* and that probably all belong to the primitive lowland race, Nal-Tel.

16. To paraphrase the concept of "primary forest efficiency," developed by J. R. CALDWELL ["Trend and Tradition in the Eastern United States," *Am. Anthropol. Assoc. Mem. No. 88* (1958)], we might think of the Cuadros phase as leaning to a "primary lagoon-estuary efficiency." We might think the same of the Ocós phase of the same region, which may date back to 1500 B.C.

17. An additional factor which may in part account for the priority of coastal Guatemala over Tehuacán in the achievement of a sedentary mode of life is the presence of an extensive system of waterways in the former region, which might have made it less necessary for local communities to move to productive sources of food. By means of canoes, a few persons could have brought the products of other niches to the village. However, our evidence indicates that the Cuadros people largely ignored the possibilities of exploiting distant niches.

Environment and Man
in Arid America

HAROLD E. MALDE[*]

The study of ancient people in the dry Southwest has long commanded the attention of scientists interested in man's response to a changing environment. Although environment is not the only factor controlling man's destiny, its influence is particularly evident in the Southwest, where small climatic changes have noticeably altered the landscape, the plants and animals, and man's way of life. In this survey I indicate only a few of the methods used to gain an understanding of man's past, emphasizing recent contributions and basing the chronology mainly on radiocarbon dating, tree-ring counts, and pottery sequences. The chronology contains numerous gaps and dubious dates, but it is the best framework available. A chronology can also be constructed by correlating local stratigraphic sequences, but such sequences are commonly incomplete and their correlation is still problematic. Moreover, many interesting biogeographic matters and isolated archeologic sites are not yet tied to geologic stratigraphy. In this article stratigraphic names from geologic and archeologic parlance are avoided, except for a few terms in general use.

Several kinds of evidence in the Southwest point to a period of cool and moist conditions, coinciding with the close of the Pleistocene, followed by warmer, drier conditions, and then by a return to a somewhat cooler and wetter climate; but the sequence of environmental change is complicated by climatic fluctuations of lesser magnitude and by differences in the impact of climate on different landscapes.

* The author is a geologist with the U.S. Geological Survey, Federal Center, Denver Colorado. This article is adapted from a paper presented 3 September 1963 at the 59th annual meeting of the Association of American Geographers in Denver.

Earliest signs of man

The age of man in the New World has not yet been satisfactorily determined, but there is undoubted evidence in the Southwest that he hunted mammoth and other large animals about 12,000 to 13,000 years ago—when the last Pleistocene glaciers still covered northern North America—using bifacial blades known as Clovis points (*1*). Some archeologists (*2*) recognize a "pre-projectile point" assemblage of less specialized tools (identified as crude scrapers, pebble choppers, and hand axes) more primitive than Clovis points and presumably older. Despite the lack of specific evidence, because of the diversity of man's environmental adaptations in early times it is not unreasonable to assume an age for man in the New World of at least 15,000 years (*3*).

A few radiocarbon samples, supposedly dating man's campfires, suggest even greater age (*4*); but for one reason or another these dates are discounted by most archeologists, though not by all.

Geologic signs of environmental change

Geologic evidence of wetter-colder climate during the late Pleistocene, and the subsequent physiographic changes, comes from the history of mountain glaciation, the rise and fall of pluvial lakes in closed basins, accumulation and dissection of alluvium, and the various effects of wind action (*5*). The position of late-Pleistocene snow line near pluvial Lake Estancia, 100 kilometers southeast of Albuquerque, implies that summer temperature was reduced 5° to 6°C (10° to 12°F) and that annual precipitation increased about 200 millimeters (8 in.) (*6*). Meteorologic study of a Pleistocene lake in Spring Valley, near Ely, Nevada, indicates a probable 30-percent decrease in evaporation, a 200-millimeter increase in precipitation, and a 7°C decrease in summer temperature (*7*). Other details concerning the rise and fall of pluvial lakes in the Great Basin are being worked out, but attempts to calculate the input and loss of salt at these lakes have not yet reckoned with complex problems of geology, hydrology, and past climatic change (*8*). Maps of several ancient soils buried in alpine deposits suggest a changing pattern of climatic zones (*9*). Measurement of alluviation and erosion in arid watersheds shows relations between precipitation, sediment transport, and valley shape that help to explain former stream deposits (*10*). Sand dunes in the plains of western Kansas show reversals of wind direction in conformity with the advance and retreat of continental glaciers (*11*). Finally, geochemical techniques have been used to show that the amounts of manganese, nitrogen, and phosphorus left by animals in cave deposits point to a period of wetter climate that ended some 12,000 years ago (*12*).

Biologic evidence of past environment

The biologic evidence for climatic change in the Southwest, as elsewhere, rests on displacement of biotic zones as recorded by fossils or by disjunct, "relict" species of living plants and animals. Recent reviews of Pleistocene biogeography (*13*) document the growing recognition of the part played by recent climatic change in the distribution of organisms.

Since Eiseley (*14*) pointed out that two land snails, *Pupilla sonorama* and *Gastrocopta ashmuni,* found with artifacts of early hunters at the Lindenmeier site, north of Fort Collins, Colorado, imply moist conditions "attendant on receding mountain glaciation," molluscan fossils have received increasing attention in Pleistocene stratigraphy and in archeology (*15*). To account for the moist conditions implied by terrestrial snails in fossil assemblages in upper Pleistocene deposits of the High Plains, for example, shifts of isotherms by several hundred kilometers north to south and large displacements of moisture belts east to west must be assumed. More ecologic studies of modern snail populations are needed (*16*).

The vertebrates of the Southwest include several isolated species, of which only a few have been studied intensively. Hall and Kelson (*17*) have mapped the distribution of 15 endemic species of mammals in the Great Basin that were probably isolated by changes in Pleistocene climate. The southern limits for several Rocky Mountain mammals and reptiles are marked by isolated populations above 2100 meters on desert mountains of southern Arizona (*18*). The shrew, *Sorex milleri,* in mountains of northeastern Mexico, is regarded as a late-Pleistocene remnant of *Sorex cinereus,* which now extends southward in boreal habitats in the mountains of northern New Mexico (*19*). The distributional and variational patterns of southwestern *Microtus* are explained by postulating a pluvial period, followed by a warm, dry interval and then a return to somewhat cooler conditions (*20*). Plethodontid salamanders in the mountains of New Mexico probably became disjunct from Rocky Mountain relatives, because of climatic warming at the close of the Pleistocene (*21*). Similarly, the distribution of iguanid lizards in the Great Basin probably resulted from climatic changes that have occurred since the last pluvial (*22*).

Disjunct distributions that indicate cooler climate during the Pleistocene are also found among insects—especially the butterflies, of which relict arctic and subarctic groups are found at mountain bogs in Colorado (*23*).

It is well known that remains of extinct animals occur in upper-Pleistocene deposits of the Southwest (*24*), but discovery of several boreal animals associated with a Clovis point in Burnet Cave, southern New Mexico, deserves emphasis (*25*). However, the recovery of *Marmota flaviventris* from the cave—a species often cited as an indicator of cold climate—is of doubtful value as evidence of Pleistocene conditions, because *M. flaviventris* is found today in Utah grasslands as low as 1400 meters (*26*).

Some plants of the Southwest also show marked distributional patterns that may reflect colder and wetter conditions during glacial stages of the Pleistocene. Among phytogeographers, the alpine tundra of Colorado is famous, being dominated by a circumboreal flora that includes numerous extraordinary arctic relicts

(*27*). The curious disjunct distribution of creosote bush in deserts of North and South America (*28*) and the puzzling taxonomic similarity of other desert plants on opposite sides of the equator suggest past climatic change in tropical zones (*29*).

Pollen records point to many biogeographic details about the former distribution of plants, but accurate interpretation of the fossil pollen requires further knowledge of pollen rain in modern environments (*30*). Looking first at records contemporaneous with the last stage of continental glaciation, we find that scattered sites in southern latitudes yield pollen of trees that now grow at higher altitudes several hundred kilometers farther north. Pollen from deposits 22,500 to 17,000 years old on the southern High Plains, now a region of short-grass prairie, suggests pine woodlands and scattered spruce (*31*), but forest-type soils are lacking; hence it appears that trees probably were not widespread in this region. Spruce pollen dated from 27,000 to 19,000 years old also is abundant in beds of ancient Lake St. Augustin in west-central New Mexico (*32*), a locality now surrounded by piñon, juniper, and pine. Pollen from pluvial Lake Cochise in southeast Arizona, from 23,000 to 20,000 years old, is dominantly (95 percent) pine but includes some spruce, fir, and Douglas fir; it suggests an environment of pine parkland such as is now found 1400 meters higher on mountains in northeast New Mexico 700 kilometers to the north (*33*). At Searles Lake, California—now a desert basin 1000 meters below the nearest woodland—a pluvial deposit 23,000 to 12,000 years old has relatively abundant pollen of juniper and pine (*34*).

Pollen records from mountain areas in the Southwest during the glacial period, although meager, suggest considerable lowering of the tree line. Sage and spruce pollen in lake sediments dated 19,400 years old, at an altitude of 2700 meters in the Chuska Mountains of northwest New Mexico, are attributed to a tundra environment; this would mean that the tree line was a least 760 meters lower than it is at present (*35*). Similarly, pollen from lakes and bogs in the San Juan Mountains of southwest Colorado indicates a former tree line 670 meters lower than the present one (*36*).

Environment of early hunters

The pollen record of the Southwest implies that the climate had already become more dry at the time of the Clovis hunters, from 13,000 to 10,500 years ago. On the southern High Plains, a decline in pollen of pine and spruce, and changes in assemblages of diatoms and mollusks, imply that ponds dried and streams diminished in volume (*37*). Spruce that had reached as far south as the Texas coastal plain disappeared from the pollen record of Texas bogs about 12,000 years ago (*38*). At the same time, pollen representing the Upper Sonoran zone at Rampart Cave in the lower Grand Canyon—a plant community of a type that now grows 600 to 1200 meters higher—disappeared (*12*). At Lehner

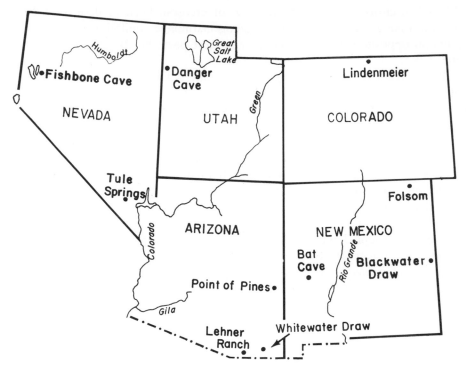

FIG. 1. Index map of archeologic sites.

Ranch in southern Arizona (see Fig. 1), pollen associated with Clovis remains about 12,000 years old suggests an environment resembling present-day grassland (*39*).

Geologic signs of increasing dryness at this time are especially clear at pluvial lakes in the Great Basin. For example, as shown by sedimentary study, water in the Bonneville Basin had evaporated to a state of high salinity by 12,000 years ago (*40*), after a previous stand about 300 meters higher.

Although the climate was becoming drier, water was nevertheless more abundant then than it is now, and Clovis Man found that ponds and streams were favorable places for hunting large animals—particularly the mammoth (*41*). Somewhat later, probably by 8000 years ago, several typically Pleistocene herding animals abruptly died out: elephant, horse, camel, and a large species of bison (*42*). Because the sudden extinction did not extend to most small vertebrates of high reproductive capacity, and because it occurred in a wide variety of environments—from the tropics to northern latitudes—circumstantial evidence points to prehistoric man as a destructive predator. That the extinction was due to purely ecologic causes seems improbable (*43*). However, the deleterious effect of climatic change on breeding habits cannot be ruled out, and the archeologic record so far fails to show that all the extinct animals were exploited as game. Resolution of this question requires more facts, but at present the role of man is one clearly identified factor.

From about 11,000 to perhaps 6500 years ago (the terminal date is poorly determined), big-game hunters other than Clovis Man, using different tools and hunting different animals, appeared on the Great Plains. As judged from remains of their camps and kill sites they were more numerous than the Clovis hunters, although increasingly arid conditions must have made for a hard life. These plains hunters depended mostly on herds of bison for food, but they also ate small game, as shown by scraps found in a few excavated campsites. Grinding tools for the preparation of plant foods appeared for the first time about 10,000 years ago and became increasingly common thereafter (*41*); such culinary objects indicate the beginning of a gathering economy and a more sedentary life.

While the bison hunters roamed the Plains, the climate was becoming drier. At first, in such regions as the southern High Plains, ponds were still abundant and supported fresh-water diatoms. Sand dunes of an earlier period were stabilized by vegetation, and cool-climate mollusks found favorable habitats near water. Later, however, the ponds dwindled, fresh-water diatoms were replaced by saline forms, widespread erosion occurred, and presumably vegetation became less dense (*37*). Parallel-flaked points dating from the latter part of this period in eastern Colorado occur in windblown sand, indicative of regional dryness (*44*), but conditions were still rather moist at the Lindenmeier site to the west, near the mountains (*45*). With loss of water supplies, hunting bands may have stayed close to familiar watering places, but travel may have been possible during wetter months, and short journeys between springs during the dry season were perhaps feasible (*46*). In winter, or under stress of increased aridity, people could find shelter in wooded valleys near the foothills (*47*). There is some archeologic evidence that survivors of the big-game hunters migrated northward (*48*), perhaps lured on by better hunting and more plentiful water in the northern plains, but eastward migration also seems likely.

People occupying the Great Basin and the southern deserts at this time were handicapped by even greater aridity and a paucity of big game (*49*). They must have depended for a livelihood on small game and edible plants. Baskets and grinding stones for collecting and preparing plant foods were in use at Danger and Fishbone caves in the Great Basin from about 9000 years ago, and they appeared in southern Arizona at about the same time.

The dry climate of this early period in the Great Basin has been inferred locally from pollen records, as well as from shrinkage of pluvial lakes and from biogeographic considerations already mentioned. Along Whitewater Draw, in southern Arizona, pollen correlated with the earliest Cochise culture (dated about 10,000 to 8000 years ago), like the pollen in earlier deposits with Clovis remains, suggests an environment resembling the present grassland (*50*). The presence of associated oak and hickory charcoal, fresh-water mollusks, and remains of water birds can be explained as evidence of a local riparian habitat within a desert region. At Nevada caves, pollen that overlies deposits yielding a high count of tree pollen dated earlier than 15,000 years ago reflects increasing aridity (*51*). Desert vegetation for the period from 13,500 to 6000 years ago is also implied by pollen from Tule Springs (*52*).

Altithermal Age

Since the pioneer work of Bryan and Antevs on the postglacial history of the Southwest, a climax of aridity from 6000 to about 4500 years ago—dated partly by analogy with European pollen records but also by radiocarbon dating of older and younger deposits—has been widely accepted and only recently disputed (*43, 53*). Such a period of warm climate is amply demonstrated in the northeastern states and in Europe (*54*) and is identifiable in pollen records from the tropics (*55*), even though the inferred rise in temperature—estimated from the tolerances of modern plants—is only a few degrees. In the Southwest, this interval is usually termed the Altithermal, and, because of evident arroyo cutting, lowered water tables, accumulation of caliche in soils, wind erosion, and dune formation, is commonly believed to have been warm and dry; but recent pollen study casts doubt on this time-worn dogma (*43*), and the assumption that certain geologic features were caused by drought is debatable. Arroyos and wind deflation, for example, are perhaps only a result of climatic shift toward less frequent but occasionally intense rainfall, without overall change in average precipitation (*56*). Such a change in the pattern of rainfall, however, would produce relatively scant vegetation and dry soils subject to erosion. Although prevailing ideas about uniformly dry climate during the Altithermal deserve critical scrutiny, and dates are needed for this period, conspicuous geologic signs characteristic of dry regions are too pervasive and too diverse to be ignored. Our knowledge is incomplete, but my guess is that the Altithermal was at first rather arid and then gradually became wetter.

Citing mainly geologic evidence, Bryan and Antevs (*57*) emphasized physical features that point to a warm and dry middle postglacial period. Local studies supply various details. In the southern Rocky Mountains, glaciers that began to shrink from moraines far down some alpine valleys slightly earlier than 6200 years ago, as estimated from radiocarbon dating, disappeared entirely and probably did not re-form until about 3800 years ago (*58*), at much reduced size. At the Lindenmeier site, a deep arroyo older than 5000 years was cut in deposits that contain artifacts of the early big-game hunters (*45*), and a similar arroyo is found at the famous Folsom site in New Mexico (*59*). An arid period, dating back to between 6300 and 4950 years ago, is expressed at Blackwater Draw on the southern High Plains by a marked disconformity, by accumulation of wind-blown sand, and by growth of gypsum crystals in desiccated lakes (*37*). A period of erosion at Whitewater Draw in southern Arizona had ended by 4500 years ago, as determined by the age of pond clay in an arroyo (*60*). Caliche formation at this time, a hallmark of arid lands, is well known from stratigraphic studies, and its past rate of development can be estimated by radiocarbon analysis

(*61*). Hack's (*62*) study of ancient sand dunes of the Hopi country, which relate to this period, is a classic in the annals of geology of the Southwest.

Biogeographic studies mentioned earlier, although still limited to a few plants and animals, support the idea of a postglacial warm period. Some botanical information from peripheral areas is also pertinent. Comparison of the present and past distribution of digger pine (*Pinus sabiniana*) in California suggests that the average winter temperature has risen 5°C since the Pleistocene (*63*). Chaparral in southwest Oregon once extended northward to Puget Sound, a finding which implies a summer rise in temperature of 5°C and a decrease of 230 millimeters in annual precipitation (*64*). Wood peat indicative of warmer-drier climate at bogs in the Northwest dated from 8300 to 3000 years ago is succeeded by sphagnum peat of the present cooler-wetter climate (*65*). In alpine bog deposits of the Colorado Front Range, a warmer period from 8000 to 3000 years ago is inferred from abundant grass pollen and reduced tree pollen (*66*), but pollen records from the San Juan Mountains of Colorado show that the warm period ended about 5000 years ago (*67*).

Archeologic remains from the Altithermal are rather scarce. On the Plains the few artifacts of this age are identified with food collectors belonging to the Archaic culture (*68*). In the Great Basin and in southern Arizona, traces of seed collectors have been found (*49*). Human populations may have dwindled as supplies of game and plant foods decreased, and men looking for water may have followed streams headward, or may have moved from shrinking lakes to higher ground (*69*). This possibility is discussed below. But I can mention two archeologic curiosities that imply necessities of the time: prehistoric wells dug in the southern High Plains (*70*) and storage cists for plant foods found in Nevada caves (*71*).

Despite the predominant view that the Altithermal was arid, Martin (*43*) believes that the climate was actually wetter, at least during summer in southern deserts. His evidence is drawn from flood-plain pollen at two sites in southern Arizona, dated from 5280 to 4120 years ago. The interpretation of pollen from flood plains is beset with unsolved problems (as Martin admits), and assignment of the pollen to the Altithermal is based only on radiocarbon dating, but the pollen clearly shows an increase in moisture indicators (pine, oak, grass, and cattail) as compared with younger beds. Interestingly, a similar increase in tree pollen in the lower sediment of Hackberry Lake, Nebraska, dated at 5040 years ago, also implies a wet period in the generally warm and dry postglacial (*72*). In support of his view that the Altithermal was wet, Martin (*18*) points out that certain lizards, snakes, and rodents in the Sierra Madre of Mexico reach their northern limits as isolated remnants on the lower slopes of the Chiricahua Mountains of Arizona and must have migrated northward along a former corridor of oak-pine woodland. The intervening divides in Sonora now support only desert grassland and scrub, but the woodland required by these animals grows about 300 meters higher. Martin attributes the inferred spreading of woodland to subtropical monsoons during the Altithermal.

Summer wetness in the Southwest during late Altithermal time is also implied by conspicuous soils that formed on landscapes suggestive of earlier aridity. The inferred period of increased moisture (5000 to 4000 years ago) coincides with a time of accelerated soil development on eolian deposits in the plains of eastern Colorado (*44*) and near Denver (*73*). At Blackwater Draw in the southern High Plains, oxidation and jointing of wind-blown sand that overlies pre-Altithermal deposits (*37*) probably indicates soil development. A characteristic soil of this age is also recognized in the La Sal Mountains of Utah and at various Rocky Mountain localities (*9*). Such soil development requires wetness as well as high temperature. Caliche soils that formed in more arid areas are readily explained by postulating additional rainfall (*74*).

Agriculture and village life

As the Altithermal drew to a close, relatively wetter and colder conditions returned, and the tempo of human life accelerated, along with evident growth in population. Many arroyos began to fill with alluvium, dry lakes in the northern Great Basin were flooded, sand dunes were overgrown with vegetation, and new glaciers formed in the Sierras and the Rockies.

The archeologic record of the Southwest shows, shortly before 5000 years ago, the first signs of agriculture and, as time went on, increased dependence on plant foods and a progressive adoption of more sedentary ways of life, ultimately resulting in villages attached to farms. Primitive corncobs at Bat Cave, a locality 2100 meters above sea level in west-central New Mexico, are dated 5600 years ago (*75*). Cultivation of corn at this altitude could have been favored by warm climate and summer rain and the subsequent cooler climate actually may have curbed agriculture for a time, because of a short growing season (*76*). Corn does not appear again in the archeologic record of the Southwest until about 4200 years ago at Point of Pines, Arizona, 200 kilometers west of Bat Cave, and at an upland site near Denver (*77, 78*). Discovery of these hints of early agriculture in uplands of the Southwest reinforces the belief that the people probably moved to higher ground during a period of warm and dry climate.

After this start, cultivation of corn spread over a wide area, especially along tributaries of large rivers, and by the time of Christ it had reached southwestward along the Gila and Salt rivers, eastward to the Rio Grande and the Pecos, and northward into the Colorado Plateau. Corn did not reach the plains of western Kansas until a thousand years ago (probably from the east), although makers of pottery, who depended on native plants, had previously clustered at sites along streams (*79*). Concurrently, squash came into use by sedentary people living along the San Pedro River, Arizona, about 4000 years ago, and beans were added a thousand years later. Thus, a populous economy evolved, based on the familiar triumvirate corn, beans, and squash. The simultaneous rise of agriculture and return of wetter climate, in the Southwest, seems to me more than coincidence. These cultivated plants were presumably imported from northern Mexico, where they had helped sustain a seed-collecting economy dating back several thousand years earlier (*80*).

During the rise of agriculture, which continued into the Christian era, the climate of the Southwest, as indicated by the slow buildup of alluvium, was characterized by intermittent rains interspersed with short intervals of drought and times of cold weather. These vicissitudes of climate, none as severe as earlier changes, brought hardships and induced human migration, but they also evoked remarkable ingenuity. The development of devices for storing and controlling available water is especially noteworthy. The chronologic framework of environmental change during this modern period is founded on a detailed sequence of pottery types first used in the Southwest 2400 years ago, and on variable growth of tree rings, for which a climate-controlled chronology extends back to just before the Christian era (*81*). The tree-ring chronology of climatic change, based on variable growth of very old bristlecone pines, may eventually embrace the past 4000 years (*82*). Because of proximity to modern times, climatic events of this period are, for convenience, referred to the Christian calendar.

As previously mentioned, agriculture was perhaps restrained by a change to a cool climate immediately after the Altithermal, although this was a time of increased moisture. Village farming was established at some sites by the beginning of the Christian era (*83*). Comparatively dry climate about the time of Christ is inferred from beams of piñon pine in archeological sites now surrounded by ponderosa pine (*84*). Buildup of alluvium continued, however, and by A.D. 550 valleys were being filled rather rapidly. For example, pit houses of this age are found buried 4½ meters deep at Chaco Canyon in northeast New Mexico (*85*), and similar situations are common elsewhere. The beginnings of town life appeared at this time, as shown by construction of pueblos dependent on farms along alluviated valleys. Alluviation ceased by A.D. 900 in some areas but lasted as late as A.D. 1200 in others (*86*). Pueblos built on the alluvial surfaces contain thousands of beams cut from pine forests that presumably grew nearby, although some of these structures are many miles from existing forests. Because of the growth of towns and farms, and the spread of population under a favorable moisture regimen, the period A.D. 700–1200, the culmination of a thousand years of village life, is commonly regarded as the cultural climax of the prehistoric Southwest. However, diminishing alluviation toward the end of this period probably reflects progressively drier conditions, higher temperatures, and consequent privation. Bones of animals from the southern part of the region that migrated northward between A.D. 1000 and 1100 are found in the village middens (*84*), and at this time elaborate techniques for controlling water—such as check dams, floodwater diversion, and irrigation ditches—became widespread (*87*). At Chaco Canyon a channel 5½ meters deep, containing pottery dating from A.D. 1100, was eroded in the early alluvium (*85*); the resultant lowering of the water table must have had a disastrous effect on farming.

After A.D. 1200, or perhaps a little earlier, the inhabitants of large villages in northern uplands of the Southwest began to abandon their villages in favor of lower sites along larger and more dependable streams. At Point of Pines,

Arizona, an upland locality with a long record of agriculture, pollen records show that corn declined and disappeared (77), suggesting that crops were no longer cultivated. By A.D. 1500, an agricultural population scattered over 600,000 square kilometers had consolidated in an area of 225,000 square kilometers, most of it south of the Mexican border, and the vacant land was not again settled until shortly before historic times (76). Within this period, great aridity is indicated in the tree-ring record from A.D. 1276 to 1299, and it has long been thought that regional drought caused crops to fail. However, a wetter climate is suggested by the expansion of coniferous forests between 1300 and 1500 (84), and Woodbury argues that skillful farming and the practice of exploiting various modes of water supply would have mitigated crop losses due to drought (76). The real cause of the abandonment of northern upland villages may have been a cool climate and a shortened growing season. Possibly these are the conditions indicated by pollen diagrams of flood-plain sediments of Rio Tesuque near Santa Fe for the period A.D. 1100–1400, which show a high proportion of tree pollen (88)—but, as I have said, interpretation of flood-plain pollen is still plagued with uncertainties. At the same time, favorable moisture conditions on the plains of Kansas (perhaps fostered by a cool climate) are indicated by the westward migration of creek-bottom agriculture; trees along valleys were cut for houses at places where trees do not now grow (79). A drought on the Plains from A.D. 1439 to 1468 is reflected in Nebraska tree rings (89), and at about this time villages along streams of the western Plains were abandoned.

Recent climatic change

Tree-ring records from Arizona and New Mexico indicate a drought about A.D. 1600 and also the death of many coniferous trees growing at low altitudes (84). It seems unlikely that the death of these trees reflects only a deficiency in winter precipitation, because these conifers depend for growth on frequent summer rains (90). In the years 1600 to 1800 forests expanded again around small stands of the older trees (those which flourished between 1300 and 1500) that had survived in sheltered habitats; it is a remarkable fact that most conifers in the Southwest are not older than 350 years, but that a few are nearly twice that age (84). On the other hand, tree-ring records from Oklahoma indicate rather constant climate on the plains since 1710, although several short droughts are evident (91).

The arroyos so common in the Southwest, which began to form about A.D. 1880, are regarded as partly a consequence of overgrazing after the arrival of white men, but contributing climatic causes cannot be discounted. Arroyo-cutting was accompanied in many places by replacement of grasslands with mesquite scrub (92), by a lowering of the water table (93), and by a deterioration of native fish faunas (94). Modern alpine glaciers reached their maximum extent about 1860 and have been retreating since this time (58). Lastly, since 1950, many low-altitude trees in the Southwest have died from drought.

Conclusion

In arid parts of America man still struggles to satisfy his need for water. He foolishly mines groundwater inherited from the past, and he has only partly learned to manage present-day water supplies, even though the study of man's response to ancient environment gives lessons for evaluating current practices. Conservation practices in vogue a millennium ago for the efficient use of occasional rain would be beneficial now if they were more widely adopted. By seeking to identify and understand past changes in the landscape, modern man might bring his surroundings under better control. There is much to learn. The earliest men and the conditions they faced in the Southwest have not yet been adequately identified, and the affairs of even the big-game hunters are reconstructed from scant evidence. Did they exterminate Pleistocene animals? Or did these animals disappear because of an elusive biologic cause? Was man driven out of some areas by drought during Altithermal time? Or are the prevailing concepts of Altithermal aridity erroneous? Do anomalous distributions of plants and animals map recent changes in climatic patterns? Or is life more tolerant of extremes than uniformitarian ideas assume? From geologic study of former episodes of alluviation, can men learn to make desert streams run again in grassy floodplains? Or is the climate now too great a hindrance? These are a few of the problems that hinge on the study of early man in arid America.

REFERENCES

1. H. M. WORMINGTON, *Ancient Man in North America* (Denver Museum of Natural History, Denver, ed. 4, 1957), pp. 42–57.
2. A. D. KRIEGER, *Am. Antiquity* **28,** 138 (1962).
3. H. M. WORMINGTON, *Am. Scientist* **50,** 230 (1962); evidence of man, in the form of burned, cut and broken bone in northern Venezuela, dated 16,375 years and 14,300 years ago, is reported by I. ROUSE and J. M. CRUXENT, *Am. Antiquity* **28,** 537 (1963).
4. M. R. HARRINGTON and R. D. SIMPSON [*Southwest Museum Papers No. 18* (1961)] report a date older than 28,000 years ago from Tule Springs, near Las Vegas, Nevada; but Richard Shutler, in a paper presented in 1963 before the Society for American Archaeology, meeting in Boulder, Colo., found no evidence of man at Tule Springs earlier than 13,000 years ago. W. W. CROOK, JR., and R. K. HARRIS [*Bull. Texas Archeol. Paleontol. Soc.* **28,** 7 (1957)] report a hearth dating back more than 37,000 years at Lewisville, Texas. G. F. CARTER [*Pleistocene Man at San Diego* (Johns Hopkins Press, Baltimore, 1957), pp. 241–242] reports charcoal from the Scripps campus at La Jolla, Calif., dated at 21,500 years ago. P. C. ORR [*Santa Barbara Museum Nat. Hist. Dept. Anthropol. Bull.* **2,** (1956)] reports dates for various charcoal layers on Santa Rosa Island, Calif., that range from 12,000 to nearly 30,000 years ago.
5. The evidence is summarized by E. ANTEVS, *Am. Antiquity* **20,** 317 (1955), and by J. P. MILLER, *Ariz. Univ. Bull.* **28,** 19 (1958); some possible periglacial effects

in southern latitudes of North America are reviewed by D. BRUNNSCHWEILER, *Biul. Peryglacjalny* **11,** 15 (1962).

6. L. B. LEOPOLD, *Am. J. Sci.* **249,** 152 (1951); ———, *ibid.,* p. 399; E. ANTEVS, *J. Geol.* **62,** 182 (1954).

7. C. T. SNYDER and W. B. LANGBEIN, *J. Geophys. Res.* **67,** 2385 (1962).

8. A. J. EARDLEY, V GVOSDETSKY, R E. MARSELL, *Bull. Geol. Soc. Am.* **68,** 1141 (1957); W. S. BROECKER and A. F. WALTON, *ibid.* **70,** 601 (1959); J. H. FETH, *ibid.,* p. 637.

9. G. M. RICHMOND, *U.S. Geol. Surv. Profess. Paper No. 324* (1962).

10. S. A. SCHUMM and R. F. HADLEY, *Am. J. Sci.* **255,** 161 (1957); W. B. LANGBEIN and S. A. SCHUMM, *Trans. Am. Geophys. Union* **39,** 1076 (1958); R. F. HADLEY, *U.S. Geol. Surv. Profess. Paper No. 352-A* (1960); S. A. SCHUMM, *U.S. Geol. Surv. Profess. Paper No. 352-B* (1960); S. A. SCHUMM, *Bull. Geol. Soc. Am.* **74,** 1089 (1963); S A. SCHUMM and R. W. LICHTY, *U.S. Geol. Surv. Profess. Paper No. 352-D* (1963).

11. D. S. SIMONETT, *Assoc. Am. Geographers Ann.* **50,** 216 (1960).

12. P. S. MARTIN, B. E. SABELS, DICK SHUTLER, JR., *Am. J. Sci.* **259,** 102 (1961).

13. E. S. DEEVEY, JR., *Bull. Geol. Soc. Am.* **60,** 1315 (1949); P. S. MARTIN, in *Zoogeography,* C. L. HUBBS, Ed. (AAAS, Washington, D.C., 1958), pp. 375–420.

14. L. C. EISELEY, *Publs. Philadelphia Anthropol. Soc.* **1,** 77 (1937); the mollusks identified by Eiseley are given different names in current studies.

15. D. W. TAYLOR, *U.S. Geol. Surv. Profess. Paper No. 337* (1960); A. B. LEONARD and J. C. FRYE, *Texas Bur. Econ. Geol. Rept. Invest. No. 45* (1962); R. J. DRAKE, *Southern Calif. Acad. Sci. Bull.* **59,** 133 (1960); ———, *ibid.* **60,** 127 (1961); D. C. ALLEN and E. P. CHEATUM, *Texas Archeol. Soc. Bull.* **31,** 293 (1961).

16. E. J. KARLIN, *Am. Midland Naturalist* **65,** 60 (1961).

17. E. R. HALL and K. R. KELSON, *The Mammals of North America* (Ronald Press, New York, 1959), vol. 1.

18. P. S. MARTIN, *New Mexico Highlands Univ. Bull.* **212,** 56 (1961).

19. J. S. FINDLEY, *Kansas Univ. Museum Nat. Hist. Publs. No. 7* (1955), pp. 613–618; B. H. SLAUGHTER and B. R. HOOVER, *Southern Methodist Univ. J. Grad. Res. Center* **31,** 143 (1963).

20. J. S. FINDLEY and C. J. JONES, *J. Mammalogy* **43,** 154 (1962).

21. R. C. STEBBINS and W. J. RIEMER, *Copeia* **1950,** 73 (1950).

22. B. H. BANTA, thesis, Stanford University, 1961.

23. A. B. KLOTS, *Proc. Intern. Congr. Entomol., 10th, Montreal, 1956* (1958), vol. 1, p. 711.

24. Geologic relations of some extinct and living vertebrates are reviewed by C. B. HUNT, *U.S. Geol. Surv. Bull. 996-A* (1953); mammalian local faunas are summarized by C. W. HIBBARD, *Papers Michigan Acad. Sci.* **43, (1957),** 3 (1958).

25. K. F. MURRAY, *Ecology* **38,** 129 (1957); the supposedly boreal forms include the fox *Vulpes macroura,* the wood rat *Neotoma cinerea,* and the hare *Lepus townsendii.*

26. P. S. MARTIN, in *Zoögeography,* C. L. HUBBS, Ed. (AAAS, Washington, D.C., 1958), p. 391.

27. W. A. WEBER, in *Recent Advances in Botany* (Univ. of Toronto Press, Toronto, 1961), vol. 1, pp. 912–914; see also P. L. JOHNSON, *Madrono* **16,** 229 (1962).
28. E. GARCIA, C. SOTO, F. MIRANDA, *Mexico Univ., Inst. Biol., Ann.* **31,** 133 (1960).
29. Pollen records that indicate forest boundaries 900 meters lower on mountains in Costa Rica and Colombia are cited by P. S. MARTIN in a paper presented before the 6th congress of the International Association for Quaternary Research, Poland, 1961, and by T. VAN DER HAMMEN and E. GONZALES, *Leidse Geol. Mededel.* **25 (1960),** 261 (1961).
30. L. D. POTTER and JOANNE ROWLEY, *Botan. Gaz.* **122,** 1 (1960); H. N. DIXON, thesis, University of New Mexico, 1962; L. J. MAHER, JR., *Bull. Geol. Soc. Am.* **74,** 1485 (1963).
31. U. HAFSTEN, in *Paleoecology of the Llano Estacado* (Fort Burgwin Research Center, Taos, N.M., 1961), pp. 59–91.
32. K. H. CLISBY, F. FOREMAN, P. B. SEARS, *Geobotan. Inst. Rübel Verhöff* **34,** 21 (1958).
33. P. S. MARTIN, *Ecology* **4,** 436 (1963).
34. A. ROOSMA, *Science* **128,** 716 (1958); R. F. FLINT and W. A. GALE, *Am. J. Sci.* **256,** 689 (1958).
35. A. M. BENT and H. E. WRIGHT, JR., *Bull. Geol. Soc. Am.* **74,** 491 (1963).
36. L. J. MAHER, JR., thesis, University of Minnesota, 1961.
37. F. WENDORF, in *Paleoecology of the Llano Estacado* (Fort Burgwin Research Center, Taos, N.M., 1961), pp. 12–21, 115–133.
38. A. GRAHAM and C. HEIMSCH, *Ecology* **41,** 751 (1960); the date is estimated from the inferred rate of sedimentation (based on a single date obtained by the radiocarbon method) and by correlating pollen records of adjacent bogs.
39. P. J. MEHRINGER, JR., paper presented before the Society for American Archaeology, meeting in Boulder, Colo., 1963.
40. A. J. EARDLEY, *Utah Geol. Mineral. Surv. Spec. Studies No. 2* (1962).
41. F. WENDORF and J. J. HESTER, *Am. Antiquity* **28,** 159 (1962).
42. J. J. HESTER, *ibid.,* **26,** 58 (1960).
43. P. S. MARTIN, *ibid.,* **29,** 67 (1963).
44. H. E. MALDE, *ibid.,* **26,** 236 (1960).
45. V. HAYNES and G. AGOGINO, *Proc. Denver Museum Nat. Hist.* **1960,** No. 9 (1960).
46. For a map of springs on the High Plains and historical accounts of them, see W. R. WEDEL, *Am. Antiquity* **29,** 1 (1963).
47. B. H. HUSCHER and H. A. HUSCHER, *Am. Phil. Soc. Yearbook 1941* (1942), pp. 226–229.
48. The evidence is summarized by H. L. ALEXANDER, JR., *Am. Antiquity* **28,** 510 (1963).
49. W. J. WALLACE, *ibid.,* p. 172; R. D. DAUGHERTY, *ibid.,* p. 144; J. D. JENNINGS and E. NORBECK, *ibid.* **21,** 1 (1955).
50. P. S. MARTIN, *The Last 10,000 Years* (Univ. of Arizona Press, Tucson, 1963).
51. P. B. SEARS and A. ROOSMA, *Am. J. Sci.* **259,** 669 (1961).
52. P. J. MEHRINGER, JR., and P. S. MARTIN, paper presented before the Society for American Archaeology, meeting in Boulder, Colo., 1963.
53. H. H. ASCHMANN, *Calif. Univ. Archaeol. Surv. Repts. No. 42* (1958), pp. 23–40.

54. E. S. DEEVEY and R. F. FLINT, *Science* **125**, 182 (1957).

55. T. VAN DER HAMMEN and E. GONZALES, *Geol. Mijnbouw* **39**, 737 (1960).

56. L. B. LEOPOLD and J. P. MILLER, *U.S. Geol. Surv. Water Supply Paper No. 1261* (1954), pp. 54–56.

57. C. C. ALBRITTON, JR., and K. BRYAN, *Bull. Geol. Soc. Am.* **50**, 1423 (1939); K. BRYAN and C. C. ALBRITTON, JR., *Am. J. Sci* **241**, 469 (1943); E. ANTEVS, *Am. Antiquity* **28**, 193 (1962).

58. G. M. RICHMOND, *Bull. Geol. Soc. Am.* **71**, 1371 (1960).

59. W. F. LIBBY, *Radiocarbon Dating* (Univ. of Chicago Press, Chicago, ed. 2, 1955), pp. 107–108.

60. E. ANTEVS, *Am. Antiquity* **20**, 329 (1955).

61. J. J. SIGALOVE, A. LONG, P. E. DAMON, *J. Geophys. Res.* **67**, 1657 (1962).

62. J. T. HACK, *Geograph. Rev.* **31**, 240 (1941); *Papers Peabody Museum Am. Archaeol. Ethnol. Harvard Univ. No. 35* (1942).

63. C. J. HEUSSER, paper presented before the 10th Pacific Science Congress, Honolulu, 1961.

64. L. E. DETLING, *Ecology* **42**, 348 (1961).

65. C. J. HEUSSER, *Am. Geog. Soc. Spec. Publ. 35* (1960), pp. 184–186.

66. R. W. PENNAK, *Ecology* **44**, 1 (1963).

67. C. L. HUBBS, G. S. BIEN, H. E. SUESS, *Radiocarbon* **5**, 271 (1963).

68. For several papers dealing with the Archaic, see *Am. Antiquity* **24**, No. 3, (1959).

69. P. B. SEARS, *Ariz. Univ. Bull* **28**, 77 (1958).

70. F. E. GREEN, *Am. Antiquity* **28**, 230 (1962).

71. R. D. DAUGHERTY, *ibid.*, p. 147.

72. P. B. SEARS, *Science* **134**, 2038 (1961).

73. G. R. SCOTT, *U.S. Geol. Surv. Profess. Paper No. 421-A* (1963), pp. 40–41.

74. C. N. BROWN, *J. Geol.* **64**, 1 (1956); W. S. MOTTS, *Bull. Geol. Soc. Am.* **69**, 1737 (1958).

75. P. C. MANGELSDORF, *Science* **128**, 1313 (1958); ———, R. S. MACNEISH, W. C. GALINAT, *ibid.* **143**, 538 (1964).

76. R. B. WOODBURY, *Ann. N.Y. Acad. Sci.* **95**, Art. 1, 705 (1961).

77. P. S MARTIN and J. SCHOENWETTER, *Science* **132**, 33 (1960) Corn of about the same age is also found at Tularosa Cave, New Mexico.

78. H. J. IRWIN and C. C. IRWIN, *Am. Antiquity* **27**, 114 (1961).

79. W. R. WEDEL, *Bur. Am. Ethnol. Bull. 174,* 626 (1959).

80. R. S. MACNEISH, *Trans. Am. Phil. Soc.* **48**, 1 (1958).

81. H. C. FRITTS, in *UNESCO and World Meteorological Organization Symposium on Changes of Climate, With Special Reference to the Arid Zones, Rome, 1961* (1963); E. SCHULMAN, *Dendroclimatic Changes in Semiarid America* (Univ. of Arizona Press, Tucson, 1956).

82. C. W. FERGUSON, JR., paper presented before the Southwestern and Rocky Mountain Division of the AAAS, 1963.

83. E. W. HAURY, *Viking Fund Publs. in Anthropol. No. 32* (1962), pp. 106–131.

84. T. L. SMILEY, *Ann. N.Y. Acad. Sci.* **95**, Art. 1, 697 (1961).

85. The relation of alluviation and climate to a prehistoric village life is discussed by K. BRYAN, *Smithsonian Inst. Misc. Collections No. 122* (1954).

86. J. P. MILLER and F. WENDORF, *J. Geol.* **66**, 177 (1958).

87. R. B. WOODBURY, *Soc. Am. Archaeol. Mem. 17* (1961).
88. L. B. LEOPOLD, E. B. LEOPOLD, F. WENDORF, *in UNESCO and World Meteorological Organization Symposium on Changes of Climate, With Special Reference to the Arid Zones, Rome, 1961* (1963), pp. 265–270.
89. H. E. WEAKLY, *Tree-ring Bull.* **6,** 18 (1940); *J. Forestry* **41,** 816 (1943).
90. W. S. GLOCK, *Trans. Am. Geophys, Union* **36,** 315 (1955).
91. H. J. HARPER, *Proc. Okla. Acad. Sci.* **41,** 23 (1961).
92. J. R. HASTINGS, *Ariz. Acad. Sci. J.* **1,** 60 (1959).
93. J. R. HARSHBARGER, *Ariz. Univ. Bull.* **28,** 51 (1958).
94. R. R. MILLER, *Papers Mich. Acad. Sci.,* **46 (1960),** 365 (1961).
95. For helpful criticism of the manuscript I am indebted to Claude C. Albritton, John T. Hack, Emil W. Haury, Charles B. Hunt, Jesse D. Jennings, Alex D. Krieger, Estella B. Leopold, Paul S. Martin, William S. Osburn, William E. Powers, Hugo G. Rodeck, and H. Marie Wormington. Publication of this article is authorized by the director of the U.S. Geological Survey.

Environmental Limitation
on the Development of Culture*

BETTY J. MEGGERS

The relationship of culture to environment is one of the oldest problems in the science of anthropology and has provided a leading source of controversy. Early students, impressed with the ways in which cultures were adjusted to the unique features of their local environments, developed the concept of environmental determinism. As more field work was done by trained observers, the variability in culture patterns became more evident and the idea of determinism was rejected. Then, as individual cultures were grouped into culture areas and recognized as specific manifestations of a general pattern, the role of environment once again compelled attention. Wissler (1926:214) expressed the correspondence that exists between culture areas and "natural" areas in the form of a law: ". . . when two sections of a continent differ in climate, florae and faunae, or in their ecological complexes, the culture of the tribal groups in one section will differ from that in the other."

In the last two decades this situation has been examined in broad-scale analyses (Forde 1934; Kroeber 1939) and detailed field studies (Steward 1938) and the relationship between environment and culture has been clarified to such an extent that Coon (1948:614) could phrase it recently in more causal terms than Wissler could use two decades before: "Differences in environment . . . are the chief if not the only reason why historical changes have proceeded at different rates in different places, and why more complicated systems have not diffused more rapidly from centers of development."

* Various versions of this paper have been read by Marshall T. Newman, Philip Drucker, Waldo Wedel, Clifford Evans, James A. Ford and Gordon Ekholm. I should like to express my gratitude to them for their constructive comments.

There are few anthropologists today who would disagree with the general statement that environment is an important conditioner of culture. However, efforts to establish the relationship more specifically seem to give negative results. The potentialities of a particular habitat can be seen reflected in the subsistence pattern, the material culture, and by extension, in the social and religious aspects of the culture that is exploiting it, but when cultures of similar subsistence patterns or general features are compared they are not found to occupy similar environments. Hunting tribes, for example, may live in semi-deserts, swamps, forests, grasslands, or mountains, and in the arctic, the tropics or the temperate zone. Conversely, areas that seem similar geographically may differ greatly culturally. This has led to the conclusion expressed by Forde (1934:464):

> Physical conditions enter intimately into every cultural development and pattern, not excluding the most abstract and non-material; they enter not as determinants, however, but as one category of the raw material of cultural elaboration. The study of the relations between cultural patterns and physical conditions is of the greatest importance for an understanding of human society, but it cannot be undertaken in terms of simple geographical controls alleged to be identifiable on sight. It must proceed inductively from the minute analysis of each actual society.

Given the traditional conception of environment, no other conclusion is possible. However, in view of the very definite evidence that cultures have an ecological aspect, which can be shown to have a determinative character particularly on the lower levels (e.g., Wedel 1953), it does not seem likely that no more general relationship exists. It is more probable that, in attempting to discover it, we have not been distinguishing the fundamental factors involved. All the efforts to correlate culture with environment have utilized the landscape classifications set up by geographers. James (1935), for example, has summarized world environments under eight principal types: dry lands or deserts, tropical forests, Mediterranean scrub forests, mid-latitude mixed forests, grasslands, boreal forests, polar lands and mountain lands. It has frequently been noted that these categories do not represent cultural uniformities or even similarities. Desert cultures range from food gatherers to high civilizations; both polar lands and boreal forests, on the other hand, are exploited by food gatherers. Since environment does have an important effect on culture, and since the usual geographical classifications fail to discriminate culturally significant units, it is logical to search for some other basis for distinction.

Definition of environment

The primary point of interaction between a culture and its environment is in terms of subsistence, and the most vital aspect of environment from the point of view of culture is its suitability for food production. Until the discovery of agriculture, this was relatively equal over the major portion of the earth's surface.

In some areas game, wild plants or fish were more abundant than in others, but the range of variation was slight in comparison with what it became following the adoption of agriculture. The cultivation of cereals was designated by Tylor (1881:215) as "the great moving power of civilization," and the cultural revolution that followed in its wake has since been commented upon frequently (Peake 1940:127; Childe 1941:66; Steward 1949a:23; White 1949:371). Most anthropologists, however, do not carry the analysis beyond the effect that agriculture has had on culture to the effect that environment has on the productivity of agriculture. Differences in soil fertility, climate and other elements determine the productivity of agriculture, which, in turn, regulates population size and concentration and through this influences the sociopolitical and even the technological development of the culture. Once this point is raised, it is evident that differential suitability of the environment for agricultural exploitation provides a potential explanation for differences in cultural development attained around the world.

To be culturally significant, a classification of environment must recognize differences in agricultural potential. Areas that permit only limited, shifting cultivation because of the poverty of the soil must be distinguished from those of enduring fertility where intensive agriculture can be practiced over long periods of time. An examination of the methods of food production suggests that four types of environment can be recognized, each with a distinct agricultural implication:

Type 1.—Areas of no agricultural potential. This includes the greatest variety of natural landscapes because only one of the many components necessary for agriculture need be absent for the area to be unsuitable. The defective element may be soil composition, temperature, rainfall, short growing season, elevation, terrain, etc. Type 1 regions include tundra, some deserts, tropical savannas, swamps, some mountain ranges, and similarly uncultivable types of land.

A few areas with no agricultural potential are suitable for a pastoral economy. These constitute a special category of Type 1 because food gathering is replaced by food production and a higher level of cultural development can be attained than is typical of Type 1 areas. Some Type 3 areas have also supported pastoral cultures on the aboriginal level. However, since pastoralism is a minor source of food production compared to agriculture among the cultures of the world, and lacks both the environmental adaptability and the variety of potentiality for cultural development characteristic of agriculture, it will receive only brief mention in this discussion.

Type 2.—Areas of limited agriculture potential. Here agriculture can be undertaken, but its productivity is minimized by limited soil fertility, which cannot economically be improved or conserved. When the natural vegetation cycle is broken by clearing, planting and harvesting, the delicate balance between what is taken from and what is returned to the soil is upset. The soil is poor to begin with, and exposed fully to the detrimental effects of the climate, it is quickly exhausted of plant nutrients. The addition of fertilizer is not feasible on a primitive level or economically practical on a modern one. Since the major cause of this condition is abundant rainfall and high humidity, Type 2 environments may be restricted to the tropics, and a good example is the South American tropical forest and selva. This does not mean, however, that all tropical environments are necessarily Type 2.

Up to the present time, no method of maintaining such areas in continuously profitable, intensive food production has been found, in spite of our extensive knowledge of plants and soils (cf. Higbee 1948). Permanent and intensive production has been achieved in some places by the introduction of tree crops (cacao, coffee, bananas, citrus, etc.) and jute, but with the possible exception of the banana, none of these could provide an adequate subsistence base. Should a solution appear in the future, the "limited" designation for Type 2 might have to be modified, but since the obstacles to the increased productivity of food crops are infinitely greater than in Type 3, a distinction between the two should still be made.

Type 3.—Areas of increasable (improvable) agricultural potential. Areas of this type contain all the essentials for agricultural production that exist in Type 2. However, being in more temperate climates where rainfall and humidity are less detrimental, soil exhaustion is caused mainly by the raising of food crops. Under a slash-and-burn type of utilization, the productivity of the land is not much greater than that of Type 2 areas. However, crop returns can be appreciably increased by techniques such as rotation, fallow and fertilization, and the same fields can be kept in almost constant production over long periods of time if not permanently. Temperate forest zones like Europe and the eastern United States belong in this category.

Other Type 3 environments are less readily improved because the deficient element is not soil fertility, but water. The Imperial Valley of California is such a case, where agriculture is made possible by water brought long distances over mountains.

Further methods of increasing agricultural potential are by the introduction of more suitable plants, such as the replacement of dry rice by wet rice in Madagascar (Linton 1936: 348–54), and the introduction of new or improved tools like the animal-drawn plow in the North American plains.

Type 4.—Areas of unlimited agricultural potential. Here the natural environment approximates as closely as possible the ideal conditions for agriculture. Climate, water and terrain are suitable and soil fertility is for the purposes of this discussion inexhaustible, so that the land can support intensive food production indefinitely. The "cradles of civilization" all belong to Type 4.

The classification of an area into one of these types is theoretically independent of the time factor. Since the introduction of agriculture in most of the world, there has been little alteration in climate or topography that has affected the agricultural potentiality of the environment. Where changes have occurred because of climatic shifts, such as the gradual northward extension of the limit of agriculture in North America, the area can be reclassified in accord with its new potential.

For purposes of practical ease in identifying an area as to type, the year 1950 can be taken as a base line. If an area is improvable by modern agricultural techniques, it is Type 3, regardless of what might have been its primitive or aboriginal usage. If it cannot be shown to have been so improved, or to be comparable to some area where similar natural deficiencies in agricultural potential have been compensated for with modern knowledge and techniques, then it is Type 2 or Type 1, depending on whether agriculture is feasible or impossible. Type 3 areas, as will be seen, are most dependent on such technical advances to develop their potential. Type 4 areas are highly productive even with relatively primitive means of exploitation.

Since this is not a common approach to the classification of environment, it may be well to risk over-repetition in order to avoid being misunderstood. The characteristics and differences between Types 1, 3 and 4 are relatively clear-cut, and probably do not need further discussion. Type 2, however, contains two pitfalls: (1) It takes a stand on a question in much dispute, namely, the agricultural potentiality of the tropics, and (2) it leads to the identification of "tropical" with "Type 2," which is not intended. Comments and information bearing on these two points will be found in the succeeding pages, but a more specific statement here may help to orient the reader.

If one wishes to make an abstract argument about the opportunities for agriculture in the South American tropics, it can be documented with quotations from visitors to the area beginning with Raleigh and La Barre in the 17th century and continuing right up to the present (Price 1952). However, a careful examination will reveal the liberal use of qualifiers such as "could," "might," "probably," "if . . . , then," etc., and considerable emphasis on the luxuriance of the wild vegetation. Such arguments are hard to refute because of their indefinite character. However, if one examines archeological, ethnographical and historical data, the efforts to initiate large-scale agricultural programs, the climatic factors influencing the vegetation cycle, and so delves beneath the promising surface, one is forced to conclude that the latter is largely an attractive camouflage. Even to grant the possibility that parts of the Amazon Basin can be brought under successful agricultural production by the use of specialized techniques and crops does not invalidate the establishment of a separate category for this and similar areas in the environmental classification. Our goal is to explain differences in cultural development, and we can do this only by observing the facts and distilling from them a general hypothesis. The assumption that underlies this process is that the situations we observe are not fortuitous or arbitrary, but are caused. The fact that cultural evolution has proceeded farther in Type 3 areas than in Type 2 areas cannot be considered accidental and dismissed as irrelevant. Although it may seem to us, possessed of the knowledge of the 20th century, that the obstacles to agricultural exploitation are no greater in one type of environment than in the other, we are not justified in projecting this view into the analysis. Unless it is a conclusion derived from an examination of the data, it cannot be brought forth to refute other generalizations founded on these facts.

Since the primary cause of this low agricultural potentiality appears to lie in the low natural fertility of the soil, worn out and broken down by long and constant exposure to leaching, it was suggested that Type 2 environments may be exclusively tropical. This is not equivalent, however, to a statement that all tropical environments are Type 2. On the contrary, one need not look far around the world to gather evidence that this is not the case. There is no reason why it should be. The primary definition of "tropical" is in terms of latitude, and latitude is perhaps the least important and most generalized factor influencing agriculture. Soil fertility, topography, rainfall pattern, temperature and similar agriculturally significant variables differ among tropical areas as they do among temperate ones, and form the basis for this environmental classification.

In correlating cultural development with environmental potentiality, the two components must be treated on the same level. The classification of the environment has been made in terms of general features that unite the landscapes placed in one category and distinguish them from those in another. The basic or primary factor, agricultural potentiality, has been deduced or abstracted from the unique or variable features, temperature, rainfall, flora, topography, that are present in any given area. In order to detect possible relationships, culture must be reduced to a similar level of generalization and specific features categorized under concepts such as "social classes," "occupational division of labor," "hierarchy of gods," etc. This has been done frequently before, especially in culture-area formulations, and its philosophical validity has been discussed by Steward (1949a: 6–7), so that it does not seem necessary to add further justification here.

If we accept as a working hypothesis the existence of a definite cause and effect relationship between these four kinds of environment and the maximum cultural development they can continuously support, the next step is to examine from this point of view some of the evidence that has been assembled about cultures. Since limitations of space do not permit coverage of the world, the greatest temporal, spatial and cultural variety may be included by using South America and Europe as test areas.

Culture and environment in South America

The aboriginal cultures of South America have been analyzed and classified in recent years into four major culture areas: Marginal, Tropical Forest, Circum-Caribbean and Andean (Steward 1946–50). Although this division was made primarily in order to present the tremendous array of data in an intelligible order, it performs the secondary function of being one of the most remarkable demonstrations available of the limiting effect of environment on culture.

The habitats of the Marginal tribes are varied geographically, including swamps, savannas, sub-Antarctic forests and arid uplands, but all belong to Type 1 because they are unfit for agriculture. A subsistence derived from hunting, fishing and gathering will normally support only small groups and these must be constantly on the move to take advantage of seasonal food plants and moving game. The combination of small population concentrations and nomadic life exerts a very definitely limiting effect on the culture, keeping it on a simple level that permits the satisfaction of basic needs and little more. Technology is limited to the manufacture of essential tools and utensils that can be made in a minimum of time and with easily accessible materials: bows and arrows, spears, coiled baskets, nets and perhaps bark canoes. Shelters are crude and temporary. Social organization is on kinship lines, since the social unit is a single family, or at best an extended family or lineage. There is no division of labor except on sex and age lines, no differentiation in rank or status among adults. The family head is the band leader, but he has no privileges or enforceable powers and few duties. Supernaturalism is poorly defined and serves individual rather than group ends; there are no offerings, sacrifices, temples or idols. Even shamans are not frequent.

That the failure to achieve a higher level of culture in Type 1 areas in South America is not the result of isolation from sources of diffusion is noted by Steward (1949*b*:691–92):

> More advanced technologies were absent to a surprising degree, even among the tribes who adjoined or formed enclaves within the Tropical Forest peoples and would seem to have had considerable opportunity for borrowing. . . . For example, simple woven and twilled baskets are easier and faster to make than coiled or twined ones, loom weaving is more efficient than netting or finger twining, and in many localities even dugout canoes would have repaid the labor of constructing them.

To explain this as the result of "a certain recklessness toward the hazards of existence," as Steward does (p. 692), is to attribute to these people an attitude that may be present at our own level of development but if held by primitive groups would soon have led them to extinction. It seems more reasonable to conclude that a powerful deterrent beyond the influence of human wishes prevents these advances from being made. Since the culture is in such intimate relationship with the environment, it is logical to look for an explanation from this source. The evidence suggests that the environment exerts an unsurmountable limiting effect on the cultures it supports as long as it permits only a hunting and gathering subsistence pattern, and that this limitation exends to all areas of the culture, even those that seem remotely or not at all related to the subsistence requirements. No amount of inventive genius or receptivity to borrowing that might be theoretically attributable to the people psychologically is sufficient to overcome this barrier.

The tribes belonging to the Tropical Forest pattern of culture occupy an environment belonging to Type 2, with limited agricultural potential. The introduction of slash-and-burn agriculture to the subsistence brings a more reliable food supply, which in turn permits a denser and more sedentary population and a release of labor from subsistence activities that is reflected in an expansion of all other aspects of the culture. More time is available for the gathering and preparation of raw materials and for the process of manufacture, and this permits the introduction of pottery and loom weaving of domesticated cotton. Other new traits are woven basketry and dugout canoes. The settlement pattern consists of semipermanent villages composed of communal or single-family houses of pole and thatch construction.

Although it represents an increase in security of food supply, slash-and-burn agriculture is not sufficiently productive or permanent of locale to support large concentrations of population or stable settlements. This is reflected in the socio-political organization which remains basically along kinship lines, the headman or chief having limited authority and few if any special privileges. Division of labor remains on sex and age lines, but the shaman begins to emerge as a part-time occupational specialist. Crisis rites are elaborated, especially at birth and puberty, and surrounded with magical observances and taboos. Deities are still mythical beings rather than objects of worship, and the most important supernatural beings are "bush spirits."

The role of the environment in the formation of this type of culture pattern is clear, but the fact that a Type 2 environment prevents any further increase in the complexity of the cultures it supports may not be so obvious. The process of evolution being typically slow, there is a possibility that the Tropical Forest pattern was too recent a development for there to have been further progress before the advent of the Europeans. This would be in line with Steward's reconstruction (1948:14–15) of the spread of culture in South America: an early expansion of the Andean pattern with some deculturation to the Circum-Caribbean level, followed by diffusion from Venezuela down the coast and up the Amazon accompanied by the loss of more advanced sociopolitical and religious patterns. If this reconstruction were true, it would place a relatively late date on the origin of the Tropical Forest pattern, since it would have to postdate the development of culture in the Andean area to a level higher than that represented in the Circum-Caribbean area and allow for the occurrence of a deculturation in the latter region and a further decline in the Tropical Forest.

Archeological evidence from the Circum-Caribbean and Tropical Forest areas has greatly increased since the publication of Steward's hypothesis, and it indicates that the actual sequence of events was in the direction of evolution rather than degeneration. Rouse's analysis (1953) of the Circum-Caribbean archeological picture shows that cultures of the Tropical Forest level precede those identifiable as Circum-Caribbean. Field work in two Tropical Forest areas (the mouth of the Amazon and British Guiana) produces a sequence from Marginal to Tropical Forest culture, rather than the Circum-Caribbean to Tropical Forest sequence needed to support Steward's analysis (Evans and Meggers n.d.; Meggers n.d.). It appears that as agriculture diffused over the continent, culture in each area was elaborated to the limit determined by the environmental potential, and having attained that level remained relatively stationary. In the Tropical Forest area it advanced from Marginal to Tropical Forest; in the Circum-Caribbean area, from Marginal to Tropical Forest to Circum-Caribbean. Thereafter local diversification in details continued but there was no noticeable further advance.

A number of examples of the degeneration of higher cultures under the influence of the tropical forest or Type 2 environment exist and constitute important evidence of the limiting force of this type of environment, although they can no longer be considered as typical of the process that created the Tropical Forest cultural pattern. One of the most striking is the failure of the highly-organized and technically-advanced Inca culture to include any of the tropical forest as an effective part of the Inca Empire. Although numerous efforts were made to extend the boundaries in this direction, they were uniformly unsuccessful. This suggests that the subsistence resources of the lowlands were so meager that they could not support such an advanced culture even when it brought with it well-developed techniques for the mass production and distribution of food.

Even less highly organized groups that attempted to colonize the lowlands were unable to maintain traits that were more advanced than the Tropical Forest pattern. One of these, the Marajoara culture at the mouth of the Amazon River, has had sufficient archeological examination to permit the reconstruction of its course to decline in detail (Meggers 1951, n.d.). The sites consist of artificial earth mounds up to 250 meters long and 7 meters high, which were used either for habitation or for burial. The variety of complex decorative styles in the pottery, the details of the burial pattern, and the size and quantity of the mounds imply a social and religious organization of the Circum-Caribbean or Sub-Andean level, with well-developed leadership, social stratification, occupational division of labor, and a religion involving idols and probably priests. The history of this culture on Marajó Island begins suddenly with the technological and sociopolitical development in its most complex form. Mounds were begun, the potters set about their work, craftsmen and specialists of other kinds devoted themselves to their special tasks, while another segment of the population undertook to secure food for all. Initially, it would not be impossible, or perhaps even difficult, for a few people to supply the needs of the group in the new environment as they had in the old one. The forested western half of the Island must have provided considerable game, and the streams and lakes were bountifully stocked with fish. Birds are abundant today and must have been so in aboriginal times.

This condition could not continue indefinitely, however. With intensive exploitation, the game would grow more wary, the fish less abundant, the birds would seek safer spots and an increasing number of man-hours would be required to feed the community. The difficulties would mount when the limited area suitable for slash-and-burn agriculture had been cut over and had to be re-used before fertility was restored. More and more individuals would have to leave their special occupations and join the quest for food. This change is reflected in the pottery, which shows a consistent decline in quality of decoration, variety of shapes and technical skill. The more elaborate decorative techniques die out approximately in the order of their complexity, those requiring the greatest expenditure of time for their execution going first. The same degeneration must have taken place in the other categories of material culture. With the breakdown of the division of labor on occupational lines, and the basis for social stratification, came a disintegration of the social system reflected archeologically in the disappearance of differential treatment of the dead. The decline continued until the culture viewed archeologically is similar in all respects to the Tropical Forest cultures, in which state it survived until Marajó Island was overrun by an invading tribe of the Tropical Forest pattern.

The evidence just reviewed brings out two major attributes of the Tropical Forest culture area: (1) advanced cultural traits did not diffuse into it from the adjacent regions of higher culture in spite of frequent "opportunity"; and (2) more advanced cultures that attempted to colonize the tropical forest were unable to preserve their more advanced culture in so doing. The conclusion seems unavoidable that there is a force at work to which man through his culture must bow. The determinant operates uniformly regardless of time, place (within the forest), psychology or race. Its leveling effect appears to be inescapable. Even modern efforts to implant civilization in the South American tropical forest have met with defeat, or survive only with constant assistance from the outside. In short, the environmental potential of the tropical forest is sufficient to allow the evolution of culture to proceed only to the level represented by the Tropical Forest culture pattern; further indigenous evolution is impossible, and any more highly evolved culture attempting to settle and maintain itself in the tropical forest environment will inevitably decline to the Tropical Forest level.

The culture of the Circum-Caribbean pattern represents a higher degree of development than was achieved in the tropical forest, manifested primarily on the social and religious level. Technological improvements are mainly in quality and variety of products, the only new category of manufactures being metallurgy. The settlement pattern is characterized by large, compact, planned villages containing several hundred to several thousand persons, with special structures for temple, chief's residence and storehouses. Social organization is in marked contrast to what exists on the Tropical Forest level: stratification into three or four classes with status partly hereditary and partly dependent on individual achievement in warfare; a chief who receives tribute and who is distinguished in life by special insignia and in death by special burial practices; divsion of labor on occupational lines; and, on the political side, union of villages or tribes into federations. Religion becomes institutionalized. Celestial beings and ancestors are among supernatural objects of worship, represented by idols housed in temples served by the shaman or chief who made offerings that sometimes included human sacrifice. Warfare was an important activity and villages were often fortified for defense.

The Circum-Caribbean and Tropical Forest cultures occupy adjacent territory along northern South America, and it has already been shown that the differences between them cannot be explained as the result of lack of opportunity for diffusion. In the light of the environmental influences operating on Tropical Forest culture, it is pertinent to examine the Circum-Caribbean area environmentally to see what the differences are that will account for the greater cultural complexity.

A diversity of geographical features is included in the Circum-Caribbean area, ranging from lowland tropical forests and alternately dry and flooded savannas up to more temperate highlands, and including both islands of varying size and the mainland. If environment and culture are related, it would be expected that this environmental diversity would be reflected in cultural diversity, which is indeed the case. Certain of these environments are Type 3, suitable for relatively intensive farming (supplemented with a good supply of seafood), and it is in those situations that the typical Circum-Caribbean cultures are found. Attempts by these to expand to the Type 2 tropical forest are traceable archeologically, especially in Central America, but none of them were successful in producing enduring settlements (Johnson 1948:196). The main distinction between Tropical Forest and Circum-Caribbean culture is in the realm of social organization. Where a stable food supply permits the establishment of good-sized, permanent communities, an elaboration of the social structure is mandatory. The village is no longer composed of relatives, and kinship is no longer a sufficient basis for regulating interpersonal relations. Chiefs exacting tribute and exercising special privileges, social classes, and occupational division of labor do not at first glance seem closely related to food supply, but the degree of dependence is readily indicated by the loss of these features when the effort is made to transplant them to the less productive Type 2 environment of the tropical forest.

In the Andean culture area with a Type 3 and Type 4 environment, the highest cultural development in South America was achieved. The Peruvian coastal valleys furnish the longest uninterrupted prehistoric sequence, partly because favorable conditions for preservation accompany favorable conditions for human occupancy. Arts and crafts, social organization, and religion were elaborated to an extent that rivaled what had been achieved in Europe in the same century. Cotton and woolen textiles were produced by a variety of techniques, some so complex that they cannot be duplicated on modern machine looms, and often ornamented with elaborate designs. Pottery was mass-produced and of high quality. Metallurgy included casting, alloying, plating of gold, silver and copper. Massive fortifications, agricultural terraces, palaces, temples and lesser buildings were constructed of carefully fitted stone masonry or adobe. Minor arts and crafts existed in profusion. Settlements ranged from small villages to cities, some of which were administrative centers attaining an estimated population of 100,000. A network of roads facilitated communication and transportation of goods between towns.

The functions of government were handled by a hierarchy of officials of increasing rank and responsibility, culminating in the divine and absolute monarch. Class distinctions were clearly defined and hereditary, with distinctive garments, insignia and other privileges for individuals of the upper class. Governmental supervision touched all aspects of life; the duties and obligations of each individual were fixed, all activities were regulated. It is almost superfluous to add that occupational division of labor was advanced to modern proportions. The religious organization paralleled the governmental one, with a hierarchy of priests headed by a close relative of the ruler. These presided over temples dedicated to gods of varying importance and housing images and ceremonial paraphernalia. The gods were approached with blood sacrifice, fasting, prayer and offerings, and ceremonies were held in accord with the ritual calendar.

The existence of so elaborate a civilization depends upon the intensive production of food and its effective distribution. Large irrigation works increased cultivatable land in the valleys on the coast, and terracing with fertilization was employed in the highlands. Specialization in crops permitted each region to grow what was best suited to its climate, altitude and soil. The surpluses of one year or area were stored for distribution in time of need. These methods were so productive that many thousands of commoners could be levied for military service, labor on public works or similar specialized tasks that contributed nothing to the basic subsistence. The closeness of the correlation between these advanced technological and sociological features and the highly productive subsistence base is demonstrated by the failure of the Inca Empire to extend its boundaries into regions with lesser agricultural potential. The failure to expand farther north or south might be laid to the slow communication and consequent difficulties in maintaining control, which were compounded as distance from the center increased. This could not excuse lack of expansion to the east, however, nor would it have prevented the diffusion of advanced pottery and weaving techniques, which were not adopted to any extent by neighboring tribes.

The evidence summarized above leads to the following conclusion: In determining the degree of evolution that a culture or culture area can attain, geographical location (in terms of proximity to centers of diffusion), intelligence (or genius) and psychological receptivity to new ideas are not as important as environment as it is reflected in the subsistence resources. If the temperature, soil, altitude, rainfall, growing season, terrain or some other factor will not permit agricultural production, then only unusual circumstances in the form of a bountiful and permanent supply of wild food (as on the Northwest Coast), or the adoption of a pastoral food production (as in parts of Asia) will permit the cultural adaptation to go beyond nomadic family bands with a minimum of material equipment and social organization. Where other factors are favorable, but the soils are of limited natural fertility that cannot be artificially increased, agriculture can be carried on although it requires constant clearing of new fields to be maintained. Even with such limitations, the effect on culture is remarkable, bringing a radically altered settlement pattern and an increase in the inventory of material traits. However, unless a method of continuing fields under permanent production is found, the culture can never proceed beyond a simple level. Where soils are of increasable or unlimited fertility and capable of permanent productivity, cultural evolution has no environmental limitation.

The close correlation between environment and culture just sketched for South America could be accidental or unique, in which case the above conclusions would have no general validity. Whether or not this is the case can easily be discovered by reviewing the relationship between cultural evolution and agricultural productivity in another part of the world. One of the best documented is Europe, a predominantly Type 3 area.

Culture and environment in Europe

The term "Neolithic Revolution" originated to describe the revolutionary alteration that took place in European culture after the introduction of cereal cultivation from the Near East. For almost a million years man had been a roving hunter and gatherer of wild foods. During this time his tool inventory increased and more effective weapons were invented, but his sociopolitical organization remained basically the same. It was only after the introduction of agriculture that a marked alteration in culture took place. The effect was similar to what occurred in South America, and Childe's description (1951:86–87) of the Danubian I period in Central Europe sounds very much like that of the Tropical Forest pattern except that slash-and-burn cultivation was supplemented with domestic cattle and pigs rather than hunting. Villages were small, composed of communal as well as individual family houses. Arts and crafts include pottery and weaving. There are no indications of differences in rank or of occupational specialization. Nor are there any temples or other evidence of well-defined religion.

In the four succeeding Danubian periods, there is little alteration in the economy that can be considered an advance. The main differences are an increasing emphasis on the pastoral aspect of the subsistence and expansion of warfare and trade, especially after the introduction of bronze. A major transformation occurred in Danubian Period VI, however, as a result of two improvements in agricultural technique: the substitution of plow for hoe cultivation, and the substitution of crop and fallow for slash-and-burn exploitation (pp. 92–94). Sheep grazed on the fallow and stubble fields, which not only provided them with a more stable food supply but also were thereby fertilized. Bronze tools facilitated the clearing of farm land and the harvesting of the grain. These innovations increased the productivity of man-hours expended in subsistence activities and this is reflected in the emergence of distinctions in rank and of occupational division of labor. Chiefs exercised local authority, and enjoyed status and wealth above the common man. War was prominent and most villages were strongly fortified. Increased village size is reflected in enlargement of the associated cemeteries.

With the introduction of iron into Europe, corresponding to Danubian VII and continuing in Period VIII, further advances in agricultural technique were initiated (pp. 96–99). Iron tools were cheaper than bronze ones and consequently more generally available. The result was more extensive clearing of land on the one hand, and more efficient cultivation with iron plows on the other. Together with other tool improvements, these permitted increased food production that resulted in further cultural advance. The population density increased substantially, and fortified towns covering twelve or more acres made their appearance. Social classes developed, with slaves at the bottom and nobility at the top. The existence of political units greater than the local community is implied by the discovery of royal tombs. Occupational division of labor was advanced and utilitarian objects like pottery were mass produced. Local manufactures were supplemented by imports from the Classical civilizations of Greece and Rome. There is little evidence of religious development except the existence of small shrines.

As Childe (p. 116) points out, the sequence just reviewed represents "not stages in the evolution of a rural economy, but rather stages in the adaptation of a rural economy, based on exotic cereals and exotic sheep, to the environment of the deciduous forest zone." It is conceivable that some of these advances could have been made without the benefit of diffusion, but the cultural evolution would have been slower in that case. As it was, the growth of culture in Europe, stimulated by diffusion, followed the same basic pattern as it did in the Near East where the discoveries originated. This is not true of all Type 3 areas. Where the techniques needed for improvement of the agricultural potentiality are more complex, the culture may skip directly from food gathering to food production in modern proportions. These changes are not accomplished by diffusion, but by transplantation of personnel and equipment into the "underdeveloped" area. The point to be emphasized is that without the application of improved agricultural techniques, Type 3 environments limit the cultures they support to the simple level represented by the Tropical Forest pattern, or in some cases even to a food-gathering economy. With these improvements, they can produce and support as high a cultural development as can environments of Type 4. Were this not the case, the history of culture would have been quite different, since Type 4 areas occupy a very small portion of the surface of the earth.

The law of environmental limitation on culture

When the four levels or stages of cultural development that have just been traced in South America and in Europe are compared, the coincidence of basic features is remarkable (Fig. 1). The same kinds of advances in settlement pat-

SOUTH AMERICA

Culture	Subsistence	Settlement Pattern	Technology	Sociopolitical System	Religion
Andean	Intensive agriculture Irrigation Fertilization	Cities to 100,000 pop.	Full occupational specialization	King Hierarchy of officials Social classes	Hierarchy of gods Hierarchy of priests Temples and idols Public ceremonies
Circum-Caribbean	Improved agriculture Seafood	Towns up to 3,000 pop.	Division of labor by occupation	Chiefs Social stratification	Shaman or chief acts as priest Temples and idols Offerings
Tropical Forest	Slash-and-burn agriculture Hunting, fishing, gathering	Villages of 50–1,000 pop.	Division of labor by sex and age	Headman No difference in rank	Bush spirits Shaman, mainly for curing
Marginal	Hunting, fishing, gathering	Nomadic single or multifamily bands	Division of labor by sex and age	Headman No difference in rank	Bush spirits

EUROPE

Culture	Subsistence	Settlement Pattern	Technology	Sociopolitical System	Religion
Danubian VII and VIII	Improved agriculture Iron plow Fertilization Fallow	Fortified cities covering 12 acres or more	Full occupational specialization	Kings and lesser chiefs Social classes	Shrines
Danubian VI	Improved agriculture Crop and fallow Wooden (?) plow Bronze ax and harvesting tools	Villages of about 38 houses	Division of labor by occupation	Chiefs with local authority Differences in rank	Ritual objects and charms
Danubian I	Slash-and-burn agriculture Domestic pigs and cattle	Hamlets of 13–26 houses	Division of labor by sex and age	No evidence of difference in rank	Female figurines
Paleolithic	Hunting, fishing, gathering	Nomadic bands	Division of labor by sex and age	No evidence of difference in rank	

FIG. 1. Correlation between agricultural productivity and culture.

tern, social organization and technology follow the same kinds of improvements in agricultural production. The major difference lies in the fact that in South America these advances were achieved spatially as well as temporally and the culture was stabilized as the agricultural limit of each area was reached, while in Europe the productivity of the soil could be increased by the application of better agricultural methods and as each improvement was put into use the culture underwent a spurt.

Since this close correlation does exist between the increased productivity of agriculture and progressive cultural development, and agricultural productivity depends upon the potentiality of the natural environment, we can rephrase the statement that culture is dependent on agriculture to read that *the level to which a culture can develop is dependent upon the agricultural potentiality of the environment it occupies.* As this potentiality is improved, culture will advance. If it cannot be improved, the culture will become stabilized at a level compatible with the food resources.

A quick mental application of this rule to a random selection of cultures will reveal many "exceptions." These are not true exceptions in the sense that they invalidate the rule, but rather are instances in which local conditions have introduced elements that disturb the "natural" course of events. This is the usual situation with scientific laws, and we are more fortunate than those in other fields in that we do have examples that illustrate the functioning of this law. Many of the laws of the physical sciences refer to ideal situations and are always distorted when viewed in the real world. Variables such as temperature, pressure, friction and gravitation explain the discrepancies between actual events and the prescriptions of physical laws. A similar variable, technology, accounts for most of the "exceptions" to the law of environmental limitation on culture. Ideally, we should expect every culture occupying a Type 3 area to have reached the level of development achieved in Europe. In reality, the level to which a culture actually does develop, or did develop aboriginally in many parts of the world, depends on the success with which the full potential of the environment is utilized. The range of variation in this respect is greatest in Type 3 areas, where technology plays the greatest role in the exploitation. Where independent discovery of improved techniques did not occur, and distance from or absence of centers of diffusion eliminated the possibility of borrowing, a culture was often stabilized at a much lower level than that set by the environmental potentiality. One only need compare the aboriginal situation in areas such as the northeastern United States, the Great Plains, and the Imperial Valley of California with modern usage to recognize the difference that technology makes in agricultural productivity in Type 3 areas.

One of the most glaring of the "exceptions" is modern civilization, which has extended itself into swamps and similarly inauspicious regions all around the world. An examination of this situation in terms of the law, however, will reveal that the basic requirement is not violated. The proposition reads: "The level to which a culture *can develop* is dependent upon the agricultural potentiality of the environment it *occupies."* There is no evidence to indicate that the technology represented in a modern base in Alaska, a mining town in the West Virginia hills or a sponge fishing community in Florida could have been achieved indigenously or can maintain itself on local resources. On the contrary, it is obvious that the existence of modern civilization in these environments is based on the special products or services which are provided to the culture as a whole, and which warrant the "underwriting" of their subsistence support. The satisfaction of thousands of secondary needs that have assumed primary significance to the consumers has spread modern technology far and wide to take advantage of everything from local natural resources to lower tax rates, and the fact that these extensions owe their existence solely to the vast food-producing capacity achieved in Type 3 environments and the extensive facilities for distribution is often obscured. The ability to maintain this kind of regional specialization is a good measure of cultural advance and a simple means of indicating how far we have progressed beyond the level represented by the Inca Empire.

This law of environmental limitation on culture has bearing on numerous current problems in anthropology. It provides a basic explanation for what seems often to be an erratic operation of diffusion. Instead of concluding that diffusion usually moves from higher cultures to lower ones, but not always, one can examine the hypothesis that diffusion proceeds most rapidly from cultures in Type 4 areas to those in Type 3 areas, and only to a limited extent from Type 4 and Type 3 areas to those of Types 1 and 2. In other words, if this is a valid law, then the barrier to acceptance of a trait or complex may often be basically environmental. A further implication is that geographical proximity to centers of diffusion is not necessarily an important determinant of degree of cultural development. Environmental limitations in adjacent Type 1 or Type 2 areas may inhibit the adoption of traits that diffuse to distant areas of Type 3.

This concept of differential cultural potential inherent in different types of environment offers an interesting explanation of both the areal distribution of cultures and the lack of stability of certain culture areas through time. The four types of environment set different limits on the level of development which a culture can attain, and the amount of latitude permitted is closely related to the stability of the cultural adjustment. Cultures occupying Type 1 areas show little basic change over thousands of years and, in fact, comprise the hunting and gathering groups surviving into the 20th century. Cultures occupying areas of Type 2 reached their optimum level of elaboration shortly after their subsistence source shifted from food gathering to slash-and-burn agriculture, and have since shown great stability. It is in areas of Type 3 and Type 4 that the greatest variation in culture through time exists, and this situation has been one of the primary obstacles to the satisfactory definition of culture areas in Asia.

The assumption of this active relationship between environment and cultural development helps to clarify some of the puzzling distributional aspects of culture, in which enclaves of lower culture are found between those of higher levels, and even along routes of diffusion. Prominent examples are the "gap" between aboriginal Mexico and the American Southeast, and tribes of Marginal level between the Andean and Tropical Forest areas in South America. These tribes are like "whistle stops," occupying areas too low in agricultural (and therefore cultural) potential to share in or profit by the diffusion moving along their "line" except in the most limited way.

If this is a true cultural law, it must have no exceptions. Either it operates as specified or one or more variables in the local situation explain the failure of the expected result. In all of the illustrations cited thus far, the total picture is well understood and the application of the law simply places the specific instance in a larger general framework. One of the most useful aspects of scientific laws, however, is that they furnish a basis for prediction and thus direct investigation of problems away from variable factors into lines that are more likely to be fruitful. An analysis of the puzzling elements surrounding the origin and development of Maya culture will serve to illustrate how the law of environmental limitation on culture can open new possibilities for investigation.

Application to the Maya problem

No one will question the statement that the Maya rank with the Aztecs and the Inca at the peak of New World cultural development. Certain of their achievements, among them calendrical, mathematical, and writing systems, are unique in this hemisphere and compare favorably with contemporary attainments in the Old World. Now, however, the marvelous sculptured stone buildings that remain as monuments to the intellectual and religious achievements of the past lie broken and concealed by luxuriant vegetation. The incongruity of this magnificent civilization in a lowland, tropical forest environment has been noted by geographers (Platt 1942:501; James 1942:675) as well as anthropologists (Steward 1949a:17; Ruppert and Denison 1943:1). The circumstance is so unusual that it has required explanation, and the one most frequently given is that geographical location at the junction between two continents in the "crossroads of culture contact" provided sufficient stimulus to compensate for the deficiencies of the environment (Hoebel 1949:483; Kroeber 1948:786; White 1949:223). The preceding discussion, however, brings us to the conclusion that diffusion of this sort can operate only after the productivity of the subsistence pattern has been increased, which was not done in the Maya case. This means that a culture of the level attained by the Classic Maya could not have developed in the Type 2 environment where the archeological remains are found, but must have been introduced from elsewhere. Furthermore, since Type 2 environments lack the resources to maintain so high a level of culture, the history of the Maya occupation of the tropical forest should represent a decline or deculturation.

These conclusions can be tested against the archeological evidence. If Classic Maya culture is an indigenous development based on increasingly or indefinitely productive agriculture, we should expect to trace a gradual transformation from something approaching the Tropical Forest pattern through a stage comparable to the Circum-Caribbean, and beyond to the developed Maya, at which level it should remain. On the other hand, if Maya culture is an example of the effort of a high civilization to colonize the tropical forest, we should expect to find that: (1) it appears suddenly in a well-developed state; (2) it does not diffuse to adjacent areas; and (3) its history is one of gradual decline. An examination of the present evidence on these points gives a promising result.

Regarding the antecedents of Classic Maya culture, it is widely acknowledged that no very definite evidence has come to light. Pre-Classic horizons have been uncovered in the Guatemala highlands and coast, in southern Veracruz and Oaxaca, and in parts of the Guatemala lowlands, but none of these seems to be directly ancestral to the lowland Classic Maya development. It is important to note that many of these areas producing pre-Classic sites are Type 3 as, for example, highland Guatemala where rotation and fertilization permit a relatively intensive utilization of the agricultural land and give an average yield of maize comparable to that in the Peruvian coastal valleys (McBryde 1947:17–21). Pre-Classic manifestations in the tropical lowland forest can easily be explained as intrusions from areas more environmentally conducive to high cultural development. If they had not been stimulated by the influence bringing the Classic Maya culture, the operation of the law of environmental limitation on culture would have resulted in their petering out as did other similar expansions into Type 2 areas.

There is a lack of transition between pre-Classic and Classic Maya culture with its specialized art and architecture, its writing and calendrical systems, that should not exist if the latter is an indigenous development. This has been pointed out often. Kidder, for example, notes (Kidder, Jennings and Shook 1946:1): "Of the first steps toward higher culture we . . . know nothing; and why this should be is one of the great puzzles of New World prehistory." In speaking of the complex chronology, Morley says (1946:45–46):

> There are no simple beginnings, no elementary first steps which must have preceded the development of the perfected system. On the contrary, when we first meet it on these two earliest-known dated objects, it is already complete with all its intricacies—a flower in full blossom, with no preliminary bud stage having survived to show how it had developed.

Strong (1948:119) speaks of "a complete break in continuity" in Honduras; Longyear (1952:82) states that Maya Early Classic culture "still seems to spring into fully developed existence from nothing, in spite of our extensive researches of the past few years." To avoid this conclusion it has been suggested that many of the characteristic Maya traits originated in a perishable medium and were only executed in stone after they had already been developed to a high degree (Morley 1946:46).

On the second point, regarding diffusion of Maya traits to adjacent tribes or regions, evidence is once again negative. The situation has been summarized by Kroeber (1939: 114–15):

> A quality of narrowness of range applies to Mayan culture as a whole. . . .
> This culture never penetrated to any serious extent beyond the territory held by
> the historic Mayan tribes. There seems to be no true Maya stratum or archaeo-
> logical horizon in Oaxaca and Vera Cruz, nor eastward beyond Salvador. Mayan
> relations or influences may be discernible as far as the Totonac and Chorotega.
> But influences are another thing from the presence of the culture; and at that,
> the distances in each direction are not great—less than from the mouth of the
> Mississippi to that of the Ohio. The generic Mayan as well as the specific Maya
> culture were nonexpansive, nonpropagandizing, self-sufficient, conservative. . . .

The third point is the question of whether the history of Maya culture
reveals an advance or a decline. Evaluations of superiority in many aesthetic
aspects of a culture are to some extent subjective, and in presenting data of
this sort it is safer to rely on an evaluation made by another person who had
no idea of using the result to demonstrate the point under discussion and therefore can be assumed not to have been prejudiced in its favor. The results
published by Morley (1946: Figs. 1 and 2, Table XI and text) suit this qualification.

Maya history begins with the earliest preserved date, A.D. 320,* and ends
with the European conquest in A.D. 1546. The intervening period is not characterized by a progressive advance as occurred in the Valley of Mexico, the
Central Andes, or in the Old World centers. Instead, the culture reaches its
climax about A.D. 790. All of the greatest achievements in stone sculpture,
stucco modeling, wood carving, featherwork, textiles, clay modeling, pottery
decoration, architecture and astronomy occurred before or about this date. The
largest city (Tikal) and the largest and tallest buildings are also of this period.
Not only are the arts and crafts most highly developed but the products are
present in the greatest quantity. Dated monuments increase in abundance until
790 and thereafter rapidly decrease (Morley 1946: Fig. 1). In other words,
there appear to have been 470 years of progress followed by more than 700
years of decline.

These figures are significant. The developmental period is too short to have
produced so advanced a culture without outside influence. However, if Maya
culture were brought into the area by a relatively small population equipped
with skills and knowledge developed elsewhere, some time would be required
to re-establish the culture in its former condition. An interesting and graphic
reconstruction of how this process appears to be reflected in the archeological
situation at Copan has been set forth by Longyear. He gives no explanation
for the sudden termination of this apparently flourishing center, noting only
that there is no evidence of violence or disaster (1951:92). This would not be
inconsistent with the conclusion that the breakdown came because the sub-

---

* Since the present problem involves elapsed time rather than absolute dates, the choice
between the correlations with the Christian calendar is immaterial.

sistence base, originally unsuited to the support of the occupational division of labor and other social features associated with advanced technology, was overtaxed to the point of collapse. The foundation weakened, the whole structure was doomed.

One question that is frequently raised at this conclusion is, "If this environment is so unsuitable, how could Maya culture have existed there for so long?" Unfortunately, no detailed study of the effect of intensive agriculture on the tropical forest environment has yet been made and theoretical analyses like that of Higbee (1948) or experiments of the type conducted by Morley (1946: 148) and Steggerda (Anon. 1938:222) are either not conclusive or not sufficiently broad to be relied upon for an accurate appraisal of the total region over a long time-span. Ecological studies examining the effect of intensive agriculture on the environment have been made, however, by Cook (1949a, 1949b) for Central Mexico, and the conclusions seem to fit the Maya archeological evidence very well. The essence of the result is expressed succinctly by Cook (1949a:54):

> So far as the Teotlalpan is concerned, it is quite clear that had Aztec (or Nahua) domination continued unchecked by external forces for another century or two, soil erosion, deforestation, and land deterioration would have reached the point where agriculture could not have supported the existing population, not to mention any further increase. At that crucial point the only solutions would have been famine and death, or wholesale emigration, which would have spelled the end of Aztec power and domination.

Here there was in the making a situation that would have ultimately caused the same sudden abandonment of flourishing centers that so puzzles us in Maya history. For a better appreciation of the way in which this interpretation fits the evidence we have on the Maya, and also because of the demonstration it makes of the importance of technology in exploiting the agricultural potential of a Type 3 environment, it might be well to quote Cook's reconstruction in greater detail (pp. 58–59):

> In the tenth century the Toltecs of Tula overran a relatively unspoiled but arid area then inhabited by Otomi who utilized the biotic environment through the use of the wild game, the nopal, the maguey, and probably some crops. The Toltecs then improved and expanded agriculture, thus permitting an increase in food supply. As a result, the population increased materially. The Toltecs were eliminated, agriculture diminished, and with it the population. During the thirteenth, fourteenth, and fifteenth centuries new races (Nahua and Otomi) entered the territory and gradually rebuilt a culture founded on agriculture, a culture which reached its peak at the end of the fifteenth and the beginning of the sixteenth centuries. As a consequence of the huge reservoir of food furnished by intensive cultivation of corn, beans, chia, huautli, and other crops and aided by extensive exploitation of the indigenous arid land plants, nopal and maguey, the population increased to the very high level of 477,000 people on 900 square miles or a density of 530 persons per square mile. This increase was possible because of a successful adaptation to the then existing physical environment, and for no other reason.

But this adaptation caused a reciprocal modification or adaptation on the part of the environment itself, and in the reverse direction. The latter consisted of a loss in agricultural potency mediated directly by erosion and indirectly by a diminution in soil water because of erosion and partial deforestation. Had events proceeded uninfluenced by external, extraneous factors [the Spanish Conquest] there would have followed a period of population decline running parallel to the diminishing food supply until at some subsequent date a new equilibrium would have been established at a lower population and agricultural level.

This area appears to have a Type 3 environment, which the application of soil conservation techniques, perhaps supplemented by other means of maintaining soil fertility, could have maintained indefinitely at the maximum level of production. In the absence of these, the environment was exploited in a manner comparable to areas of Type 2. The result was overtaxation followed by exhaustion, with marked effects on the incumbent culture. This was not an immediate thing, but required several centuries of gradual aggravation to reach the crucial point where a radical adjustment was forced on the part of the culture. This whole reaction closely fits the known archeological circumstances of Classic Maya development and decline and suggests that a similar process of increasing imbalance between the demands of the culture and the ability of the environment to meet them was in operation there. While this interpretation appears to have justification on the basis of present knowledge, only a detailed study of Maya environment in terms of subsistence capacity and the effects of intensive agriculture similar to that undertaken by Cook for central Mexico can establish finally and conclusively whether a similar reaction actually did take place.

Having suggested how this law may be of use in cultural interpretation, it may be pertinent to be equally specific about what it cannot do. It is not to be confused with a universal explanation for cultural decline. Cultures decline for a great many reasons other than the deficiencies of the environment, and have frequently done so in areas of Type 3 and Type 4. The environmental explanation is only primary when a highly developed culture invades a Type 2 area, and thereby taxes the environment beyond its capacity. Nor can this law explain the differential level of development attained aboriginally by cultures in areas of equal agricultural potentiality in different parts of the world. Western Europe and the eastern United States are both Type 3 areas, yet in A.D. 1492 the cultural level attained by the former was far above that of the latter. In terms of environment, both had equal opportunity, so that environment is obviously not the cause of cultural evolution. Nor has it been so stated or implied. The environmental limitation on culture simply establishes a ceiling on indigenous cultural evolution. Whether or not this limit is reached depends upon many other factors, some of which may turn out to be constant, others of which are undoubtedly local and "accidental." This law gives us a clue to why certain areas produced high cultures while in others cultural development was stabilized at a much lower level. Its application in many instances, however, consists in establishing the potential ceiling to cultural evolution, so that the local conditions that prevented the culture from realizing the environmenal possibilities are brought into sharper focus.

In concluding, it may be well to state specifically that it is not my intention to convey the impression that the analysis and conclusions presented here are in any way the final and complete answer to the problem of the relationship between environment and culture. They are only tentative and will require much more exploration than has been given here before we can confidently accept or reject them. In either event, the conclusion should be based on the evidence itself. To dismiss this hypothesis because of conflicts that might exist between it and other generalizations on this subject is unfair not only to this attempt and to the other theories, but harmful to our science as a whole. Only by continually re-examining our conclusions in the light of new data and confirming or rejecting them as the new situation warrants can we discover new avenues of investigation and continue to advance our understanding of culture and its behavior.

Summary

The relationship between environment and culture has been of increasing interest to anthropologists in recent years. There has also been a certain amount of attention directed to defining the relationship of the subsistence pattern to the sociopolitical and religious aspects of a culture. Since subsistence is dependent on environmental characteristics and appears also to be largely responsible for the level of development attained by the culture it supports, some cause and effect relationship between environment and culture is implied.

Since geographical classifications of environment do not isolate culturally significant types, an attempt was made to subdivide environments on the basis of their subsistence potential in terms of agriculture. Four types of environment were distinguished: Type 1, with no agricultural potential; Type 2, with limited agricultural potential; Type 3, with increasable agricultural potential; and Type 4, with unlimited agricultural potential. An analysis of the cultures of South America in areal terms and those of Europe in historical terms suggests that definite limitations and possibilities for cultural development are associated with each of the four types of environment. These were expressed in the form of a law: the level to which a culture can develop is dependent upon the agricultural potentiality of the environment it occupies.

If this analysis is valid, it suggests that previous attempts at explaining differences in level of cultural development in terms of geographical position, proximity to continental junctions, accessibility to centers of diffusion, genius or other psychological factors attributable to the population may not penetrate to the level of primary cause. Absence of a suitable source of diffusion can explain the failure of a culture to realize the potentiality of the environment it occupies, but where the environment is Type 1 or Type 2, no amount of opportunity for diffusion can effect a cultural advance beyond the limitations set by the environment.

REFERENCES

ANONYMOUS 1938 Maize and the Maya. Carnegie Institution of Washington News Service Bulletin, School Edition, Vol. IV, No. 26.

CHILDE, V. GORDON 1941 Man makes himself. Thinker's Library, No. 87. London. 1951 Social evolution. London.

COOK, SHERBURNE F. 1949*a* The historical demography and ecology of the Teotlalpan. Ibero-Americana 33. Berkeley. 1949*b* Soil erosion and population in central Mexico. Ibero-Americana 34. Berkeley.

COON, C. S. 1948 A reader in general anthropology. New York.

EVANS, CLIFFORD and BETTY J. MEGGERS n.d. Field notes on British Guiana archeology.

FORDE, C. DARYLL 1934 Habitat, economy and society. London.

HIGBEE, EDWARD 1948 Agriculture in the Maya homeland. Geographical Review 38:457–64.

HOEBEL, E. ADAMSON 1949 Man in the primitive world. New York.

JAMES, PRESTON 1935 An outline of geography. Boston. 1942 Latin America. New York.

JOHNSON, FREDERICK 1948 The post-conquest ethnology of Central America: an introduction. Handbook of South American Indians 4:195–98. (Bureau of American Ethnology Bulletin 143.)

KIDDER, A. V., J. D. JENNINGS and E. M. SHOOK 1946 Excavations at Kaminaljuyu. Carnegie Institution of Washington, Publication 561.

KROEBER, A. L. 1939 Cultural and natural areas of native North America. Berkeley. 1948 Anthropology: race, language, culture, psychology, prehistory. New York.

LINTON, RALPH 1936 The study of man. New York.

LONGYEAR, JOHN M., III 1951 A historical interpretation of Copan archeology. The Civilizations of Ancient America, Selected Papers of the XXIX International Congress of Americanists, pp. 86–92. 1952 Copan ceramics: a study of southeastern Maya pottery. Carnegie Institution of Washington, Publication 597.

McBRYDE, F. WEBSTER 1947 Cultural and historical geography of southwest Guatemala. Smithsonian Institution, Institute of Social Anthropology, Publication No. 4. Washington.

MEGGERS, BETTY J. 1951 A pre-Columbian colonization of the Amazon. Archeology 4:110–14. n.d. The archeological sequence on Marajó Island, Brazil, with special reference to the Marajoara culture. Ph.D. dissertation on deposit at Columbia University, New York.

MORLEY, S. G. 1946 The ancient Maya. Stanford.

PEAKE, HAROLD E. 1940 The study of prehistoric times. Journal of the Royal Anthropological Institute 70:103–46.

PLATT, ROBERT S. 1942 Latin America: countrysides and united regions. New York.

PRICE, WILLARD 1952 The Amazing Amazon. New York.

ROUSE, IRVING 1953 The circum-Caribbean theory, an archeological test. American Anthropologist 55:188–200.

RUPPERT, KARL and J. H. DENISON, JR. 1943 Archaeological reconnaissance in Campeche, Quintana Roo, and Peten. Carnegie Institution of Washington, Publication 543.

STEWARD, JULIAN H. 1938 Basin-plateau aboriginal sociopolitical groups. Bureau of American Ethnology Bulletin 120. Washington. 1948 The Circum-Caribbean tribes: an introduction. Handbook of South American Indians 4:1–41. (Bureau of American Ethnology Bulletin 143.) 1949a Cultural causality and law: a trial formulation of the development of early civilization. American Anthropologist 51:1–27. 1949b South American cultures: an interpretative summary. Handbook of South American Indians 5:669–772. (Bureau of American Ethnology Bulletin 143.)

STEWARD, JULIAN H. (ed.) 1946–50 Handbook of South American Indians. Bureau of American Ethnology Bulletin 143, Vols. 1–6. Washington, D.C.

STRONG, W. D. 1948 The archeology of Honduras. Handbook of South American Indians 4:71–120. (Bureau of American Ethnology Bulletin 143.)

TYLOR, EDWARD B. 1881 Anthropology. New York.

WEDEL, WALDO R. 1953 Some aspects of human ecology in the central plains. American Anthropologist 55:499–514.

WISSLER, CLARK 1923 Man and culture. New York. 1926 The relation of nature to man in aboriginal America. New York.

WHITE, LESLIE A. 1949 The science of culture. New York.

TEMPERATURE AND THE EVOLUTION OF MAN

If human populations remained in one environment for a long period of time it would be relatively simple to assess the environmental effects upon human anatomy and physiology. However, human groups have migrated and have been exposed to various environments. To further complicate the problem, many matings have taken place between different ethnic groups and this has brought changes in genetic predispositions to environmental factors. In spite of these difficulties, many investigators have sought to understand the interactions of man and his environment.

In all probability more papers have been written about the adaptation of human beings to temperature than to any other ecological factor. One group of investigators contends that human adaptations are largely morphological and usually tend to follow the ecological rules of Bergmann and Allen. Another group opposes this view and contends that the adaptation is largely physiological. The arguments are, of course, very intricate. The papers in this section should be read in the sequence presented for an adequate chronological review of arguments and rebuttals about these two opposing views.

SUPPLEMENTARY READINGS

BAKER, PAUL T., The Biological Adaptation of Man to Hot Deserts. 1958, *American Naturalist,* **92:** 337–357.

BAKER, PAUL T., Climate, Culture and Evolution. 1960, *Human Biology,* **32:** 3–16.

BURKITT, DENIS, A Children's Cancer Dependent on Climatic Factors. 1962, *Nature,* **194:** 232–234.

GOLDSMITH, R., Use of Clothing Records to Demonstrate Acclimatization to Cold in Man. 1960, *Journal of Applied Physiology,* **15:** 776–780.

NEWMAN, RUSSELL W., and ELLA H. MUNRO, The Relation of Climate and Body Size in U.S. Males. 1955, *American Journal of Physical Anthropology,* **13:** 1–17.

SCHOLANDER, P. F., H. T. HAMMEL, J. S. HART, D. H. LeMESSURIER and J. STEEN, Cold Adaptation in Australian Aborigines. 1958, *Journal of Applied Physiology,* **13:** 211–218.

The Application
of Ecological Rules
to the Racial Anthropology
of the Aboriginal New World*

MARSHALL T. NEWMAN

Introduction

Correlations between the physical characters of warm-blooded vertebrates and their environments have led zoologists to the formulation of several ecological rules (Allee & Schmidt 1951:457, 460–472). The generally accepted interpretation of these correlations is that through natural selection, adaptive changes have occurred as the result of environmental stresses. Application of these rules to man has rarely been attempted. As far as I can determine, the first general suggestion that ecological rules were applicable to man came from Ridgeway (1908:833). Schreider (1951:823–824) interpreted the regular changes in human body weight/body surface area ratios in terms of two of these ecological rules. Unaware of Schreider's work, I pointed out the specific applicability of several ecological rules to man (Newman 1951:191). In May, 1952, before the American Academy of Arts and Sciences, Coon applied these rules to man on a world-wide basis. Nevertheless the occurrence of adaptive alterations in recent man has been denied (Howells 1944:217; Kroeber 1948:167; Lundman 1952: 5–6). In large part this denial seems only to reflect an insistence that such human adaptation be demonstrated. It is the purpose of this paper, therefore, to test two of the best validated ecological rules on the aborigines of the New World, namely, Bergmann's (1847) and Allen's (1877). Both of these rules deal with the fostering of bodily heat retention or dissipation by respectively reducing or increasing the radiating skin surface per unit of body mass.

---

* A shorter version of this paper was presented before the American Association of Physical Anthropologists, December 27, 1952. Published with the permission of the Secretary of the Smithsonian Institution.

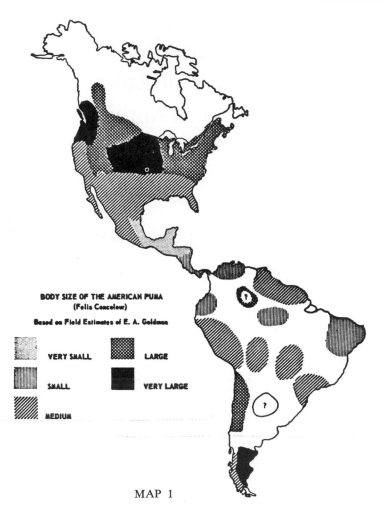

BODY SIZE OF THE AMERICAN PUMA
(Felis Concolor)

Based on Field Estimates of E. A. Goldman

VERY SMALL   LARGE

SMALL   VERY LARGE

MEDIUM

MAP 1

   Bergmann's rule holds that within a single wide-ranging species of warm-blooded animal, the subspecies or races in colder climates attain greater body size than those in warmer climates. Illustrative of this rule is the distribution of body size in the American puma (Young & Goldman 1946), second only to man in the extent of its New World range. Map 1 shows that the average increase in the puma's body size with higher latitudes forms a sustained gradient or cline for each New World continent. The same body size clines are demonstrated by other mammals of more restricted range. For example, the ermine of northeastern Asia and northwestern North America shows steep and sustained size clines for each continental area (Hall 1951:88). Again the eight subspecies of the mule deer show average body size reductions from south Alaska to Lower California (Cowan 1936:173).

Basic to Bergmann's rule is the principle that ". . . in otherwise similar bodies, the larger one has the smaller skin surface in proportion to mass, since volume and mass increase as the cube of the linear measurements and surface only as the square" (Allee & Schmidt 1951:462). Greater body size, therefore, increases the body mass/body surface ratio. Chunkier and more compact body builds do the same thing. Increasing this ratio reduces body heat loss by radiation and therefore seems to be a cold climate adaptation. On the other hand, as Schreider (1951:823) points out, ". . . the body mass/body surface ratio tends to decrease in climates which, at least during part of the year, put a stress on heat-eliminating mechanisms." In comparable fashion, small body size, or a slender build, increases the skin surface relative to mass, and by fostering body cooling in this way, appears to be a hot-climate adaptation. Although unaware of the Bergmann principle, Coon, Garn and Birdsell (1950:36–44, Fig. 1) developed the same idea and applied it to arctic- and desert-dwelling humans.

Allen's rule holds that warm-blooded animals living in cold climates have their heat radiating body surfaces further reduced by decreases in the size of their extremities and appendages. An example of this rule is seen in the reduction of ear length toward the north among the several North American species of rabbits (Allee & Schmidt 1951:467). Comparable shortening of extremities is seen in a number of other mammals. This sort of reduction also raises the body mass/body surface ratio, and as such seems to be an additional cold-climate adaptation.

In mammals and birds there are a number of exceptions to these rules: 10 to 30 percent for Bergmann's rule, calculated only from subspecies in the most contrasting climates of the species range (Rensch 1938:282). Among these exceptions are occasional reversals in the body size clines, as in raccoons which show a northward decrease in size. Allen has suggested that such reversals of Bergmann's rule may correspond to transitions into a less suitable climate (Allee & Schmidt 1951:465). It is also possible that in some cases the extension of the species range into colder climates is so recent that selection has not had time to operate. In addition to the reversals, there are some species showing no sustained size clines at all. In some cases the lack of clines is real, particularly with animals that by living in burrows and by other means escape part of the climatic extremes; in others, simply a matter of inadequate data. Yet as stated by Allee and Schmidt (1951:465), ". . . when one recalls the many other means at hand for reducing the radiation of heat and the many other factors that serve to regulate body size, the small number of such exceptions is astonishing."

While the general validity of Bergmann's and Allen's rules seems to be recognized (cf. Mayr 1942), in practice their usefulness as interpretative tools in mammalian taxonomy is hampered by certain limitations not present in human studies. For example, in some mammals, especially the Rodentia, the small growth increments throughout life render the determination of adult body size an approximation foreign to students of man. Then, quantitative analyses of body size and proportions demand larger subspecies samples than can usually be amassed, since few taxonomists spend their lives studying one species, as anthropologists do. Moreover, most species, of mammals at least, have rather restricted ranges, which limit the gross climatic variations to which they are exposed. Thus many subspecies differences, if of an adaptive nature, are more likely attributable to local conditions, such as microclimate, than to the gross climatic variations underlying the operation of Bergmann's and Allen's rules.

In contrast, for man we have much larger series of measurements on wholly adult groups distributed over wide areas with tremendous climatic variations. In addition, the considerable body of data on post-Pleistocene human skeletons provides a third dimension usually lacking in taxonomic studies. For these reasons, it is likely that Bergmann's and Allen's rules may be more closely operative in man than in other animals. Man's assets as a test species for ecological rules need not be vitiated by the possession of a culture, since the strongly shielding effect of high culture is only 5–6000 years old anywhere, and in some parts of the world has hardly been felt.

Although testing of Bergmann's and Allen's rules is confined here to New World peoples, I am aware that in certain parts of the Old World they do not seem applicable. Upon superficial examination, the rules do not appear operative in Africa south of the Sahara. Yet, in Europe and the Near and Middle East and in East Asia and Malaysia, there seem to be north-south body size clines conforming to Bergmann's rule. The explanation of these discrepancies in Africa and perhaps elsewhere is not yet apparent.

Method

In the course of testing the rules, I have plotted the distribution of a number of mean male bodily and other dimensions and indices on linguistic and tribal maps of the New World (Coon, Johnson & Kluckhohn 1935; Steward 1950). Where only one series is available for a wide-spread group, I have assumed that this series is wholly representative of it. Areas for which mean figures are either lacking or wholly inadequate have been left blank on the maps. However, Biasutti (1941) and Lundman (1952), from whom I have borrowed maps 7, 9, and 10 were not so cautious, and with or without adequate data shaded in all areas. Where I have plotted skeletal measurements (maps 5, 6 and 8) I have eliminated series of considerable known antiquity, but can make no claim that these maps represent a single time level. It is more than likely that they span at least the last 1000 years. In maps 4 and 6, covering head and face size, I have simply derived the averages from the mean dimensions. In all, the categories used in these maps are arbitrary, and in some areas the data are inadequate, but probably the maps represent reasonable approaches to the real distributions. Taken as a group, the maps tend to reinforce each other and therefore present a much more solid case than could be achieved by one map alone. This is especially the case where maps of a measurement or index on the living are confirmed by maps covering the skeletal aspects (see maps 5, 8 and 10).

It is clear, in view of the emphasis on the body mass/body surface ratio in Bergmann's rule that a plotting of this figure would be more meaningful than linear figures. Unfortunately, individual height-weight figures for Indians and Eskimos, from which body surface may be calculated, are rather scanty and therefore do not have the Point Barrow-to-Beagle Channel distribution of the more standard measurements. And only recently were the calculation formulae found to be reasonably applicable to Eskimos (Rodahl 1952:246). Indians have not as yet been tested in this regard. Yet this body mass/body surface approach has much merit, as Schreider (1951) is beginning to show for Old World groups, and will be needed for a more conclusive demonstration of the pertinence of Bergmann's and Allen's rules for the peoples of the Americas.

Clines in body, head and face size in Indians and Eskimos

The distribution of average male stature in map 2, shows a conspicuous concentration of short peoples in the lower latitudes. To the north and south there is a progressive irregular increase in stature closely comparable to the body size clines for the puma (map 1). In American Indians the sustained nature of these stature clines is the more remarkable in view of the number and scope of well-documented intracontinental movements of people, for example: The Athabaskan push into the Southwest, the late movements into the Plains, the Tupí spread down the Brazilian coast, and the historic invasion of the Pampas by Araucanians. The regularity of the clines is also remarkable in view of the more obvious deficiencies of the basic data—inaccuracies of measurement, small size of some series and the chances of White and other admixture. In northern North America, however, the stature cline is broken by the shorter Eskimo. But as map 3 demonstrates, the Western Eskimo are not inferior in sitting height to the tallest Indians. Their shorter stature, then, is attributable solely to their short legs. This reduction of extremity length is in accordance with Allen's rule, and probably represents an adaptation fostering body-heat retention. Judging from their equally high relative-sitting-heights (Lundman 1952: map 3), the Eastern Eskimo also conform to Allen's rule, but are smaller in both stature and sitting height than are the Indians south of them. Possibly the use of heavy tailored clothing in combination with factors of uncertain food supply and periodic undernutrition may cancel out the selective advantage of larger bodies in colder climates, but this cannot be demonstrated. Other than in this way, I cannot account for the Eastern Eskimo's smaller body size, although in Labrador and West Greenland, Stewart (1939:65, 68) suggests there may have been a stature decrease since European contact, due possibly to a less adequate diet occasioned by acculturation. This view is reinforced by the fact that, despite the heavy increments of White genes they have received, these particular Eskimo are still shorter than their Baffin Island and East Greenland neighbors. In North America, other short-statured people surrounded by taller groups are the Yuki of northern California, and the Harrison Lake Lillouet of southern British Columbia.

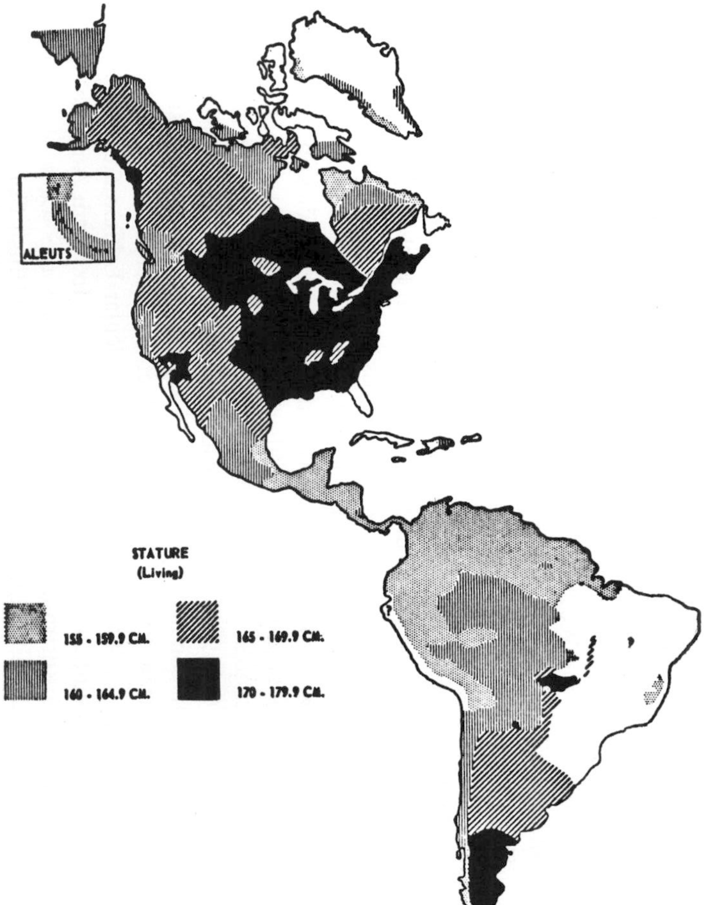

154

SITTING HEIGHT
(Living)

75 - 81 MM.

82 - 84 MM.

85 - 87 MM.

88 - 91 MM.

MAP 3

ALEUTS

STATURE
(Living)

155 - 159.9 CM.

160 - 164.9 CM.

165 - 169.9 CM.

170 - 179.9 CM.

MAP 2

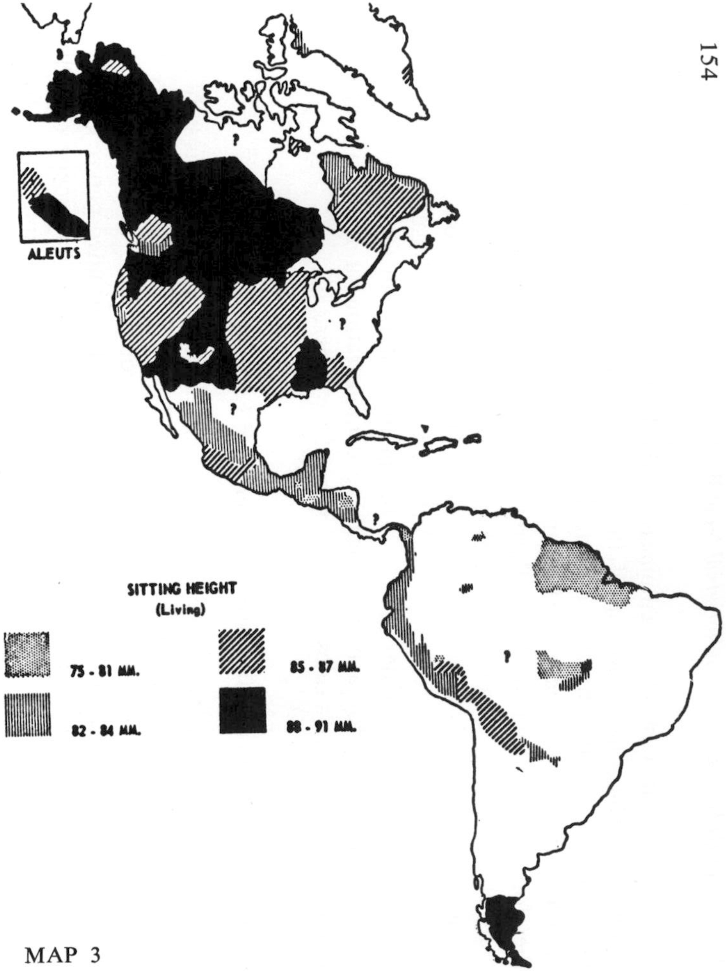

ALEUTS

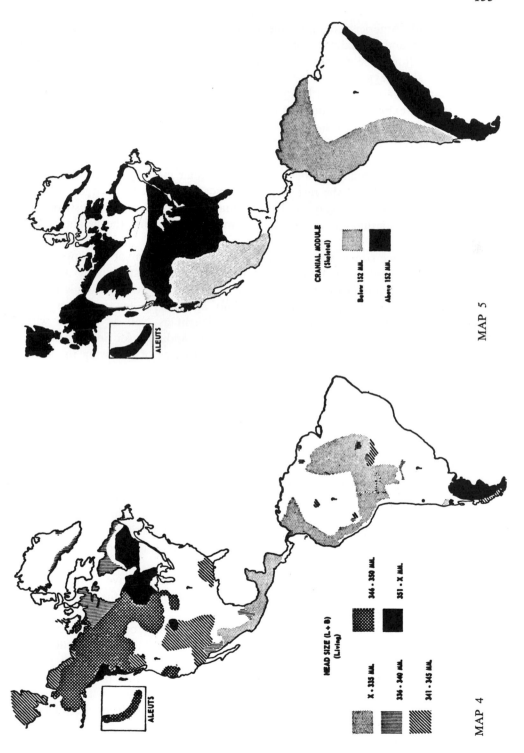

CRANIAL MODULE
(Skeletal)

Below 152 MM.

Above 152 MM.

ALEUTS

MAP 5

HEAD SIZE (L + B)
(Living)

X - 335 MM.

336 - 340 MM.

341 - 345 MM.

346 - 350 MM.

351 - X MM.

ALEUTS

MAP 4

The South American stature cline is broken in the extreme south by the short Yahgan and Alakaluf of the Magellanic archipelago. No sitting heights are available for these people, but other measurements indicate they are not particularly short-legged.

In map 4, head size in the living shows essentially the same sustained clines as stature, but exhibits exceptions in the Eastern Eskimo and along the southern Chilean coast. Since head size as used here is simply a length + breadth calculation, the vertical height is ignored. Thus the low-headed peoples of western North America (Stewart 1940: Fig. 3) and northeastern South America (Stewart 1943: Fig. 2) are actually smaller in head size than map 4 indicates, and the higher-headed peoples of the rest of the Americas are somewhat larger-headed. These discrepancies are largely resolved by map 5, which shows the distribution of the mean cranial module of the skull, a measure including the height of the vault.

The upper-face size of the skull, as expressed by the sum of the upper-face height and bizygomatic breadth, shows the same clinal distributions as head size. On map 6, large faces characterize the northern and southern ends of the native range, although the Labrador Eskimo again form an exception (see above). That there is increased upper-facial height as well as breadth with latitude is shown by Lundman's (1952) map 6. In addition, for South America at least, size of the eye orbits in skulls shows indications of following the same clines (Stewart & Newman 1950:26).

Clines in body, face and nose proportions in Indians and Eskimos

So far only body size clines have been considered, all of which appear to follow Bergmann's rule. The trunk-leg proportions of the Eskimo are in accordance with Allen's rule (see map 3 and p. 153). Confirmatory of the body-build characters of the Eskimo is Rodahl's summary (1952 table 2), giving the surface area of different parts of the body in percentage of the total calculated surface area. Forty-two male and 11 female Eskimo from Alaska, and a patently insufficient series of 7 Whites are used. Percentagewise the Eskimo have the larger skin surface of the head, trunk, and hands; the Whites for the arms, thighs, lower legs, and feet.

In facial proportions of the living, map 7 shows the relative elongation of the face with higher latitude. These clines are confirmed by the upper facial index on skulls (map 8).

Doubtless related to the progressive elongation of the face is the narrowing of the nose with latitude first pointed out by Thomson (1913). In addition, Davies (1932:349) has offered the unverified explanation that narrow noses represent an adaptation to cold climates where the temperature of the air must be adjusted to a warmth and humidity suitable to the lung tissue, just as a broad nose is of value in providing maximum egress for heated air from the lungs in climates hot enough to render optimum heat dissipation a selective advantage.

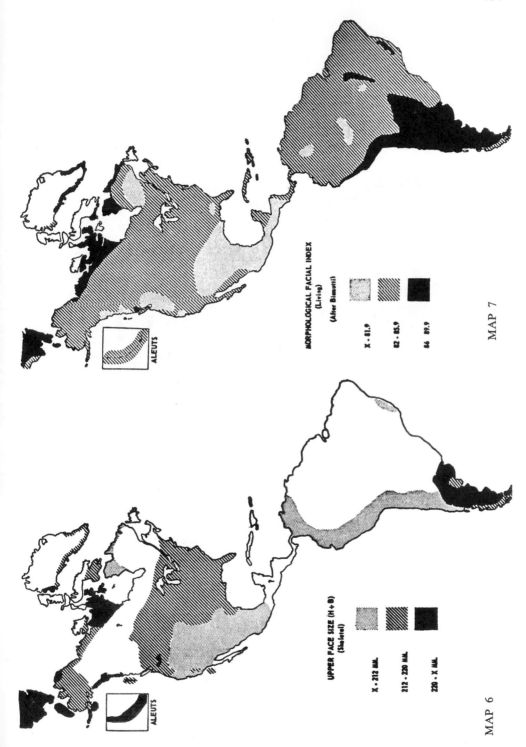

MORPHOLOGICAL FACIAL INDEX
(Living)

(After Bieswsti)

X - 81.9

82 - 85.9

86 - 89.9

MAP 7

ALEUTS

UPPER FACE SIZE (H + B)
(Skeletal)

X - 212 MM.

212 - 220 MM.

220 - X MM.

MAP 6

ALEUTS

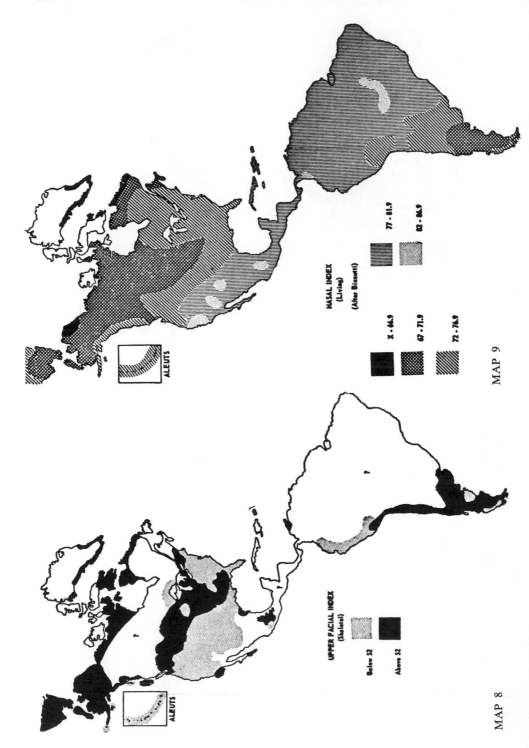

NASAL INDEX
(Living)
(After Biasutti)

X - 66.9
67 - 71.9
72 - 76.9
77 - 81.9
82 - 86.9

ALEUTS

MAP 9

UPPER FACIAL INDEX
(Skeletal)

Below 52
Above 52

ALEUTS

MAP 8

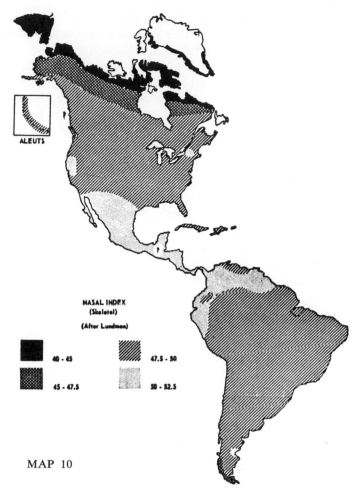

NASAL INDEX
(Skeletal)

(After Lundman)

40 - 45		47.5 - 50
45 - 47.5		50 - 52.5

MAP 10

The distribution of the nasal index on the living is shown in map 9, where the regular and sustained quality of the clines is remarkable in view of the technical difficulties in the location of nasion. Some, at least, of the five patches of higher indices between California and Central Brazil can probably be attributed to overly low location of nasion in the series reported from there (Newman 1953: 131). The clines for nasal indices on the living are paralleled by those on the skull, judging by map 10.

The biological nature of the clines in body size and proportions in American aborigines

The sustained clines in body size and proportions are, in my opinion, due to adaptive changes that took place largely since the New World was first peopled about 15,000 years ago (Willey 1951:3). In their pattern of adaptive change the body size clines seem to follow Bergmann's rule. While the body proportions of the Eskimo probably follow Allen's rule, the clines in facial and nasal proportions are not directly attributable to either rule, although in all likelihood they are due to the same factors of temperature and humidity.

Although gross climatic effect is undoubtedly important in controlling body size and proportions, there are almost certainly other factors. Possibly indications of the presence of such other factors are provided by the exceptions to the sustained nature of the clines: The smaller body size of the Eastern Eskimo, Canoe Indians, Yuki, and Harrison Lake Lillouet. Assuming the samples to be adequate, which is questionable in the last two mentioned, these peoples may be smaller because of inadequacies in food supply and nutrition. Another sort of exception is provided by the Indians living in high altitude cold along the Andes, who are small in body size though relatively large in chest dimensions, and give all indications of a separate problem in adaptation from those considered here.

In the American tropics, and perhaps elsewhere, it seems likely that food supply and nutrition may be as important as temperature and humidity in determining body size. Although we know less about human nutritional requirements in the tropics than in any other broad climatic zone, there are several indications of extra stresses in that area. Mills (1941:525) contends that the thiamine requirements of experimental animals are increased in hot environments, but whether this holds true for man is not wholly certain. Again, there are indications that due to higher excretory and other losses, the iron and possibly the calcium requirements of tropic-dwelling man are also heightened (Mitchell & Edman 1951:94). Against these and other possibilities of higher nutritional requirements for man in the tropics, there is Mills' further contention that tropic-raised meats are lower in thiamine content than those raised in temperate climates (Mills 1942:5). If these factors stand up under the scrutiny of controlled assays and other experiments, it is apparent that humans residing in the tropics and subsisting upon locally raised foods are faced with a real dietary dilemma lending selective value to smaller body size.

The extent to which adaptations in body size and proportions are inherited cannot as yet be determined. There are at present only general indications as to the hereditary nature of body build in man (Davenport 1923:153). These indications are supported by evidence from other animals. As noted by Rensch (1938:282), when several subspecies are placed in a common environment, without intermixture, there is no apparent convergence in physical characters over a number of generations. He also cites instances where body-size clines do not correspond to recent climatic zones, but rather to those of the preceding geological period. Finally he notes that there is a higher rate of cell division in the larger-bodied subspecies than in the smaller-bodied ones. Another sort of evidence favoring the inherited nature of body build is provided by production in the laboratory of large-bodied and small-bodied races of mice by pedigree selection for eight generations (MacArthur & Chiasson 1945).

On the other hand, there is convincing evidence that changes in the environment can have a direct non-genic effect on human body build. Lasker (1946:274–277) has summarized the cases where there are definite but limited physical changes that took place in the descendants of immigrants: Europeans, Japanese, Chinese and Mexicans in the United States, Japanese in Hawaii, and North Americans in Panama. Particularly pertinent to the present study are Mills' (1942:6–9) findings that, age for age, Panama-born North American children are slightly shorter in stature and lighter in weight than those just arrived from the United States. He attributes the retardation of the Panama-born to the growth depression caused by difficulties in dissipation of body heat. If so, the growth depression may be viewed as a non-genic adaptation to a body mass/body surface ratio more favorable to hot-climate living. This point is illustrated by Robinson's (1942) determination that in terms of standard physiological criteria, such as pulse rate, small men showed greater physical endurance than large men when both were placed at hard labor under conditions of difficult heat dissipation. Baker's (1953) recent findings that White and Negro soldiers lost body fat under conditions of desert stress, may be interpreted as a rapid somatic adjustment to the problem of body heat loss.

Animal experiments strongly support the evidence for man that the environment can have a direct, non-genic effect on body build. For example, white mice raised at about 65°F. have significantly longer and heavier bodies and shorter extremities and appendages than those from the same stock raised at 90°F. (Ogle 1934; Mills 1939). The same findings, without the increase in body length, also apply to chicks (Allee & Lutherman 1940). Thus the Bergmann and Allen effects are easily duplicated in the laboratory.

From the foregoing, it seems clear that body build is influenced by both hereditary and direct environmental factors. It is likely that the same environmental pressures that provide a selective screen favoring the better adapted body types, also make a somatic impression on the individual during his life span. As Angel (1952:261) has pointed out, through the mechanism of relative growth, both factors—natural selection of hereditary phenotypes and direct non-genic effect of the environment—can produce striking alterations in body size and proportions. The relative potencies of these two factors in man, then, is a problem for future research.

The significance of the clines in body size and proportions in New World racial studies

Whatever the relative potencies of the factors producing the clines shown in maps 2–10, the clines themselves are based upon most of the standard dimensions usually taken by anthropometrists. Otherwise there would have been insufficient data to plot the clines. Of the remaining standard dimensions, only head form and relative head height show distributional patterns not readily interpreted as adaptive ones. Indeed, the earlier and marginal distribution of long heads (Dixon 1923:404) and the apparently late arrival of low heads (Stewart 1940:43–45; 1943:151–152) seems best explained by migrations of peoples differing in these regards. But since the diagnostic criteria of most racial classifications of New World aborigines are principally the body size and proportion traits shown here to be adaptive, it is most curious that if explanations of these classifications are attempted at all, they are in terms of a separate migration from Asia to account for each race (Stewart & Newman 1950:28–30). Even Neumann (1952) used 4 to 6 migrations to account for his 8 North American varieties although he leaned more heavily upon morphological characters in defining his racial varieties than upon the metric features considered here. The extent to which his diagnostic morphological characters are influenced by adaptive changes in head, face, and nose size and proportions remains to be determined.

This extreme hereditarianism of most classifiers makes no allowance for physical change in the Americas except by interbreeding. Without denying that the New World was peopled by successive migrations or infiltrations of physically differing peoples, it is very likely that the American races of the classifiers are at least partly the products of adaptive changes that took place in the New World. This view does not necessarily contest any reality the classifiers' American races may have, since ecological races have definite validity in biology. Rather, it questions the classifiers' insistence that phenotypic traits involving body size and proportions could survive unaltered the vicissitudes of varying environmental pressures for 80 to 600 generations (i.e., 2,000 to 15,000 years) in the New World. It is much more probable that the sharpness of metric resemblance to Asiatic peoples fades with the number of generations in the Americas. Changes in the Asiatic parent- and the American daughter-populations, occasioned by mutation, random genetic drift, adaptation, and intermixture, would certainly blur the original closeness of phenotypic resemblance. On this basis it seems likely that the traditional metric analyses have only short range applicability in space and time to problems of racial affiliations. Effective coverage of the longer ranges may come only from morphological studies using traits whose functional and adaptive natures are understood, and, as Birdsell (1952:358) has suggested, from controlled analyses of the genetically more complicated characters.

Summary

The adaptive responses of bodily form to environment in warm-blooded animals have led, largely in the last century, to the formulation of several ecological rules. These rules constitute today an important and developing aspect of modern systematic studies, but only in the last several years have they been recognized as possibly operative in man. Extensive testing of these rules on human materials, however, has not been performed. For this reason, I have examined the applicability of two of the best validated of these rules—Bergmann's and Allen's—to the body forms of New World aborigines.

The principle behind both rules is that the maximum retention of body heat in cold climates occurs when the radiating skin surface is small relative to body mass. Since this ratio can be achieved by larger body size, Bergmann's rule holds that within a wide-ranging species, the subspecies in colder climates attain greater size than those in warmer climates. Allen's rule holds that in addition the cold climate subspecies have reduced extremities and appendages, thus further reducing the body surface. In warmer climates, following Bergmann's rule, easier dissipation of body heat goes with the low body mass/body surface ratio achieved by smaller body size.

Using stature as a measure of body size, map 2 shows a concentration of short peoples in the lower latitudes astride the equator, bearing out part of Bergmann's rule. Then stature shows somewhat irregular increases toward the north and south. These gradients or clines are sustained up to the northern continental fringe where the Eskimo show shorter statures due largely to their shorter legs. This shortness of extremities conforms to Allen's rule. Other measures indicative of body size (head size, maps 4 and 5; face size, map 6) show clines confirming those for stature.

In addition to these body size clines, maps 7 through 10 show comparable patterns of distribution in facial and nasal proportions. Both the face and nose become relatively longer and narrower with increasing latitude in North and South America.

It is important to note that these changes in body form corroborate each other, and together form a distributional pattern too closely associated with gross climatic variations to be fortuitous. That this distributional pattern in body form follows Bergmann's and Allen's rules indicates that we are dealing with adaptive changes. How much of the adaptations is due to natural selection of inherited body forms, and how much to direct non-genic effect during individual life span cannot now be determined. It seems fairly certain, however, that both factors operate in concert.

In all likelihood these adaptive changes took place since the New World was first peopled about 15,000 years ago. Now the dimensions upon which these changes are based constitute most of the traditionally taken measurements on the anthropometric blank. These same measurements are also the principal criteria used in most classifications of New World races. If the classifiers explain these races at all, they do so in terms of a separate migration from Asia for each one. This explanation seems erroneous in view of the high probability that the racial criteria themselves are of an adaptive nature. More likely, the races of the classifiers are at least partly ecological races formed in the New World.

REFERENCES

ALLEE, W. C. and C. Z. LUTHERMAN 1940 An Experimental Study of Certain Effects of Temperature on Differential Growth of Pullets, Ecology, Vol. 21, pp. 29–33.

ALLEE, W. C. and K. P. SCHMIDT 1951 Ecological Animal Geography, 2nd ed., New York.

ALLEN, J. A. 1877 The Influence of Physical Conditions in the Genesis of Species. Radical Review, Vol. 1, pp. 108–140.

ANGEL, J. L. 1952 The Human Skeletal Remains from Hotu Cave, Iran. Proceedings of the American Philosophical Society, Vol. 96, No. 3, pp. 258–269.

BAKER, P. T. 1953 Heat stress and gross morphology, Report no. 197, Environmental Protection Branch, Quartermaster Climatic Research Laboratory.

BERGMANN, C. 1847 Ueber die Verhältnisse der Warmeokonomie der Thiere zu ihrer Grösse. Göttinger Studien, Vol. 3, pp. 595–708.

BIASUTTI, R. 1941 Le Razze e i Popoli della Terra, Vol. 1. Torino.

BIRDSELL, J. B. 1952 On various levels of objectivity in genetical anthropology. American Journal of Physical Anthropology 10 No. 3: 355–362.

COON, C. S., S. M. GARN and J. B. BIRDSELL 1950 Races: A Study of the Problems of Race Formation in Man, Springfield, Ill.

COON, C. S., F. JOHNSON and C. KLUCKHOHN 1935 The Indian Languages of North America (map), Harvard Univ., photocopy.

COWAN, I. A. 1936 Distribution and Variation in Deer (Genus *Odocoileus*), of the Pacific Coastal Region of North America, California Fish and Game, Vol. 22, no. 3, pp. 155–246.

DAVENPORT, C. B. 1923 Body Build and its Inheritance, Carnegie Institution of Washington, publ. no. 329.

DAVIES, A. 1932 A Re-survey of the Morphology of the Nose in Relation to Climate, Journal of the Royal Anthropological Institute, Vol. 62, pp. 337–360.

DIXON, R. B. 1923 The Racial History of Man, New York.

HALL, E. R. 1951 American Weasels, University of Kansas Publications of the Museum of Natural History, Vol. 4, pp. 1–466.

HOWELLS, W. W. 1944 Mankind So Far, Garden City, New York.

KROEBER, A. L. 1948 Anthropology, New York.

LASKER, G. W. 1946 Migration and Physical Differentiation: A Comparison of Immigrant with American-born Chinese, American Journal of Physical Anthropology, Vol. 4, n.s., No. 3, pp. 273–300.

LUNDMAN, B. 1952 Umriss der Rassenkunde des Menschen in Geschichtlicher Zeit, Ejnar Munksgaard, Copenhagen.

MACARTHUR, J. W. and L. P. CHIASSON 1945 Relative Growth in Races of Mice Produced by Selection, Growth, Vol. 9, No. 4, Paper #289, pp. 303–315.

MAYR, E. 1942 Systematics and the Origin of Species, Columbia University Press, New York.

MILLS, C. A. 1939 Medical Climatology, Springfield, Ill.

——, 1941 Environmental Temperatures and Thiamine Requirements, American Journal of Physiology, Vol. 133, pp. 525–531.

——, 1942 Climatic Effects on Growth and Development, with Particular Reference to the Effects of Tropical Residence, American Anthropologist, Vol. 44, n.s., No. 1, pp. 1–13.

MITCHELL, H. H. and M. EDMAN 1951 Nutrition and Climatic Stress, with Particular Reference to Man, Springfield, Ill.

NEUMANN, G. K. 1952 Archeology and Race in the American Indian, pp. 13–34 in Archeology of the Eastern United States, Chicago.

NEWMAN, M. T. 1951 Review of *Races . . .* by Coon, Garn and Birdsell, *Boletín Bibliográfico de Antropología Americana,* Vol. 8, Pt. 2, pp. 188–192.

———, 1953 Anthropometry of the Umotina, Nambicuara and Iranxe, with Comparative Data from Other Northern Mato Grosso Tribes, Institute of Social Anthropology publ. No. 15: 128–135.

OGLE, C. 1934 Climatic Influence on the Growth of the Male Albino Mouse, American Journal of Physiology, Vol. 107, pp. 635–640.

RENSCH, B. 1938 Some Problems of Geographical Variation and Species Formation, Proceedings of the Linnean Society of London, 150th Session, Pt. 4, pp. 275–285.

RIDGEWAY, W. 1908 The Application of Zoological Laws to Man, Report, British Association for the Advancement of Science, pp. 832–847.

ROBINSON, S. 1942 The Effect of Body Size Upon Energy Exchange in Work, American Journal of Physiology, Vol. 136, pp. 363–368.

RODAHL, K. 1952 The Body Surface Area of the Eskimo, Journal of Applied Physiology, Vol. 5, no. 3, pp. 242–246.

SCHREIDER, E. 1951 Anatomical Factors of Body-heat Regulation, Nature, Vol. 167, No. 4255, May 19, pp. 823–824.

STEWARD, J. H. (ed.) 1950 Handbook of South American Indians, Bulletin Bureau of American Ethnology, No. 143, Vol. 6.

STEWART, T. D. 1939 Anthropometric Observations on the Eskimos and Indians of Labrador, Field Museum of Natural History, Anthropological Series, Vol. 31, No. 1, 163 pp.

———, 1940 Some Historical Implications of Physical Anthropology in North America, Smithsonian Miscellaneous Collections, Vol. 100, pp. 15–50.

———, 1943 Distribution of Cranial Height in South America, American Journal of Physical Anthropology, Vol. 1, n.s., no. 2, pp. 143–155.

———, and M. T. NEWMAN 1950 Anthropometry of South American Indian Skeletal Remains, Bureau of American Ethnology Bulletin 143, Vol. 6, pp. 19–42.

———, 1951 An Historical Résumé of the Concept of Differences in Indian Types, American Anthropologist, Vol. 53, No. 1, pp. 19–36.

THOMSON, A. 1913 The Correlations of Isotherms with Variations in the Nasal Index, International Congress of Medicine, London, Vol. 17, Sect. 1–2, pp. 89–90.

WILLEY, G. R. 1951 American Archaeology, Science, Vol. 114, no. 2959, Sept. 14, p. 3.

YOUNG, S. P. and E. A. GOLDMAN 1946 The Puma: Mysterious American Cat, American Wildlife Institute, Washington, D.C.

Evolution of Climatic
Adaptation in Homeotherms*

P. F. SCHOLANDER

Climatic adaptation in warm-blooded animals has been a subject of much concern to ecologists and evolutionists. With the formulation of the climatic rules of Bergmann and Allen it has become almost dogma that a reduction in the surface area relative to weight is a morphogenic factor of prime importance in the evolution of cold-hardy species or races. This idea is based on the simple reasoning that, other factors being equal, the less surface an animal has the less heat it would lose. Natural selection would therefore favor an arctic fauna tending towards large globular woolly balls with the least possible ears, tail, snout and legs. Tropical animals would tend in the opposite direction, towards smaller skinny forms, with long legs, snout, ears and tail. Clines of this sort have been looked for and have been found in many mammals and birds, and are given in textbooks on evolution as classical examples of the workings of adaptation by selection. Lately anthropologists have seen in the climatic rules a powerful tool by which to explain many racial features in man.

Adaptation, in the sense of "rendered fit for," implies an understanding of how and why the observed trend or response is useful, and is hence linked up with physiology. Sufficient information on the physiological adjustments of arctic and tropical animals is now available so that we may attempt an analysis of what phylogenetic pathways evolution has actually followed in the engineering of climatic adaptation of warm-blooded animals.

Climatic adaptations found in Arctic and Tropical mammals and birds

Most homeothermic animals require maintenance of a constant internal body temperature. This is generally higher than the environmental temperature. In arctic latitudes the temperature gradient to the outside is so great that the main

* Contribution No. 755 from the Woods Hole Oceanographic Institution.

166

problem becomes one of keeping warm. Thermally speaking there are three avenues open for adaptation to the arctic environment: (1) by lowering the gradient, (2) by increasing the heat production, and (3) by decreasing the heat dissipation. In a tropical environment overheating would be checked by changes in the opposite direction.

It is known that the body temperature is the same in species from all climates. (Compare Morrison and Ryser, 1952, and Irving and Krog, 1954.) Also the basal heat production has been found to be essentially the same in all climates, inasmuch as most arctic, temperate and tropical mammals fit the mouse-to-elephant curve of Benedict (1938). Birds show this regularity too. This leaves the heat dissipation as the only major avenue for phylogenetic adaptation to climate. (Compare the three papers by Scholander, Hock, Walters, Johnson and Irving, 1950.)

Major adaptations are traceable not only in the overall heat dissipation but also in the heat dissipation of localized peripheral structures. We shall consider the overall heat dissipation first.

Adaptation of the overall heat dissipation

At thermal equilibrium the heat dissipation balances the heat production. The latter is usually determined indirectly from the oxygen consumption or the carbon dioxide output. It is reasonable to assume that a mammal or a bird when fully adapted to its normal environment can rest and sleep in it at essentially basal heat production. A fundamental measure of the overall adaptation to cold is therefore to determine the lowest air temperature at which the animal can maintain a resting or basal metabolic rate, without losing body temperature. This is its *critical temperature*.

If the temperature of the environment drops, our resting mammal or bird will compensate for it by decreasing the heat loss. This is done by raising hairs or feathers, decreasing peripheral circulation and by balling up. At the critical temperature the overall insulation has reached its maximal value. If the environmental temperature is lowered still further, shivering sets in as a gross sign of incipient metabolic heat regulation. From this point on there is an increase in the heat production which is approximately proportional to the difference between the body and air temperature, such as would be expected from Newton's law of cooling (cp. Fig. 1).

In tropical mammals the critical temperature was found to be 25–27°C., the same as in naked man. In the arctic fox and husky the critical temperature was not yet reached at −30° in laboratory experiments. In these and larger arctic mammals it is probably −40° or lower since they can sleep unprotected on the snow at these temperatures. When curled up on the snow they may be likened to a man resting comfortably in an arctic sleeping bag at −40°.

Mammals and birds smaller than a rabbit have critical temperatures higher than the larger animals. Lemmings had a critical temperature of around +10°

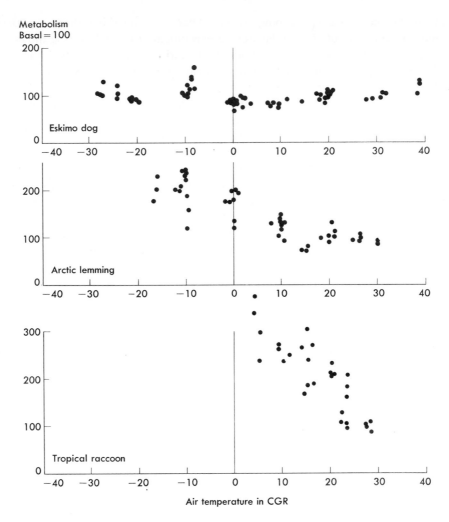

FIG. 1. Heat production versus environmental temperature in the husky, the lemming and the tropical raccoon. Resting or basal rate is set at 100. Critical temperature is below −30° in the husky, 10–15° in the lemming and 25–27° in the tropical raccoon. (From Scholander, Hock, Walters, Johnson and Irving 1950.)

and a little shrew with much less body insulation must have one still higher. These and many other small mammals live in the cold northern forests or on the tundra through the winter, but they all seek shelter, often under the snow, where microclimates may be found which are only a few degrees below freezing (Johnson, 1951). Many of them build warm nests. If shelter is not available such small animals may have to pull through cold spells by sustained high metabolic rate. Snow buntings were kept outside in an open wire cage at

Point Barrow, Alaska, during the whole winter. These birds had a critical temperature of 0° and nevertheless spent several months at −20° or lower. They normally migrate south in the winter.

In humans the critical temperature is only known for the white man and is about 27°. In spite of much recent work on the Eskimo this, his most fundamental index of overall temperature adaptation, has not been determined. Neither has the microclimate inside his clothing or sleeping bags been defined, but it is most likely as warm as ours. At least, his mittens, footwear and other clothing are excellent and sufficient to keep us warm. The really cold people, such as the Tierra del Fuegians of former days, or the Australian aborigines, have not been tested conclusively. Hicks, Moore, and Eldridge (1934) found that the Australians were able to rest at a basal heat production naked at 0° air temperature, but as they were surrounded by little fires their environmental temperature is unknown (Goldby, Hicks, O'Connor, and Sinclair, 1938).

How have the observed great differences in the critical temperature come about? There are two major avenues available. One is the increase in body insulation as we go towards colder climates; another is an adaptation of extremities and other peripheral parts to tolerate, and remain functional at, low tissue temperatures, sometimes even approaching zero degrees.

Body insulation

Measurement of the body insulation of mammals from the tropics to the arctic, on detached pieces of fur taken from the trunk, shows that it increases from warmer to colder climates (Fig. 2). In arctic mammals the trunk insulation increases from the shrew to the rabbit, but from then on as the animals get bigger the insulation remains approximately constant (Fig. 3). In the same environment a 5 kg hare or fox has about the same insulation as a 500 kg moose. For these animals the body-to-air gradient is the same, and hence the heat transfer per surface area should be about the same. This may be derived independently from the fact that the resting metabolic rate of a mammal is in general roughly proportional to the ¾ power of the weight (Brody and Procter, 1932; Brody, 1945; Kleiber, 1932, 1947). This makes it close enough to be proportional also to the ⅔ power of the weight, which is the relationship the surface area bears to weight. We should therefore not be surprised to find about the same insulation in all of the larger arctic species, including fur-clad man.

The non-adaptability of the resting rate shows that the heat production is not determined by the heat loss, as one might infer from the surface law of Rubner (1883), but vice versa. Whatever the surface area happens to be, the heat loss from it must be so regulated by various means that it balances the heat production. In a homeotherm one might say that body temperature plays the first violin, metabolic rate the second, and heat loss the third. The surface area is but one of the several factors which determine the heat loss.

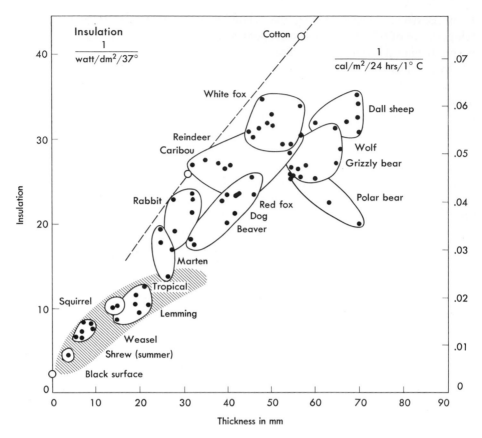

FIG. 2. Insulation of winter fur from arctic and tropical mammals. (Modified from Scholander, Walters, Hock, and Irving, 1950.)

In tropical animals the body insulation varies from almost complete nakedness to a sizeable amount of fur. A tropical sloth has a fur on its trunk as warm as that of an arctic lemming. This somewhat astounding fact is undoubtedly linked up with the very low metabolic rate of the sloth, which is no more than half of that of an ordinary mammal.

Adaptation in peripheral parts

It was shown that an arctic mammal like the husky or fox may sleep on the snow at −40° at a resting metabolic rate (Fig. 1). This is possible because of the very high overall body insulation. If this animal were to get up and run, let us say on a warm sunny winter day, it would have to increase suddenly its heat dissipation by some 10 to 20 times, in order not to heat up. Such a latitude in heat dissipation cannot be accomplished through the dense, thick body fur, but

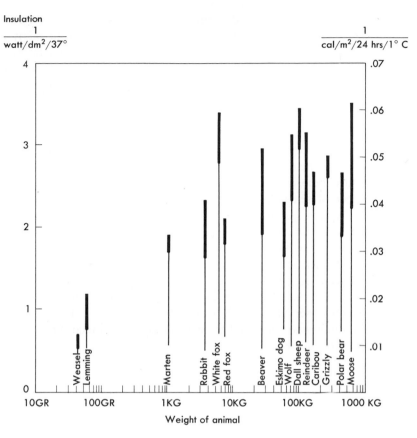

FIG. 3. Insulation of the winter fur versus size of arctic mammals. (From Scholander, Walters, Hock, and Irving, 1950).

is achieved by other means. All arctic mammals and birds present a conspicuously uneven insulation. The extremities and face are generally very poorly insulated; in most mammals this is also true for the belly. A caribou, reindeer, or mountain sheep has three to five times less insulation on the legs than on the trunk (Scholander, Walters, Hock, and Irving, 1950).

It is a reasonable assumption that these poorly insulated parts, when warmed by increased circulation, would serve as essential avenues for an increased heat loss. Penguins and seals when out of water may keep their feet and flippers very hot, and seals are known to have an extremely efficient vasomotor control in the flippers (Scholander, 1940; Irving, Scholander, and Grinnell, 1942). Arctic sea gulls (*Larus glaucus*) avoid freezing their legs in subzero weather by increased circulation (Scholander, Walters, Hock, and Irving, 1950). Panting and exposure of the tongue are other well known avenues for increased heat dissipation.

When heat must be conserved the bare areas or parts may cool very considerably. This has been shown by measuring the leg temperature in many arctic mammals and birds (Irving, 1951). In cold weather reindeer and huskies and other arctic mammals and birds maintained their legs at 10°C. or even lower for prolonged periods. When resting, the animals usually coil up, shielding the bare parts from the cold.

Many species of more or less aquatic mammals and birds keep their naked feet, and sometimes the tail, in ice water for a long time. We may mention ducks, sea gulls, penguins, wading birds, whales, seals, beavers, muskrats, otters, moose and others. Some of these have greatly expanded flukes, fins, flippers or webbed feet. Temperature records from these structures are few. Irving found, however, that the feet of sea gulls (*Larus argentatus* and *L. glaucescens*) may be kept near zero degrees (Chatfield, Lyman, and Irving, 1953). When the feet of an arctic gull (*L. glaucus*) were kept in a thermos bottle of ice water their caloric output over two hours was only 1.5% of the basal rate of the bird. (Scholander, Walters, Hock, and Irving, 1950). From the handling of subarctic porpoises (*Phocaena*) in cold water and young arctic seals (*Cystophora*) in ice water it is known that their flukes or flippers may keep close to the water temperature (personal observations). It would be difficult to conceive how such animals could remain warm if they had to keep these expanded and thin organs at body temperature in the ice water.

As a corollary to the conspicuously low temperature which we may find in peripheral parts the nerves in the cold tolerant legs of a herring gull were found to conduct impulses at temperatures so low as to render the nerves of a hen's legs useless (Chatfield, Lyman, and Irving, 1953).

Vascular heat exchangers

Many mammals and birds show a vascular pattern in the extremities or other peripheral parts which may be interpreted as an adaptation to heat conservation. Claude Bernhard (1876) considered that some of the heat from the arteries would be transmitted over to the cooler blood returning through the neighboring veins. Bazett and his coworkers (1948) through numerous measurements in man showed that temperature gradients of as much as 3 degrees per decimeter could develop along a brachial or radial artery, mainly because of heat transfer from the artery across to the *venae commitantes*. The principle of operation of such a counter current exchange system will be seen from the diagram in Figure 4.* The heat exchange system as we find it in man is a mere rudiment

---

* The theory for a multi-channel counter current exchange system of this sort has been elaborated for the *rete mirabile* of the swimbladder of deep sea fishes. Here an oxygen gradient of some 100–200 atmospheres is maintained across the swimbladder wall, and the *rete* can be calculated to cut down the oxygen tension of the leaving blood to only a few millimeters of mercury (Scholander, 1954).

compared to those we find in many mammals and birds. The multi-channel arteriovenous *rete* systems to be described below are by physical necessity heat exchangers and economizers of the body heat. Whether or not this is their primary or sole function is another matter.

In the manatee the flippers and tail are supplied with blood through a bundle of hundreds of arteries and veins intermingled in a *rete* (Murie, 1872; Fawcett, 1942). Fan-shaped arteriovenous bundles are prevalent in the peripheral structures of seals (Zuckerkandl, 1894; Müller, 1904; and personal observations). The tail and flippers of whales are supplied through arteriovenous *retes* (Stannius, 1841; Wilson, 1879; Braun, 1905; Slijper, 1936; Fawcett, 1942). The arteries in the tail fluke are surrounded by venous channels (personal observations). The capybara and to less extent the nutria, amphibious rodents of South America, have arteriovenous *retes* in the legs (Müller, 1904).

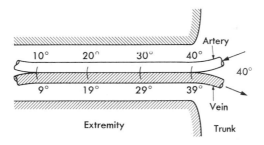

FIG. 4. Schematic presentation of arteriovenous counter current heat exchange in an extremity, resulting in a steep linear temperature gradient and consequent reduced peripheral heat loss.

Penguins have an arterial *rete* in the axilla suggestive of heat exchange with the veins, which are fewer in number (Watson, 1883; Müller, 1908). Tall wading birds like cranes, herons, flamingos have tarsial arteriovenous *retes,* as have also several long-legged land birds (Hyrtl, 1863). Sea or lake waters are cooling even in the tropics, considering that the cooling power of water is some 20 to 50 times that of air of the same temperature.

Many terrestrial tropical mammals have arteriovenous bundles running out into the extremities and tail instead of, or in addition to, the conventional single arteries with their *venae commitantes.* The most striking development of such bundles or *retes* is found in sloths, anteaters, armadillos, pangolins, loris, tarsiers, and monotremes (Hyrtl, 1853, 1854; Zuckerkandl, 1894, 1895, 1907; Leche and Göppert, 1902–1906; Müller, 1904; Wislocki, 1928; Rau and Rao, 1930; Wislocki and Straus, 1932; Davies, 1947). Of these animals the sloth is known to be extremely temperature sensitive, and at times it may well need to keep its long arms and legs at a low reptilian temperature to be able to keep the trunk warm. Its resting metabolic rate is only half that of an ordinary mammal (Scholander, Hock, Walters, and Irving, 1950). Monotremes are normally very temperature sensitive in their metabolic response to cold and have a low metabolic rate (Martin, 1902). The loris are very sluggish animals.

Other animals, such as ducks, geese, swans, sea gulls, have not been found to have macroscopic heat exchangers in their legs (Hyrtl, 1863), although one might well at first thought expect that they would need them. Irving found a steep temperature gradient below the feathered part of the leg in a sea gull (*L. glaucescens*) suggestive of a vascular heat exchange mechanism (Chatfield, Lyman, and Irving, 1953).

In any attempt to evaluate the thermal significance of the *retes,* one must remember that in well insulated animals, like the fox, which is capable of sleeping on the snow at −40°, there may arise a serious problem of heat dissipation, when the weather turns warm, or when the animal is running. Where heat conservation is the main problem one might find vascular heat exchangers; where heat dissipation is the more important point one might not find them. Final evaluation of the thermal significance of these striking structures must of course await experimental measurements. At all events the extremities and sometimes the tail and other bare parts of the body are essential for the heat regulation in northern species and show very significant adaptations to climate.

Bergmann's and Allen's rules

In the above brief outline of known physiological pathways in the phylogenetic adaptation to hot and cold climates no mention is made of the possible importance of the overall size of the animal. Neither is there any reference to the absolute or relative size of the protruding parts such as legs, tail, and ears. Behind both Bergmann's and Allen's rules lies the idea that as we go to colder environments the surface of animals relative to weight should become reduced, bringing about a decrease in heat loss. These rules are conceived as applicable primarily on a sub-species level. (Compare Goldschmidt, 1940; Huxley, 1943.) There are two aspects here which are of interest to us: To what extent are clines of this sort of general occurrence, and what evidence is there that they are caused by a physiological response to cold?

To the first question one may point out that there is disagreement as to whether these clines constitute clear trends. Rensch (1936) is the chief proponent of the validity of the rules, whereas Reinig (1939) denies them, finding size clines radiating more or less in any direction from a common distribution center. Well-known cases where size increases southwards are among many others, the puma, the raccoon and the otter (Allen, 1906). The rules evidently are not entirely above debate. For the physiological interpretation of established cases this does not matter a great deal, inasmuch as the basic measurements are often thermally irrelevant or reveal differences so small that they cannot be appraised.

The Biometrical Data.   In the arguments for the validity of Bergmann's and Allen's rules Rensch has, for example, made use of data from Ridgeway's "The Birds of North and Middle America" (1904–1914). The measurements are based on dried museum skins. The size is taken as the wing length, which is the length from the wrist bend to the tip of the longest primary. There are a few short finger bones in this measurement, the rest is just wing feathers. These measurements may correlate with flight but bear no useful thermal significance. If we consider a five millimeter's difference in length of these feathers as thermally uninterpretable we find that 16 subspecies pairs out of a total of 43 have slightly longer feathers going north. If we consider it uninterpretable whether the tarsus is 30% or 32% of the length of the wing feathers then also Allen's rule disappears from physiology.

Rensch also compared subspecies pairs of southern and northern mammals based on skin measurements given in Anthony's "Field Book of North American Mammals" (1928). In a series of 30 pairs 80% of the subspecies were longer in the north; in a similar series of European forms 60% were longer in the north. The length difference was mostly less than 10%. The relative length of feet and tail versus body length was often a trifle smaller in the northern form of a pair. The correlation was considered positive at a difference of only 0.2% (i.e., 20.0% instead of 20.2%).

Physiological Significance.   If, contrary to the view of Reinig, the slight biometrical trends found by Rensch are taken to reflect a general tendency, what is the evidence that they represent a physiological adaptation to temperature?

Exposure and resulting adaptation to cold do, of course, affect the whole population of northern mammals and birds. From a purely physiological standpoint, if relative surface reduction were a point of general adaptive importance, we should expect this to modify the animals not only on a subspecific level, but the whole northern warm-blooded fauna should by convergence tend towards large globular species. This quite obviously is not so. In some of the coldest areas on earth, the great northern Canadian and Siberian forests, there is a wide variety of sizes and shapes in both birds and mammals. There are little birds with naked legs thinner than match sticks, such as red-polls and chickadees, there are tiny shrews and mice, there are long-tailed foxes, long-legged, long-eared mammals, like the moose and deer. Some of the mammals of the cold forests or tundra have a considerable expanse of horns.

In the icy polar lakes and seas swim mammals and birds, such as whales, seals, and penguins, not with surface-saving, reduced extremities but with legs or tail naked and expanded into swimming surfaces. We also find numerous wading birds walking about with their tall, thin legs in ice water. Nowhere are extremities so regularly exposed to more severe chilling. Yet here we find no tangible evidence that the size of the surface area, absolute or relative, is in any way a critical factor in arctic or northern phylogenetic adaptation.* The prime point is *conservation of heat,* true enough, but in this the size of the surface area of the animal is of minor importance, at best. The factors that count are the *thermal properties of the surface*—its insulation, its exposure, its vascularization, and its ability to tolerate a cold tissue temperature. Poorly insulated and expanded areas do not disappear but are essential adjuncts in heavily insulated animals which ensure sufficient latitude in the heat regulation.

In the tropics the assortment of mammals and birds is similar to that in the arctic, but less well insulated. There are tiny birds and large ones, tiny mammals and large ones, some chubby and stocky like the rhinoceros, others long and lanky like the giraffe.

We are unable to see any evidence that the surface area as such has played a detectable role in the phylogenetic engineering of warm-blooded animals for hot and cold climates. The heat loss from the available surfaces, as a function of their insulation, their exposure and their surface temperature, drowns out in importance the numerical value of the areas.†

We may conclude that there is no physiological evidence to indicate that those cases of subspecific clines which accord with Bergmann's and Allen's rules are the result of a heat-conserving adaptation. One must be open for other inter-pretations. Cold climates do not produce a fauna tending towards large-sized globular forms with small protruding parts. The phylogenetic adaptation to heat conservation in the arctic took place through other means, which have been measured, which are understood, and which apply to every individual of every species.

Bergmann's and Allen's rules applied to man

Hardly anywhere have these "rules" been taken more seriously than in modern anthropology. Coon, Garn and Birdsell (1950) in their stimulating book "Races. A Study of the Problems of Race Formation in Man" take the racial features of many people to be the result of an interaction between the climate and the surface area of man.

The stockiness and relatively short extremities found in many Eskimos are interpreted as the result of cold, working through generations on the hands and feet of these people, giving short-limbedness a selective advantage. Similarly the Mongolian face has been engineered by the cold wind and weather. This is evi-

---

* The hopeless inadequacy of cold adaptation via Bergmann's rule may be seen by the following consideration. Take a body-to-air gradient in the tropics of 7° and in the arctic of 70°, i.e., a tenfold increase. A tenfold greater cooling in the arctic animal is prevented by covering the surface with fur a few centimeters thick. A relative surface reduction of ten times would require a weight increase of the animal of one thousand times.

† For these same reasons it is conceptually an unfortunate custom to express basal or resting metabolic rate as per surface area.

dently based on the concept that the Eskimo is a people perpetually shivering from cold. As already mentioned, there are no measurements to substantiate such an idea. They are clever in clothing. You are warm when you stay with them and when you use their mittens and leg wear. Furthermore, it would seem that tall Eskimos could easily cheat evolution out of shortening arms and legs simply by getting long enough sleeves on their parkas and long enough legs on their pants. Extra mittens and socks could also be had if needed. Where then would be the stimulus to drive the selection?

If subjected to a suitable cold stress, circulation will improve in our hands and feet so that they may remain warm and functional at an exposure which would render unadapted digits numb and useless (Balke, Cremer, Kramer, and Reichel, 1944; Carlson, Burns, Holmes, and Webb, 1953). In Eskimos adapted hands remain conspicuously well circulated and warm on cold exposure (Brown and Page, 1952, and personal observations in the field). This is a heat-wasting tropical type of emergency reaction. In sharp contrast to this we have the heat-preserving, cold, but functional extremities of arctic mammals and birds. This ultimate adaptation evolved in animals compelled to submit to the environment. In the Eskimo the main adaptation lies not in physiology, but in an age-long experience and technical skill in ducking the cold. They conquered the arctic not by submitting to it but by surrounding themselves successfully with a little piece of the same tropical microclimate upon which we also depend.

As the opposite of the allegedly cold-engineered Eskimos the tall Tuaregs of the hot and dry Sahara have been cited, and with them the Australian aborigines. Several tribes of the latter were studied by Hicks, Moore, and Eldridge (1934), who observed that these *naked* people expose themselves seasonally to very low, even freezing, temperatures, something neither we nor an Eskimo would ever venture to do naked. This certainly confuses the idea that the Eskimo features are a result of cold exposure and the Australian features a result of heat exposure. There is hardly any valid evidence from physiology that the surface area as such, in man or beast, is a factor of general morphogenic importance in the evolution of races inhabiting hot or cold climates.

Summary

Mammals and birds have the same body temperature in hot and cold climates, and within the same weight range they have roughly the same basal heat production per unit weight. This leaves them with *heat dissipation* as the only main avenue for climatic thermal adaptation. The lowest air temperature at which a mammal or bird can rest at a basal heat production, maintaining its body temperature, is the critical temperature. This is 25–27° in naked man and in many tropical species, and −40° in the larger arctic species, and is a fundamental measure of the overall climatic thermal adaptation. The major reason for the low critical temperature in the arctic species is the heavy body insulation provided by fur or feather coats, combined with an outstanding tolerance of low tissue temperature (often near 0°) in poorly insulated peripheral parts such as legs, tail and face. There are good indications that arctic species depend upon vascular control of these poorly insulated parts for heat dissipation. Without them they would over-heat during exercise when the heat output may be increased 10–20 times over the resting rate. Aquatic species, especially, expose their naked feet, fins or tail to the most severe chilling in ice water. Yet these organs are usually thin and greatly expanded for swimming. In many arctic and tropical species cold extremities, and consequently low heat loss, are assured by arteriovenous counter current heat exchangers at the base of the limbs or tail. In spite of the low temperature which may prevail in the extremities when the animal needs heat conservation, these organs are fully functional.

There is no physiological evidence, in beast or man, that the minor and erratic subspecific trends expressed in Bergmann's and Allen's rules reflect phylogenetic pathways of heat-conserving adaptation. Arctic species do not tend towards large spheres with reduced extremities and tail. The phylogenetic adaptations which have taken place are fairly well known in their main physiological aspects, as outlined above. They are major and general, as is the stimulus of the climate, and they know no taxonomic barriers.

REFERENCES

ALLEN, J. A. 1906. The influence of physical conditions in the genesis of species. Ann. Rep. Smithsonian Inst. (1905), pp. 375–402.

ANTHONY, H. E. 1928. Field Book of North American Mammals. G. P. Putnam's Sons, New York.

BALKE, B., H. D. CREMER, K. KRAMER, and H. REICHEL. 1944. Untersuchungen zur Kälteanpassung. Klin. Wochenschr., 23: 204–210.

BAZETT, H. C., L. LOVE, M. NEWTON, L. EISENBERG, R. DAY, and R. FORSTER, II. 1948. Temperature changes in blood flowing in arteries and veins in man. Jour. Applied Physiol., 1: 3–19.

BAZETT, H. C., E. S. MENDELSON, L. LOVE, and B. LIBET. 1948. Precooling of blood in the arteries, effective heat capacity and evaporative cooling as factors modifying cooling of the extremities. Jour. Applied Physiol., 1: 169–182.

BENEDICT, F. G. 1938. Vital energetics. Carnegie Inst. Washington Publ. no. 503.

BERGMANN, C. 1847. Ueber die Verhältnisse der Wärmeökonomie der Thiere zu ihrer Grösse. Göttinger Studien, pt. 1, 595–708.

BERNARD, C. 1876. Leçons sur la chaleur animale. Libr. J.-B. Baillière et Fils, Paris.

BRAUN, M. 1905. Einiges über *Phocaena communis* Less. Zool. Anz., 29: 145–149.

BRODY, S. 1945. Bioenergetics and Growth. Reinhold Publ. Corp., New York.

BRODY, S., and R. C. PROCTER. 1932. Relation between basal metabolism and mature body weight in different species of mammals and birds. Univ. Missouri Agr. Exper. Sta. Res. Bull., 166: 89–101.

BROWN, G. M. and J. PAGE. 1952. The effect of chronic exposure to cold on temperature and blood flow of the hand. Jour. Applied Physiol., 5: 221–227.

CARLSON, L. D., H. L. BURNS, T. H. HOLMES, and P. P. WEBB. 1953. Adaptive changes during exposure to cold. Jour. Applied Physiol, 5: 672–676.

CHATFIELD, P. O., C. P. LYMAN, and L. IRVING. 1953. Physiological adaptation to cold of peripheral nerve in the leg of the herring gull (*Larus argentatus*). Amer. Jour. Physiol., 172: 639–644.

COON, C. S., S. M. GARN, and J. R. BIRDSELL. 1950. Races. A Study of the Problems of Race Formation in Man. Charles C. Thomas, Springfield, Ill.

DAVIES, D. V. 1947. The cardiovascular system of the slow loris (*Nycticebus tardigradus malaianus*). Proc. Zool. Soc. London, 117: 377–410.

FAWCETT, D. W. 1942. A comparative study of blood-vascular bundles in the Florida manatee (*Trichechus latirostris*) and in certain cetaceans and edentates. Jour. Morph., 71: 105–133.

GOLDSCHMIDT, R. 1940. The Material Basis of Evolution. Yale Univ. Press, New Haven.

HICKS, C. S., H. O. MOORE, and E. ELDRIDGE. 1934. The respiratory exchange of the Australian aborigine. Australian Jour. Exper. Biol. Med. Sci., 12: 79–89.

HUXLEY, J. 1943. Evolution. The Modern Synthesis. Harper and Bros., New York.

HYRTL, J. 1853. Beiträge zur vergleichenden Angiologie. IV. Das arterielle Gefäss-System der Monotremen. Denkschr. K. Akad. Wissensch., Math.-Naturwiss. Classe, Wien, vol. 5, Abth. 1, 1–20.

HYRTL, J., 1854. Beiträge zur vergleichenden Angiologie. V. Das arterielle Gefäss-System der Edentaten. Denkschr. K. Akad. Wissensch., Math.-Naturwiss. Classe, Wien, vol. 6, Abth. 1, 21–64.

HYRTL, J. 1863. Neue Wundernetze und Geflechte bei Vögeln und Säugethieren. Denkschr. K. Akad. Wissensch., Math.-Naturwiss. Classe, Wien, 22: 113–152.

IRVING, L. 1951. Physiological adaptation to cold in arctic and tropic animals. Fed. Proc., Amer. Soc. Exper. Biol., 10: 543–545.

IRVING, L., and J. KROG. 1954. Body temperatures of arctic and subarctic birds and mammals. Jour. Applied Physiol., 6: 667–680.

IRVING, L., P. F. SCHOLANDER, and S. W. GRINNELL. 1942. The regulation of arterial blood pressure in the seal during diving. Amer. Jour. Physiol., 135: 557–566.

JOHNSON, H. M. 1951. Preliminary ecological studies of microclimates inhabited by the smaller arctic and subarctic mammals. Science in Alaska, 1951. Proc. Second Alaska Sci. Conf., Alaska Div. AAAS, pp. 125–131.

KLEIBER, M. 1932. Body size and metabolism. Hilgardia, 6: 315–353.

KLEIBER, M. 1947. Body size and metabolic rate. Physiol. Rev., 27: 511–541.

LECHE, W., and E. GÖPPERT. 1902–1906. Das Gefässsystem. *In* H. G. Bronn, Klassen und Ordnungen des Thier-Reichs, vol. 6, Abt. 5, Buch 5, Teil 1, 1171–1330.

MARTIN, C. J. 1902. Thermal adjustment and respiratory exchange in monotremes and marsupials.—A study in the development of homoeothermism. Phil. Trans. Roy. Soc. London, ser. B. 195: 1–37.

MORRISON, P. R., and F. A. RYSER. 1952. Weight and body temperature in mammals. Science, 116: 231–232.

MÜLLER, E. 1904. Beiträge zur Morphologie des Gefässsystems. II. Die Amarterien der Säugetiere. Anat. Hefte, 27: 71–241.

MÜLLER, E. 1908. Beiträge zur Morphologie des Gefässsystems. III. Zur Kenntnis der Flügelarterien der Pinguine. Anat. Hefte, 35: 553–648.

MURIE, J. 1872. On the form and structure of the manatee (*Manatus americanus*). Trans. Zool. Soc. London, 8: 127–202.

RAU, A. SUBBA, and P. KRISHNA RAO. 1930. Contributions to our knowledge of the anatomy of the Lemuroidea. I. Arterial system of *Loris lyddekerianus*. Half-Yearly Jour. Mysore Univ., 4: 90–121.

REINIG, W. F. 1939. Besteht die Bergmannsche Regel zu Recht? Arch. Naturgesch., N.F., 8: 70–88.

RENSCH, B. 1936. Studien über klimatische Parallelität der Merkmalsausprägung bei Vögeln und Säugern. Arch. Naturgesch., N.F., 5: 317–363.

RIDGEWAY, R. 1904–1914. The birds of North and Middle America. Bull. U.S. Natl. Mus. no. 50, pts. 2–6.

RUBNER, M. 1883. Ueber den Einfluss der Körpergrösse auf Stoff-und Kraftwechsel. Zeitschr. Biol., 19: 535–562.

SCHOLANDER, P. F. 1940. Experimental investigations on the respiratory function in diving mammals and birds. Hvalraadets Skr. no. 22.

SCHOLANDER, P. F. 1954. Secretion of gases against high pressures in the swim-bladder of deep sea fishes. II. The *rete mirable*. Biol. Bull., 107: 260–277.

SCHOLANDER, P. F., R. HOCK, V. WALTERS, and L. IRVING. 1950. Adaptation to cold in arctic and tropical mammals and birds in relation to body temperature, insulation, and basal metabolic rate. Biol. Bull., 99: 259–271.

SCHOLANDER, P. F., R. HOCK, V. WALTERS, F. JOHNSON, and L. IRVING. 1950. Heat regulation in some arctic and tropical mammals and birds. Biol. Bull., 99: 237–258.

SCHOLANDER, P. F., V. WALTERS, R. HOCK, and L. IRVING. 1950. Body insulation of some arctic and tropical mammals and birds. Biol. Bull., 99: 225–236.

SLIJPER, E. J. 1936. Die Cetaceen vergleichend-anatomisch und systematisch. Capita Zool., vol. 7.

STANNIUS, H. 1841. Ueber den Verlauf der Arterien bei *Delphinus phocaena*. Arch. Anat., Physiol. Wissensch. Med., 379–402.

WATSON, M. 1883. Report on the anatomy of the Spheniscidae collected during the voyage of H.M.S. Challenger. Rep. Sci. Results Voyage H.M.S. Challenger, Zool., vol. 7, pt. 18

WILSON, H. S. 1879. The *rete mirabile* of the narwhal. Jour. Anat. Physiol., 14: 377–398.

WISLOCKI, G. B. 1928. Observations on the gross and microscopic anatomy of the sloths (*Bradypus griseus griseus* Gray and *Choloepus hoffmani* Peters). Jour. Morph., 46: 317–397.

WISLOCKI, G. B., and W. L. STRAUS, JR. 1932. On the blood vascular bundles in the limbs of certain edentates and lemurs. Bull. Mus. Comp. Zool., 74: 1–15.

ZUCKERKANDL, E. 1894. Zur Anatomie und Entwickelungsgeschichte der Arterien des Vorderarmes (1. Teil). Anat. Hefte, 4: 1–98.

ZUCKERKANDL, E. 1895. Zur Anatomie und Entwickelungsgeschichte der Arterien des Unterschenkels und des Fusses. Anat. Hefte, 5: 207–291.

ZUCKERKANDL, E. 1907. Zur Anatomie und Morphologie der Extremitatenarterien. Sitzungsber. K. Akad. Wissensch., Wien, Math.-Naturwiss. Klasse, vol. 116, Abt. 3, 459–730.

Adaptation of Man
to Cold Climates

MARSHALL T. NEWMAN

The purpose of this note is to agree broadly with Scholander's view (1955, 15–26) on the adaptation of homeotherms to cold climates, and to outline the bodily adaptations of man in the arctic that were not mentioned. Scholander is certainly correct that decrease of heat dissipation in man as in other homeotherms plays the major role in adaptation to cold. While heavy insulation in the form of fur is obviously no phylogenetic adaptation for man, specially designed fur clothing and some efficient means of shelter are the two prime factors permitting man's late Pleistocene shift from a warm Pontian to a cold Holarctic fauna. Indeed it seems likely that the clo

$$\left(\frac{1 \text{ clo} = 0.18°C.}{\text{cal./sq.m./hr.}} \right)$$

units of native attire closely parallel the insulating values of winter fur cited in Scholander's Figure 2.

In view of man's relatively recent emergence from the tropics, and because of his cultural accoutrements to cope with cold, the efficient vascular control of the less well insulated extremities seen in arctic fauna cannot be matched by humans. Nevertheless man shows some adjustments in this direction. While some cold climate mammals and birds can maintain leg temperatures at 10°C. and lower (Scholander, 1955, p. 19), tests on American Whites show that under more moderate cold at 15°C., the surface of the feet can remain without apparent injury at 17°C. for a month (Spealman, 1949, p. 236). Possibly cold-adapted people like the Eskimos could maintain lower temperatures in their extremities, but this has not been tested. Clearly the Eskimos have not achieved full physiological adaptation to cold. To cite two sorts of evidence, the most common

181

operation performed on Alaskan Eskimos is said to be amputation of frozen toes (Coon, Garn, and Birdsell, 1950, p. 43).

While Scholander is largely correct when he says, "In the Eskimo the main adaptation lies not in the physiology, but in an age-long experience and technical skill in ducking the cold," in the long view he has underplayed two factors. First, the technical skill in ducking the cold probably resulted only from long-term experimentation, and during this time the cold would have a more drastic screening effect upon the experimenters. Secondly, while Eskimos surround ". . . themselves with a little piece of the same tropical microclimate upon which we also depend," this is contingent upon plentiful supplies of high calorie food. Since the Eskimo winter house is heated largely by the bodies of its inhabitants, up to around 60°F. with possibly a 100°F. indoor-outdoor gradient (Stefansson, 1955, p. 36), these radiators need constant stoking. An Eskimo outdoors, though clad in a cold resistant double garment of as much as 4 clo in insulating value, needs food to keep warm enough for effective hunting. Any doubt that short supply and starvation are the principal hazards of Eskimo life may be dispelled by the many references listed by Weyer (1932, pp. 116–117 ff.). It seems likely that Scholander has also underplayed the apparent physiological superiority under cold stressing that Eskimos show over Whites, and particularly Negroes (Meehan, 1955, pp. 333–334). The higher surface temperatures maintained by Eskimos whose fingers are immersed in an ice bath may be, as Scholander notes, a heat-wasting tropical type of emergency reaction. These higher finger temperatures corroborate Brown and Page's (1952, p. 229) data on the greater blood flow in Eskimo than in Whites' hands during an ice bath. Yet heat-wasting emergency reaction or not, it seems clear that the ability to maintain sufficient extremity temperatures to prevent freezing has selective value in cold climates. Military annals provide practical demonstrations of this, with the higher incidence of cold injuries in Negro than in White troops during the Korean winter of 1950–51, and the two subsequent winters at Ladd Air Force Base, Alaska (Meehan, 1955, p. 330).

Similar finger-ice bath experiments were conducted in Manchuria, where the highest temperatures were maintained by a series of Tungus-speaking mountain people, the Orochons (Yoshimura and Iida, 1952, p. 179). Mongols and Chinese ranked together, and the Japanese then living in Manchuria showed the lowest temperatures. Furthermore, Manchurian-born Chinese showed higher finger temperatures than those born in Shantung, and Japanese from the colder areas of their home islands had higher figures than those from the warmer areas. It is likely that in both the Eskimo-White-Negro and the Orochon-Mongol-Chinese-Japanese studies acclimatization during the individuals' life span and racial heredity served as complementing factors. In addition, Coffey (1955) found manual dexterity under arctic conditions to be very superior in young Eskimo and Indian men as compared to acclimatized Whites.

Sargent (1953) has provided a summary of our physiological knowledge of short-term acclimatization in Whites. With the pituitary-adrenal system as the controlling mechanism, a reactive syndrome of changes occur. Some of these are vasoconstriction and shifting of the blood from superficial areas to the pulmonary and probably splancnic regions, reduced skin temperatures, blood plasma diminution, hemoconcentration, and metabolic increases.

Whether these short-term changes are similar to the physiological patterns of Eskimos and other arctic peoples has not been determined. The decrease of blood volume in Southampton Island Eskimos during the summer months (Brown et. al. 1954, p. 254) seems antithetical to the White syndrome. Yet a similarity is suggested by Roberts' (1952 a and b) findings that among native peoples, including those from the arctic, basal metabolic rates and blood pressures seem to rise with lowered mean annual temperatures, while pulse and respiration rates are lowered. Possibly the higher blood pressures of cold climate peoples are principally a reflection of vasoconstriction, but here some proof is needed.

Basal metabolic rates of Eskimos are consistently high, ranging in means from $+12$ to $+33$ during the wintertime (Bollerud, Edwards, and Blakely, 1950, pp. 1–2). Repeated determinations on the same Southampton Island Eskimos under strictly basal conditions gave high BMRs, although about a 6 percent drop occurred during the summertime (Brown et. al. 1954, p. 253). The reasons for the higher basal metabolic rates in Eskimos are not wholly clear. Rodahl (1952) made 340 tests on 73 healthy Eskimos, and found that while subsisting on native food their BMRs averaged $+8\%$ over White norms. When they changed to a White diet, their BMRs fell to an average of -8%. This should indicate that the significantly higher basal metabolic rates of Eskimos are largely dietary in origin. In connection with U.S. Military personnel in the arctic, Gray, Consolazio, and Kark (1947) have evidence that the metabolic increase due to the hobbling effect of clothing on military personnel seems at least twice as great as that due to lowered temperature. In this connection Stefansson (1955, p. 51) states that Eskimo winter clothing only weighs 7–10 pounds, as compared to 15–25 pounds for the usual military arctic gear, and would, I assume, have a lessened hobbling effect. Another explanation for the higher metabolic rates and caloric intake in the arctic comes from Webster (1952, p. 134), who views them as compensation for the considerable heat lost in warming and humidifying inspired air to body temperature.

In addition to calorie increase as a subsidiary means of adjusting to the cold, experiments show (Swift and French, 1954, p. 221) that high-fat diets are superior in maintaining tissue temperature to high carbohydrate and especially high protein diets. Heinbecker (1928, p. 474 ff.) speaks of the Eskimos' remarkable capacity to oxidize the plentiful fats in their diet. In explaining the superiority of high fat diets, Swift and French (idem) suggest that it is more concerned with reducing heat dissipation than increasing heat production, and ". . . may involve a temporary deposition of dietary fat in the subdermal tissues following a high-fat meal." No proper measure has been made of the subcutaneous fat covering of people like the Eskimo, but it is generally assured to be thicker than in temperate climate people. If this is actually true, the facts that subcutaneous fat has insulating qualities ⅓ to ½ better than muscle (Edholm, 1954, p. 210), and that 1 cm of fat has a 1 clo insulating rating (Bazett, 1949, p. 145), should give Eskimos a clear adaptative advantage.

Besides these physiological alterations contributing to withstanding the cold, there are significant morphological changes as well. While the causal relationship between the body mass/body surface ratio and climate has not been demonstrated, the correlation between the two cannot be denied for man. Roberts (1953, p. 542) found a correlation of -0.60 between mean body weights in 116 native groups, including 11 from the arctic, and mean annual temperatures of their locations. The range of means ran from about 42 to 72 kg, and there was an average increase of .305 kg for 1°F. decrease. Corroboration of Roberts' work comes from R. W. Newman and Munro's (1955, p. 10) determination of a correlation of -0.611 betwen body weight and estimated skin surface in 15,000 U.S. Army inductees with the mean January temperature of their state of birth. Here the regression is .109 kg increase with 1°F. decrease. Then R. W. Newman (1955) found high negative correlations in U.S. troops between (1) fat free or lean body weights and mean January temperatures of their birth areas, and (2) subcutaneous fat and mean July temperatures of their birth areas. These findings suggest that in colder climates the proportion of metabolically active tissue to inert tissue is higher than in warm climates.

Additional confirmation comes from Schreider's (1951) demonstration that mean body weight/body surface ratios run about 38 in colder climates, while in hot climates minimum means of 30 kg/m² are attained. Since he used the Du Bois height-weight formula which tends to overestimate body surface in cold climate peoples and to underestimate it in hot climate peoples, his mean ranges may actually be slightly extended over those stated. The body size trends in these several studies support the view that Bergmann's rule is operative in man, and in civilized man at that.

Allen's rule has not had such extensive testing in man. There is some evidence in New World aborigines (Newman, 1953, maps 2 and 3) and in the Old World (Lundman, 1952, K. 3) that cold climate peoples have relatively longer trunks and shorter legs than others. R. W. Newman's (1953) clothing study on 2,450 Koreans clearly demonstrates their longer trunks and shorter legs as compared with American Whites. Little or no shortening of the arms, however, is apparent in cold climate peoples, whose arm/stature ratios run about one index unit lower than Europeans. Whereas the feet of cold climate peoples are said to be small (Coon, 1954, p. 292), Rodahl's (1952, p. 424) skin surface study on Eskimos shows their hands to be relatively large. Perhaps the arms and hands of arctic peoples serve, when needed, as a means of heat dissipation, as do the flippers of seals and penguins (Scholander, 1955, p. 19 and 24).

The so-called "climatic engineering" of the Mongoloid face—involving reduction of brow-ridges with their cold-vulnerable sinuses, orbital and malar adjustments to permit more fat padding, and reduction of nasal saliency (Coon, Garn, and Birdsell, 1950, pp. 67–71)—is a model of morphological logic, but needs testing. Some data on the superior fat padding of the eye-ball in Chinese is provided by Wen (1934). The reduced beard and beard growth of Mongoloid peoples (Coon, Garn, and Birdsell, 1950, p. 72) may also be a cold weather adaptation since in cold the exhaled breath will freeze in beards, along with the skin underneath.

All these data should make it clear why anthropologists have paid serious attention to the application of the ecological rules to man. If anything, these rules seem to be more closely operative in man than in other species of homeotherms (see Newman, M. T., 1953, pp. 312–313). Basic experiments on human subjects are proceeding apace, with the view of tying in morphology to physiology, and the two to the environmental setting. Although within the total environment, anthropologists have over-emphasized temperature and humidity, they are well aware that other less readily measurable factors such as nutrition and workload may be equally significant. In researches upon human adaptation, perhaps the most pressing need is some means of differentiating between the short-term non-genic alterations and the long-term phylogenetic changes. As Scholander infers, this means more and better controlled studies on native peoples.

REFERENCES

BAZETT, H. C. 1949. The regulation of body temperatures, pp. 109–192, in Newburgh, L. H.., Ed., Physiology of Heat Regulation and the Science of Clothing. W. B. Saunders, Philadelphia.

BOLLERUD, J., J. EDWARDS and R. A. BLAKELY. 1950. Survey of the basal metabolism of Eskimos. Project Report (No. 21–01–020) from the Arctic Aeromedical Laboratory.

BROWN, G. H., and J. PAGE. 1952. The effect of chronic exposure to cold on temperature and blood flow of the hand. Jour. of Applied Physiol., 5 (5): 221–227.

BROWN, M. G., G. S. BIRD, L. M. BOAG, D. J. DELAHAYE, J. E. GREEN, J. D. HATCHER, and J. PAGE. 1954. Blood volume and basal metabolic rate of Eskimos. Metabolism, 3 (3): 247–254.

COFFEY, M. F. 1955. A comparative study of young Eskimo and Indian males with acclimatized White males. In Ferrer, M. I., ed., Cold Injury. Transactions of the 3rd Conference February 22, 23, 24, 25, 1954. Fort Churchill, Manitoba, Canada. 226 pp. Josiah Macy Jr. Foundation, New York.

COON, C. S. 1954. Climate and race, in Shapely, H., ed., Climatic Change. Harvard University Press.

———, S. M. GARN and J. B. BIRDSELL. 1950. Races: A Study of the Problems of Race Formation in Man. C. C. Thomas, Springfield.

EDHOLM, O. G. 1954. Physiological effects of cold environments on man, pp. 207–212, in Cloudley-Thompson, J. L., ed., Biology of Deserts. Institute of Biology, Tavistock Houses, London.

GRAY, E. LEB., F. C. CONSOLAZIO and R. M. KARK. 1947. Nutritional requirements for men at work. QMC-W11-009-gm-70250, Report No. 3.

HEIBECKER, P. 1928. Studies on the metabolism of Eskimos. Journal of Biological Chemistry, **80** (2).

LUNDMAN, B. 1952. Umriss der Dassendunde des Mensch in Geschichtlicker Zeit. Ejnar Munksgaard, Copenhagen.

MEEHAN, J. P. 1955. Individual and racial variations in a vascular response to a cold stimulus. Military Medicine, **116** (5): 330–334.

NEWMAN, M. T. 1953. The application of ecological rules to the racial anthropology of the aboriginal New World. American Anthropologist, **55** (3): 311–327.

NEWMAN, R. W. 1953. Clothing for Korean personnel. Report No. 206, Environmental Protection Branch, OQMG.

———. 1955. The relation of climate and body fat in young American males. Am. J. Phys. Anthrop., **13** (2), abst.

———, and E. H. MUNRO. 1955. The relation of climate and body size in U.S. males, Am. J. Phys. Anthrop., H. S., **13** (1): 1–18.

ROBERTS, D. F. 1952a. Basal metabolism, race and climate. Jour. Royal Anthrop. Inst., **32** (2): 169–183.

———. 1952b. An ecological approach to physical anthropology: environmental temperature and physiological features. Acts du IV Cong. Internat. de Sci. Anthrop. et Ethnol., Vienna, **1:** 145–148.

———. 1953. Body weight, race and climate. Am. J. Phys. Anthrop., N. S., **11** (4): 533–558.

RODAHL, K. 1952. The body surface area of Eskimo as determined by the linear and the height-weight formulas. Am. J. Phys. Anthrop., N. S., **10** (4): 419–426.

SARGENT, F. 1953. Weather stress. A bioclimatological hypothesis. Ann. Human Ecology, **3,** (1): 1–13.

SCHOLANDER, P. F. 1955. Evolution of climatic adaptation in homeotherms. Evolution, **9** (1): 15–26.

SCHREIDER, E. 1951. Anatomical factors of body-heat regulation. Nature, **167** (4255): 823–824.

SPEALMAN, C. R. 1949. Physiologic adjustments to cold, pp. 232–239, in Newburgh, L. H., ed., Physiology of Heat Regulation and the Science of Clothing. W. B. Saunders Co., Phila.

STEFANSSON, V. 1955. Clothes made the Eskimo. Nat. Hist., **64** (1): 32–41.

SWIFT, R. W., and C. E. FRENCH. 1954. Energy Metabolism and Nutrition. Scarecrow Press, Washington, D.C.

WEBSTER, A. P. 1952. Caloric requirements of man in cold climates: theoretical consideration. J. Applied Physiol., **5** (3): 134–142.

WEN, I. C. 1934. The development of the upper eyelid of the Chinese with special reference to the Mongolic fold. Chinese Med. J., **48:** 1216–1227.

WEYER, E. M. 1932. The Eskimos. Yale University Press.

YOSHIMURA, H., and T. IIDA. 1952. Studies on the reactivity of skin vessels to extreme cold. Part II. Factors governing the individual difference of the reactivity or the resistance against frost-bite. The Japanese Jour. of Physiol., **2** (3): 177–185.

Geographical Character Gradients and Climatic Adaptation

ERNST MAYR

The recent discussion by Scholander (1955) of the so-called "ecological rules" indicates a number of misunderstandings. It might be worthwhile to scrutinize the meaning and validity of these rules in some detail, since some of these misunderstandings seem to be based on widespread misconceptions, to judge from discussions with various biologists. Before the discussion a word should be said on terminology. There is no good, generally accepted collective term available for such rules as Bergmann's rule, Allen's rule, etc. The terms "climatic rules" and "ecological rules" have been used, both being rather broader than justified by the phenomena which they describe. The term ecogeographical rules, although by no means ideal, will be used in the subsequent discussions, being less inclusive than the term ecological rules.

What do the ecogeographical rules signify?—They are purely empirical generalizations describing parallelisms between morphological variation and physiographic features. For instance, Bergmann's rule states that "Races of warm blooded vertebrates from cooler climates tend to be larger than races of the same species from warmer climates." As Rensch has emphasized consistently, this is a purely empirical finding which can be proven or disproven no matter to what physiological theory one might ascribe this size trend. The validity of an ecological rule then does not depend on the validity of the physiological interpretation, but merely on the reliability of the empirical finding. To prove that an ecological rule is invalid one would have to prove that it is not valid in the majority of relevant cases. For instance, one would have to prove that races of warm blooded vertebrates in cooler climates do not tend to be of larger average size than races in warmer climates.

This clear separation between empirical findings and interpretation has not always been observed by some of the early authors (e.g., Bergmann) or in some

187

of the textbooks. It is therefore necessary to emphasize once more that two independent steps are involved: first, the establishment of a regularity (and these regularities may be very different in mammals, fishes, or insects) and second, the physiological interpretation given to this regularity.

Laws or rules?

A few authors, mostly those without first-hand experience with the phenomenon, have assumed that these regularities are "laws" that are invariably true. However, right from the beginning authors like Gloger (1833) and Bergmann (1849) have stressed that these rules have only statistical validity. They are true for "most" species or "many" races. Rensch in particular has emphasized this point and has devoted a series of papers (Rensch, 1936, 1938, 1939, 1940, 1948) to a determination of the percentage of cases in which the stated regularities have validity. These rules work only "other things being equal." The principal object of Rensch's investigation was not so much to prove the climatic rules, but rather to determine the degree of their validity for different kinds of animals in different regions.

Do the ecogeographical rules apply to species as well as to races?

Bergmann and other early authors applied these rules equally to species and races, but it must be admitted that most of their "species" are considered geographic races by modern authors. It is true that these rules are sometimes valid on the species level, and Hesse, Allee, and Schmidt (1951) have listed a number of such cases. Yet nearly all contemporary supporters of the ecogeographical rules have pointed out carefully that they have validity only for populations within species. The general viewpoint concerning the limits in the application of the ecogeographical rules has been stated by Mayr (1954) as follows: "It has long been known that the validity of the so-called ecological rules, so far as it exists at all, is restricted to intraspecific variation. . . . A more northerly species is by no means always larger than its nearest more southern relative." The fact that "cold climates do not produce a fauna tending towards large-sized globular forms with small protruding parts" (Scholander, 1955) is not in the least in conflict with Bergmann's or Allen's rule.

The physiological interpretation of the ecogeographical rules

A number of recent authors have stressed that there is a difference, at least in degree if not in kind, between the adaptation of a population to local conditions and the adaptation of a new kind of animals or plants to a novel ecological niche. Adaptation to local conditions has been referred to as ecotypic adaptation (Turesson) or existential adaptation (Goldschmidt). It is quite evident that the ecogeographical rules formulate empirical findings concerning the local type of adaptation. They have never been interpreted by evolutionists as playing "a detectable role in the phylogenetic engineering of warm-blooded animals for hot and cold climates" (Scholander). Nor have evolutionists contended that the ecological rules "reflect phylogenetic pathways of heat conserving adaptation." They are an ecotypic, not a phylogenetic phenomenon.

The physiological interpretation will be different on the whole for each eco-geographical rule, depending on whether it concerns size, proportions or coloration, warm-blooded or cold-blooded animals. All interpretations, however, have in common the endeavor to establish a correlation between a character gradient and a gradient in the environment. Rensch's (1939) investigation of the increase in size in *Parus montanus* in correlation with temperature gradients may be selected as an example of this method. A first attempt to correlate the size gradient within the European range of this species with the annual isotherms was unsuccessful. However, when the isotherms of the coldest month were taken, which in Europe is January, they were found to parallel closely the size cline in *P. montanus*. Similarly ichthyologists have established for fishes a correlation between decreasing water temperatures and a tendency toward an increase in certain meristic elements. A close parallelism between character gradients and environmental gradients, if found to have a genetic basis, is interpreted with good reason as being the result of natural selection.

If we take specifically the case of Bergmann's rule, it is entirely consistent with the known facts to assume that the parallelism between temperature gradient and size gradient is correlated with the change in the body surface–volume ratio which is the consequence of a simple law of geometry. The explanation then that the increase of size to the north serves heat conservation and that the decrease of size to the south facilitates heat dissipation is entirely consistent with all the known facts. The hypothesis then that Bergmann's rule is the result of natural selection in favor of an optimal surface to volume ratio is a legitimate one. It is axiomatic in scientific methodology that a hypothesis is considered valid until it has either been disproven or until a better one has been proposed.

The role of exceptions

The need for heat conservation is only one of many possible selection pressures affecting absolute or relative body size. It is to be expected that under certain conditions other factors may affect geographic variation in size more strongly than the need for heat conservation. For instance, if a small mammal lives in burrows during the winter, selection pressure for heat conservation will be greatly lessened and there may be no size increase toward the north. Indeed since an increase in size results in an increased demand for food, size may actually decrease to the north where food is the limiting factor. This was indeed demonstrated by Stein (1951) for the European mole (*Talpa europaea*). The phenotype of an animal is the result of a compromise between many conflicting selection pressures. Every exception to the ecogeographical rules is an indication of such a conflict. These rules are now sufficiently firmly established so that the emphasis of research should be shifted to a study of the exceptions. Snow's (1954) study of trends of geographic variation in palearctic titmice illuminates the reason for some exceptions in this family. Relative bill size, for instance, decreases rapidly northward in these titmice until a minimum size is reached. It appears that the size and the amount of food taken by these birds precludes a further reduction in bill size. This minimum size then is the ultimate compromise of conflicting selection pressures. Exceptions to the rules in other groups of animals should be analyzed in a similar manner.

Length of bird wing and Bergmann's rule

In all studies on the validity of Bergmann's rule for birds the length of the wing is used as an indication of body size. Scholander criticizes the use of this measurement by Rensch because "there are a few short finger bones in this measurement, the rest is just wing feathers. These measurements correlate with flight, but bear no useful thermal significance." He does not appear to realize that Rensch has nowhere treated the wing as a heat radiating body part. The wing is used as an indication of general body size, in the absence of a better measure, since "wing load" necessitates a fairly close correlation between wing length and body weight, and the latter is an indication of general size (Amadon, 1943). It is unknown and badly in need of investigation how close this correlation is. A number of studies which have revealed exceptions are already available. It has been pointed out by several authors, including Rensch himself, that a new variable is introduced if northerly populations of an otherwise sedentary species are migratory. In most cases this leads to an attenuation and considerable lengthening of the wing of the northern population. The better a flyer the particular species is, however, the less effect the annual migration will have on wing shape and wing size, and the fact that the populations will spend both summer and winter in a warm climate will become the dominating factor. In *Dicrurus leucophaeus,* for instance, wing length in the highly migratory race of North China (*leucogenis*) (adult males av. 142.8) is no greater than in the more or less sedentary race of South China (*salangensis*) (adult males av. 143.0) (Mayr and Vaurie, 1948).

Special uses of the wing in courtship may set up a new selection pressure which entirely upsets the need for a "normal" wing load. Adult males of the Regent Bower Bird (*Sericulus chrysocephalus*) have a wing which averages 5 mm and a tail which averages 15 mm shorter than that of immature males (Mayr and Jennings, 1952). In the African weaver, *Euplectes hordaceus,* likewise the wing is much shorter in the nuptial plumage (76.3) than in the eclipse plumage (82.7) (Verheyen, 1953).

These findings again are evidence of the multiplicity of selection pressures to which an organ is exposed and of which the final phenotype is a compromise.

Does the existence of other heat conserving mechanisms invalidate the ecogeographical rules?

Scholander's criticism of the physiological interpretation of Bergmann's and Allen's rules is based on the fact that other heat conserving mechanisms, such as an increased density of fur or plumage, fat deposits, or vascular mechanisms, are immeasurably more efficient than the slight shifts in surface to volume ratios demonstrated by the ecological rules. The facts of physiological adaptation to life in a cold climate discovered by Irving, Scholander, and other recent investigators are of the greatest interest and can be considered as unequivocally established. Yet they do not permit the conclusions drawn by Scholander.

The philosophy of "all or none" solutions is exceedingly widespread not only in science but in all human affairs. Unfortunately no philosophy could be worse suited for evolutionary studies. All or none solutions are based on typological thinking and alien to the facts of variation. Multiple solutions for biological needs are the general rule in evolution. An animal is protected against a predator not by speed *or* an armor *or* by cryptic coloration *or* poison *or* bad taste *or* by hiding *or* by nocturnal habits, but always by a combination of several of these. Simple answers are nearly always misleading. It took ornithologists a long time before they got away from such shortsighted single aspect statements as "birds start breeding in spring because of increasing day length," or "birds migrate in fall because of a drop in temperature." Does the fact that a thicker fur or denser plumage increases protection against the cold completely eliminate any selective advantage of an improved body surface to volume ratio? Surely not!

The true meaning of geographical character gradients

The regularities in the geographic variation of general size and of proportions are a simple matter of fact, as pointed out above. Vaurie, for instance, showed that all species of drongos show variation of wing length correlated with latitude except those restricted to a single island or those that live in a single restricted climatic zone (Mayr and Vaurie, 1948). Adherence to the ecological rules is, however, usually not found in the case of isolated populations (Mayr, 1942), a fact which is an important clue in the solution of this problem. It is becoming increasingly evident that such ecotypic adaptations as manifest themselves in the ecological rules are the means of a local population for reaching a balance between (1) the need for adaptedness to local conditions and (2) partaking at the same time of the heritage of the species as a whole, which includes all physiological mechanisms that are species specific. A species is a single large Mendelian population pervaded in all directions by gene flow. It is this cohesive force of gene flow which is primarily responsible for the validity of the climatic rules. It gives physiological unity to a species but increases the necessity for local adjustments to local conditions. That these local adjustments, reflected in the ecological rules, have only limited effectiveness is evident from the fact that even the species which obey the rules find northern and southern limits to their geographic range.

The sensitivity of this process of local adaptation is evidence of the universality of natural selection and this is the crucial point of the entire question. Even genes with a selective advantage of only a fraction of one percent tend to accumulate in populations, as shown by R. A. Fisher (1930) and others. Natural selection is particularly efficient during catastrophes and other periods of great environmental stress. Let us look at a model of the effect of such a catastrophe on the survival of two alternate mechanisms adding to the survival value. Let us assume that in a population of mammals, which is at rare intervals exposed to very severe winter conditions, there are 10 individuals with a superior vascular heat conserving mechanism and also 10 with a greatly reduced tail length among the total population of 1,000 individuals. After a severe winter the 10 individuals with the superior vascular mechanism might survive as well as two with the greatly reduced tail length. After an even more severe winter only one individual might survive which happens to have the combination of the superior vascular mechanism and the reduced length of tail. Students of natural selection know that such a model is quite realistic and that genes accumulate in a population, independently of each other, in accordance with the contribution they make to fitness. Problems of selection are simply statistical problems and the prevailing phenotype of a population will be the result of a balance between opposing selection pressures. This is the meaning of the ecogeographical rules, nothing more and nothing less.

It appears to me that there is no contradiction between Scholander's interesting findings on the heat preserving adaptations of arctic species of birds and mammals, and rules like Bergmann's and Allen's rules, which deal with adaptation of intraspecific populations to local conditions. Either set of factors does not disprove the other.

I greatly appreciate the kindness of Prof. P. F. Scholander, Oslo, for criticizing an earlier draft of these comments. This has greatly helped in stating more concisely existing differences in interpretation. Prof. B. Rensch, Münster, likewise had the kindness to read these comments in manuscript.

REFERENCES

AMADON, D. 1943. Bird weights as an aid in taxonomy. Wilson Bull., **55**: 164–177.
HESSE, R., W. C. ALLEE and K. P. SCHMIDT. 1951. Ecological Animal Geography. J. Wiley and Sons. New York. xiii + 715.
MAYR, E. 1942. Systematics and the Origin of Species. Columbia Univ. Press, New York. xiv + 344.
———. 1954. Change of genetic environment and evolution, in Huxley et al., Evolution as a Process. Unwin Brothers, Woking and London. pp. 157–180.

————, and K. JENNINGS. 1952. Geographic variation and plumages in Australian bowerbirds (Ptilonorhynchidae). Amer. Mus. Novit. no. 1602, pp. 1–18.

————, and C. VAURIE. 1948. Evolution in the family Dicruridae (birds). *Evolution*, **2:** 238–265.

RENSCH, B. 1936. Studien über klimatische Parallelität der Merkmalsausprägung bei Vögeln und Säugern. Arch. f. Naturgesch., N.F., **5:** 317–363.

————. 1938. Bestehen die Regeln klimatischer Parallelität bei der Merkmalsausprägung von homöothermen Tieren zu Recht? Ibid., **7:** 364–389.

————. 1939. Klimatische Auslese von Grössenvarianten. Ibid., **8:** 89–129.

————. 1940. Die ganzheitliche Auswirkung der Grössenauslese am Vogelskelett. Journ. f. Orn., **88:** 373–388.

————. 1948. Organproportionen und Körpergrösse bei Vögeln und Säugetieren. Zool. Jb. (Physiol.), **61:** 337–450.

SCHOLANDER, P. F. 1955. Evolution of climatic adaptation in homeotherms. *Evolution*, **9:** 15–26.

SNOW, D. W. 1954. Trends in geographical variation in Palaearctic members of the genus Parus. *Evolution*, **8:** 19–28.

STEIN, G. H. W. 1951. Populationsanalytische Untersuchungen am europäischen Maulwurf. II. Über zeitliche Grössenschwankungen. Zool. Jahrb. Abt. f. Syst. Ökol. und Geog. der Tiere, **79:** 567–590.

VERHEYEN, R. 1953. Exploration du Parc National de l'Upemba. Mission G. F. DeWitte.—Oiseaux. Inst. des Parcs Nat. du Congo Belge, **19:** 1–687.

Climatic Rules

P. F. SCHOLANDER

In reply to the interesting comments by Newman and Mayr (*Evolution* 1956) on my article "Evolution of Climatic Adaptation in Homeotherms" (*Evolution* 1955) I shall restate the issue I raised, namely: What is the evidence that the slight biometrical trends expressed in Bergmann's and Allen's rules represent a physiological adaptation to temperature?

Clearly, the first prerequisite must be to establish that the observed size cline is associated with a falling environmental temperature going north. Among Eskimos, Lapps and other northern people the thermal environment which is most relevant to our problem exists inside the clothing, and so far this has not been measured. The indications are that it is as tropical as ours. The argument that Eskimos frequently suffer loss of toes from frostbite seems to be controversial; it was termed utter nonsense by a physician stationed among the Thule Eskimos in North Greenland, and statements to the same effect were made to me by people who have intimate knowledge of the Lapps and Chukchees. Whether, as Newman suggests, the primeval Eskimos went through "long-term experimentation" and considerable freezing before they learned to make clothing is something else again.

I pointed out that the biometrical clines expressed in Bergmann's and Allen's rules are based on measurements which are irrelevant or at best uninterpretable as a means for appraising the thermal adjustment of the animal. Whether or not the subspecific, generally minute and erratic size trends have anything to do with heat conservation and thermo adaptation cannot therefore be determined from such data. But the whole thesis is badly shaken, not to say demolished, by the flagrant lack of general validity of the rules which is apparent when we look for similar trends on a species level. Here neither the biometry of the rules nor their fancied physiological interpretation hold. It should also sound a warning that similar size clines are found in many cold-blooded animals where thermal implications clearly are out of the question.

Mayr, banking on geometry and logics, nevertheless considers the thermo adaptive implications of the rules so firmly established that the emphasis of research should rather be shifted to an analysis of the exceptions. As an example of such an analysis, i.e., of an exception to an unproven thesis, is cited among others the case of the titmouse (Snow, *Evolution* 1954). In several species of European titmice the length of the beak, divided by that of the wing feathers, decreases going northward. This, of course, harmonizes with Allen's rule, and is constructed as a straightforward effect of cold on the beak. In two species, however, it is remarkable that beyond a certain northern limit the bill shrinks no farther. Since every exception to the ecogeographical rules is considered to be an indication of a selection conflict, what is the conflicting selection pressure that has checked the shrinking of the titmouse's bill? Clearly if the cold had shrunk the beak away, eating would be difficult, and so the conflicting pressure must lie in the eating process. This inference is indeed supported by unpublished quantitative observations to the effect that not only the size of food particles but also the amount taken by these birds is such that eating would be seriously hampered if the bill should shrink any more. I take it that the result of these fanciful constructions must be a scrawny titmouse striving to attain a size to fit the climate, but frustrated by a cold beak not much good to eat with.

The titmouse shows another equally remarkable deviation from Allen's rule: Its tail feathers, oblivious to the cold, grow longer going north. This must also be an adaptation, according to Mayr, because "a close parallelism between character gradients and environmental gradients, if found to have a genetic basis, is interpreted with good reason as being the result of natural selection." One may well ask: Selection of a long tail for what? I shall abstain from joining a free-for-all on the question of how the titmouse got its tail.

Mayr suggests that exceptions to the rules in other groups of animals should be analyzed in a similar way, so let us consider the American otter. This animal defies Bergmann's rule by getting smaller going north. What is the selection pressure that shrank the northern otter? I would like to suggest that the conflicting pressure may be traced to the squeeze of the ice-hole. Whenever the ice-hole tends to freeze shut in the winter the otter cannot pass through it without being subjected to a certain degree of "selection squeeze," and the fact that today this pressure may be so slight as to be unmeasurable serves only to prove the great delicacy of the selection process, or if this argument is not adequate we need only invoke the Pleistocene, when the otters must certainly have undergone a "long-term experimentation" and considerable squeezing while they were learning how to make proper holes. Now, according to Mayr, "it is axiomatic in scientific methodology that a hypothesis is considered valid until it has either been disproven or until a better one has been proposed." So I take it this hypothesis must for the present be respected.

It is unnecessary to point out my admiration in general for the great modern synthesis which the science of evolution represents, but I may venture to observe that some examples of adaptive mechanisms are being paraded where the physiological interpretations are taken much too lightly. I appreciate very much that I have been given the opportunity to enter the lions' den and confront morphologically oriented evolutionists with some physiological aspects of a subject of interest to both.

Ecological Rules, Body-Heat Regulation, and Human Evolution

EUGENE SCHREIDER

During the last ten years ecological rules related to body-heat regulation have been discussed by many authors.* It seems to me that their points of view can be summarized as follows:

Supporters of classical rules, named after Bergmann (1847) and Allen (1877), believe that variations in size and body-build of a homeotherm species, observed in different parts of its geographical range, must be considered as evolutionary adaptations to thermal environment. Zoologists are mostly concerned with size, while anthropologists usually put the stress on body-build.

An opposite view is held by some physiologists in whose opinion the actual existence of geographical gradients of this kind is doubtful, as there are many exceptions to the rule. Be that as it may, such gradients could not be explained by adaptive changes because the adaptation to thermal environment is achieved by physiological, rather than by anatomical means.

A third point of view has been expressed by some authors who do not seem to be generally concerned with ecological rules, but who emphatically deny their applicability to human species. In their opinion, man modifies his natural surroundings so efficiently that he escapes the pressure of climatic factors.

In my own opinion, these points of view should be revised critically, but sympathetically, as, in spite of conflicting conclusions, the evidence quoted in support of them is generally good.

---

* Among the recent authors, entirely or partly favorable to ecological rules, the following should be quoted: Baker (1960), Bodenheimer (1957), Coon et al. (1950), Coon (1955), Garn (1958), Mayr (1956), Newman (1953), Rensch (1959), Salt (1952), and Snow (1954, 1958); the "rules" have been criticized mostly by Hensel (1959), Scholander, (1955, 1956), Irving (1957), and Wilber (1957). A "synthetic" view, which is not inconsistent with the present writer's opinion, has been expressed by Hamilton (1961).

The efficiency of artificial microclimates

Although the idea that man can modify his environment at will is largely correct, it leads to faulty interpretations if it is forgotten that far-reaching changes continue to take place even in our time, without the demands of the human organism being taken into account.

Regarding protection against extremes of temperature, the situation varies considerably according to the technique standards used, the materials available, and local customs. Wherever social distinctions are marked, it also differs according to economic resources. Even in modern houses, heating, for economic reasons, may be highly inadequate.

Tradition and routine may also impede changes desirable from the physiological point of view. The average temperature in most houses in the British Isles is markedly lower than in American dwellings. From the physiological viewpoint it is insufficient, so insufficient, in fact, that some doctors are of the opinion that in certain conditions it is responsible for perinatal mortality: "prevention which is of paramount importance because of high mortality, can be achieved only by safeguarding against a fall of room temperature" (Mann and Elliot, 1957).

The American microclimate is more satisfactory probably because the harder winter demands stricter precautions being taken. Negligence is more liable to occur in countries whose winter is reputedly mild. This explains why chilblains are more common in France and Italy than in Russia, Sweden, or Canada.

Improvements are possible only if knowledge and technical means permit. Numbers of Arctic populations have been unable to solve the problem of heating. The portable tent used by certain Siberian autochtons provided no effective protection against low temperatures (Bogoraz, 1901, 1904–1909). A similar observation has been made about certain Canadian aboriginal tribes (Stefansson, 1943). The Eskimo igloo, with its "tropical" heat, should not be too exclusively singled out for quotation. The igloo is of relatively recent invention, and is not the only dwelling known to the Eskimos. In certain Eskimo huts, it may be cold (Birket-Smith, 1937).

Man, however, even with inferior material resources, but with a knowledge of fire going back to time immemorial, is capable of protecting himself with varying success against the cold. On the other hand, even with advanced techniques, he is generally defenseless against excesses of heat. Air conditioning is an extremely rare privilege, and the thermal environment in which, for instance, farm work is done, cannot be modified at will.

In damp tropical countries, as well as in deserts, the heat puts the organism to a severe test. Shade does not necessarily offer protection. In dry regions in Soviet Asia, the temperature in summer may reach 40°C. inside the homes. In some regions of the Sahara, the heat is so hard to bear, even at night, that, for part of the year, the inhabitants of certain towns sleep on terraces, unless they leave their permanent dwellings for reed huts (Rochefort, 1957).

It is true that in certain hot and arid regions the nights, at least in winter, are very cold. It has sometimes even been thought that it is the cold, rather than the heat, to which the inhabitants must have adapted themselves. Now, whatever the level of civilization, man has to work in order to live, and his work is generally done before nightfall: *the daytime environment counts above all,* for this is the environment in which his active life is lived, with the main expenditure of energy and the highest calories production (Schreider, 1962).

In the lower latitudes, the daytime environment, unless moderated by altitude or other local peculiarities, is characterized by the intense heat which man, impelled by economic needs, cannot escape. However ingenious he may be, he cannot entirely withdraw from the climatic environment, particularly the heat. It is therefore impossible to dismiss the problem of selective pressure exercised by the thermal environment.

Human ecological gradients

Let us now study the question whether gradients exist in man. A certain regularity in the geographical distribution of human characters was observed by the early naturalists. They noted, for example, that the inhabitants of cold mountainous regions are short but compact, whereas those of the neighboring lowlands with a damp, warm climate are more slender in form (Orbigny, 1839). Some authors judged it possible to group Eskimos and Fuegians in a single "hyperborean race," by basing their argument on the fact that all of them are of short and massive build.

Other similar generalizations have been made more recently, and they are on the whole correct. However, like the earlier conclusions, they are still based on impressions, rather than upon direct evidence, and, for want of quantitative data, propose one simple gradient for a given morphological "character," such as "body-build," without taking into account that the same biological result can be obtained, as we shall see, in different anatomical ways.

I have chosen a strictly biometrical approach to the problem. The first stage was the study of ten metric characters in eleven human populations, which permitted an approximate estimation of trunk volume and surface. It then appeared that the volume/surface ratio is very similar in groups as distinct as Parisian workmen and Somali nomads. It fluctuates around 0.5 liter per square decimeter, which leads one to believe that in spite of their obvious imperfection, estimated volume and surface reflect an anatomical fact. And, despite the small variation, the ratio appeared higher in European populations than in tropical populations.

If the body weight/estimated trunk surface ratio is found, closely related figures are still obtained, the European samples, however, forming one group $(1.26-1.30 \text{ kg/dm}^2)$, and the tropical samples another $(1.09-1.24 \text{ kg/dm}^2)$ (Schreider, 1950a, 1951a). These initial observations allow the assumption that a geographical gradient exists for the body weight/body surface ratio (W/S).

In fact, it proved impossible to pursue the work along these lines, because human samples, for whom measurements are available allowing the estimation of the trunk volume and surface, are extremely rare. I therefore had to use the much greater number of samples for which each individual body height and weight was known; this allowed the calculation of the body surface, by means of a well-known formula: Surface area (cm^2) = Weight in kg$^{0.425}$ Height in cm$^{0.725}$ 71.84 (Du Bois).

Published information so far relates to a hundred or so male samples, which represent all the main subdivisions of the human species, and about twenty female samples. For all these samples, the body height, the body weight, the body surface, and the body weight/body surface ratio are known, but in a fairly large number of cases, additional measurements are available, allowing the body structure to be estimated, which is highly important.

Figures now available confirm on the whole the geographical gradient of the W/S ratio, which tends to decrease in hot countries. They reveal, however, a more complex situation than had at first been thought, for they suggest that there is either an exception to the rule, or else that there is a plurality of distinct gradients for the various races.

As regards the European leucoderm group, no complication occurs. In Europe itself the ratio which can attain 39 kg/m^2 in Germany, more than 38 in northern Ireland and Finland and 37.9 in France, falls to 37.0 in Calabria and 37.4 in Sicily. It drops still further in North Africa (37.1–36.5), to 36 among the Arabs of the Yemen, and to 35.4 in a Berber population in the Sahara. The existence of the W/S ratio gradients in the white races has been moreover confirmed in the United States (Newman and Munro, 1955).

The only important exception to the W/S ratio gradient concerns the melanoderm (black) racial group. This exception is less important than one might believe at first sight, for although it is represented by almost twenty populations, it is limited geographically to neighboring tribes all grouped in the west of Africa (partly Mali and especially Haute Volta).

Beginning with this group of tribes whose W/S ratio fluctuates between 37.2 and 37.9 kg/m^2, the figures decrease towards the north, in the direction of the Sahara (36.5–36.8), towards the Atlantic coast (35.9–36.6), as well as towards the interior of the African continent, where the average figures are in the region of 33.5–36.2. If this territorial unit of relatively high values did not exist, the conclusion might have been reached that there is one single gradient of the body weight/body surface ratio, with progressive decrease in figures from northern Europe to East Africa (32.8–36.3) and South Africa (33.9).

Several populations of Somalia, a country close to the hot desert, give averages ranging between 34 and 35. We do not know whether it is permissible to include these human groups in the Black gradient, as their anthropological status is uncertain. And we naturally have to put in a class apart the Bushmen (30.2), as well as the Congo Pygmies (31.4–31.5) who give low figures but cannot mingle with the racial groups of Black Africa.

It has not been possible to find documentary material concerning the Siberian or Central Asiatic populations. We know, however, that the inhabitants of hot Asiatic countries, whether Tonkinese or Southern Indians, give low averages, especially the latter (32.4–34.6). Low figures are also found for a small group of Autochtons in the Australian desert (35.6) and for the pygmy inhabitants of the Andaman Islands (32.4), the Philippines (31.4–31.9), and Malaya (30.91).

There is a distinct shortage of information about the aborigines of the New World. Nevertheless, the few figures available clearly suggest the existence of a gradient. The highest are found in cold climates, among the Mapuches in the Andes (39.2), the Eskimos of Greenland (38.0) and of Canada (39.1), and some distinctly lower values in Guatemala (36.9), Venezuela (35.6), and Mexico (34.9–36.4).

This undoubtedly tallies with the classical ecological rules, and provides a satisfactory biometric confirmation of them. But I have further attempted, by testing it on human populations, to verify the rule that in closely related homeotherm forms, protruding and exposed organs tend to become shorter as the average temperature of the habitat decreases (Allen, 1877). In order to carry out this verification, I found the ratio, to the body weight, of the total length of the limbs,* which, as was shown long ago in physiology, are "thermolytic" organs (Bernard, 1858, 1878). It then appeared that the limbs/weight ratio shows a definite increase in populations dwelling in hot climates (Table 1).

The collected results confirm, therefore, the generalization made over ten years ago, namely, that "in races or closely related homeotherm species, the relative value of the body surface, expressed as a ratio of the volume or the mass, increases in climates which, at least during part of the year, subject the thermolytic mechanisms to stress. The inverse tendency appears in climates which over-facilitate the elimination of heat" (Schreider, 1951a). This last sentence should, I think, be emphasized, since the idea that the heat stress alone plays a role has been erroneously ascribed to me. This, however, concerns the interpretation of the results, to which we shall have occasion to return later. For the moment, the essential fact is the existence of gradients, namely anatomical changes whose parallelism with certain aspects of the enviroment it is hard to deny.

What, one may ask, are these anatomical changes? A number of anthropologists apparently consider that there is a correlative modification of stature and body-build, somewhat short stature and thickset, stocky figures typifying Arctic peoples, whereas inhabitants of the tropical belt tend to be characterized by tall stature combined with slenderness (Coon et al., 1950; Coon, 1955). The example, popularized by a number of publications (e.g., Barnett, 1961), is given, on the one hand, by the Eskimo, with its bulky shape, and on the other, by the tall, thin Nilotic. This conception is an oversimplification of the facts, and is utterly incompatible with the anthropometric data and the two gradients brought to light by my results.

---

* Total length of limbs = [(acromion − dactylion) + symphysion height] × 2.

TABLE 1. Limb length/body weight ratios (cm/kg) for adult males (Schreider, 1957a and b and unpublished data).

	Limbs/weight ratio		Body height average
	Average	SD	
73 Parisian workers	4.88	0.47	168.8
47 Finns	4.89	0.41	169.5
80 French soldiers	4.91	0.47	166.2
50 French students	4.94	0.43	174.6
300 British soldiers*	5.00	—	170.9
113 French soldiers	5.02	0.41	168.9
504 Ukrainians*	5.08	—	167.3
120 Sicilian soldiers	5.09	0.43	169.1
100 Tonkinese	5.37	0.36	159.9
82 Otomis (Mexico)	5.51	0.49	157.6
31 Arabs (Yemen)	5.63	0.47	162.2
18 Asheraf (Somalia)	5.64	0.56	170.9
119 Nhungues (Mozamb.)	5.66	0.52	167.9
123 Darod (Somalia)	5.74	0.54	172.2
119 Rahanoween (Somalia)	5.83	0.59	169.4
51 Gobaween (Somalia)	5.90	0.51	168.4
47 Dir (Somalia)	6.01	0.49	172.9
26 Antumba (Mozambique)	6.06	0.64	164.9
87 Hawyah (Somalia)	6.21	0.51	170.0
18 Korana (S. Africa)	6.21	0.58	159.8
35 Indians (Madras)	6.61	0.71	168.4
95 Aka Pygmies (Congo)	6.98	0.67	144.1
115 Basua Pygm. (Congo)	7.03	0.77	144.3

* Calculated from published averages. All other figures calculated from individual measurements. Data concerning Finns and Madras Indians communicated by M. Pelosse (Paris) and Dr. Henrotte (Liége), respectively.

In fact, if brachymorphic Eskimos give a high W/S ratio (38–39), the Otomi of Mexico, like other Indians of the tropical regions, are also brachymorphic, but show a much lower figure (W/S ratio = 34.9; stature = 157.6), which is close to that of the Darod of Somalia, leptomorphs of tall stature (W/S ratio = 35.1; stature = 172.2), whose anatomy is rather similar to that of Nilotics. There is no *exact* parallelism between the two gradients shown by my results, and the geographical distribution of weight, stature, or body-build. This is explained by the fact that the same result, like the reduction of the W/S ratio, is obtainable by different anatomical variations, namely, the diminution of all body dimensions, as in the case of the Otomi, and, to a more marked extent, the Pygmies; or by the considerable shortening of the trunk, accompanied by lengthening of limbs, as in the case of Somalis.

The opposition of the Eskimo and the Nilotic is, therefore, in some way fallacious and even from the didactic angle, it may lead to error. There exist in tropical regions brachymorphs of small size, with a low W/S ratio and a high limbs/weight ratio. The facts are such that there appears to be a convergence for the biologically important ratios in human groups which originally did not enjoy the same evolutionary opportunities. But, before we can accept this conclusion, we must be backed by a number of guarantees of certainty.

The value of basic data

The first task is to find how much reliance can be placed in the figures which allowed the existence of the weight/surface and limbs/weight ratios to be shown. Some understandable initial reserve can be expressed on the account of the body surface having been estimated by using a formula in which weight is a factor. In connection with this, it is worth recalling that the first rough draft of a gradient was obtained in a totally different way, the trunk surface having been estimated from a set of anthropometrical measurements. The facts show that the weight/ total surface ratio gives the same results as the weight/trunk surface ratio.

By way of a check, we have also worked out, separately for the two sexes, correlations between the weight/*surface calculated by the formula* ratio, and the weight/*surface measured by integrator* ratio: these correlations amount to 0.83 for adult males, and 0.84 for females (Schreider, 1951a). There is a sufficient degree of agreement, if it is borne in mind that we have only to compare the averages.

It is true that the formula used for obtaining the total surface was established on individuals of white race, so that some correction might be necessary before applying it to other human groups. No correction appears, however, to be needed for the Eskimos (Rodahl, 1952); and for the yellow races, if one is necessary, it is not an extensive one (Necheles and Loo, 1932). The formula seems to imply a relatively important error only in the case of African and Australia black races, because it does not take into account the considerable length of limbs which characterizes the two racial groups. But if this is the case, a corrected formula could only still further accentuate the geographical gradient of the W/S ratio (Newman, 1956).

Doubt can, however, be expressed about the value or the significance of a character such as weight. The question is important, but is directly related to the biological interpretation of the gradients, and they will be studied together.

The biological meaning of gradients

In an interesting study confirming the geographical gradient of the W/S ratio in the United States, two American authors reach the conclusion that the cause of it is to be sought in the influence of the climate over food consumption, the latter being greater in regions where cold winters are experienced (Newman and Munro, 1955).

No one will question the influence of nutrition on body weight, and since this is the case, one is tempted to think that the low W/S ratio of populations living for the most part in underdeveloped countries is simply a reflection of their insufficient nutritional state. This explanation is too simple to be correct. Body weight's normal fluctuations are *loosely* correlated with calorie intake (Thomson et al., 1961). And as far as I know, I did not take into account data concerning populations stricken by famine or abnormally overnourished.

Certain samples, indeed, benefited from unusually plentiful nourishment, but they are found in tropical countries, and are military series from former colonial armies, whose average weight is greater than that of civilians of the same origin. However, their W/S ratio generally does not reach temperate climate figures. Such is the case, notably, of certain Somali samples. This is also the case of our Tonkinese, who were studied while stationed in France. Inversely, French soldiers who had, on the average, lost some kilograms during the last war, gave a W/S ratio comparable to that of the French samples studied in less exceptional circumstances. Other similar cases could be quoted.

This may well appear strange should it be forgotten that, if nutrition influences body weight, it is not the sole determining factor. The situation becomes clearer if, instead of confining oneself exclusively to weight, one takes into account a set of anthropometric data. Fortunately this is possible in a number of cases. It is then observed that, in the populations under study, the *average man* is neither skeleton-like nor obese, whatever his weight. In fact, the average weight of a population is dependent primarily on its average dimensions and its morphology, which limit ponderal fluctuations.

The short trunk and very long limbs of the Nilotics, Somalis, and Australians (Abbie, 1957, 1958), can no more be explained by a particular nutritional status than can the structure of the trunk of European populations which, out of geometrical necessity, shows excessive volume in relation to its surface (Schreider, 1950a). Moreover, direct observation of some human groups showing a low W/S ratio or a "deficient" body weight leads one to state that their nutrition is sufficient (Schreider, 1953–1955; Roberts, 1960).

One of the main arguments against the purely nutritional interpretation of the weight/surface ratio differences resides in the fact that the W/S ratio gradient, which is so clearly defined in men, is *non-existent in women,* who are nevertheless represented by about twenty populations (Schreider, 1950a, 1951a, and unpublished material). It is difficult to conceive that the men's diet should be insufficient, whereas the women of the same tribe may sometimes appear overnourished, for their averages, for both body weight and the W/S ratio, may even be above the male averages: such is the case of Andaman Islands aborigines and two populations of Somalia.*

---

* The fact of women showing no gradient comparable with that of men may be explained by the fact that body-heat regulation in females has peculiarities not found in males (Hardy and Milhorat, 1939; Hardy, Milhorat, and Du Bois, 1941; Du Bois, Ebaugh, and Hardy, 1952). Account has also to be taken of the possible influence of sexual selection, which favors corpulent women (Baker, 1960).

It is, in short, impossible to suppose, when human groups whose dimensions and body structure are fairly well known, that the differences in their average body weight are due solely, or even essentially, to the nutritional regimen. Food may be a disturbing factor likely to invert the ranking of similar averages, without, however, perturbing the whole gradient.

The problem is somewhat different for irregularities appearing as true departures from the rule. Exceptions, in the case of certain animals, had been known for some time. They are partly explained by ecological adaptation, i.e., by the behavior characterizing the species. Moreover, various physiological mechanisms may reduce the role of the body mass in relation to its thermolytic surfaces. It is, nevertheless, equally certain that the importance of the W/S ratio is not to be dismissed in homeotherms as a whole, as seems to be the opinion of physiologists who deny all relationship between anatomical dimensions and structures, on the one hand, and climatic characteristics on the other. In polar bear, whose coat, when completely soaked with water, offers no protection, the heat is probably retained by peripheral vasoconstriction. However, "the polar bear is also a very large animal with large heat capacity and has a proportionately small surface" (Scholander et al., 1950). If it is granted that the polar bear benefits from its very considerable mass compared to its relatively small surface, it is difficult to see why it should not be the case with other mammals, particularly with man.

As regards the human species, the problem is simplified for man's hairy coating does not show physiologically important variations. Moreover, we have multiple proofs of the influence exercised by the W/S ratio over his thermal balance. In heat, individuals with a high ratio perspire more freely than others, but this is useless waste, since the excessive sweat drips away and is largely lost from a physiological point of view (Schreider, 1951b). On the other hand, we observe, in 120 French soldiers, that those who stand up to heat well include a high proportion of individuals having a W/S ratio lower than 36 kg/m^2, whereas this proportion is low in those who find it difficult to stand high temperatures. The difference between the two percentages is equal to $23.2\% \pm 6.4$ and the probabilities are fewer than one in a thousand that this is due to mere chance. Furthermore, by keeping men walking at a speed of 7 km/hr for fifteen minutes on the treadmill, we find, despite the short test time, a positive correlation of 0.31 between the W/S ratio and the final temperature of the subjects.

Does the limbs/weight ratio, in its turn, play a part in thermoregulation? In heat, with an environmental temperature of 35°–36.9°C., the negative correlation between the body temperature and the ratio amounts to -0.38 ($P = 0.03$). Like the previous one, this correlation is not very marked, but there is no reason to suppose that it ought to have been more so; the anatomical conditions of thermoregulation are not the only determining cause of this. The plurality of cross-factors partly explains why, in physiology, correlations are generally low. If we neglected the low coefficients, we should run the risk of rejecting, one by one, all the factors which, taken together, ensure the physiological success of the species (Schreider, 1958, 1960).

Summary

There are serious grounds for considering geographical gradients of biometrical characters such as the weight/surface ratio or limbs/weight ratio as true ecological gradients, linked in the course of evolution to climatic conditions and thermoregulation. We must not be deterred by the existence of exceptions. The sole important exception in man known at present is limited territorially to part of West Africa. It may be due to compensating physiological mechanisms, or be considered as the beginning of a gradient peculiar to African melanoderms: our present state of knowledge allows no clear choice to be made between these two hypotheses. Finally, it has to be borne in mind that certain exceptions might well be due to relatively recent migrations.

The most plausible hypothesis is that these ecological gradients are, in fact, the product of natural selection. Nutritional habits cannot explain the gradients even if they may influence them. The wide differences revealed by the figures do not admit of this interpretation: both gradients, like the average body mass of the populations, are linked in the first place to the very marked variations in average sizes and anatomical proportions which are largely, if not exclusively, hereditary. The outstanding fact is that, in similar climatic conditions, populations differing greatly in stature, weight, or other metric characters give closely related and sometimes identical figures for the weight/surface or limbs/weight ratio. This can only be explained by a phenomenon of convergence which, in partly differing anatomical ways, but under similar environmental conditions, has led to biologically equivalent results.

REFERENCES

ABBIE, A. A. 1957. Metrical characters of a central Australian tribe. Oceania, **27:** 220–243.

———. 1958. Timing in human evolution. Proc. Linn. Soc. N. S. Wales, **83** (2): 197–213.

ALLEN, J. A. 1877. The influence of physical conditions in the genesis of species. Radical Review, **1:** 108–140.

BAKER, P. T. 1960. Climate, culture and evolution. Human Biol., **32:** 3–16.

BARNETT, A. 1961. The human species. Revised ed., Penguin Books, Harmondsworth.

BERGMANN, C. 1847. Ueber die Verhaltnisse der Wärmeökonomie des Thiere zu ihrer Grösse. Göttinger Studien, **3:** 595–708.

BERNARD, CL. 1859. Leçons sur les propriétés physiologiques et les altérations pathologiques des liquides de l'organisme. **Vol. I,** Paris.

————. 1878. Leçons sur les phénomènes de la vie communs aux animaux et aux végétaux. Paris.

BIRKET-SMITH, K. 1937. Moeurs et coutumes des Esquimaux. Payot, Paris.

BODENHEIMER, F. S. 1957. The ecology of mammals in arid zones. Recherches sur al Zone Aride. Ecologie humaine et animale, p. 100–137, UNESCO, Paris.

BOGORAZ, W. C. 1901. Otcherk materialnovo byta olennikh Tchouktchei. Sbornik Muzeia po anthropologhii i etnografii. Vol. 2, St. Petersbourg.

————. 1904–1909. The Chukchee. Memoires of the Jesup North Pacific expedition. Vol. 7, Amer. Mus. Nat. Hist., New York.

COON, C. S. 1955. Some problems of human variability and natural selection in climate and culture. Amer. Nat., **89:** 257–280.

————, S. M. GARN, and J. B. BIRDSELL. 1950. Races. Thomas, Springfield.

DU BOIS, E. F., F. G. EBAUGH, and J. D. HARDY. 1952. Basal heat production and elimination of thirteen women at temperatures from 22°C. to 35°C. J. Nutr., **48:** 257–293.

GARN, S. M. 1958. A comment on Wilber's "Origin of human types." Human Biol., **30:** 338–340.

HAMILTON, T. H. 1961. The adaptive significance of intraspecific trends of variation in wing length and body size among bird species. Evolution, **15:** 180–195.

HARDY, J. D., and A. T. MILHORAT. 1939. Basal heat loss and production in women at temperatures from 23 to 36°C. Proc. Soc. Exp. Biol. Med., **41:** 9.

————, ————, and E. F. DU BOIS. 1941. Basal metabolism and heat loss of young women at temperatures from 22 to 35°C. J. Nutr., **21:** 383.

HENSEL, H. 1959. Heat and cold. Ann. Rev. Physiol., **21:** 91–116. Palo Alto.

IRVING, L. 1957. The usefulness Scholander's views on adaptive insulation of animals. Evolution, **11:** 257–259.

MANN, T. P., and R. I. K. ELLIOTT. 1957. Neonatal cold injury. Lancet, **272:** 229–233.

MAYR, E. 1956. Geographical character gradients and climatic adaptation. Evolution, **10:** 105–108.

NECHELES, H., and T. C. LOO. 1932. Uber den Stoffwechsel der Chinesen. I. Die Körperoberflache. Chinese J. Physiol., **6:** 129.

NEWMAN, M. T. 1953. The application of ecological rules to the racial anthropology of the aboriginal New World. Amer. Anthr. (n.s.), **55:** 311–327.

————. 1956. Adaptation of man to cold climates. Evolution, **10:** 101–104.

NEWMAN, R. W., and E. H. MUNRO. 1955. The relation of climate and body size in U.S. males. Amer. J. Phys. Anthr., **13:** 1–17.

ORBIGNY (D'), A. 1839. L'homme américain. Vol. I, Paris.

RENSCH, B. 1959. Evolution above the species level. Methuen, London.

ROBERTS, D. F. 1960. Effects of race and climate on human growth as exemplified by studies on African children. *In* Tanner, J. M., Human growth, p. 59–72, Pergamon, London.

ROCHEFORT, R. 1957. Les effets du milieu sur les communautés humaines des régions arides, adaptation de ces communautés aux conditions locales de milieu. *In* Recherches sur la zone aride, VIII, Ecologie humaine et animale, p. 11–42, UNESCO, Paris.

RODAHL, K. 1952. The body surface area of Eskimos as determined by the linear and the height-weight formulas. Amer. J. Phys. Anthr., **10:** 419–426.

SALT, G. W. 1952. The relation of metabolism to climate and distribution in three finches of the genus Carpodacus. Ecol. Monogr., **22**: 122–152.

SCHOLANDER, P. F. 1955. Evolution of climatic adaptation in homeotherms. Evolution, **9**: 15–26.

———. 1956. Climatic rules. Evolution, **10**: 339–340.

———, R. HOCK, V. WALTERS, and L. IRVING. 1950. Body insulation of some arctic and tropical mammals and birds. Biol. Bull., **99**: 225–236.

SCHREIDER, E. 1950a. Les variations raciales et sexuelles du tronc humain. L'Anthropologie, **54**: 67–81, 228–261.

———. 1950b. Geographical distribution of the body-weight/body-surface ratio. Nature, **165**: 286.

———. 1951a. Race, constitution, thermolyse. Rev. Sci., **89**: 110–119.

———. 1951b. Anatomical factors of body-heat regulation. Nature, **167**: 823–825.

———. 1953. Régulation thermique et évolution humaine. Bull. Mem. Soc. Anthr. Paris, (10) 4: 138–148.

———. 1953–1955. Recherches anthropologiques sur les Otomis de la région d'Ixmiquilpan (Mexique). L'Anthropologie, **57**: 453–489; **59**: 253–296.

———. 1957a. Ecological rules and body-heat regulation in man. Nature, **179**: 915–916.

———. 1957b. Gradients écologiques régulation thermique et différénciation humaine. Biotypologie, **18**: 168–183.

———. 1958. Les régulations physiologiques. Essai de révision biométrique du problème de l'homéostasie. Biotypologie, **19**: 127–215.

———. 1960. La biométrie. Presses Univ. de France, Paris.

———. 1962. Anthropologie physiologique et variations climatiques. Natural Sci. Dept., Arid Zone Report, UNESCO, Paris (in press).

SNOW, D. W. 1954. Trends in geographical variation in Palaearctic members of the genus Parus. Evolution, **8**: 19–28.

———. 1958. Climate and geographical variation in birds. New Biology, **25**: 64–84.

STEFANSSON, F. V. 1943. The friendly arctic. Macmillan, New York.

THOMSON, A. M., W. Z. BILLEWICZ, and R. PASSMORE. 1961. The relation between calorie intake and body weight in man. Lancet, **1**: 1027–1028.

WILBER, C. G. 1957. Physiological regulations and the origin of human types. Human Biol., **29**: 329–336.

TEMPERATURE AND HUMAN REPRODUCTION

Many facets of human reproduction are dependent upon optimal temperature conditions. This paper is representative of current research in this field.

SUPPLEMENTARY READINGS

CHANG, K. S. F., S. T. CHAN, W. D. LOW, C. K. NG, Climate and Conception Rates in Hong Kong. 1963, *Human Biology,* **35:** 366–376.

Temperature
and the Production
of Spermatozoa*

T. D. GLOVER
AND D. H. YOUNG

A number of factors well known to seminologists prevent a well-planned and clear-cut experiment from being carried out on the fertility of the human male. Largely for this reason, it would seem, a lot of data on male fertility have been obtained from experiments on animals, and many aspects of function in the human testis have necessarily involved considerable speculation. The question of temperature and its effect on male fertility is outstanding in this connection, for experimental results have been obtained on only a limited number of subjects, while other data have been derived from clinical observations where adequate control measures are often difficult to ensure. However, it is well recognized that in a wide variety of mammals, including man, the testes function at a temperature which is lower than that of the abdominal viscera. Furthermore, many experiments with animals have revealed that the production of male gametes is extremely susceptible to any increase in the temperature of the testes. It would therefore seem worthwhile to review some of the experiments and examine the situation as it applies to human problems. The present paper is an attempt to do this, and it is hoped that it might provide some perspective upon which future experiments with the human subject could be based.

Experiments on the importance of testicular temperatures

Harrison listed differences between abdominal and testicular temperatures in several mammals and pointed out that it was greatest in the rat and mouse (mean

* From the Department of Veterinary Anatomy, University of Liverpool, and the Male Infertility Clinic, The Royal Infirmary, Liverpool, England.

211

values being 8.3 and 8.5°C., respectively), intermediate in the rabbit and ram
(6.2 and 7.1°C.) and least in the macaque monkey (2.0°C.). In man, this
temperature difference is between 2.0 and 2.5°C. While the delicacy of thermoregulation in the human testis has never been firmly established, it is recognized
in laboratory animals that spermatogenesis is sensitive to relatively small increases in environmental temperature.[43, 44, 50] By means of artificial cryptorchidism in guinea pigs, these workers induced testicular degeneration and established
the thermoregulatory role of the scrotum. Under these circumstances the
temperature of the testes would, according to Harrison's data, be raised only
4.0°C. above normal. These findings were confirmed by Moore and Oslund,[48, 49]
and already similar effects had been observed in dogs by Griffiths. More direct
evidence of the susceptibility of the testes to heat was provided by Fukui,[12, 13]
who found that application of heat rays to the testes of rabbits resulted in defective spermatogenesis. Moore and Chase also reported this result from the
direct application of heat to the scrotum.

Cunningham and Osborn sterilized rats with 5-min. treatments of infrared
radiation at 48°C., and Fukui[12, 13] showed that bathing the scrotum in hot water
at this temperature destroyed the spermatogenic epithelium of rabbits within 1 hr.
These results are not really surprising, since physiologic mechanisms, such as
enzyme systems, are likely to be impaired if not inhibited by temperatures approaching 50°C. By contrast, it appears from Fukui's work that at 40°C. very
long periods of exposure are needed to produce complete degeneration of
spermatogenic tissue. He gave 180–200 hr. of continuous exposure as examples.
Yet Asdell and Salisbury reported damage in the rabbit testis after only 24 hr.
of experimental cryptorchidism, but in comparing the two results, the degree of
spermatogenic interference must be taken into account. In addition, it would
seem incautious on existing evidence to regard the effects of cryptorchidism as
exclusively due to increased testicular temperature. This is particularly so in
clinical cases of the disorder, and this point was emphasized by Klein and Mayer.
Nevertheless, it is clear that spermatogenic activity is sensitive to localized increase in temperature irrespective of its mode of induction. Guieyesse-Pellisier,
for example, claimed a sterilizing effect of hot steam when applied to the scrotum
of dogs, and insulation of the scrotum in bulls and rams, where an increase in
the temperature of the testes is unquestionable, results in characteristically deficient sperm production;[16, 24, 35, 39] similar effects have also been produced by
artificial cryptorchidism in rabbits.[18] In man, subfertility is sometimes reported
in association with varicocele,[57–60, 66, 67] and it has been suggested that this
may be a reflection of a localized temperature effect.[26] Apparently hydroceles
act similarly, and it is also likely that increased temperature plays a part in
the manifestations of orchitis. In rams, for instance, Gunn et al. reported defective sperm production due to inflammation caused by blowfly maggot on the
scrotum.

The detrimental effects of increased temperature on the function of the testes are not confined to local applications, however, for exposure of animals to high environmental temperatures also induces degeneration in the quality of ejaculated semen.[4, 39] In the human being MacLeod and Hotchkiss showed, too, that by increasing body temperature experimentally the concentration of spermatozoa in ejaculated semen could be reduced. It has been claimed also that in clinical cases involving pyrexia, the normal function of the human testis can be impaired, and pneumonia and typhoid have been mentioned in this connection.[27, 42] Further evidence of the effects of pneumonia was produced by MacLeod, who also showed that chicken pox can cause a temporary disturbance of sperm production. Gunn *et al.* demonstrated seminal degeneration in rams as a result of the intraperitoneal injection of pus from acute abscesses. The purpose of this procedure was simply to produce an experimental pyrexia.

It therefore seems clear that elevation of temperature, whether local or general, affects spermatogenic tissue adversely in mammals whose testes are normally resident in a scrotum.

Possible causes of "heat degeneration"

Fukui[12, 13] suggested that damage to the testes incurred by increased temperature was due to the thermolability of certain "spermatogenous" proteins. The contention has never been confirmed or refuted in subsequent work, but it is more often held that circulatory changes are involved. Barron believed that "heat degeneration" could be due to hyperemia resulting from vasodilatation, while Moore[44] gave vascular stagnation and oxygen lack as a possible explanation. If heat is applied to an exposed testicle, a hyperemia is apparent, as would be expected, but in the rabbit a characteristic cyanosis ensues. It would seem possible that when the temperature is elevated, blood flow to the testes might be slowed because of back pressure, and an alteration in the capillary-reduction curve might follow,[36] but Cross and Silver (1962) have shown that oxygen tension in the testis of rabbits increases when the scrotum is warmed. Circulatory factors, therefore, need more study—but certainly even slight changes in the circulation of the testes can affect spermatogenesis.[30] A relationship between circulatory and temperature effects has been demonstrated by Moule and Knapp, who showed that in the ram, ligation of the external pudendal artery causes a rise in the temperature of the testes.

An entirely different suggestion as to the mechanism of "heat degeneration" was put forward by Meschaks, who showed that seminal degeneration in bulls following insulation of the scrotum is closely related to the excretion of neutral steroids in the urine; he suggested that abnormal function of the testes under these conditions might be due to excessive production of testicular and adrenal cortical hormones.

The matter remains unsettled, but as far as the effects of circulation are concerned, quantitative data on blood flow such as those recently provided by Waites and Moule[63, 64] are the most helpful contribution. With regard to hormonal effects, consideration of the problem makes painfully clear the dearth of precise information on the endocrine control of the testes. It is perhaps for this reason that results obtained on the hormonal activity of the testes in conditions of increased temperature are difficult to interpret.

Endocrine function of the testes during "heat degeneration"

Moore and Gallagher reported that in guinea pigs 8 months of artificial cryptorchidism produced no apparent effect on the secretion of testicular hormone, and Jeffries, using the cytology of the accessory organs as an indicator, made a similar claim for the rat. Nelson,[52] however, observed changes in the seminal vesicles of rats after 240 days of experimental cryptorchidism. Moore[45] also used rats as experimental animals and took the weight of the seminal vesicles as an indicator of male-sex-hormone activity. He found that confinement of the testes in the abdomen reduced hormonal activity, although, if the condition was continued, the hormone output appeared to attain some constancy after 20–80 days. Pfeiffer showed a reduction in the size of the seminal vesicles of the rat following an increase in environmental temperature, and Elfving obtained similar results in the guinea pig with direct application of heat to the scrotum.

All these experiments relied on the weight or cytology of the accessory glands as indicators of the male sex hormone. More recently Clegg[6] used levels of seminal fructose and citric acid as indicators of male sex hormone activity in artificial cryptorchidism in rats. This was based on the work of Mann *et al.,* who had shown these levels to be accurate indicators of circulating androgen. By using these technics, Clegg was able to show that reduction in androgenic activity during cryptorchidism was preceded by a sharp rise. The finding was later confirmed[7] by means of a detailed histologic examination of the interstitial cells of the testes. Earlier, increase in seminal fructose during insulation of the scrotum in rams had been demonstrated,[17] and a similar increase in excretion of 17-ketosteroids was shown by Meschaks in bulls. This apparent increase in androgenic activity during the early stages of artificial cryptorchidism doubtless explains the findings of Bouin and Ancel, Hanes and Hooker, and others that the interstitial tissue of the testes increases in amount in cryptorchidism. Nevertheless, Engberg claimed in the human being that bilateral cryptorchidism reduced androgenic activity by half, and explanation of the cause of these fluctuations must remain speculative at present.

Possible differences in effect between naturally occurring and artificial cryptorchidism should be borne in mind, however, since in the former condition the testes have generally been exposed to an abnormal environment for a longer period of time.

The response of spermatozoa to increased temperature

Since it is necessary for spermatozoa to traverse the epididymis before they are ejaculated, it is of obvious importance to consider the effects of high temperature upon the spermatozoa themselves during their prolonged sojourn in the excurrent ducts. It might be emphasized in this regard that spermatozoa spend much of their adolescence and often their entire adult life in the epididymis. This structure is permanently packed with spermatozoa, and its length in many mammals is striking, being more than 70 M. in the stallion, at least 40 M. in bulls,[14] and roughly 6 M. in man.[62]

If spermatozoa in the epididymis were unaffected by variations in temperature, the adverse effects of cryptorchidism or insulation of the scrotum would not be revealed in ejaculated semen for some time, because the epididymis would first have to be emptied of its contents (normal spermatozoa) unless defective spermatozoa could squeeze their way through the main sperm mass. This would necessitate an extra impetus to the passage of abnormal spermatozoa, and on present evidence it would seem highly unlikely. However, during insulation of the scrotum in rams, degenerated (decapitate) spermatozoa do not appear in ejaculates for about 1–2 weeks,[16, 56] so it is relevant to ask whether this delay represents the time of migration through the epididymis. If it does, the assumption must be made that decapitation occurs only in the testes. This would not be justified for rabbits, where it has been shown that artificial crpytorchidism exerts a profound effect on spermatozoa already in the epididymis.[19, 20] In this species, however, the effect appears to vary according to the level of the epididymis at which the spermatozoa are located. Decapitation of so-called mature spermatozoa from the tail of the epididymis is not seen in artificial cryptorchidism for 7–11 days while it appears to occur more rapidly in spermatozoa situated in the head of the epididymis.[21] It thus appears that the action of increased temperature on the morphology of mature spermatozoa in the tail of the epididymis is cumulative. Nevertheless Knaus showed that rabbits become infertile after only three days of experimental cryptorchidism, and thus it seems that their fertilizing capacity is lost before decapitation occurs, and that a cumulative action of increased temperature relates only to the morphology of spermatozoa. This important possibility requires further investigation, especially since Young[68] showed that in vitro, sperms from the tail of the epididymis were most susceptible to high temperatures. This would seem to be the exact converse of the situation in vivo.

Decapitate spermatozoa can be produced in rams by a short 24-hour period of insulation of the scrotum[15] where accumulation of effect could hardly occur, but in these cases, abnormal sperms are not ejaculated for some 17–24 days, which closely resembles the time of migration of spermatozoa through the epididymis.[54] It thus seems possible that in the ram also, spermatozoa in the testes and upper regions of the epididymis react more readily to the effects of elevated temperature.

The effect of low temperature on the production of spermatozoa

Harris and Harrison demonstrated, by surrounding the exposed rat testis with a mixture of ice and salt, that application of a temperature of $-5°C$. for 1 hr. caused some destruction of spermatogenic epithelium. A temperature of $-11°C$. was needed, however, to bring about severe spermatogenic damage. These workers suggested that the effects were related to induced ischemia, presumably due to vascular spasm, and the results Cross and Silver (1962) obtained following the application of ethyl chloride to the scrotum of the rabbit appear to confirm this, since marked reduction in testicular oxygen tension was recorded. But it is again important to have some knowledge of the response of spermatozoa in the epididymis to such variations in temperature, and Chang showed that the application of ice to the scrotum of rabbits caused rapid decapitation of spermatozoa in the tail of the epididymis. Excessively low temperature therefore seems to have rapid effects on sperm production, but the effects of minor decreases in temperature need to be studied more critically.

It would seem important indeed to establish more precisely the range of temperature in which testes situated in a scrotum normally function, for the peculiar vascular pattern of the mammalian testis, the cremaster muscles, and the dartos muscle indicate in themselves that efficient thermoregulation of the testes is vital.

Conclusions

From relatively limited information on temperature and testicular function in man, together with more abundant data in animals, it is justifiable to conclude that increasing the temperature of the human testis is likely to reduce fertility. But the "population explosion" detracts from attaching too much importance to this as far as the average man is concerned. Nevertheless, it might well be profitable for the subfertile male to keep his testes "cool" for perhaps they might be especially prone to damage from high temperatures. Some reports,[9] in fact, have indicated that subfertility has been overcome by bathing the scrotum in cold water or casting away close-fitting underclothes. The evidence is, however, by no means conclusive, and a controlled experiment on the subject is strongly indicated.

A vital question today is, could a human male be *temporarily* sterilized by insulation of his scrotum, or by taking frequent hot baths? The answer would seem to be in the affirmative, provided that the insulation was adequate, the baths sufficiently frequent, and the water hot enough. An interpretation of these nebulous terms must, however, await the results of further experiments, of which some are in progress and others might usefully be undertaken in the future. Little progress can be made until more quantitative data are available and since fertility trials on the human being cannot easily be planned, particularly when background knowledge is scanty, conventional semen tests could afford valuable information as an initial approach. It would be worthwhile to establish conclusively the effects of local applications of heat to the human scrotum on the motility, morphology, and metabolic activity of ejaculated spermatozoa.

An accurate appraisal of semen samples in mammals must take into account the differences in the structure of the male organs of reproduction in different species, as well as possible specificity in function.

Perhaps the testes of various mammalian species differ in their response to body temperature. The fact that Montremata, Cetacea, Proboscidea, Xenarthra, Hyracoidea and some of the Insectivora retain their testes permanently in the abdomen lends support to the possibility. This is particularly so where there appears to be no close correlation between body temperature and the position of the testes.[65]

That the length of the ductus epididymidis also differs between species might be of additional importance, since wide variations in the number of contained spermatozoa must occur. The time at which testicular abnormalities are revealed in ejaculated semen in different species might thus vary considerably. Figure 1 illustrates, as an example, differences in basic structure between the epididymis of the ram and that of man. Apart from over-all size differences, the tail of the epididymis of the ram is extensive when compared with that of the human being. Therefore, if spermatozoa are damaged in the testes or upper regions of the epididymis only (as, for instance, after short periods of temperature elevation), it seems likely that they might appear in human ejaculates sooner than they would in those of the ram. It could be, of course, that the response of human spermatozoa to elevated temperature is entirely different from that of

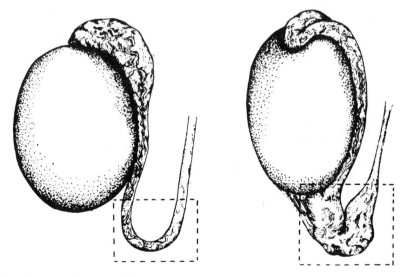

FIG. 1. Diagrams of human (*left*) and ram (*right*) testis and epididymis, illustrating form of tail of epididymis relative to rest of epididymis. (See text.)

spermatozoa in experimental animals, and also, the time of migration of spermatozoa through the human epididymis needs to be established beyond all doubt.

From this survey, we suggest that experiments on the influence of increased testicular temperature on the fertility of the human male are desirable, for it might be significant in certain cases of infertility or subfertility. In addition, application of the effects of increased testicular temperature to the problems of birth control cannot be altogether dismissed. It seems that severe heat treatment is needed in animals before the testes are damaged irreversibly, that spermatozoa in the epididymis readily respond to increased temperature by first losing their fertilizing capacity and then rapidly disintegrating. Furthermore, libido does not appear to be affected by short-term treatments. If sperm production is not completely abolished or the adverse response of spermatozoa is not total, the effects may still be of value in solving a world problem though they may be disappointing in individual cases. Certainly it seems from experiments with animals that local heat treatment of the testes is systemically innocuous, and the possibility of side effects can be disregarded. When a number of noxious agents, some of which might upset general physiologic functions, are being tested, it would seem appropriate also to investigate seriously the applicability of a well-known and apparently harmless phenomenon to the problem of population control.

REFERENCES

1. ASDELL, S. A., and SALISBURY, C. W. *Am. J. Physiol.* *132:*791, 1941.
2. BARRON, D. H. *Anat. Rec.* *55:* suppl. 6, 1933.
3. BOUIN, P., and ANCEL, P. *Arch. Zool. exp. gen.* *1:*437, 1903.
4. CASADY, R. B., MYERS, R. M., and LEGATE, J. E. *J. Dairy Sc.* *1:*14, 1953.
5. CHANG, M. C. *J. Exper. Biol.* *20:*16, 1943.
6. CLEGG, E. J. *J. Endocrinol.* *20:*210, 1960.
7. CLEGG, E. J. *J. Endocrinol.* *21:*433, 1961.
7a. CROSS, B. A., and SILVER, I. A. *J. Endocrinol.* *3:*377, 1962.
8. CUNNINGHAM, B., and OSBORN, T. I. *Endocrinology* *13:*93, 1929.
9. DAVIDSON, H. A. *Practitioner* *173:*703, 1954.
10. ELFVING, G. *Effects of the Local Application of Heat on the Physiology of Testis.* T. A. Sahalan Kirjapaino, Oy., Helsinki, 1950.
11. ENGBERG, H. *Proc. Roy. Soc. Med.* *42:*652, 1949.
12. FUKUI, N. *Jap. Med. World 3:*27, 1923.
13. FUKUI, N. *Jap. Med. World 3:*160, 1923.
14. GHETIE, E. *Anat. Anz.* *87:*369, 1939.
15. GLOVER, T. D. *J. Physiol.* *128:*22P, 1955.
16. GLOVER, T. D. *Stud. Fertil.* *7:*66, 1955.
17. GLOVER, T. D. *J. Endocrinol.* *13:*235, 1956.
18. GLOVER, T. D. *Stud. Fertil.* *10:*80, 1959.
19. GLOVER, T. D. *J. Endocrinol.* *18:*xi, 1959.

20. GLOVER, T. D. *J. Reprod. Fertil. 1:*121, 1960.
21. GLOVER, T. D. *J. Endocrinol. 23:*317, 1962.
22. GRIFFITHS, J. *J. Anat. Physiol. 27:*482, 1893.
23. GUIEYESSE-PELLISSIER, A. *Arch. d'anat. microscop. 33:*5, 1937.
24. GUNN, R. M. C., SAUNDERS, R. N., and GRANGER, W. *Bull. Counc. Sci. Industr. Res. Australia* No. 148, 1942.
25. HANES, F. M., and HOOKER, C. W., *Proc. Soc. Exper. Biol. & Med. 35:*583, 1937.
26. HANLEY, H. G. *Proc. 2nd World Cong. Fertil. & Steril.,* 1956, p. 93.
27. HANSEMANN, D. *Virchow's Arch. Path. Anat. 142:*538, 1895.
28. HARRIS, R., and HARRISON, R. G. *Stud. Fertil. 7:*23, 1955.
29. HARRISON, R. G., in *Conference on Infertility.* The Family Planning Association, London, 1948, p. 14.
30. HARRISON, R. G., and OETTLE, A. G. *Proc. Soc. Study. Fertil. 2:*6, 1950.
31. JEFFRIES, M. E. *Anat. Rec. 48:*131, 1931.
32. KLEIN, M., and MAYER, G. *Abstracts of xvii Int. Physiol. Congr.* 1947, p. 193.
33. KNAUS, H. *Arch. Gynäk. 151:*302, 1932.
34. KNUDSEN, O. *Acta Path. Microbiol. Scandinav.,* Suppl. Cl, 1954.
35. LAGERLOF, N. *Acta Path. Microbiol. Scandinav.,* Suppl. 19, 1934.
36. LUNSGAARD, C., and VAN SLYKE, D. D. *Cyanosis.* Williams & Wilkins, Baltimore, 1923.
37. MACLEOD, J. *Fertil. & Steril. 2:*523, 1951.
38. MACLEOD, J., and HOTCHKISS, R. S. *Endocrinology 28:*780, 1941.
39. McKENZIE, F. F., and BERLINER, V. *Res. Bull. Mo. agric. exper. Sta.,* No. 265, 1937.
40. MANN, T., DAVIES, D. V., and HUMPHREY, G. F. *J. Endocrinol. 6:*75, 1949.
41. MESCHAKS, P. *CIBA Symposium on Mammalian Germ Cells.* Churchill, London, 1953.
42. MILLS, R. G. *J. Exper. Zool. 30:*505, 1919.
43. MOORE, C. R. *Anat. Rec. 24:*383, 1923.
44. MOORE, C. R. *Am. J. Anat. 24:*269, 1924.
45. MOORE, C. R. *Yale J. Biol. & Med. 17:*203, 1944.
46. MOORE, C. R., and CHASE, H. D. *Anat. Rec. 26:*344, 1923.
47. MOORE, C. R., and GALLAGHER, T. F. *Am. J. Anat. 45:*39, 1930.
48. MOORE, C. R., and OSLUND, R. *Anat. Rec. 26:*343, 1923.
49. MOORE, C. R., and OSLUND, R. *Am. J. Physiol. 67:*595, 1924.
50. MOORE, C. R., and QUICK, W. J. *Am. J. Physiol. 68:*70, 1924.
51. MOULE, G. R., and KNAPP, B. *Australian J. agric. Res. 1:*456, 1950.
52. NELSON, W. O. *Cold Spring Harb. Symp. quant. Biol. 5:*123, 1937.
53. NELSON, W. O. *J. Urol. 69:*325, 1953.
54. ORTAVANT, R. C. *R. Soc. Biol. 148:*866, 1954.
55. PFEIFFER, G. A. *Endocrinology 21:*260, 1937.
56. PHILLIPS, R. W., and McKENZIE, F. F. *Res. Bull. Mo. agric. exper. Sta.* No. 217, 1934
57. RUSSELL, J. K. *Brit. M. J. 1:*1231, 1954.
58. RUSSELL, J. K. *Lancet 2:*222, 1957.
59. SCOTT, L. S. *Stud. Fertil. 10:*33, 1958.
60. SCOTT, L. S. *J. Obst. & Gynaec. Brit. Emp. 65:*904, 1958.

61. Scott, L. S., and Young, D. *Fertil. & Steril.* *13:*325, 1962.
62. Testut, L. *Traité d'Anatomie humaine,* ed. 18. Paris, 1934.
63. Waites, G. M. H., and Moule, G. R. *J. Reprod. Fertil.* *1:*223, 1960.
64. Waites, G. M. H., and Moule, G. R. *J. Reprod. Fertil.* *2:*213, 1961.
65. Wislocki, G. B. *Quart. Rev. Biol.* *8:*385, 1933.
66. Young, D. H. *Proc. Soc. Study Fertil.* *5:*27, 1953.
67. Young, D. H. *Brit. J. Urol.* *28:*426, 1956.
68. Young, W. C. *J. Exper. Zool.* *49:*459, 1927.

THE LAND
AND
DISEASE PATTERNS

*We have only now begun to realize that the land on which
we live affects our health. Gentry, Parkhurst, and Bulin
have produced one of the most provocative articles
to appear in recent years. It has been well received and
many accept its results. Others, like Grahn and
Kratchman in the next section on altitude, recognize
it as a study carefully done but disagree with some of the
results. MacMahon and Sowa (Supplementary
Readings) present a further assessment of the paper.*

SUPPLEMENTARY READINGS

LUDWIG, T. G., Recent Marine Soils and Resistance to Dental Caries. 1963, *Australian Dental Journal,* **8:** 109–113.

LUDWIG, T. G., W. B. HEALY and CAPT. F. L. LOSEE, An Association Between Dental Caries and Certain Soil Conditions in New Zealand. 1960, *Nature,* **186:** 695–696.

MACMAHON, BRIAN, and JAMES M. SOWA, Physical Damage to the Fetus. 1961, *The Milbank Memorial Fund,* **39:** 1–60.

An Epidemiological Study of Congenital Malformations in New York State*

JOHN T. GENTRY,
ELIZABETH PARKHURST,
AND GEORGE V. BULIN, JR.

Congenital malformation rates, based on information entered on birth and death certificates, are higher in certain areas of New York State than in others. Available geological data indicate a correlation between areas with high malformation rates and geographical locations containing natural materials with relatively high concentrations of radioactive elements.

The initial clue to this association was uncovered by the senior author in 1954 after his attention was directed to an "unusually large number of cleft palate patients" who were residents of a northern New York county.† Information obtained from the Office of Vital Statistics of the New York State Department of Health showed relatively high reported rates for all congenital malformations in townships within one portion of this county. Data from the Atomic Energy Commission pertaining to a reconnaissance of radioactive rocks of the Hudson Valley and Adirondack Mountains[1] revealed that the townships with a high reported malformation rate were located in an area with igneous bedrock outcrops having relatively high levels of radioactivity and an average range of equivalent uranium content between 0.003 and 0.004 percent.

A review of the reported congenital malformation rates for all townships within Upstate New York‡ indicated that additional areas with elevated rates

---

* The association of elevated malformation rates in man with residence in areas containing natural materials with relatively high concentrations of radioactive elements.
† Observation by Louis M. DiCarlo, Ed.D., director, Syracuse University Speech and Hearing Center.
‡ The term Upstate New York is synonymous with New York State, exclusive of New York City, and will be used in the material which follows.

223

were located primarily in the Adirondack Mountains, Hudson Highlands, and portions of the Allegheny Plateau section of southern New York. These areas also contain igneous or black shale bedrock having relatively high radioactivity levels[2-5] or glacial deposits of these materials associated with advances and retreats of the ice sheets.

As a result of these leads, an epidemiological study was initiated in Upstate New York with the following objectives:

1. Determination of the incidence of congenital malformations reported on birth and death certificates by county, city, township, and village.
2. Determination of the type, amount, and distribution of natural materials with relatively high concentrations of the radioactive elements.
3. Determination of the association, if any, between the incidence of congenital malformations and the distribution of such materials.
4. Evaluation of the roles which known teratogenics, including radiation, may have had in producing congenital malformations within relatively high and low malformation rate areas.

Incidence of congenital malformations

Number and types of malformations reported on birth and death certificates. Birth and death certificate information was used exclusively for the purpose of compiling congenital malformation data. Information from the Medical Rehabilitation (physically handicapped children) Program in New York State was not utilized because of the high degree of selection of cases under the program. Stillbirth data were also excluded because of the unreliable nature of the reported causes of stillbirth.

The birth certificate used in Upstate New York contains on the reverse side a confidential medical supplement. Attending physicians are asked to answer a number of questions, including "Congenital malformation of infant: No___, Yes___. If yes, describe." This question is answered in the negative or with a specified anomaly on 90 percent of the certificates. Recorded anomalies are subsequently classified by the Office of Vital Statistics as to congenital malformation type according to the "International Statistical Classification of Diseases, Injuries, and Causes of Death." Nonphysician deliveries in New York State are for all practical purposes nonexistent.

The number of malformations reported on birth certificates is inevitably incomplete, since a certificate must be filed not later than five days after birth, and some malformations are not diagnosed within this time. For the years 1948–1955 all certificates of death for children under five years of age, stated to have been born in Upstate New York, were also available and were matched to their corresponding birth certificates. Malformations which were reported only on the death certificate were added to those which were reported on the birth certificates.

TABLE 1. Births recorded in New York State, exclusive of New York City, to residents of that area and the incidence of congenital malformations among them, as reported on birth certificates or on the death certificates of children under five years of age, 1948–1955.

Year	Live Births	No. with Malformations Reported by Death Certificate Only			Rate per 1,000 Live Births		
		Birth Certificate	Under 1 Year	1–4 Years	Birth or Death Certificate	Reported on Birth Certificate	Reported on Birth or Death Certificate
1948	141,098	1,481	401	74	1,956	10.5	13.9
1949	142,044	1,537	331	49	1,917	10.8	13.5
1950	143,163	1,475	325	40	1,840	10.3	12.9
1951	151,773	1,678	374	51	2,103	11.1	13.9
1952	159,760	1,760	349	42	2,151	11.0	13.5
1953	161,154	1,751	355	36	2,142	10.9	13.3
1954	168,822	1,796	330	15	2,141	10.6	12.7
1955	174,930	1,770	349	—	2,119	10.1	12.1
1948–1955	1,242,744	13,248	2,814	307	16,369	10.7	13.2

Table 1 shows, for each of the years 1948–1955, the number of live births to residents of Upstate New York; the number of these births with malformations reported on the birth certificates; and the number of children with malformations unrecorded at birth but subsequently reported by death certificate. This latter information is further differentiated for individuals who at death were under one year or from one to four years of age. The information for the one-to-four-age group is, of course, incomplete for children who were born in the years 1951–1954 and wholly lacking for those born in 1955.

For the entire period there were 13,248 births with malformations reported by birth certificate, and 3,121 by death certificate only—a total of 16,369 individuals, representing an average annual incidence of 13.2 congenital malformations per 1,000 live births.

Table 2 shows the total number of cases for the period of 1948–1955 by general malformation categories according to whether reported on the birth certificate or by death certificate only. When two or more malformations appeared on the birth certificate, the case was allocated to the more serious category. When a child with a malformation reported on its birth certificate died from another malformation, it was classified to the malformation reported as the cause of death.

Malformation rates for cities, villages, and towns. Births recorded Upstate are allocated to the usual place of residence of the mother. The 1948–1955 births and recorded malformations were tabulated by residence for each city and village over 2,500 population and for each township, exclusive of any villages over 2,500 located within the township. Rates per 1,000 live births were then computed for each of the areas.

TABLE 2. Malformations reported on the birth certificates or on the certificates of death under five years of age, according to type of malformation: New York State, exclusive of New York City, 1948–1955.

Type of Malformation	Total	Malformation Reported on Birth Certificate			Malformation Reported on Death Certificate Only
		Not Known to Have Died	Died from:		
			Malformation*	Other Causes	
All malformations	16,369	9,465	2,725	1,058	3,121
Central nervous system	2,595	578	1,459	142	416
Monstrosity	476	31	356	33	56
Spina bifida and meningocele	1,223	379	703	61	80
Hydrocephalus	631	66	343	26	196
Other	265	102	57	22	84
Circulatory system	2,715	194	617	80	1,824
Hare lip, cleft palate	1,414	1,267	41	102	4
Digestive system	1,072	195	237	53	587
Genitourinary system	1,270	1,037	102	41	90
Skeletal system	2,276	2,131	5	136	4
Bones and joints	1,461	1,276	41	123	21
Mongolism	392	257	19	78	38
Other and unspecified malformations	3,174	2,530	204	303	137

* When cause of death was a malformation different from the malformation stated on birth certificate case was allocated to malformation given as cause of death.

FIG. 1. Distribution of cities and towns with congenital malformation rates over 20/1,000 live births, 1948–1955.

There is little state-wide difference in the incidence of malformations for urban and rural areas. The rates are 12.9 per 1,000 live births for cities over 10,000, 13.4 for incorporated communities 2,500–10,000, and 13.5 for rural areas. In all, 186 out of 942 townships have rates of 20.0, or more. These are shown on the map in Figure 1. While these are scattered throughout the state, seven counties have no township with a rate this high, and 12 counties have only one each. In many counties the high rates are in adjacent townships, forming a cluster. For example, in St. Lawrence County seven of the eight high rate townships are adjoined and are adjacent to the one high-rate township in Lewis County. Similar clusters are also located in the Adirondack portion of Essex, Franklin, Warren, and Saratoga Counties; in the Catskills; and in the counties of the Allegheny Plateau. All of the counties with no high-rate townships lie in the Erie-Niagara-Mohawk plain, in the Hudson Valley lowlands, and on Long Island.

Type, amount, and distribution of natural materials with relatively high concentrations of the radioactive elements

All rocks contain at least minute quantities of the radioactive elements. The most important of the naturally occurring radionuclides are C^{14}, K^{40}, Ra^{226}, Th^{232}, U^{238}, as well as the decay daughters of the last three nuclides.[6]

Rocks containing these materials may occur as bedrock or as less massive, fragmentary products of erosion. Large quantities of these smaller rock particles are associated with extensive morainal deposits of the glacial ice sheets.

Radionuclides from rocks, or their erosion products, may leach into ground waters, be utilized by plant life, or be disseminated into the atmosphere as gases or as particulate matter. The amounts of these materials in the environment are usually greater when associated with rocks with relatively high concentrations of the radioactive elements.

Bedrock. Most of the common rock types occur within the boundaries of New York State. These include igneous and metamorphic rocks, and the sedimentary shales, limestones and sandstones. The general distribution of these bedrock materials within New York has been extensively mapped by geological workers and is illustrated in Figure 2.[7]

Generally, more silicic igneous rocks, such as granite and syenite, have a higher concentration of radioactive elements than do less silicic igneous types, such as basalts or the sedimentary rocks. Among the sedimentary rocks, limestones and sandstones are relatively low in radioactivity, while shales are somewhat higher. Organic black shales have been found to be especially high.[4] Differences in the occurrence of radioactive elements in granite versus sedimentary rock types are in the magnitude of as much as five to one as illustrated in Table 3.[8]

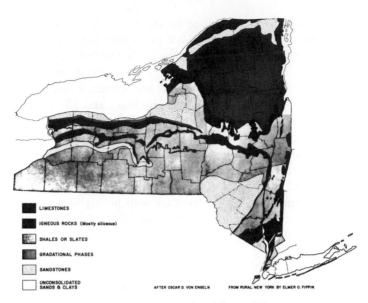

FIG. 2. Underlying rock formations.

Most of the area of what is known as the Adirondack Province is underlaid by igneous and metamorphic rocks. Outside of this region their only extensive occurrence as surface rock is in the Hudson Highlands, a narrow strip in the southeastern part of the state that includes Putnam County and part of Orange and Rockland Counties.

The Atomic Energy Commission has published four reports dealing with reconnaissance of radioactive rocks in New York State.[1-3, 5] Vickers also made a study of the radioactivity of various sedimentary rocks in central New York.[4] Additional unpublished studies of the organic black shales have been made by staff members of the New York State Geological Survey.

The areas with the greatest concentrations of materials with unusually high radioactivity levels were found by Narten and McKeown[1] to occur in the northwestern and southeastern Adirondacks where there are numerous contacts between gneisses of the Grenville series and the granosyenite complex. The Hudson Highland gneisses were found by McKeown[3] to have an average percentage of equivalent uranium from 0.003 to 0.004 percent which is higher than the 0.002 percent that is considered to be normal.

TABLE 3. Natural occurrence of radioactive elements.

	Ra^{266} (10^{-12} gm/gm)	Th^{232} (10^{-6} gm/gm)	K^{40} (10^{-6} gm/gm)
Granite rock	1.6–4.7	8–33	3.5
Sedimentary rock	0.3–1.0	1–5	0.1–1.0

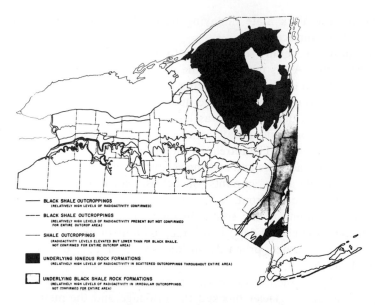

FIG. 3. Rock outcroppings and areas with underlying rock having relatively high levels of radioactivity.

A state-wide compilation of these data is illustrated in Figure 3. This includes mapping of surface outcrops of organic black shales containing at least 0.003 percent equivalent uranium. Shale outcrops with radioactivity levels elevated but lower than that for black shale are also indicated. The underlying igneous rock formations of the Adirondack and Hudson Highland provinces are shown where relatively high levels of radioactivity are present in scattered exposures. Black shale formations also underlie a considerable part of the Hudson Valley area. Here the formations with elevated radioactive content outcrop in an irregular manner which has not been mapped in detail for the entire area.

These maps include all generalized radiological information available at the time of report preparation. It should be emphasized, however, that the data are not complete. Little or no information based on field measurements is available for much of the unmarked areas. The absence of data does not, therefore, necessarily indicate the complete absence of rocks with relatively high levels of radioactivity. Spot anomalies may be expected in many areas. Major surface exposure of such materials, however, may be assumed to be recorded.

Glacial material. Except for a small area in southern Cattaraugus County, all of New York State has been glaciated. During the Pleistocene epoch of geologic time when glaciation was occurring in North America, at least four separate ice advances took place. Of these, the last, or the Wisconsin advance, was the most important in New York State in laying down the glacial deposits which now underlie the land surface.

The ice moved generally southward into New York from centers of accumulation to the north. At its maximum, the glacier was probably several thousand feet thick over much of the state. During its movement, the glacier abraded the underlying rock and incorporated huge quantities of it into the ice. When the ice retreated by melting, this material was left as a deposit over the land in various forms. Glacial till, or boulder clay, an unsorted deposit, was left by the melting ice over most of the state. The retreat to the north was marked by several periods of equilibrium of ice advance and melting so that the ice front remained stationary long enough to pile large amounts of debris, called recessional or terminal moraines, at the static ice front.

Melt water draining to the south through valleys which had been widened and deepened by the glacier deposited large amounts of glacial outwash in them. These valleys are located primarily in the southern part of the state in the Allegheny Plateau.

When the edge of the ice was melted back to a position north of the drainage divide, the bulk of the glacier blocked the drainage and the melt water became ponded between the glacier edge and the higher land of the divide. Debris was washed into these ice dammed lakes with a sorting of the rock material during deposition which produced deposits of fine silt and sand. These latter types of deposits are extensively developed in the Hudson Valley, north of Kingston, in the Black River Valley which is located along the southwestern boundary of the Adirondacks, over the lake plain between Lake Ontario and the front of the Allegheny Plateau, and on the St. Lawrence Lowland.

Composition of the different types of glacial deposits is extremely variable. Composition is, however, directly related to the nearby bedrock which usually supplied the predominant material in the deposit. Shales, having been formed originally from clay material and being generally less resistant than other rock types, yielded glacial deposits with much clay. Igneous rocks eroded by the glacier are deposited predominantly as sands and gravels or generally coarse debris. The relative resistance of the rock determined the persistence of the rock in the drift. The igneous rocks, being the hardest, are often found hundreds of miles from the outcrop.

Depth of deposits is also variable. The more extensive deposits are located in the valleys and where material was deposited in lakes or in the sea (water-laid). Generally, deposits are thin over the uplands and on steep slopes. Accurate information as to depth of deposits is lacking for much of the state.

Radioactivity levels for glacial material are directly related to the type and level of the parent bedrock and the composition of the overburden. McKeown[3] found abnormally radioactive glacial material up to ten miles from the bedrock source. The fine sands and silts of water-laid deposits are generally lower in radioactivity than the till, or ice-laid morainal material, in the same area.

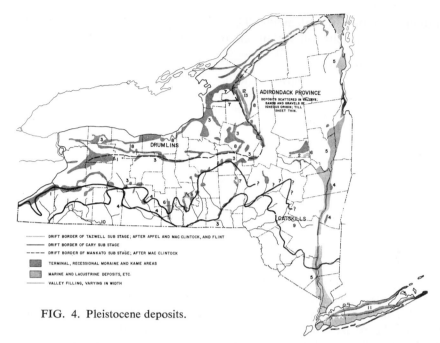

FIG. 4. Pleistocene deposits.

EXPLANATION—This map is a compilation of data from various sources. Only those deposits extensive enough to be important are shown. The following reference sources were used: 1 Fairchild, 1907; 2 Brigham, 1929; 3 Fairchild, 1932; 4 Woodworth N. Y. S. Mus. Bull. No. 83; 5 Woodworth N. Y. S. Mus. Bull. No. 34; 6 Tarr, 1909; 7 Brigham G.S.A. Bull. No. 8; 8 Taylor, 1924; 9 Rich, 1935; 10 Apfel, 1944; 11 Fuller, 1914; 12 Fairchild N. Y. S. Mus. Bull. No. 160; 13 Langey, 1952; 14 ground water bulletins.

A state-wide mapping of the distribution of glacial material is illustrated in Figure 4. This represents a compilation of available data from various authorities. Fairchild[9] mapped glacial deposits for the central and western parts of the state and his maps were used extensively. Mapping of moraines in the eastern part of the state was spotty and the data were gathered, where available, from various authors. Major terminal and recessional moraine deposits are mapped under the designation of "drift border." General till cover was not included in the mapping because of its wide distribution.

Association of the incidence of malformations with the distribution of materials with relatively high concentrations of radioactive elements

Classification of townships on the basis of geological data. Before the malformation data for all local areas became available, a classification of all townships and cities in Upstate New York was made pertaining to the probable or unlikely presence of extensive quantities of materials with relatively high concentrations of radioactive elements. The classification of "probable" was made when a township or city fell within one of the three following categories:

1. Igneous bedrock areas.
2. River valleys in the Allegheny Plateau.
3. Terminal or recessional moraine areas with igneous or black shale outcrops occurring within a 25-mile distance to the north of the center of the city or township.

Townships and cities not falling within these three categories were classified as "unlikely."

The igneous bedrock category was selected because this rock type contains the highest concentration of radioactive elements found in natural materials within New York State. River valleys in the Allegheny Plateau were included because of the extensive glacial deposits in these locations with the presence of both igneous and black shale components. Morainal areas were also included, despite smaller deposits on upland slopes, when a confirmed outcrop of igneous or black shale material was present within an arbitrary 25-mile distance from the direction of glacial ice movement. The 25-mile distance was selected on the assumption that the great majority of all radioactive glacial materials present would have been derived from bedrock sources within this area. Areas with mapped water-laid glacial deposits were excluded because of the relatively lower radioactivity levels of these materials.

Classifications were based exclusively on the state-wide maps of bedrock and glacial material illustrated in Figures 3 and 4. Townships were classified as "probable" only when more than one-half of the total township area or the major population centers were associated with one of the designated categories.

Additional state-wide classifications were made as to the presence of bedrock exposures of igneous or black shale material within a ten-mile distance to the north of the center of a city or township. A more restrictive ten-mile distance was used in this classification because of the definitive findings by McKeown[3] of abnormally radioactive glacial materials as far as ten miles from a bedrock source. A classification was also made based on the presence of any mapped glacial deposits and whether these covered more than one-half of the area of the township or the population centers.

Malformation rates for townships classified according to geology.   Malformation rates among children of residents of all urban and rural areas, classified as to the probable or unlikely presence of extensive quantities of natural materials with relatively high concentrations of the radioactive elements, are shown in Table 4. For all "probable" areas the rate is 15.1 per 1,000 births, as compared with the rate of 12.8 for the "unlikely."

If geology is a factor in the incidence of malformation, one would expect the association to be less marked in the urban than in the rural areas, where there

TABLE 4. Malformation rates per 1,000 resident live births* in areas classified as to probable or unlikely presence of extensive quantities of materials with relatively high concentrations of the radioactive elements: New York State, exclusive of New York City, 1948–1955.

Presence of Extensive Quantities of Radioactive Materials	Total			Urban†			Rural		
		Malformations			Malformations			Malformations	
	Births	No.	Rate	Births	No.	Rate	Births	No.	Rate
Total	1,242,744	16,369	13.2	690,506	8,925	12.9	552,238	7,444	13.5
"Probable"	191,003	2,893	15.1	76,670	1,084	14.1	114,333	1,809	15.8
Igneous bedrock areas, except those covered with water-laid glacial deposits	27,521	462	16.8	4,298	56	13.0	23,223	406	17.5
River valleys in the Allegheny Plateau, and/or drift border areas	163,482	2,431	14.9	72,372	1,028	14.2	91,110	1,403	15.4
"Unlikely"	1,051,741	13,476	12.8	613,836	7,841	12.8	437,905	5,635	12.9

* Exclusive of births to residents recorded in New York City and other states.
† Incorporated places having a population of 2,500 or more in the 1950 Census.

should be greater exposure to natural materials. Table 4 shows that this is the case, with rates for the "probable" and "unlikely" rural areas being 15.8 and 12.9, as compared with the corresponding urban rates of 14.1 and 12.8.

Within the rural areas, the presence of igneous bedrock is associated with a rate of 17.5. River valleys in the Allegheny Plateau and/or drift borders (terminal or recessional moraines) have a rate of 15.4. For river valleys the rate is 15.5, and for drift border areas, 15.0.

Analysis of more detailed geological classifications of rural townships indicate that the location of a township within a river valley or a drift border area is apparently more significant than the presence of bedrock outcrops of igneous or black shale material within the township or within a distance of ten miles to the north. However, outside the river valley and drift border areas, the rates of townships with and without such outcrops are 13.4 and 12.4, respectively. Where glacial deposits have been mapped, the rates for townships in river valley and drift border areas, which are more than half covered with glacial deposits, are higher than in those areas which are less than half covered: 18.0 versus 15.1.

Table 5 shows malformation rates by type of malformation in the "probable" and "unlikely" rural areas. For every type of malformation, except Mongolism, the rate is higher in the "probable" areas.

It is difficult to test these differences for statistical significance since their standard deviations are certainly larger than those obtained by assuming binomial distribution. It is possible however to test for the consistency of the pattern throughout the state.

TABLE 5. Malformation rates per 1,000 resident live births, 1948–1955, by type of malformation in rural areas of New York State classified as to probable or unlikely presence of extensive quantities of materials with relatively high concentrations of the radioactive elements.

Malformation Classification	"Probable" Areas		"Unlikely" Areas	
	Malformation	Rate	Malformation	Rate
All malformations	1,809	15.8	5,635	12.9
Central nervous system	254	2.2	857	2.0
Circulatory system	299	2.6	939	2.1
Hare lip, cleft palate	181	1.6	529	1.2
Digestive system	122	1.1	384	0.9
Genitourinary system	150	1.3	440	1.0
Skeletal system (club foot)	264	2.3	779	1.8
Bones and joints	148	1.3	466	1.1
Other unspecified malformations	356	3.1	1,104	2.5
Mongolism	35	0.3	137	0.3

Grouping the counties of the state into the six standard geographical regions shown in Table 6, we find that in each region the malformation rate for "probable" towns is greater than for the "unlikely," although the difference is very small for the Catskill-Pocono Highlands.

Of the 57 Upstate counties, 38 contain townships classified as "probable." The average difference in these counties between the rates for "probable" and "unlikely" areas is 2.9, with a standard error of 0.95. The probability of this difference occurring by chance is less than three in 1,000. In three counties all townships were classified as "probable," with an average rate of 14.3. In 16 counties all townships were classified as "unlikely," with an average rate of 11.3.

TABLE 6. Regional malformation rates per 1,000 resident live births, by probable or unlikely presence of extensive quantities of materials with relatively high concentrations of the radioactive elements: rural area of New York State, 1948–1955.

Region	"Probable" Areas		"Unlikely" Areas	
	Births	Malformation Rate	Births	Malformation Rate
Total rural area	114,333	15.8	437,905	12.9
Adirondack Highlands	18,613	17.8	37,018	12.1
Catskill-Pocono Highlands	10,895	14.2	11,430	14.0
Northern Allegheny Plateau	42,981	16.1	27,682	14.6
Northwestern Allegheny Plateau Border	16,989	15.3	11,020	13.7
Erie-Ontario-Mohawk Plain	19,136	14.8	165,103	12.1
Hudson Valley and Long Island	5,719	15.4	185,652	13.2

TABLE 7. Malformation data by occupation of father.

| | | | Rural Area of 20 Nonmetropolitan Counties, 1952 | | | | | |
| | | Death Rate from Malformations* Upstate Area | "Probable" Areas | | | "Unlikely" Areas | | |
Code No.	Occupation of Father		Births	Malforma-tions No.	Rate	Births	Malforma-tions No.	Rate
	Total	2.86	7,689	126	16.4	6,671	89	13.3
0, 2	Professional, managers, and officials	2.60	1,275	24	18.8	791	12	15.2
3, 4, 5	Clerical and sales personnel, skilled workers	2.75	2,090	30	14.4	1,747	21	12.0
6	Semiskilled workers	2.76	1,659	26	15.7	1,290	16	12.4
7, 9, X	Service workers, laborers, and not reported	3.59	1,553	22	14.2	1,396	22	15.8
1, 8	Farmers and farm laborers	3.15	1,112	24	21.6	1,447	18	12.4

* Neonatal mortality (under 28 weeks) per 1,000 single white live births recorded Upstate to residents of that area, 1950–1952.

Association of the incidence of malformation with geology and socioeconomic status. If the association of malformation rates with geology is not an accidental phenomenon, the question arises as to what factor, or factors, might be associated with both a higher incidence of malformations and geology. One such factor is the socioeconomic status of the population. Unfortunately, there are no population data from the United States Census available for townships sufficient to classify the townships in this regard. However, for a special study of reproductive wastage now under way in the New York State Health Department, all births for the years 1950–1952, recorded to residents of the Upstate area, were coded for occupation of the father according to the 10-digit classification employed by the Bureau of the Census. The incidence of malformations among these births is not yet available, but neonatal mortality (under 28 days) from malformations as a cause of death could be computed for single white births for each occupation group. This information is shown in Table 7.

These data show a relationship between the neonatal death rate from malformations and occupation of the father, which suggests a similar relationship between occupation (or socioeconomic status) and the total incidence of malformations.

To test whether the differences in malformation rates between "probable" and "unlikely" areas could be due to differences in the occupation of the father, as stated on the birth certificates, punch cards for the 1952 births to residents of the rural areas of 20 nonmetropolitan counties were selected for tabulation. These included all the counties in the Adirondack Highlands and the northern

Allegheny Plateau, except the metropolitan county of Albany. These were divided into residents of "probable" and "unlikely" areas, and each group tabulated into the five occupation categories shown in Table 7.

Applying the malformation death rates prevailing in Upstate New York in 1950–1952 to each of these occupation groups, the expected death rates for the "probable" and "unlikely" areas are 2.95 and 3.00, respectively. Differences in occupational distribution could thus not account for a higher death rate from malformations in the "probable" areas of these counties.

The incidence of malformations as reported on birth and death certificates for these areas in 1952 was also obtained. For all births in the "probable" and "unlikely" areas, the malformation rates were 16.4 and 13.3. For each occupation group the rate was higher in the "probable" than in the "unlikely" area, except for the group "service workers, laborers, and occupation not reported." The greatest difference was for the farmers and for the farm laborers: 21.6 versus 12.4.

Association of the incidence of malformations with geology and type of public water supply.   In areas of probable presence of extensive quantities of radioactive materials one would expect relatively higher levels of radioactivity in water supplies derived from ground sources (wells and springs), than in those derived from large surface waters (lakes and rivers).

There are 555 communities under 10,000 population in New York State, 499 of which are served by public water supplies. The sources of water for these systems include 255 from ground waters, 72 from lakes and rivers, 83 from brooks and streams, and 89 from mixed sources.[10]

Table 8 shows the births, malformations, and malformation rates for the residents of these communities, classified by type of supply according to their location in areas of probable or unlikely presence of extensive quantities of radioactive materials. In the "probable" areas the rate is highest, 16.9, in those com-

TABLE 8. Malformation rates per 1,000 resident live births, according to source of public water supply and the probable or unlikely presence of extensive quantities of radioactive materials: incorporated places under 10,000 population, New York State, 1948–1955.

Source of Public Water Supply	"Probable" Areas			"Unlikely" Areas		
		Malformations			Malformations	
	Births	No.	Rate	Births	No.	Rate
Total	50,333	732	14.5	150,742	1,936	12.8
Wells and springs	15,307	259	16.9	60,894	783	12.9
Large surface (lakes, rivers)	11,195	139	12.4	31,275	371	11.9
Small surface (brooks, streams)	11,213	149	13.3	24,008	304	12.7
Mixed	12,618	185	14.7	34,565	478	13.8

munities deriving their water supply from wells and springs, and lowest, 12.4, in those utilizing large surface waters. In the "unlikely" areas the rates differ very little by source of supply, with those communities which derive their supply from wells and springs having a rate of 12.9, and from large surface waters, 11.9.

Evaluation of the role of possible etiological agents in producing congenital malformations in areas with elevated malformation rates

An epidemiological field investigation was undertaken in an attempt to obtain information as to differences in the frequency of occurrence of known etiological factors between relatively high and low malformation rate townships. Comprehensive family interviews were carried out and more detailed geological field studies were made of these areas. Preliminary measurements were also made of external radiation levels and the radioactivity of water supplies. The number of cases of rubella reported during each of the years 1949–1955 in the townships selected for field study was compared with the distribution of malformation cases during the same period. Possible biases in the malformation rates due to different reporting practices by hospitals and the role of sampling variation in the selection of high and low rate townships for special study were also evaluated.

Selection of areas for field study. Groups of four or more contiguous rural townships with unusually high malformation rates were selected in different parts of the state to obtain approximately 300 families with malformed children recorded on birth or death certificates during the years 1950–1955. Rates for the 55 individual high rate townships selected ranged from 14.6 to 66.7 per 1,000 live births. Groups of four or more contiguous low rate townships were also selected to obtain an equal number of families with malformed children. These townships were located either adjacent to the high rate areas or were in sections of the state with predominantly low rate townships.

The malformation rates for the 108 low rate townships ranged from zero to 16.9 per 1,000 live births. The slight overlapping of rates of the high and low rate township groups is due to the inclusion of several normal rate townships with contiguous groups of both high and low rate townships. These townships were included because of their small populations and the questionable statistical significance of their rates and their location as part of what appeared to be an otherwise uniform grouping of relatively high or low rate townships. The location of the 163 townships selected for study is shown in Figure 5.

For the townships selected comparable malformation data for the four-year period 1944–1948 were obtained to confirm the high or low rate grouping. For the high rate towns the rate for the earlier period was 16.3, for the low rate towns, 11.1. This would suggest that the malformation rates of a substantial number of the high rate towns were "truly" high and not merely the result of chance variation due to the small numbers involved.

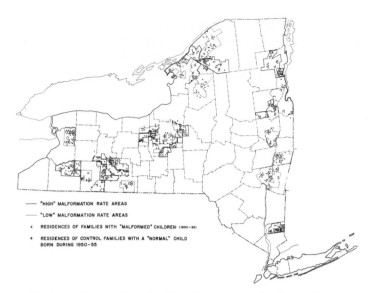

FIG. 5. Distribution of field study areas and family residences.

The possibility that the rates in the high and low rate areas might reflect different reporting practices on the part of physicians and hospitals was also considered. Punch cards for all births to residents of the selected areas for one year, 1952, were obtained and tabulated according to the place of birth. Births occurred in 132 different hospitals. In 63 of these hospitals births were recorded to residents of both high and low rate townships. In these 63 hospitals the malformation rates associated with residents of high and low rate townships were 27.8 and 9.6, respectively. For deliveries in these same 63 hospitals to women residing in townships not included in the field study areas the rate was 12.7. From this it appears extremely unlikely that reporting practices alone could account for the differences in malformation rates between high and low rate areas.

Demographic data for field study areas.   All births to residents of the field study areas for one year, 1952, were tabulated according to birth weight, age of mother, age of father, number of previous children ever born to mother, and occupation of the father. No significant differences between high and low rate areas were found in the distribution of the births by any of these variables, although the percent of births weighing 2,500 gm or less was slightly higher in the high rate areas, 7.8 percent, than in the low rate areas, 6.6 percent.

Neonatal mortality for 1952 was higher in the high rate area (24.2 versus 19.0 per 1,000 live births) entirely because of the higher death rate from malformations. Mortality from 28 days up to five years of age was 10.8 per 1,000 live births in the high rate area, 11.6 in the low.

The stillbirth rate per 1,000 total births in the two areas for the period 1948–1955 was 16.6 in the high rate area and 16.8 in the low.

Rubella. A tabulation of the annual incidence of rubella during the years 1949–1955 in each field study township revealed no association with the incidence of malformations.

Geological field data. Of the 55 high rate townships selected, 22 were classified as igneous bedrock areas, 18 as river valley-drift border areas, and 15 as "unlikely" areas. Of the 108 low rate townships, eight were igneous, 13 river valley-drift border areas, and 87 "unlikely."

Geological field work was carried out in the selected townships without knowledge by the worker of the high or low malformation rate status of the townships. Each town was classified as to underlying bedrock and glacial deposits, taking into account the extent of areal distribution in relation to population concentration.

Malformation rates per 1,000 live births were computed for all field study townships which had been placed in the same bedrock and glacial material categories. To reduce sampling variation and possible bias resulting from the method of selection of field study areas on the basis of their relatively high or low rates for the period 1948-1955, rates were based upon the births for the entire period 1944-1955.

Rates did not vary by type of bedrock when the type of glacial material was held constant. Table 9 shows the rates by type of glacial material. Rates in areas with ice-laid material are consistently higher than in areas with water-laid material. Within the ice-laid category, the highest rate, 19.5, is associated

TABLE 9. Malformation rates per 1,000 resident live births, in areas selected for field investigation classified according to type of unconsolidated glacial material, 1944–1955.

| Type of Glacial Material | Total | | | Ice Laid | | | Water Laid | | |
	Births	Malformations No.	Rate	Births	Malformations No.	Rate	Births	Malformations No.	Rate
Total	88,810	1,093	12.3	74,054	959	13.0	14,756	134	9.1
Igneous	12,625	234	18.5	11,254	219	19.5	1,371	15	10.9
Mixed igneous*	13,516	187	13.8	9,831	146	14.9	3,685	41	11.1
Mixed shale† "Extensive" quantities (areal distribution and depth)	17,234	246	14.3	17,234	246	14.3	—	—	—
"Limited" quantities	27,387	281	10.3	26,868	278	10.3	519	3	5.8
Shale	18,048	145	8.0	8,867	70	7.9	9,181	75	8.2

* Igneous glacial material in which there are quantities of limestone, sandstone, and similar sedimentary debris included.
† Deposits associated with the alternating shale, sandstone, and siltstone beds of the upper Devonian of southwestern and south central New York.

with igneous glacial material. In the "mixed shale" classification, the rate is higher for those areas with extensive quantities of this material, 14.3, than for areas with limited amounts, 10.3.

Family interview data. In the high rate areas there were 299 births with malformations recorded during the period 1950-1955. However, 13 of these were not investigated because the child was born out of wedlock or had been adopted since birth, or was in a family for which an index case had already been selected. The net total represented 286 families. In the low rate areas 307 cases netted a total of 292 families.

For each of the index families a control family was selected by taking from the bound volume of birth certificates the next certificate of birth to a mother resident of the same area. The location of the residences of study and control families is shown in Figure 5.

Families were interviewed by staff public health nurses to obtain detailed family residence and occupation data extending through the grandparents of children designated on the certificates. The residence history included urban-rural status, source of drinking water, utilization of natural stone as a home construction material, presence of dust as a nuisance condition, and the utilization of a home garden for family produce needs. A history of all pregnancies as well as number, birth dates, weights, and health status of other children in the family was obtained. A familial history of malformations was recorded along with miscellaneous information pertaining to socioeconomic level, consanguinity, national stock, and religion. Data on the nutritional status of study families were not collected because of the difficulty of obtaining reliable information and the doubtful relationship in man between malnutrition and congenital malformations.[11]

Interviews were completed for 836 families, or 72 percent of the total. Most of the families not interviewed had moved out of the area. Only 30 families refused to cooperate.

Of the 440 control individuals for whom interviews were completed, 15 were stated by the mother to have a malformation. There were eight in the high rate area and seven in the low, representing a rate among the total control group of 34.1 per 1,000 from interviews alone.* This rate is almost three times the state-wide rate obtained from birth and death certificates, indicating the incompleteness of reporting on the birth certificates. Of the 15 cases found by interview, six represented conditions which could not have been detected at

---

* McIntosh, R. et al., report an incidence of malformations in live born infants of 7.4 percent, based upon examinations at birth, at six months and 12 months of age.[16] For infants surviving the neonatal period the rate was 7.0, but only 43.2 per cent of the malformations were observed at birth. The rate for those observed at later examination was therefore 4.0 percent, very similar to the rate reported here.

TABLE 10. Incidence of malformations, stillbirths, and abortions among siblings of index cases and controls.

	Index Cases with Malformation			Index Cases without Malformation		
	Total	High Rate Areas	Low Rate Areas	Total	High Rate Areas	Low Rate Areas
Families interviewed	411	203	208	425	211	214
Live born siblings	1,207	650	557	1,189	631	558
With malformations	71	37	34	51	36	15
Rate per 1,000	58.8	56.9	61.0	42.9	57.1	26.9
With Mongolism, epilepsy, cerebral palsy, mental retardation	7	5	2	10	7	3
Rate per 1,000	5.8	7.7	3.6	8.4	11.1	5.4
Stillbirths	43	25	18	30	20	10
Abortions	125	57	68	149	75	74
Total stillbirths and abortions	168	82	86	179	95	84
Rate per 1,000 total sibling pregnancies	122.2	112.0	133.7	130.8	130.9	130.8

birth, such as pyloric stenosis and congenital dislocation of the hip. These were equally divided between high and low rate areas. The remaining nine cases were associated with minor conditions, such as tongue tie, hammer toes, cyst under the tongue, etc. The equal number of previously unknown cases found by interview among control cases in both high and low rate areas indicates that incompleteness of reporting has not of itself been responsible for the differences in rates obtained from birth and death records.

The 15 cases found among the controls were added to the index cases, resulting in 411 cases and 425 controls. Table 10 shows the total number of live siblings of these children and the incidence of malformations among them, and also the incidence of stillbirths and abortions in all sibling pregnancies. There are no consistent differences in any of these rates either between cases and controls or between high and low rate areas.

Few pregnancies in families with or without malformations were associated during the first trimester with German measles, two versus three, or pelvic radiation, five versus three. There were no reported associations between malformations and the occurrence of other infectious diseases during the first trimester of pregnancy. There was a slight difference between the percentages of the two groups having a history of pelvic radiation following the first trimester, 11.4 versus 9.4 percent. A slightly higher percentage of women with malformed children were reported by their physicians to have experienced toxemia as a complication of pregnancy, 16.4 percent versus 13.0 percent.

The number of reported consanguineous cousin marriages between parents or grandparents in families with and without a malformed child was 14 and 4.

Additional family history data showed a greater incidence of anomalies on both the husband's and wife's side of the family in families with a malformed child as compared to those without a malformed child. This was true also for cases of epilepsy, cerebral palsy, mental retardation and Mongolism. For diabetes a high incidence was reported on the wife's side only.

Miscellaneous data revealed that approximately 30 percent of families in high and low rate areas reported dust as a nuisance condition; only 20 percent of all families raised more than 50 percent of their own garden produce; and that approximately one-half of all homes used stone as a building material. Igneous rock was used in one-third of all homes in the high rate areas. In 20 percent of the families in the high rate areas and 12 percent of those in the low rate areas, there was a history of residence of some member of the family in the area over 75 years.

Radiological data. Precise and reliable measurements of radiation exposures are limited. In connection with the present study 38 external environmental radiation measurements were made in Upstate New York by Leonard Solon, acting director of the Radiation Branch of the New York Operations Office, AEC, and his coworkers.[13] A 20-liter ionization chamber was used in conjunction with a vibrating reed electrometer. This equipment was mounted in the rear of an automobile with all but one reading taken with the instrument being in this location. The latter reading was taken inside a church which was constructed of granite rock.

The outdoor penetrating environmental radiation levels were found to lie primarily in the interval of 8 to 12 microroentgens per hour. This represents 2.1 to 3.2 r per 30-year period. The radiation associated with igneous rock areas was generally responsible for the higher levels. Appreciable departures from this range were found at points adjacent to exposed rocks having relatively high concentrations of radioactive materials. Occupational exposure associated with such materials was recorded as high as 40 μr per hour. Exceptions also occurred in association with buildings constructed with materials with elevated radioactivity. A reading of 18.5 μr per hour was made in the one building constructed with granite rock in which an ionization chamber measurement was made. This latter measurement was in contrast to a general environmental reading of 9.5 made outside the building.

Through the cooperation of the Atomic Energy Project at the University of Rochester School of Medicine and Dentistry, 18 water samples were analyzed for radioactivity levels by Dr. John Hursh. A description of Dr. Hursh's analysis procedures has already been published.[14]

Preliminary screening measurements of water samples from both high and low malformation rate areas were made with the intent of picking up any highly radioactive ground source. A sample from a drilled well containing 29×10^{-16}

gm of Ra266 per ml represents such a source. This sample was taken from the igneous rock area of the Adirondacks. The sample showing the next highest level at 5.2×10^{-16} gm was also taken from an igneous section in Putnam County, within the Hudson Highlands. These levels are in contrast to a general range of from 0.0 to 1.7×10^{-16} gm of radium per ml found in public water supplies.[14] Measurements of emitters from the thorium chain are not complete. Initial findings, however, reveal no evidence of substantial amounts of these emitters in the samples collected. Preliminary examinations for trace elements have not revealed any notable differences between samples from the various areas.

Radon measurements for mines in the Adirondacks, which were carried out by the New York State Department of Labor and the New York Operations Office of the Atomic Energy Commission, were found to be between 10^{-10} and 10^{-11} curies per liter in the majority of places sampled.[12] The former levels exceed the present maximum permissible concentration of radon and radon daughter products of 10^{-11} c per liter.

Bone and tissue specimens from lifetime residents coming to autopsy are also being collected in certain study areas for future radiological measurements by the Atomic Energy Commission's New York Operations Office.

Discussion

The foregoing data represent an epidemiological fact-finding study. The associations noted are statistical in nature and represent a first step in establishing possible cause-effect relationships. It should be stressed that the associations relate to total malformation rates and the location of geographical areas containing materials with relatively high concentrations of radioactive elements. This is not tantamount to a direct relationship with external environmental radiation levels or "background" radiation.

The study and the study data are also not comparable to the studies of the effects of atomic blast radiation in Japan[15] or to the majority of animal studies dealing with ionizing radiation. The latter studies have been related almost exclusively to high dose, external radiation administered over short periods of time. In contrast, the environmental radiation factors herein described pertain to low dosage levels over long periods of time. With many families, the time factor has included several generations. The sources of radiation, in addition to external radiation, include internal emitters which may have been ingested with food or drinking water, or inhaled.

The data upon which this report is based relate to such a substantial number of births that most of the differences indicated would be statistically significant by whatever tests devised. However, the real significance lies in the overwhelming consistency of the pattern which is shown in the relationship of malformation rates to geology. The data are crude with factors other than chance variation operating. Some of the most convincing evidence may be found in a comparison of the maps of bedrock, glacial material, and malformation rates illustrated in Figures 1–4. Interrelationships of these three items are perhaps most readily illustrated in the area immediately to the south and southeast of Rochester. A 150-mile eastwest section of the drift border of the Mankato glacial substage is associated with elevated malformation rates only in a 40-mile section which lies immediately to the south of an outcrop of relatively highly radioactive black shale.

Special attention should be directed to the general range of external environmental radiation of 8–12 μr per hour and the fact that the higher readings are primarily associated with igneous bedrock areas. Although possibly of significance only in the matter of relative values, the 50 percent increase in the level of the higher radiation figure over the lower is similar to the difference between the malformation rates of 12.9 and 17.5 found in Table 4. These latter rates reflect the differences found between rural areas classified as probably not containing relatively large quantities of materials with elevated radioactivity versus those containing more highly radioactive igneous materials.

The general absence of unusually high external environmental radiation levels in river valley and morainal areas is offset by the potential radiation exposures to man via ground water used for drinking purposes. Epidemiological justification for this consideration is found in Table 8 where higher rates in these areas are associated with consumers of ground water supplies in contrast to large surface supplies. These data suggest that an internal factor acquired through drinking water may play a more important role than an external agent.

The association of increased malformation rates with residence in areas containing materials with relatively high levels of radioactivity strongly suggests radiation as a primary etiological agent. However, another etiological agent which may be associated with radioactive materials may be responsible for the differences noted. Such an agent, however, is presently unknown and no known etiological factor other than radiation has the same statistical association with the malformation differences which are recorded. This applies to rubella, medical radiation, socioeconomic status, consanguinity, and the many other factors investigated in this study. Until such time as the existence of an alternate agent can be elicited, it would appear desirable to consider radiation as a causal agent. If such a causal association can be confirmed, it would serve as the basis for establishing more realistic and reliable information and standards pertaining to the long-range effects on man of low level, environmental radiation than those which have been extrapolated from laboratory experimentation with Drosophila and mice. Such information would be of special value in evaluating the hazards of environmental contamination by radioactive wastes and of fallout materials. Extensive additional radiological measurements will be required, however, before accurate estimates of these possible relationships can be made.

Summary

1. A tabulation was made of all congenital malformations recorded for children born during 1948–1955 in New York State, exclusive of New York City. Birth certificates, or certificates of death of children under five years of age, were used as sources of information. There were 16,369 malformations among 1,242,744 live births, an incidence of 13.2 per 1,000 live births. For the rural area the rate was 13.5. Rates of 20.0 or higher occurred in 186 out of a total of 942 townships. Contiguous groupings of these high rate townships occurred primarily in the Adirondack Mountains, Hudson Highlands, and Allegheny Plateau portions of the state.

2. An independent compilation was made of all available geological data pertaining to deposits of materials with relatively high levels of radioactivity. These data were used to classify all townships as to the probable or unlikely presence of extensive quantities of natural materials with relatively high levels of radioactivity. The malformation rate for all rural areas classified as "probable" was 15.8 per 1,000 live births. For "unlikely" rural areas the rate was 12.9. The most highly radioactive materials in New York State are found in areas with outcrops of igneous rocks. These areas had the highest malformation rate, 17.5. Areas with extensive deposits of glacial materials had a rate of 15.4. These included river valleys in the Allegheny Plateau and glacial moraine areas. Areas with less extensive glacial deposits had a lower rate.

3. Birth record data pertaining to occupation of father were used to evaluate the relationship between malformation rates, presence of radioactive materials, and socioeconomic status. The neonatal mortality rate from malformations was inversely related to socioeconomic status as indicated by occupation of father. However, there was no relationship between socioeconomic status and the presence of radioactive materials. In "probable" radioactive material areas malformation rates were higher than in "unlikely" areas for all but one occupational group.

4. Data pertaining to source of public water supply were used to evaluate the relationship between malformation rates, presence of radioactive materials, and drinking water from wells and springs as contrasted with large surface supplies (lakes and rivers). In areas of "probable" radioactive materials the malformation rate was highest, 16.9, in communities deriving their water supplies from wells and springs, and lowest, 12.4, in those utilizing surface waters. In the "unlikely" areas the corresponding rates were 12.9 and 11.9.

5. Groups of contiguous townships with relatively high and relatively low malformation rates were selected for special epidemiological field study. There were no differences between the high and low rate areas in the distribution of births by age of mother, age of father, number of previous children born to mother, or occupation of father. There were also no differences in infant mor-

tality after the first month, or in the stillbirth rate. Possible biases associated with different reporting practices by hospitals, sampling variation in the selection of field study areas, and general under-reporting of malformations were investigated and could not account for the difference in rates between the high and low rate townships. There was no association between the incidence of rubella and malformations in any of the townships. Extensive family interview data revealed that medical radiation, infectious disease during the first trimester of pregnancy, and other potential etiological factors were not responsible for the malformation rate differences noted.

6. Field measurements of external environmental radiation levels were found to lie mainly in the interval of 8–12 μr per hour with appreciable departures from this range at points adjacent to exposed minerals having an elevated radioactive content. These levels represent a range of from 2.1 to 3.2 r per 30-year period. Preliminary screening measurements of radium 226 for a limited number of water supplies revealed one highly radioactive supply, from an igneous rock outcrop area, which contained 29.0×10^{-16} gm per ml. This level is in contrast to a general range of from 0.0 to 1.7×10^{-16} gm of radium per ml found in public water supplies.[14]

Acknowledgments

The authors wish to express their sincere appreciation for the assistance and guidance received from Dr. Earl T. Apfel, professor and chairman of the Department of Geology, Syracuse University; Dr. Donald Fisher, New York State paleontologist; Dr. John Prucha, former senior geologist, and other staff members of the office of the New York State Geological Survey who have given freely of their time.

As noted in the text, radiological measurements were carried out by Dr. John Hursh and Leonard Solon and his co-workers. Additional staff members of the Atomic Energy Commission have been most helpful.

Dr. John Fertig, professor of biostatistics, Columbia University School of Public Health and Administrative Medicine, and William M. Haenszel, head, Biometrics Section, National Cancer Institute, reviewed the statistical data and made helpful suggestions.

Many other professional associates, particularly those in the New York State Department of Health, have given valued assistance. Special thanks are due the county public health nurses who carried out the family interviews under the general direction of the health officers and supervising nurses in participating jurisdictions.

REFERENCES

1. NARTEN, P. F., and MCKEOWN, F. A. Reconnaissance of Radioactive Rocks of the Hudson Valley and Adirondack Mountains, New York. USAEC Technical Information Service, Oak Ridge, Tenn., TEI Bull. No. 70 (May), 1952.

2. McKeown, F. A., and Klemic, Harry. Reconnaissance for Radioactive Materials in Northeastern U.S. During 1952. USAEC Technical Information Service, Oak Ridge, Tenn., TEI Bull. No. 317-A (June), 1953.

3. McKeown, Frank. Reconnaissance of Radioactive Rocks of Vermont, New Hampshire, Connecticut, Rhode Island, and Southeastern New York. USAEC Technical Information Service, Oak Ridge, Tenn., TEI Bull. No. 67 (June) 1951.

4. Vickers, Rollin C. A Radioactivity Study of the Sedimentary Rocks of Central New York State and a Description of the Methods and Apparatus Used. Master's thesis, Syracuse University, 1951.

5. Vickers, R., and Schnabel, R. W. Reconnaissance of the Clinton Formation in New York, Pennsylvania, Maryland and New Jersey. USAEC Technical Information Service, Oak Ridge, Tenn., TEI Bull. No. 434, 1953.

6. Lowder, W. M., and Solon, L. R. Background Radiation: A Literature Search. USAEC Health and Safety Laboratory, New York Operations Office (July), 1956.

7. Modified from New York State Planning Board. A Graphic Compendium of Planning Studies. Albany, N.Y., 1935, p. 7.

8. Modified from Hultquist, Bengt. Studies on Naturally Occurring Ionizing Radiation. Kungl-Svenska Vetenskapsakademiens Handlingar, 6:19; 1956.

9. Fairchild, H. L. New York Moraines. GSA Bull., 43:627–662, 1932.

10. New York State Department of Health, Bureau of Environmental Sanitation. Public Water Supply Data. Bull. No. 19, 1954.

11. Warkany, Joseph. Congenital Malformations Induced by Maternal Dietary Deficiency. Nutrition Rev. 13:289–291 (Oct.), 1955.

12. Harris, Saul J. Radon Levels in Mines in New York State. Monthly Rev. New York State Department of Labor, Division of Industrial Hygiene, 33, 10:37 (Oct.), 1954.

13. Solon, L. R.; Lowder, W. M.; Zila, A. V.; Levine, H. D.; Blatz, H.; and Eisenbud, M. External Environmental Radiation Measurements in the United States. USAEC Health and Safety Laboratory, New York Operations Office (Mar.), 1958.

14. Hursh, J. B. Radium Content of Public Water Supplies. J. Am. Water Works A. 46, 1:43–54 (Jan.), 1954.

15. Neel, J., and Schull, W. J. The Effect of Exposure to the Atomic Bombs on Pregnancy Termination in Hiroshima and Nagasaki. Washington, D.C.: National Academy of Sciences, Publ. No. 461, 1956.

16. McIntosh, Rustin; Merritt, Katherine K.; Richards, Mary R.; Samuels, Mary H.; and Bellows, Marjorie T. The Incidence of Congenital Malformations: A Study of 5,964 Pregnancies. Pediatrics, 14, 5:505–522 (Nov.), 1954.

ALTITUDE

Differences in altitude imply differences in temperature, wind, light, oxygen pressures, radiation, and other factors. Grahn and Kratchman have dealt admirably with a most complex problem of human reproduction in a most complex ecological setting.

SUPPLEMENTARY READINGS

SWAN, LAWRENCE W., Some Environmental Conditions Influencing Life at High Altitudes. 1952, *Ecology,* **33:** 109–111.

TOMPKINS, PENDLETON, Altitude and Fertility. 1950, *Fertility and Sterility,* **1:** 184–186.

WEBB, WILSE B., and HARLOW ADES, Sleep Tendencies: Effects of Barometric Pressure. 1964, *Science,* **143:** 263–264.

Variation in Neonatal Death Rate and Birth Weight in the United States and Possible Relations to Environmental Radiation, Geology and Altitude[*]

DOUGLAS GRAHN
AND JACK KRATCHMAN

The potential biological hazards for man exposed to extremely low levels of ionizing radiation continue to be the subject of much debate. Ideally, the hazards are best evaluated in man himself, though there are many difficulties inherent in any survey or study of a human population. The United States population, for example, contains widely different social customs, economic levels, educational attainments, racial origins, and health practices. In addition, the age structure varies among the different regions and states, and a high degree of mobility is a population characteristic. In spite of these variables, there have been several attempts to evaluate the effects of environmental radiation on man, largely by means of the published vital statistics records. These have included the study of bone tumor incidence (Bugher and Mead, 1958), congenital malformations (Gentry, Parkhurst and Bulin, 1959; Kratchman and Grahn, 1959; Wesley, 1960), and leukemia incidence (Court Brown *et al.,* 1960; Craig and Seidman, 1961). The results of the tumor and leukemia incidence studies have all been negative. The malformation studies have been suggestive of a radiation effect, though alternative explanations and hidden biases were not entirely accounted for.

The present study is a more detailed follow-up of our previous preliminary report (Kratchman and Grahn, 1959). This study is not restricted to congenital malformation deaths, as these are not believed to be uniformly diagnosed in all regions. In addition, deaths from this cause are not presented in the vital statistics by age intervals. The calculation of comparative mortality rates would therefore require the age-standardization of all population groups. The neonatal

[*] This work was performed under the auspices of the U.S. Atomic Energy Commission.

251

death rate (deaths occurring within the first 28 days of life) is used instead, since it is normally based on the number of live births and therefore avoids the difficulties of a shifting population base. About 10 to 15 percent of the neonatal deaths are attributed to malformations, and in addition, there is a sufficient variety of causes of death to permit the measure to reflect the effect of a number of intrinsic and extrinsic factors. The birth weight parameter was examined because of the high negative correlation that exists between it and the neonatal death rate.

Methods

Vital statistics data. The published vital statistics data of the U.S.A. (U.S. Department of Health, Education and Welfare) for the eight years 1950 through 1957 have been the source of all neonatal mortality and birth weight data, though the latter were not available for the years 1950 and 1951 in the form employed. The neonatal deaths and live births were tabulated by county of residence for the white population. The published listings are separated into "white" and "non-white" whenever 10 percent of the population or 10,000 of their number are non-white. This category includes Negro, American Indian and Oriental races. When the 10 percent or 10,000 criteria are not met, no separation is given, and therefore tabulations by county contain a small, but variable, proportion of non-white births and deaths. The sum effect of this is to raise the death rates a little above those published for the white population of a given state or region.

The birth weight data are published, by county, in two broad categories: "2,500 grams or less" and "2,501 grams or more." County tabulations for this study were re-expressed in terms of the percentage of births weighing 2,500 grams or less. Births of this category are classed as "immature," according to the Sixth Revision of the International Lists of Diseases and Causes of Death; therefore the weight parameter expresses the frequency of immature births in the population. The same breakdown of racial information pertains to both the weight and mortality data.

Several additional tabulations were made for selected states, regions, or years. These include: gestation length, mean birth weight, percent born in hospitals, cause of death, and time of death. For the states of Delaware, Illinois, Indiana, Idaho and Montana, which contain virtually no uranium ore reserves, neonatal mortality rates were tabulated on a state-wide basis rather than by summation of individual counties for the purpose of rough comparison across an array of geologic environments.

Census data. Certain characteristics of the surveyed population groups were tabulated to evaluate differences in age and socioeconomic level. Median family income and median age values were tabulated, by county, from the published 1950 U.S. census data (U.S. Bureau of the Census, 1953). Where needed, other characteristics, such as median school years completed, percent non-white, total population number, and population growth figures were also derived from the census reports.

Geologic data. The geologic provinces of the U.S. were carefully defined in order that every county in the study could be assigned to a province. Where geologic borders did not coincide with political boundaries, assignment was made according to the location of the majority of the land area of the county.

Data as of January 1, 1962, on the location and magnitude of known uranium ore reserves in terms of tons of U_3O_8 were obtained from the Division of Raw Materials, U.S. Atomic Energy Commission.

Altitude estimates were drawn from several sources, such as road maps and commercial atlases. However, most of the available figures, regardless of immediate source, are drawn from the accumulated data of the U.S. Geological Survey.

The mean county-altitude values finally employed are not mean values for the total physical topography, but are better classed as "mean populated altitude" figures. Individual locality elevations were multiplied (weighted) by the population number for the given locality. These were summed within the county and divided by the total population number to yield a weighted mean altitude. When county values are assembled into larger units, as states or provinces, the county altitudes were weighted by the number of live births. Thus, state altitude values are, for example, mean populated altitudes weighted by the number of live births at risk. The above procedure is critical for the present survey since mean physical elevations are nearly always well above the populated elevations.

Radiation data. In the absence of detailed radiation dosimetry data, the preliminary report (Kratchman and Grahn, 1959), relied on the geographical distribution of uranium ore deposits as an indication of higher than average concentration of radioactive material in the natural environment. Although this presumption recognized the fact that most uranium reserves are highly localized, frequently deeply-buried, and in remote unpopulated areas, it was selected as a preliminary hypothesis on the assumption that an area containing large uranium deposits was presumed to be an environment which has a greater amount of disseminated uranium than an area which lacks deposits.

Since the publication of the preliminary report, additional studies have indicated that the assumption that uranium ore reserves are indicative of higher radiation levels may not be entirely appropriate. Nevertheless, there is a generally higher terrestrial radiation level in the mountain areas than in the midwestern region (Solon *et al.,* 1959). The average of 27 independent readings of environmental radiation (excluding terrestrial beta rays) is 11.7 microroentgens per hour or 103 milliroentgens per year for Ohio, Indiana, Illinois and Wisconsin. Of this, 66 mr is terrestrial, 37 cosmic. Forty-nine readings in Colorado, Wyoming, Utah and New Mexico averaged 20.2 μr per hour or 177 mr per

year. Of this, 104 mr is terrestrial and 73 cosmic. The terrestrial gamma radiation is therefore about 50 percent and cosmic radiation nearly 100 percent
higher in the sampled regions of the mountain states.

These data of Solon *et al.* are the only direct measures available for the
regions of interest and provide only a broad definition of the differences in radiation intensity. In view of the above remarks concerning the probable lack of
close correlation between radiation levels and uranium reserves, Solon's data
are probably sufficient for the question of external radiation levels. Radiation
levels from the deposition of internal emitters have not been measured.

The dose rate from cosmic radiation was also measured and reported by Solon
et al. (1959, 1960) for altitudes up to 17,000 feet after adjustment to a latitude
of about 41° N, which very nearly bisects the continental U.S. No attempt was
made to correct for latitude variation since the cosmic flux rises only 14 percent

TABLE 1. Geologic provinces and states included in the analysis of neonatal mortality
rates.

Geologic Province	State	No. of counties	
		With U_3O_8 reserves	Without U_3O_8 reserves
Colorado Plateau	Arizona	3	0
	Colorado	6	5
	New Mexico	3	2
	Utah	7	7
Rocky Mountains	Colorado	9	18
	New Mexico	1	2
	Utah	0	5
	Washington	2	2
	Wyoming	4	9
Basin and Range	Arizona	3	8
	Nevada	4	13
	New Mexico	3	5
	Utah	2	8
Western Stable Region	Colorado	1	24
	Kansas	5[a]	9[b]
	Nebraska	0	11
	N. Dakota ⎱ S. Dakota ⎰	5	7
	New Mexico	0	16
	Texas	9[a]	8[b]
	Wyoming	5	5
Coastal Plain	Texas	6	7
Coast Ranges	California	2	9
		80	180

[a] With known helium reserves.   [b] Without known helium reserves.

FIG. 1. Geologic provinces of the Continental United States.

between 30° and 50° N at an altitude of 6,500 feet and less than 10 percent at
sea level. The altitude effect on radiation intensity is considerably greater and
the majority of the populations studied reside in the more limited latitude range
between 35° and 45° N.

Geographic areas selected for study.   Table 1 presents the number of counties in the study with and without known ore reserves by geologic province and
state west of the Mississippi River. Figure 1 outlines the geologic provinces in
the U.S. and Fig. 2 indicates the states and counties included in the study.
The map does not encompass the Texas Coastal Plain counties of Colorado,
DeWitt, Fayette, Gonzales, Karnes and Lavaca.
    Only portions of some states are included. These are:
    (1) California and Washington: Counties containing large granite batholiths
         and including several ore deposits.
    (2) North and South Dakota: Limited ore bearing areas with non-uranium
         areas for controls.
    (3) Nebraska: A non-uranium control area at moderate altitude.
    (4) Kansas and Texas Panhandle: Helium reserve area with non-helium
         areas as controls.
    (5) Texas Coast: Limited ore-bearing area with non-uranium areas as
         controls.
Control counties, in the specified instances, were chosen from geologic maps
according to two criteria; contiguity with an ore bearing county and similarity
of the geology.

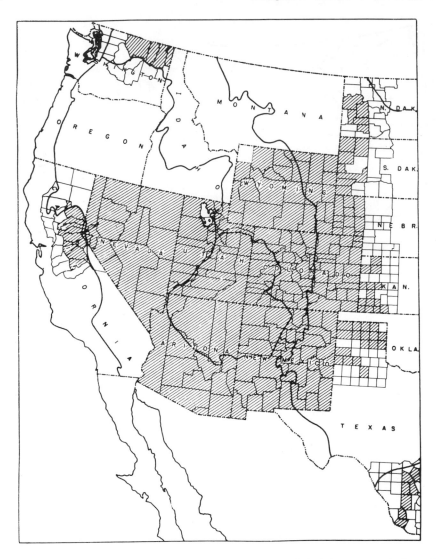

FIG. 2. Western portion of United States. Counties included in survey indicated by cross hatch. Heavy lines outline geologic provinces defined in Fig. 1.

Results

Neonatal mortality: standardization of the population. During the eight-year study period, a 15 percent decline in neonatal mortality has occurred. The rate of change is essentially the same for the mountain states as for the whole U.S. (Fig. 3). This suggested that the time trend could be ignored and the data were pooled across the eight years.

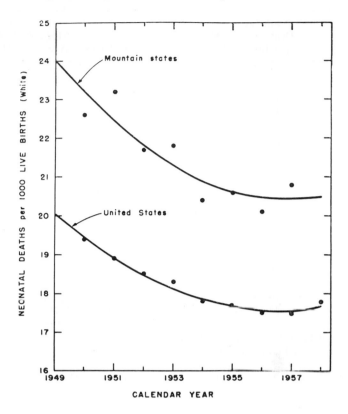

FIG. 3. Regression of neonatal death rate on time in years for U.S. and mountain states.

An analysis of socioeconomic factors was done for the years 1951–1954 for the nine geographic census divisions of the U.S. (these do not coincide with the geologic provinces and are defined in Volume II, Part 1, U.S. Summary, 1950 census). The eight states of the Mountain Division were also separately evaluated. The data for this analysis are given in Table 2.

Several assumptions can be made concerning these measures of the socioeconomic characteristics of the population: (a) median income reflects educational attainment and age, (b) neonatal mortality decreases as the probability of being born in a hospital increases and the latter is in turn positively related to income, (c) neonatal mortality decreases with increasing income. Income therefore appears to characterize the general educational and social attainments and level of medical care in the population. Variation in median family income has consequently been used to account for the effect of differences in socioeconomic level on neonatal mortality among the individual counties and states. The regression is −2.0/1000 live births per $1,000 median income, and all county values were adjusted to a common income of $3,000.

TABLE 2. Socioeconomic values for U.S. census divisions and mountain states.

Division or State	Neonatal[a] Death Rate per 1,000	Median[b] School yrs.	Median Family[b] Income-Thous.	Median[b] Age yrs.	% Born in[a] Hospitals
New England	17.58	10.4	$3.25	32.4	98.8
Middle Atlantic	17.43	9.5	3.40	33.0	98.3
E. North Central	17.85	9.7	3.43	31.4	98.1
W. North Central	17.88	9.1	2.90	31.2	97.0
South Atlantic	18.90	9.2	2.41	28.3	93.6
E. South Central	20.93	8.7	1.79	27.0	87.0
W. South Central	19.68	9.3	2.36	28.2	89.6
Mountain	20.98	10.9	3.10	27.8	95.1
Pacific	17.68	11.6	3.55	32.0	98.8
United States (Total)	18.37	9.7	3.07	30.8	95.9
Arizona	22.05	10.6	2.85	27.8	95.2
Colorado	22.40	10.9	3.07	29.6	96.2
Idaho	18.63	11.0	3.05	27.5	98.6
Montana	18.83	10.3	3.26	30.2	98.9
Nevada	20.80	11.7	3.61	32.1	99.4
New Mexico	25.03	9.5	2.65	24.4	82.1
Utah	16.63	12.0	3.26	25.0	98.9
Wyoming	22.25	11.1	3.48	28.0	98.9

[a] Based on 1951–54 data for white population only.
[b] From 1950 U.S. census data; income for 1949.

TABLE 3. Age and income adjusted neonatal death rates and associated physical variables by state: 1950–57 white population only.

State	Altitude (feet)	U_3O_8 Reserves (tons)	Atm. Press (mm Hg)	Cosmic rad. (mr/yr)	No. of Live Births	Neonatal Deaths ± SE (Per 1,000 births)
Texas (Coast)	310	570	752	35.1	37,216	18.13 ± 0.98
Washington	1,440	a	721	41.9	11,078	18.01 ± 1.80
California	1,490	40	720	42.1	26,203	18.33 ± 1.17
Arizona	2,080	2,240	703	46.4	179,659	20.67 ± 0.47
Kansas	3,080	(Helium)	678	53.6	15,007	20.90 ± 1.65
Dakotas	3,180	2,680	676	54.2	33,975	20.10 ± 1.08
Texas (Panhandle)	3,370	(Helium)	672	55.3	35,192	21.26 ± 1.09
Nevada	3,690	190	664	58.0	40,360	22.64 ± 1.04
Nebraska	3,920	—	657	60.2	22,790	21.72 ± 1.37
New Mexico	5,010	80,330	632	69.6	189,242	23.41 ± 0.49
Colorado	5,390	11,670	623	73.1	306,818	22.19 ± 0.38
Wyoming	5,390	60,830	623	73.1	66,728	22.65 ± 0.82
Delaware	60	—	758	34.0	63,648	17.10 ± 0.73
Illinois and Indiana	630	—	744	36.8	2,285,385	17.40 ± 0.12
Idaho	3,320	—	673	55.1	131,306	18.25 ± 0.52
Montana	3,490	50	668	56.7	127,660	18.66 ± 0.54
Utah	4,590	12,190	642	65.6	191,042	16.63 ± 0.41

a Data not available for publication.

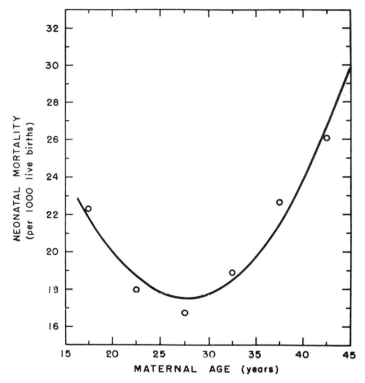

FIG. 4. Regression of neonatal death rate on maternal age, 1950 white population.

The relationship between maternal age and neonatal mortality is shown in Fig. 4. This is based upon data from a limited special study of live births that occurred during the first quarter of 1950 (U.S. Department of Health, Education and Welfare, 1958). Individual county mortality ratios were adjusted to a constant maternal age of 27.5 years by means of the equation: $Y = 49.8 - 2.33A + 0.042A^2$ where A is the maternal age. At 27.5 years, $Y = 17.5$, and is at a minimum value. For ages above or below 27.5, the mortality rate, Y_X, is always greater and the difference, $Y_X - 17.5$, is subtracted from the observed county value for adjustment purposes.

Comparison of states and geologic provinces. The age and income adjusted neonatal mortality figures for the individual states, or portions thereof, are given in Table 3. Significant differences exist between Colorado, for example, and the Texas Coastal Plain counties, sampled regions of Washington and California, or the states of Delaware, Illinois and Indiana. The most striking difference involves the state of Utah, which has the lowest neonatal death rate in the U.S., significantly below its neighboring states. This is not associated with a high fetal death rate, so it apparently cannot be attributed to a classification difference for perinatal mortality. The individual county values in Utah are uniformly

TABLE 4. Age and income adjusted neonatal death rates by geologic province.

Geologic Province	U_3O_8 Reserves (tons)	Altitude (feet)	No. of Live Births	Neonatal Death Rate $\pm$ SE
Basin and Range	670	3,550	74,180	20.96 ± 0.74
	Non-Ur.	2,700	213,699	21.89 ± 0.45
	Total	2,920	287,879	21.65 ± 0.38
Coastal Plain	570	330	20,024	18.74 ± 1.36
	Non-Ur.	280	17,192	17.43 ± 1.41
	Total	310	37,216	18.13 ± 0.98
Coast Ranges	40	2,390	2,371	19.51 ± 4.02
	Non-Ur.	1,400	23,832	18.21 ± 1.23
	Total	1,490	26,203	18.33 ± 1.17
Colorado Plateau	104,230	5,670	38,921	21.65 ± 1.05
	Non-Ur.	6,240	18,098	21.19 ± 1.52
	Total	5,850	57,019	21.51 ± 0.86
Rocky Mountains	62,580	5,440	66,864	21.30 ± 0.79
	Non-Ur.	6,100	59,827	21.56 ± 0.84
	Total	5,750	126,691	21.42 ± 0.58
Western Stable Region	2,700	4,320	37,127	21.04 ± 1.05
	Non-Ur.	4,790	341,934	22.81 ± 0.36
	Helium	3,220	27,508	21.04 ± 1.22
	Non-Helium	3,360	22,691	21.28 ± 1.36
	Total	4,570	429,260	22.46 ± 0.32

low but do vary from about 10/1000 to 24/1000, though this is a more limited range as compared to other states. A further analysis of the Utah data will be given below and it will be shown that Utah, although it is an exception, does adhere to certain basic relationships to be brought out. However, because of its unexplained deviation from other states, Utah is not included in subsequent analyses.

A comparison of geologic provinces (Table 4) reveals differences that were already evident from the examination of their composite states. Significant differences do exist, but these are associated with the extremes of geographic location. The data in both Tables 3 and 4 point to altitude as an important variable. However, ore reserves also are larger in the provinces and states at the higher altitudes where the higher mortality rates prevail, even though there appears to be no consistent effect that can be associated with the presence of uranium ore within the geologic provinces.

Altitude is not a simple variable. There is an increase in cosmic ray intensity, a decrease in oxygen partial pressure, an increase in ultraviolet radiation, and a decrease in average humidity and temperature accompanying altitude increase. Although a search for radiation effects underlies this study, oxygen tension is

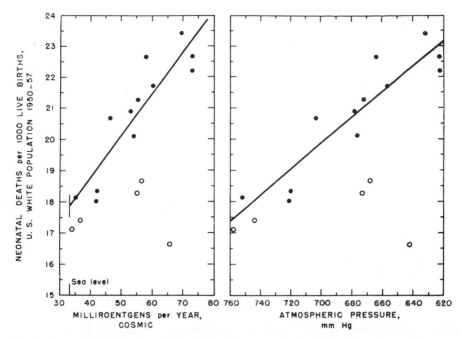

FIG. 5. Regressions of age and income-adjusted neonatal death rate on annual cosmic radiation dose and atmospheric pressure. Open circles not included in calculation (see text and Table 3). To facilitate comparison, values for atmospheric pressure are plotted from high to low.

one environmental factor that cannot easily be dismissed, since it has long been recognized as a factor in the disturbed reproductive physiology seen at high altitudes (Monge, 1948). Figure 5 presents the mortality data from Table 3 plotted against cosmic ray intensity and atmospheric pressure in terms of mm of mercury. The latter can be re-expressed as the partial pressure of oxygen by multiplying the abscissal values by 0.2096. The equations for the two relationships are:

$$Y_1 = 13.42 + (0.1343 \pm 0.0205)D$$

and

$$Y_2 = 48.92 - (0.415 \pm 0.0058)P$$

where Y_1 and Y_2 are the predicted neonatal death rates per 1,000 live births, D is annual cosmic ray dose in milliroentgens, and P is atmospheric pressure in millimeters of mercury. Both regressions are highly significant ($r_{Y \cdot D} = +0.900$; $r_{Y \cdot P} = -0.914$) and the regression on atmospheric pressure is slightly, but not significantly, the better fit. The values of Y at sea level are:

$$Y_1 = 17.89, \quad D = 33.3 \text{ mr}$$
$$Y_2 = 17.38, \quad P = 760 \text{ mm}$$

The regression of mortality rate (Y_3) on altitude in feet (A) is

$$Y_3 = 17.51 + (1.04 \times 10^{-3} \pm 0.15 \times 10^{-3})A.$$

This regression fits the data about as well as that for atmospheric pressure and is used for certain data adjustments and comparisons. It should be noted that neither cosmic radiation intensity nor atmospheric pressure is linearly related to altitude.

In all three cases, the regression coefficient is the least squares estimate from the data in the upper portion of Table 3. Data for the states of Delaware, Illinois, Indiana, Idaho and Montana are not employed since, as noted previously, these data are not summarized by county and therefore do not include the small portion of non-white births and deaths which invariably elevate the final mortality rates. Utah is the exception, but within the state the data are consistent with the relationships noted in Fig. 5. Individual counties in Utah range from 3,500 to 7,000 feet and a progressive increase in mortality rate is detectable across this range. The rate of change is similar to the above noted regressions and the equation for Utah is

$$Y = 7.78 + (1.83 \times 10^{-3} \pm 0.79 \times 10^{-3})A.$$

Comparison of areas with and without uranium ore. The data in Table 4 also present the mortality rates in the six provinces according to the presence or absence of uranium ore and, for western Kansas and the Texas Panhandle, the presence or absence of helium reserves. The helium reserves are considered since, as Kratchman and Grahn (1959) indicated, these reserves may be the result of the disintegration of localized disseminations of uranium and therefore reflect a higher than average level of environmental radiation. The differences within provinces are not significant and uranium-bearing counties are as likely to have mortality rates above as below their control areas. There is, however, a small confounding of altitude in these comparisons.

In order to ascertain if any relationship may exist between mortality and the presence of uranium ore in the absence of the altitude variable, the 57 counties with ore reserves (excluding Utah) were adjusted to a constant altitude of 3,000 feet. These adjusted mortality rates were plotted against a crude measure of ore concentration; tons of U_3O_8 per 1,000 square miles. No correlation was evident even across six log cycles of difference in ore concentration. The regression coefficient of death rate on log ore concentration is $+0.113 \pm 0.625$. *Thus, it can be concluded that the quantity of uranium ore reserves is unassociated with the probability of neonatal mortality.* However, in the absence of direct measurement of radiation levels in the 57 counties, these results cannot be considered as having entirely eliminated an interpretation based on radiation-induced injury.

Birth weight and associated parameters. In the course of the analysis of neonatal mortality, it became increasingly apparent that other measures associated with

TABLE 5. Duration of gestation and birth weight for selected states; 1956 and 1958 white population only.

State	Altitude (feet)	Duration of gestation (wks)	Birth weight (grams)
Illinois-Indiana	630	40.40	3,342
Arizona	2,080	40.28	3,300
Idaho-Montana	3,400	40.13	3,290
Utah	4,590	40.23	3,288
New Mexico	5,010	40.17	3,169
Colorado	5,390	40.01	3,152

the birth event had to be examined, since the observed relationship with altitude strongly suggested the existence of an underlying subtle disturbance of reproductive physiology.

Table 5 presents data drawn from the 1956 and 1958 statistics on gestation length and birth weight for the indicated states that were selected for their distribution between sea level and 6,000 feet and the adequacy of sample size for live births. There is a decline in the duration of gestation with increasing altitude, but the maximum difference is only about 1 percent of the average duration, or about 0.4 weeks. This is not significant and will not explain the

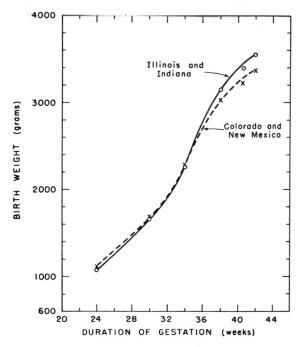

FIG. 6. Fetal growth curves derived from data on live birth weights for 1950–51 white population.

birth weight difference of 190 grams between Colorado and Illinois-Indiana. Figure 6 describes the fetal growth curves for Illinois-Indiana versus Colorado-New Mexico for the years 1950–51. This suggests that during the last 10 weeks of gestation the growth rate of the fetus at 5,000 feet or more progressively falls behind that for the fetus at or near sea level.

It would thus appear that, all other factors being equal, the duration of gestation may be slightly shorter at higher altitudes. In addition, birth weight is several hundred grams lower, apparently because of a depressed growth rate in the third trimester. With these observations in mind, the 1952–57 birth-weight classification data can be examined as an indication of more extensive physiological perturbation.

TABLE 6. Percentage of live births at 2,500 grams or less by altitude interval: 1952–57 white population only, Utah not included.

Altitude Interval (feet)	Mean Alt.	Atm. Press (mm Hg)	No. Live Births	% 2,500 grams or less
0–500	263	753	35,166	6.57
501–1,000	633	743	7,147	6.66
1,001–1,500	1,118	729	73,318	6.17
1,501–2,000	1,786	713	13,809	7.97
2,001–2,500	2,286	699	56,570	7.78
2,501–3,000	2,864	684	12,207	7.14
3,001–3,500	3,256	674	50,933	8.24
3,501–4,000	3,756	662	60,226	8.46
4,001–4,500	4,287	649	63,160	8.67
4,501–5,000	4,824	636	100,420	9.47
5,001–5,500	5,237	627	133,617	10.37
5,501–6,000	5,661	617	28,011	9.80
6,001–6,500	6,149	605	53,899	10.74
6,501–7,000	6,767	591	26,619	11.54
7,001–7,500	7,213	582	10,712	11.17
7,501–8,000	7,721	570	9,427	13.04
8,001–9,000	8,519	553	2,474	12.93
9,001–10,000	9,568	532	887	16.57
10,001–11,000	10,410	513	1,697	23.7

The percentage of live births falling in the category, "immature," 2,500 grams or less, is summarized by altitude intervals in Table 6. This summary is based upon the county altitude values without regard to state or geologic province, for all states except Utah. In the 1952–57 period, between 3 percent and 5 percent of the birth weights were not reported. Although these are generally distributed across all weight categories, failure to report tends to occur more frequently for small infants. If so, there is probably a slightly greater rate of increase in frequency of immaturity with altitude than noted here.

In Fig. 7, the data are fitted with two equations; a first and a second degree polynomial. The equations are:

$$Y_1 = 30.6 - (0.033 \pm 0.003)P \text{ and}$$

$$Y_2 = 83.8 - (0.195 \pm 0.052)P + (0.000122 \pm 0.000039)P^2,$$

where Y is percentage of live births at 2,500 grams or less, and P is atmospheric pressure in mm of Hg. Sea level values are:

$$Y_1 = 5.6 \qquad Y_2 = 6.4.$$

The data for Utah are shown separately in Fig. 7. As noted previously for the neonatal death rate, the values lie below the trend but conform to it. Thus, the basic environmental factor, or factors, associated with altitude has the same effect on all fetuses and newborn. The "intercept" of the relationship can be shifted, however, by other undefined aspects of the general environment.

As birth weight drops below 3,500 grams, the probability of death in the neonatal period increases exponentially (U.S. Department of Health, Education, and Welfare, 1954). In the special study referred to, the neonatal mor-

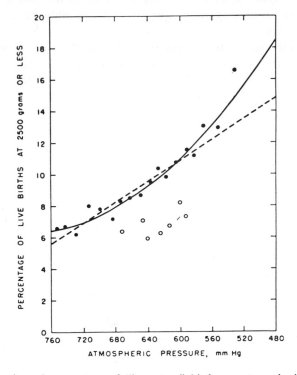

FIG. 7. Regression of percentage of "immature" births on atmospheric pressure. Dotted line: $Y = 30.6 - 0.033\ P$; solid line: $Y = 83.8 - 0.195\ P + 0.000122\ P^2$. Open circles: Utah. Solid circles: All other surveyed counties.

tality rate was 175.8/1000 live births at 2,500 grams or less than 7.1/1000 at 2,501 grams or more. Although directly applicable statistics are not available, it is possible to combine birth weight distribution data with the mortality— weight data and calculate neonatal death rates for Colorado, for example, that are reasonably close to the observed values. Apparently, most of the excess mortality in the mountain states can be attributed to their lower birth weights. In this regard, it should be noted that the published weight distribution data clearly indicate that the whole distribution of birth weights is shifted downward in the mountain states. The increased frequency of immature births is not due to a skewing of the distribution or to an accumulation of births in a few weight-class intervals below the mean. This is an extremely important factor since it indicates the existence of a generalized phenomenon affecting fetal growth and development, not a factor with a limited effect, such as one causing only an increase in premature delivery of extremely small fetuses.

Age-specific mortality and causes of death.   The time and causes of death have been examined for several selected states with the hope this might reveal differences that could assist in the interpretation of the mortality and birth weight data. It should be emphasized, however, that the cause of death data are subject to considerable difference of diagnostic opinion and can only be evaluated in a broad sense.

Table 7 gives the death rate, by specific cause, for the total neonatal period, of Illinois-Indiana and Colorado-Wyoming. This comparison is emphasized on the assumption that these four states would be more similar in their levels of medical practice and socioeconomic status than comparisons involving the border states. About 95 percent of all deaths are included in the selected categories.

Most of the deaths fall into a few classes: malformations, birth injuries, postnatal asphyxia and atelectasis, and immaturity. The death rate from birth injuries and immaturity is 30 to 50 percent higher in Colorado-Wyoming than in Illinois-Indiana, while only slight increases are noted for malformations and asphyxia. Other causes vary in the degree of excess, but a few points bear mention. Several causes of death are predominantly of genetic origin; congenital malformation, erythroblastosis, hernia and intestinal obstructions, and possibly asphyxia and atelectasis. These causes are elevated in frequency by only 2 to 18 percent in the mountain states, while the oher causes are elevated by 35 to 137 percent. Since birth weight is lower at higher altitudes, it is not surprising to find an excess of mortality associated with immaturity as a concurrent qualification or as an unqualified cause.

Data for New Mexico and Utah are also presented in Table 7. Although Utah has a total death-rate ratio to Illinois-Indiana of 0.95, there is an array of causes of death that are in excess. These include maternal toxemia, erythroblastosis, hemorrhagic diseases and the ill-defined diseases (largely nutritional maladjustment and congenital debility).

TABLE 7. Mortality ratios for selected causes of death; 1950–57 white population only. Illinois-Indiana = 1.00.

Cause of Death	Ill.-Ind. Death Rate (per 10,000 live births)	Mortality Ratio		
		Colorado-Wyoming	New Mexico	Utah
Hernia; intest. obst.	1.73	1.18	1.14	0.92
Cong. malformation	25.91	1.02	1.05	0.98
Birth injury	26.08	1.48	1.21	0.89
w/o immat.	11.28	1.12	1.24	0.86
with immat.	14.80	1.76	1.19	0.91
Postnatal asphyxia and atelectasis	47.80	1.07	0.81	0.80
w/o immat.	13.92	0.81	0.96	0.79
with immat.	33.88	1.17	0.75	0.81
Pneumonia	6.66	1.44	1.43	0.51
w/o immat.	4.55	1.26	1.48	0.47
with immat.	2.11	1.84	1.35	0.60
Diarrhea	0.88	2.19	5.50	0.72
Matern. toxemia	1.24	1.59	1.59	1.80
Erythroblastosis	6.97	1.06	1.12	1.23
Hemorrhagic dis.	1.73	1.64	0.95	1.19
Ill defined dis.	3.55	2.37	3.89	1.69
w/o immat.	0.66	1.51	4.05	1.60
with immat.	2.89	2.57	3.86	1.71
Immaturity	43.63	1.35	1.81	1.03
Accidents	1.07	1.65	2.59	0.84
All causes	173.03	1.28	1.40	0.95

While variation in diagnostic accuracy and completeness certainly exists, immaturity and the ill-defined diseases are definitely excessive as causes of death in New Mexico, Utah, Colorado, and Wyoming. Except for erythroblastosis in Utah, the causes that may be more genetic in origin are not particularly in excess in these states.

During the first 28 days of life, the death rate drops almost exponentially. The mountain states, exclusive of Utah, have a higher rate of mortality through-out the whole time period, but it is not uniformly in excess of the Illinois-Indiana base line. The data in Table 8 and Fig. 8 indicate the existence of a sharp increase in the mortality ratio for Colorado-Wyoming during the second and third full days of life. This drops back rapidly in the latter half of the first week, then rises again to a more steady level of excess mortality during the second through fourth weeks of life. This plateau continues throughout most of the first year. The early peak also appears in the data of New Mexico and Arizona though less markedly for Arizona. Since the latter has a mean altitude of about 2,000 feet compared to the 5,000 feet or more in the other states, this early period of high risk may be a characteristic of high altitude populations.

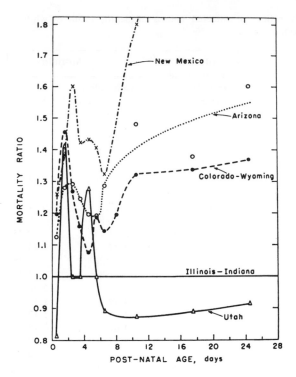

FIG. 8. Mortality ratios for age-specific mortality from all causes. Ratio equals New Mexico/Illinois-Indiana, etc.

TABLE 8. Mortality ratios for all causes of death during neonatal period; 1950–57 white population only. Illinois-Indiana = 1.00.

Age (days)	Ill.-Ind. Death Rate (per 10,000 per day)	Mortality Ratio			
		Colo.-Wyo.	New Mexico	Ariz.	Utah
0	927	1.20	1.26	1.13	0.81
1	250	1.46	1.38	1.28	1.41
2	171	1.27	1.60	1.29	1.00
3	90	1.16	1.42	1.24	1.00
4	51	1.08	1.43	1.20	1.28
5	37	1.19	1.41	1.19	1.00
6	28	1.14	1.32	1.29	0.89
7–13	13.7	1.32	1.80	1.48	0.88
14–20	7.7	1.34	2.17	1.38	0.89
21–27	5.4	1.37	2.38	1.60	0.92

Unfortunately, the published data are not reported in a way that permits the calculation of age-specific mortality rates by cause for the individual states, so it is not possible to associate the early period of high risk with specific causes.

The mortality ratios for the state of Utah generally conform to the results for the surrounding mountain states. There is a higher level of mortality during the first week, though it tends to broaden out over most of the week before dropping to a lower stable level. Since the Utah data demonstrate a small mortality excess due to immaturity, the early peak may be the result of a more rapid selection against the immature infant when subject to the additional stress of a lower ambient partial pressure of oxygen.

Discussion

The neonatal mortality rate is unquestionably higher in most of the mountain states than in the coastal and midwestern regions. The analysis clearly indicates that there is a regular increase in neonatal death rate with increasing altitude and that this relationship is probably independent of the geologic environment. The correlation with altitude, however, may be due to a number of factors, but the associated increase in cosmic ray intensity and decrease in oxygen partial pressure would appear to require special attention.

For the most part, the increased neonatal death rate appears to be a direct function of the lower birth weight that characterizes the higher altitude populations. The proportion of live births classed as immature progressively increases with altitude, and there is evidence that this may be due to a depression of fetal growth. In addition, the age-specific mortality rates indicate the existence of a peak of the mortality-ratio in the first days of life for the infants at higher altitude compared to Illinois and Indiana.

Radiation as a causative agent. The original working hypothesis of this study, that increased levels of environmental radiation underlie the higher neonatal mortality rates, is based on genetic concepts. Specifically, it was assumed that higher radiation levels would result in an increased mutation rate that would express itself in part by an increase in early mortality. However, it is extremely difficult either to prove or disprove a genetic argument on the basis of only the published vital statistics data.

Although neonatal mortality is known to have a genetic component (see summary by Stern, 1960), different studies vary in the importance accorded the genotype for the control of perinatal and neonatal deaths. There is apparently no simple way of calculating the proportion of genetic deaths occurring in the neonatal period; we roughly estimate the figure to be about 20 percent. This assumes that all of the erythroblastosis, one-half of the hernia and malformation, one-fifth of the atelectasis and one-tenth of the pneumonia and immature categories are genetic in origin. Most of these deaths are in the erythroblastosis and congenital malformation categories. Examination of the data revealed that the mortality rates for these two causes of death are very similar in the different parts of the United States that were surveyed. This is particularly true for malformation deaths, which would suggest that a genetic hypothesis to explain the higher neonatal death rates is not appropriate.

Data of the present type have sometimes been employed for the calculation of the genetic doubling dose for man. Such efforts are not appropriate. A brief exploration of the concept will emphasize this and indicate the tenuous nature of any radiation genetic hypothesis to interpret these or similar data reported by Gentry *et al.* (1959) and Wesley (1960). If a doubling dose were to be calculated, two assumptions concerning the population are implicit. One, it is assumed that the population is in genetic equilibrium with respect to the induction and elimination of detrimental genes. Two, it is further assumed that all excess mortality can be attributed to genetic factors. Neither of these assumptions can be met. If one now assumes that excess neonatal death is due to dominant genes, only a single generation would be required to reach equilibrium. However, if this were the case, the Hiroshima-Nagasaki survivorship should have demonstrated tremendous increases in the incidence of early mortality, whereas the actual changes were either negative or insignificantly positive (Neel and Schull, 1956). The average dose to the exposed Japanese population was between 35 to 40 r while that to the U.S. mountain population is only about 2 r/generation/gamete above the sea level exposure.

Certainly, the U.S. population is not in genetic equilibrium. In most of the mountain regions, there have been only about three generations at risk. The average generation number would be less, since these populations have grown by a factor of about 70 in the last 100 years while the balance of the U.S. has grown by a factor of only 6 or 7. Most of this difference must be due to migration, which reduces the rate of approach to equilibrium. Therefore, if one did then assume the population to be in equilibrium for recessive genes, the probability of death of the heterozygote would have to be over 30 percent, which is about 10 times greater than generally noted (Morton, Crow and Muller, 1956; Fraser, 1962).

Birth weight also has a genetic component (Morton, 1955, 1958; Penrose, 1954), but the amount of genetic variation appears small. If weight is controlled by a polymorphic genetic system where weights in the 2,500 to 4,000 gram interval represent the adaptive norm, as suggested by Stern (1960), then the observed changes in birth weight distribution are contrary to genetic expectation. In this study, the whole distribution of weights is shifted, rather than an increase occurring in only the extreme weight classes, as would be expected if there were an increased segregation of detrimental homozygous gene combinations. A polygenic, additive genetic system under the pressure of an increased frequency of detrimental genes would behave in the manner observed, but again, the 190-gram weight shift is far in excess of any reasonable expectation according to experience (Neel and Schull, 1956; Morton, 1958).

Direct irradiation of the fetus must also be considered as a possible basis for the decreased birth weight and increased mortality rate. In the mountain states, the fetus would receive a dose of 50 to 60 mr over that at sea level, and protracted over the full gestation period. There are no comparative experimental or clinical data at this extremely low dose rate or total dose. There are some data, however, on mice (Russell, Badgett and Saylors, 1960) and rats (Brown *et al.,* 1962) exposed at rates between 2 r and 20 r/day. At doses of 10 r/day or less there is no significant effect on birth weight.

Microcephaly and other deformities have been observed among children exposed *in utero* at Hiroshima and Nagasaki (Plummer, 1952). These were all among the more heavily irradiated as judged by radiation injury and distance from the hypocenter. Doses of several hundred roentgens or more were probably involved. A search for abnormal skeletal development among children irradiated *in utero* was negative (Sutow and West, 1955). Birth weight data are not available on these children.

The observed weight and mortality parameters in the U.S. mountain states are similar to those of radiation-induced injury from exposure *in utero,* but, as with genetic considerations, the present data indicate changes far in excess of any clinical or experimental radiation experience. If radiation were the predominant causative agent through either genetic or somatic pathways, man would be characterized by such an extremely high level of radiosensitivity that it would almost certainly have been detected many years ago, and particularly in the Japanese studies. As the data stand, there is no evidence for the existence of such an extreme radiosensitivity.

Hypoxia as a causative agent. It has been mentioned above that a reduced partial pressure of oxygen has a detrimental effect on reproductive physiology. A fascinating report by Monge (1948) portrayed the historical and even evolutionary significance of this problem in the Spanish colonization of Peru. For example, the original Spanish capital city, Jauja, situated at 10,800 feet, was moved to the present location, Lima, near sea level, because of the relative infertility and high neonatal death rate among the livestock.

Reduced viability and an increased probability of early death has been observed in domestic and laboratory animals as well as in man, and the problem is of some economic importance for poultry breeding in the U.S. mountain states. Smith and Abbott (1961) noted that White Leghorn chickens have only 3 percent hatchability at 10,150 feet, although 93 percent of the eggs are fertile. Sixty percent hatch at sea level, and eggs laid at high altitude but brought to sea level for incubation have a normal hatch rate. Thus, the effect of altitude is transient. Additional evidence of the importance of oxygen was given by Davis (1955) and Moreng and Hartung (1959) who noted the improvement of hatch rate when the incubator air is supplemented with oxygen.

In the Sprague-Dawley rat, exposure to a simulated altitude of 18,000 feet for four hours a day reduces the average litter size by over 40 percent, and survival between birth and 21 days of age drops from 90 percent to 60 to 70 percent (Altland, 1949). Most of the drop in litter size was attributed to fetal resorption. The only persistently noted lesion was marginal necrosis and hemorrhage of the placenta, which was attributed to hypoxia. An additional report by Chiodi (1953) indicated that 35 percent mortality occurred in the first three days of life among rats born at 12,000 feet. This is prevented by raising the oxygen tension to sea level values.

The most significant data on man were derived from a study of infants born in Lake County, Colorado (10,000+ feet), which is the highest county in the U.S. Lake County infants are 380 grams lighter than Denver infants (Lichty *et al.,* 1957) but congenital defects were no more frequent there than in Denver or New York. There was no effect attributable to race, socioeconomic status or diet. Body length and head size were also smaller, but in accordance with normal relations between weight and length or circumference (Howard, Lichty and Bruns, 1957). Thus the reduced birth weight was due to an over-all reduction of growth. These clinical measures conform to the earlier statistical observation that the whole distribution of birth weights is shifted to lower values.

One additional observation in the study by Howard *et al.* is particularly significant. This relates to the infants of mothers who had previously borne children outside of Lake County. For 120 mothers who met this criterion, there were 293 prior children with a mean birth weight of 3,130 grams and 261 children born in Lake County with an average weight of 2,840 grams. The 290-gram difference is more striking when considering that mean birth weight normally rises slightly with increasing maternal age. This observation emphasizes the direct nature of the altitude effect on the maternal-fetal physiological relationships.

The exact physiologic mechanism of the effect of reduced oxygen tension on fetal growth and neonatal mortality is somewhat obscure. An attempt to synthesize the observations and considerations of a number of investigators does offer the following as a possible interpretation (Barcroft, 1938; Boell, 1955; Windle, 1941; Acheson, Dawes and Mott, 1957; Metcalfe *et al.,* 1962). During the period of major differentiation and organogenesis, the oxygen supply is more than adequate as growth of the placenta is in excess of the demand placed upon it. The placenta, however, is structurally limited and therefore the blood volume it can handle is ultimately limited. Although minor fluctuations in oxygen exchange normally occur, there appear to be effective compensating mechanisms for this. When the available oxygen is limited by the physical environment, however, compensation by the fetus will take the form of a reduced oxygen requirement and the amount available for growth must therefore be reduced. In this way, average fetal growth rate in the last trimester could easily be depressed at higher altitudes, where the maternal and uterine environments are unable to provide the normal O_2 requirements.

Since the altitudes in the U.S. are not exceptionally high and the fetal death rates in the mountain states are not excessive, it can be concluded that the lower birth weight and subsequently increased neonatal death rate are an expression of minor adaptive failures detectable only in large populations.

The study has thus touched upon some interesting considerations of human ecology and the adaptive capabilities of man. Neonatal death might well be considered an extended expression of "pregnancy wastage," and of the most expensive form, both biologically and economically. The mountain states have a 20 percent to 30 percent higher rate of wastage than the U.S. averages but the pregnancy losses appear to be more than compensated by a greater reproductive activity. The preliminary reports of the 1960 census (U.S. Bureau of the Census, 1961) presented a measure of reproductive performance, the "fertility ratio," for all U.S. regions and states. This ratio is the number of children under 5 years of age per 1,000 women between the ages 15 and 49. The mountain region has the highest fertility ratio in the U.S.; 560, compared to the U.S. average of 488. There is also a generally positive relationship between this ratio and the neonatal death rate across the whole U.S.

Very likely, the non-transient residents of the mountain states become progressively acclimatized and less susceptible to pregnancy loss. However, early death is also a very effective means of natural selection for parent stock of greater adaptability. The existence of what would now be recognized as a genetic basis for resistance to hypoxia was described centuries ago by the Spanish colonists in Peru (Monge, 1948). Intermarriage of Peruvian Indian and Spanish produced offspring more capable of survival at high altitude. It was noted that infants with one parent of pure Indian descent enjoyed greater viability than those with one-quarter, one-eighth or less admixtures of the native genotype. Selection for fertile and fecund breeding stock in sheep has also been successful in the Andes. In this country, selection experiments with poultry have succeeded in improving the viability of standard breeds at elevations above 7,000 feet (Davis, 1955; Smith and Abbott, 1961). Heritability of resistance to the hypoxic environment has been estimated to be between 0.30 and 0.65, comparable to other estimates of heritability of viability in poultry (Lerner, 1950). Thus, the high-altitude environment is an excellent example of a general environmental stress factor to which man and the domestic animals can or have responded in the most classical manner, by selection for the viable genotype.

In conclusion, a word should be said about previous efforts to relate congenital malformation frequency and death rate to environmental radiation. The study by Wesley (1960) hardly deserves mention, since it was inappropriate to accept world-wide figures on malformation deaths as diagnostically accurate and comparable. The study by Gentry *et al.* (1959) was carefully done and relatively complete. Although New York state has some areas with altitudes above 3,000 feet, as in the Adirondacks, the results probably cannot be attributed to altitude, since altitude appears to have little influence on malformation incidence, even though brief periods of severe anoxia are known to induce malformations in mice (Ingalls, Curley and Prindle, 1952). It is difficult to interpret the New York study, but the present study certainly would not support a radiation genetic hypothesis, as put forth by Gentry *et al.* The completeness of ascertainment of malformations is open to question, since the original study detected an under-reporting that may have been as high as 50 percent. Urban-rural differences in the continuity of medical observation may also be a problem. Lastly, in spite of the existence in the mountain states of local uranium concentrations many times greater than in New York, no detrimental effects could be attributed solely to the geologic environment.

Summary

Variation in the neonatal death rate in selected areas of the Western United States has been evaluated with reference to the geologic environment and the presence or absence of known uranium and helium reserves. While the neonatal death rate is unquestionably higher in the mountain regions, this does not appear to be attributable to higher levels of terrestrial radiation. A significant positive relationship does exist between death rate and altitude. The increased death rate can be largely attributed to a lower birth weight, since the frequency of immature births, on a weight criterion, progressively increases with altitude. The observed correlations with altitude have been evaluated in terms of either the increase in cosmic radiation intensity or the decrease in oxygen partial pressure, or both. The data have been evaluated in terms of three hypotheses; radiation-induced mutation, radiation-induced injury to the fetus, and hypoxia-induced depression of fetal growth. Very little of the excess neonatal death can be attributed to the readily-defined genetic factors, and direct fetal irradiation was concluded to be of no significance. The weight of the evidence—historical, experimental, and clinical—strongly suggests that the reduced partial pressure of oxygen is responsible for the reduced fetal growth and subsequently increased neonatal death rate.

REFERENCES

ACHESON, G. H., DAWES, G. S., and MOTT, J. C. 1957. Oxygen consumption and the arterial oxygen saturation in fetal and newborn lambs. *J. Physiol* (Lond.) **135:** 623–642.

ALTLAND, P. D. 1949. Breeding performance of rats exposed repeatedly to 18,000 feet simulated altitude. *Physiol. Zool.* **22:** 235–246.

BARCROFT, J. 1938. *Features in the architecture of physiological function.* Cambridge: Cambridge Univ. Press.

BOELL, E. J. 1955. Energy exchange and enzyme development during embryogenesis. In: *Analysis of Development,* B. H. Willier, P. A. Weiss, and V. Hamburger, Eds. Philadelphia: W. B. Saunders Co., p. 520–555.

BROWN, S. O., KRISE, G. M., PACE, H. B., SORG, V., and TRIGG, J. 1962. The effects of pre- and postnatal irradiation on the development, growth and maturation of the albino rat. *Annual Prog. Report, Rad. Biol. Lab., Texas Eng. Exp. Sta., College Station, Texas.*

BUGHER, J. C., and MEAD, P. A. 1958. Frequency of bone sarcoma in the U.S. in relation to low level radiation exposure. *Proc. II. Intern. Conf. Peaceful Uses of Atomic Energy* **23:** 165–170.

CHIODI, H. 1953. Mortality of young rats at mountain heights. *J.A.M.A.* **153:** 162.

COURT BROWN, W. M., SPIERS, F. W., DOLL, R., DUFFY, B. J., and McHUGH, M. J. 1960. Geographical variation in leukemia mortality in relation to background radiation and other factors. *Brit. Med. J.* **1:** 1753–1759.

CRAIG, L., and SEIDMAN, H. 1961. Leukemia and lymphoma mortality in relation to cosmic radiation. *Blood* **17:** 319–327.

DAVIS, G. T. 1955. Influence of oxygen concentration on hatchability and on selecting for hatchability. *Poultry Sci.* **34:** 107–113.

FRASER, G. R. 1962. Our genetic 'load.' A review of some aspects of genetical variation. *Ann. Hum. Genet.* **25:** 387–415.

GENTRY, J. T., PARKHURST, E., and BULIN, E. V., JR. 1959. An epidemiological study of congenital malformations in New York State. *Amer. J. Public Health* **49:** 497–513.

HOWARD, R. C., LICHTY, J. A., and BRUNS, P. D. 1957. Studies of babies born at high altitude. II. Measurement of birth weight, body length and head size. *Amer. J. Dis. Child.* **93:** 670–674.

INGALLS, T. H., CURLEY, F. J., and PRINDLE, R. A. 1952. Experimental production of congenital anomalies. *New Engl. J. Med.* **247:** 758–768.

KRATCHMAN, J., and GRAHN, D. 1959. Relationships between the geologic environment and mortality from congenital malformation. *U.S. Atomic Energy Comm. Report. TID-8204.*

LERNER, I. M. 1950. *Population genetics and animal improvement.* Cambridge: Cambridge Univ. Press.

LICHTY, J. A., TING, T. Y., BRUNS, P. D., and DYAR, E. 1957. Studies of babies born at high altitude. I. Relation of altitude to birth weight. *Amer. J. Dis. Child* **93:** 666–669.

METCALFE, J., GIACOMO, M., HELLEGERS, A., PRYSTOWSKY, H., HUCKABEE, W., and BARRON, D. H. 1962. Observations on the placental exchange of the respiratory gases in pregnant ewes at high altitude. *Quart. J. Exp. Physiol.* **47:** 74–92.

MONGE, C. 1948. *Acclimatization in the Andes.* Baltimore: Johns Hopkins Press.

MORENG, R. E., and HARTUNG, T. E. 1959. Turkey breeding practices. *Colorado State Univ. Exp. Station Bull. 520-S, Fort Collins, Colorado.*

MORTON, N. E. 1955. The inheritance of human birth weight. *Ann. Hum. Genet.* **20:** 125–134.

MORTON, N. E. 1958. Empirical risks in consanguineous marriages: birth weight, gestation time, and measurements of infants. *Amer. J. Hum. Genet.* **10:** 344–349.

MORTON, N. E., CROW, J. F., and MULLER, H. J. 1956. An estimate of the mutational damage in man from data on consanguineous marriages. *Proc. Nat. Acad. Sci.* **42:** 855–863.

NEEL, J. V., and SCHULL, W. J. 1956. The effect of exposure to the atomic bombs on pregnancy termination in Hiroshima and Nagasaki. *Nat. Acad. Sci.-Nat. Research Council, Publ. 461, Washington, D.C.*

PENROSE, L. S. 1954. Some recent trends in human genetics. *Proc. IX Intern. Cong. Genet., Caryologia (Suppl.)* **6:** 521–530.

PLUMMER, G. 1952. Anomalies occurring in children exposed *in utero* to the atomic bomb in Hiroshima. *Pediatrics* **10:** 687–693.

RUSSELL, L. B., BADGETT, S. K., and SAYLORS, C. L. 1960. Comparison of the effects of acute, continuous and fractionated irradiation during embryonic development. In:*Immediate and low level effects of ionizing irradiation,* A. A. Buzzati-Traverso, Ed. London: Taylor and Francis, Ltd., p. 343–359.

SMITH, A. H., and ABBOTT, U. K. 1961. Adaptation of the domestic fowl to high altitude. *Poultry Sci.* **40:** 1459.

SOLON, L. R., LOWDER, W. M., SHAMBON, A., and BLATZ, H. 1959. Further investigations of natural environmental radiation. *Health and Safety Laboratory, U.S. Atomic Energy Comm. Report HASL-73.*

SOLON, L. R., LOWDER, W. M., SHAMBON, A., and BLATZ, H. 1960. Investigations of natural environmental radiation. *Science* **131:** 903–906.

STERN, C. 1960. *Principles of Human Genetics,* 2nd Ed. San Francisco: W. H. Freeman Co.

SUTOW, W. W., and WEST, E. 1955. Studies on Nagasaki (Japan) children exposed *in utero* to the atomic bomb. *Amer. J. Roentgenol.* **74:** 493–499.

U.S. Bureau of the Census. 1953. *U.S. Census of Population: 1950. Vol. II, Characteristics of the population. Parts 1, 3, 5, 6, 16, 27, 28, 31, 34, 41, 43, 44, 47, 50.* Washington: U.S. Gov't. Printing Office.

U.S. Bureau of the Census. 1961. *U.S. Census of Population: 1960. General population characteristics, United States Summary. Report PC(1)-113.* Washington: U.S. Gov't. Printing Office.

U.S. Department of Health, Education and Welfare. *Vital Statistics of the United States, Vol. I., 1950–1958.* Washington: U.S. Gov't. Printing Office.

U.S. Department of Health, Education and Welfare. 1954. *Weight at birth and its effect on survival of the newborn in the United States, early 1950. Vital Statistics-Special Reports, Selected Studies, Vol. 39, No. 1.*

U.S. Department of Health, Education and Welfare. 1958. *Weight at birth and survival of newborn by age of mother and total-birth order: United States, early 1950. Vital Statistics-Special Reports, Selected Studies, Vol. 47, No. 2.*

WESLEY, J. P. 1960. Background radiation as the cause of fatal congenital malformation. *Int. J. Radiat. Biol.* **2:** 97–118.

WINDLE, W. F. 1941. *Physiology of the fetus.* Philadelphia: W. B. Saunders Co.

CYCLES IN MAN

It is a common observation that biological cycles are associated with the rhythms of the physical world. Within the past ten years a great volume of research has been done on man and his cycles. The paper by Knobloch and Pasamanick deals with a theme which is common in current studies of cycles in man.

Consult the paper by MacMahon and Sowa (Supplementary Readings) for a positive reaction and the paper by Lander, Forssman, and Akesson (Supplementary Readings) for a negative reaction. Other cycles in man are mentioned in the paper by Dubos.

SUPPLEMENTARY READINGS

BUNNING, ERWIN, The Physiological Clock. 1964, Academic Press.

CLOUDSLEY-THOMPSON, J. L., Rhythmic Activity in Animal Physiology and Behaviour. 1961, Academic Press.

COLE, LAMONT C., Biological Clock in the Unicorn. 1957, *Science,* **125:** 874–876.

GOLDSCHMIDT, LEONTINE, Monthly Variations in Thermal Fragility of Erythrocytes in Man: Influence of Age and Sex. 1964, *Nature,* **201:** 791–793.

LANDER, ELVIR, HANS FORSSMAN and HANS OLOF AKESSON, Season of Birth and Mental Deficiency. 1964, *Acta Genetica et Statistica Medica,* **14:** 265–280.

ORME, J. E., An Ante-natal Determinant of Intelligence. 1963, *Nature,* **200:** 1239.

Seasonal Variation
in the Births
of the Mentally Deficient

HILDA KNOBLOCH,
AND BENJAMIN PASAMANICK

It is well known that the time at which injury to the developing fetus occurs results in a differential effect on the production of congenital anomalies. The embryonic stage, rather than the specific nature of the prenatal stress, appears to determine the type of malformation that will appear. Defects will manifest themselves in those organ systems that are undergoing the greatest amount of differentiation or organization at the time of the injury.[1] In the central nervous system[2] damage which occurs prior to the eighth week of fetal life usually results in gross anomalies, many of which are incompatible with life. During the eighth to twelfth week the cerebral cortex is undergoing its organization into the various molecular layers, and this period would be the critical time during which maternal stress would be apt to lead to those neuropsychiatric disabilities which result from cortical disorganization.

Infectious diseases play prominent roles in the production of central nervous system damage. Congenital lues in the past was one of the major conditions which acted during fetal life to produce remote as well as immediate damage to the brain. In the more recent past reports have appeared about the effect of rubella in the first trimester of pregnancy in the production of several central nervous system defects. Viral infections operate in the postnatal period to damage the brain and their effects are easily observed. The influence of similar infections in the mother during pregnancy is not as easily subjected to investigation, but it may be equally if not more important.

As a starting point, one of a series of neuropsychiatric disabilities—mental deficiency—was selected and a study designed to test the hypothesis that, because of the variation in the prevalence of viral infection, differences in the incidence of mental deficiency would occur which would be dependent on the season of birth. Infants conceived in the winter months it was postulated would have an in-

279

creased incidence of mental deficiency when compared to infants conceived in the summer months, because of the increase in the prevalence of these infections during the colder seasons.

Materials and method of study

The birth dates of all individuals who had ever been admitted to the Columbus State School were supplied by the Statistical Bureau of the Division of Mental Hygiene; patients who were born between 1860 and 1949 were included. The number of admissions in the years before the turn of the century and even well into the twentieth century was obviously small, either because of the incompleteness of the records or because of the limited facilities available. Likewise, because of the policy of the school of not admitting children under the age of six years, less than a dozen were born after 1948 at the time that the list was compiled. Since a minimum of 100 individuals per year was admitted from 1913 through 1948, the analysis was made on patients born in those years.

The number of births in each month was supplied by the Ohio State Health Department. These data were available for all of the years during which adequate numbers of admissions occurred with the exception of 1946, and this year was consequently eliminated from consideration. A rate which can be considered a "first admission rate" was then calculated according to the month of birth for those years already delineated above. This rate would express the seasonal variation in births of the mentally deficient. It is obviously not a precise expression of the differential incidence of mental deficiency, but is sufficiently analogous to permit substitution of the single word "incidence" for the more cumbersome phraseology.

It was recognized that, at the very most, only 10 percent of all of the mental defectives born in the state were admitted to the Columbus State School. Admissions are allocated to the 88 counties of the state strictly on the basis of county population, some counties having 24 admissions per year and some many times that number. Since the children are six years of age by the time that they are admitted, month of birth is not likely to be a factor taken into consideration in any decision to admit a child. It was also recognized that neither could account be taken of the precise amount of in- and out-migration; we do not believe that a decision to move is influenced by the month in which a child is born, however. There is no reason to believe, therefore, that bias would be introduced by either of these factors because of season of birth.

Findings and discussion

There is variation in the "first admission rate" for mental deficiency and the rate per 1,000 live births by month of birth is shown in Table 1. Contrary to what was predicted by the hypothesis, however, the greatest incidence occurs not in the late summer and early fall months but rather in the winter months,

TABLE 1. Mental deficiency first admission rates by month of birth, Columbus State School, 1913–1948 (excluding 1946).

Months	No. of Births	No. of Admissions	Rate/1,000
January	358,848	503	1.402
February	339,704	512	1.507
March	365,631	520	1.422
April	342,624	475	1.386
May	350,131	485	1.385
June	349,894	472	1.349
July	373,853	494	1.321
August	377,085	489	1.297
September	361,995	484	1.337
October	354,558	463	1.306
November	334,113	473	1.416
December	342,881	485	1.414
Total	4,251,317	5,855	1.377

the peak being found in February. This highest rate of 1.507 per 1,000 births for February is significantly higher than the rate of 1.297 for its seasonal counterpart for August (C.R. = 2.36; $P < 0.02$). Likewise, the rate of 1.442 for the first three months of the year is significantly higher than the rate of 1.318 for the contrasting months of July, August, and September (C.R. = 2.43; $P < 0.02$). These data are shown in Table 2. For the infants born in February the critical eighth to twelfth week of the gestation period would be the month of July.

Several possible explanations for this finding immediately come to mind. Since there is a higher admission rate to the Columbus State School from the lower socioeconomic groups and also a higher incidence of mental deficiency in

TABLE 2. "First admission rates" for mental deficiency by season of birth, Columbus State School, 1913–1948 (excluding 1946).

Season	No. of Births	No. of Admissions	Rate/1,000	
February	339,704	512	1.507	
				C.R. = 2.3 $P < 0.02$
August	377,085	489	1.297	
January, February, and March	1,064,183	1535	1.442	
				C.R. = 2.4 $P < 0.02$
July, August, and September	1,112,933	1467	1.318	

these groups, any differential between upper and lower socioeconomic groups in the planning of pregnancies would be reflected in the number of patients born in each of the different seasons. The assumption would be, then, that the upper economic groups planned their pregnancies so that their babies were delivered in July and August. This explanation has already been suggested by Goodenough[3] as the explanation for her observation of a slight superiority in IQ's of school children born in the summer months. It would not seem logical to plan to have children in the two hottest months of the year, but fortunately data are available and it is possible to examine the facts without having to inquire into motives.

There is a significant difference in the number of births by month. Analysis of some four million births in Ohio in the period from 1910 to 1955 indicates that the highest birth rates occur in July, August, and September. There is, curiously enough, another peak in February. Data on over 160,000 births in New York City in 1956 show a similar pattern. Data on approximately 23,000 births in Baltimore were used in comparing the upper and lower socioeconomic groups. Census tract of residence was the criterion for placing a birth into a given economic 10th of the population. The peak number of births for the smaller series tends to be in September, October, and November. There are, however, no significant differences according to socioeconomic status; if anything, there appears to be a somewhat higher birth rate for the upper socioeconomic groups for the winter period when compared to the lower socioeconomic groups. Differential planning of birth appears, therefore, to be an inadequate explanation for the seasonal variations in the births of the mentally deficient.

Mills has written extensively on the effects of climate on health and disease in man and animals. He indicates,[4] for instance, that in the rat thiamin requirement doubles as the temperature changes from 65°F. to 90°F. Members of the vitamin B complex act as catalysts at specific stages in glucose combustion and there has been much speculation about the effects of the alteration in the metabolism of glucose on the functioning of the central nervous system. In rats there are also many differences in learning and retention when litter mates kept on uniform diets for three months are reared in temperatures of 55°F., 75°F., and 90°F.[5] This effect apparently carries over to human beings as well. As only one example, students taking college entrance examinations during the summer achieve only about 60 percent of the ratings obtained on the same examination given in the winter.

More important than performance under diverse environmental conditions, perhaps, is the relation of the month of conception to certain later functions. Mills reports that children in the Cincinnati latitudes who are conceived in the summer months have just half the chance of entering college as those conceived in the winter months. There is a low likelihood of being included in "Who's Who" if there is a summer conception and only four out of the 33 presidents were conceived in the third quarter of the year. Peterson[6] has shown findings similar to those of our own, namely that feeble-minded children are more frequently conceived in the summer months. Mills[7] tends to attribute all of these findings to the beneficial effects of atmospheric instability and environmental stimulation, and the consequent greater metabolic potential of the germ cells.

Mills[5] also mentions that it has been shown, in animals at least, that it is possible to control the depressing effects of heat by adequate diet, particularly in respect to the vitamins and protein, and he points out that it is probably necessary to have proportionately more protein to meet the minimum requirements during the summer months when the total caloric intake is reduced.

In a study of a group of New Haven Negro infants born during the years of World War II[8] we demonstrated that white physical and behavioral developmental norms were followed. The only intragroup correlation was the significant superiority of those infants who were above weight at birth, as well as at the time of examination, over the infants who were below the median in weight at both times. It was felt that these findings could be explained on the basis of adequate prenatal care and adequate nutrition during pregnancy consequent to increased employment and wartime rationing.

On the basis of these findings it was postulated that the relationship between temperature and intellectual performance might, perhaps, be greatly influenced by the fact that the diet of the mothers may be poor in the hotter months of the year, and that this lowered dietary intake exerts its greatest effect during the eighth to twelfth week of gestation. If this were true, then it should be possible to demonstrate a difference in the incidence of mental deficiency on the basis of variations in temperature from one year to another.

Accordingly, the monthly mean temperatures for the six largest Ohio cities for which data were available were averaged. The temperatures during June, July, and August were those considered, since these were the months in which the eighth to twelfth week of gestation corresponded to those months of the year with the highest incidence of mental deficiency. The years in which the mean temperature was above the median were then contrasted with those years in which the temperature was below the median. These data were also based on the years from 1913 to 1948.

The differences in the "first admission rates" for mental deficiency, according to whether the mean temperature for the month was above or below the median, are shown in Table 3. When the eighth to twelfth week of pregnancy occurred in June, there are no significant differences in the incidence of mental deficiency between those years with temperatures below and above the median. For July and August the differences are highly significant. The rates in those years where the average temperature was above the median were 1.658 per 1,000 births for July and 1.519 for August, compared to rates of 1.276 and 1.206, respectively, in those years when the average temperature was below the median. Likewise, the differences for the total three-month period of June, July, and August were highly significant, being 1.524 for those years where the weather

TABLE 3. "First admission rates" for mental deficiency by month of birth according to mean temperature during the 8th to 12th week of pregnancy, Columbus State School, 1913–1948 (excluding 1946).

		8th to 12th Week of Pregnancy			
		June	July	August	Total
Mean Temperature		70.19	74.30	72.73	....
Temperature Below Median	No. of Births	170,788	175,522	186,494	532,804
	Admission Rate/1,000 Births	1.411	1.276	1.206	1.295
Temperature Above Median	No. of Births	181,126	171,293	187,598	540,017
	Admission Rate/1,000 Births	1.402	1.658	1.519	1.524

$X^2 = 10.02$
$P < 0.001$

was hot compared to 1.295 for the cooler years ($X^2 = 10.02$; $P < 0.001$). These differences between the warmer and cooler summers are greater than the differences observed between babies born in the first three months of the year and those born in the third quarter. The difference for the month of July on the basis of mean temperature is actually three times as great as the difference between the first and third quarters of all of the years under investigation. These highly significant differences would tend to support the hypothesis that inadequate dietary intake in early pregnancy during the hot summer months has an adverse effect on the development of the child. The number of cases was too small to permit analysis of variations from one season to another from year to year. Before combining all of the years together, however, variation in rates from one year to the next was examined. It was immediately obvious that in the depression years the rates were very much higher than in the nondepression years in both the post-World War I depression and the depression of the 1930's. However, the temperature differences for the so-called "boom years" and for the "depression years" were the same as for the total. Within each group the hotter summers were followed by a higher incidence of mental deficiency in the winter months, regardless of whether the over-all rate for the block of years was high, as in the depression years, or low, as in the boom group.

These findings appear to form one more link in the chain of events demonstrated by our previous studies of the association of prenatal and paranatal factors with the development of neuropsychiatric disabilities and the hypothesis of a continuum of reproductive casualty. These previous studies indicated that the complications of pre- and paranatal periods, particularly the chronic anoxia producing ones, such as toxemia and bleeding, and prematurity, were associated with an increased incidence of a series of clinical conditions ranging from cerebral palsy[9] through epilepsy,[10] mental deficiency,[11] behavior disturbances,[12] reading disturbances,[13] and tics.[14] A higher incidence of these complications of pregnancy was demonstrated in the lower socioeconomic groups[15,16] where dietary factors might be of considerable importance. Some authors[17] have demonstrated that toxemia of pregnancy can be prevented by supplying a diet adequate in protein and vitamins to the mother during gestation and at this time probably the most widely accepted theory of the cause of the toxemias of pregnancy is inadequate protein intake. There may, of course, also be a direct effect of protein deprivation on the production of mental deficiency per se without the necessity of the intermediary influence of toxemia. There have been many reports on a number of differences in infants whose mothers' diets have varied during pregnancy.

Under these theoretical assumptions one would expect to find differences similar to those in mental deficiency in the incidence of complications of pregnancy, and obstetricians are aware of a seasonal variation in toxemia. The New York City Health Department supplied data on the proportion of live birth certificates reporting one or more pathological conditions during pregnancy in 1956. Findings to be reported elsewhere indicate that all of the complications of pregnancy predicted by the hypothesis are significantly higher in the winter months.

These findings do not invalidate the infection hypothesis or preclude other explanations for the differences found. Infectious diseases probably play an important role prenatally. Since it is more likely that they act to a larger extent in the winter months rather than in the summer, these findings are only strengthened. As a matter of fact, the incidence of summer encephalitis was examined in an attempt to correlate it with the rates of admissions for mental deficiency and it was found that the rates were lower in the years when encephalitis was high in the summer months, although not significantly so. Another factor that immediately comes to mind as being associated with hot summer weather is salt depletion and this may very well play a role, the exact nature of which is not immediately clear at the present time.

There are, undoubtedly, complex interactions of many environmental influences which alter susceptibilities and change the manifestations of central nervous system damage. We are engaged in further investigations which may elucidate the etiologic factors and open up greater possibilities for prevention. A host of additional epidemiologic studies immediately comes to mind—an investigation of all the neuropsychiatric disabilities and complications of pregnancy by seasonal and temperature variation; the effect of geographic location on the production of differences in incidence; the influence of hyperemesis gravidarum on the development of the child. Intensification of dietary and behavioral experimentation with laboratory animals, where the experimenter can vary conditions at will, also appears indicated.

These findings also add to the mounting body of evidence, based on studies done by others as well as ourselves, that the characteristics of a human being are far from being immutably determined by the genes at the moment of conception. Environmental factors act continuously on the fetus from this moment, if they have not already significantly affected the parents also, to determine the anatomical structure as well as behavioral functioning. Except for a comparatively few and rare hereditary disorders, life experiences, rather than inherited characteristics, may be the primary factors making one individual significantly different from the next.

It does not appear necessary, however, to wait until the last iota of evidence is in, proving the association of diet and disability. Present knowledge, exclusive of the results of this study, would appear sufficient to demand that public health workers turn their attention more directly to this problem. We are well beyond the stage of paying lip service to the importance of the chronic diseases; possible avenues for prevention should be seized upon—and action taken. In a field as complex as behavioral functioning, prevention of dysfunction is often the only method of demonstrating etiology.

The possibility of dietary control in the prevention of disability need not be confined to efforts in this country, even though we recognize the tremendous cost of the neuropsychiatric disabilities in terms of chronicity, loss of productivity, family dislocation, and the need for provision of care.

There may be much more to gain in the developing countries which are, by and large, the tropical ones. The inability to improve productivity to support their increase in population, which is largely a result of public health measures in controlling acute infectious diseases, may well hinge on the long-term effects of diets which we know to be suboptimal. It seems likely that this damaging influence is acting not only on the present generation, but also on future individuals yet unborn to produce a whole series of neuropsychiatric disabilities. Breaking the vicious cycle by a concerted attack at one point, namely, women in the child-bearing period, could be extremely rewarding.

Summary

In studying the admissions of mentally defective children, born in the years 1913–1948, to the Columbus State School, it was found that significantly more had been born in the winter months, January, February, and March. Since the third month after conception is known to be the period during pregnancy when the cerebral cortex of the unborn child is becoming organized, any damage which occurred at that time could affect intellectual functioning. The months when this might happen would be June, July, and August, the hot summer months, when pregnant women might decrease their food intake, particularly protein, to dangerously low levels and consequently damage their developing babies. If this were so, one would expect that hotter summers would result in significantly more mental defectives born than following cooler summers. This was exactly what was found to a highly significant degree. Possible explanations of the above findings were sought in the occurrence of summer encephalitis and an increased birth rate in the lower socioeconomic group, but these were not confirmed.

These findings have wide public health implications, since the writers have shown previously not only that physical growth is affected by what happens to the unborn child but also that cerebral palsy, epilepsy, and even behavior and reading disorders may follow damage during this period. There is a growing body of evidence which indicates that it is very important for women in the child-bearing age to have good diets if they are to produce healthy, normally developing children. Inadequate dietary intake during pregnancy, because of heat as well as substandard economic conditions, may be an important link in the vicious cycle that results in poor physical and mental growth.

REFERENCES

1. INGALLS, THEODORE H. The Epidemiology of Congenital Malformations. In Mechanisms of Congenital Malformation. Proc. Second Conference of the Association for the Aid of Crippled Children. New York, N.Y.: Watkins 1954, pp. 10–20.

2. OSTERTAG, B. Die Einzelformen der Verbildung. In Handbuch der Speziellen Pathologischen Anatomie und Histologie. Berlin, Germany: Springer-Verlag, 1956, Vol. 13, Part IV, pp. 362–601.

3. GOODENOUGH, FLORENCE. Intelligence and Month of Birth. Psychological Bull. **37:** 442, 1940.

4. MILLS, CLARENCE A. Influence of Environmental Temperature on Warm-Blooded Animals. Ann. New York Acad. Sc. XLVI: 97–105, 1945.

5. ———. Temperature Dominance Over Human Life. Science 110, 267–271, 1949.

6. PETERSEN, WILLIAM F. The Patient and the Weather. Vol. III. Mental and Nervous Diseases. Ann Arbor, Mich.: Edwards Bros., 1934.

7. MILLS, CLARENCE A. Mental and Physical Development as Influenced by Season of Conception. Human Biol. 13, 3: 378–389, 1941.

8. PASAMANICK, BENJAMIN. A Comparative Study of the Behavioral Development of Negro Infants. J. Gen. Psychol. **59:** 3–44, 1946.

9. LILIENFELD, ABRAHAM M., and PASAMANICK, BENJAMIN. The Association of Prenatal and Paranatal Factors with the Development of Cerebral Palsy and Epilepsy. Am. J. Obst. & Gynec. **70:** 93–101, 1955.

10. LILIENFELD, ABRAHAM M., and PASAMANICK, BENJAMIN. Association of Maternal and Fetal Factors with the Development of Epilepsy. Abnormalities in the Prenatal and Paranatal Periods. J.A.M.A. **155:** 719–724, 1954.

11. PASAMANICK, BENJAMIN, and LILIENFELD, ABRAHAM M. Association of Maternal and Fetal Factors with the Development of Mental Deficiency. I. Abnormalities in the Prenatal and Paranatal Periods. Ibid. **159:** 155–160, 1955.

12. PASAMANICK, BENJAMIN; ROGERS, MARTHA E.; and LILIENFELD, ABRAHAM M. Pregnancy Experience and the Development of Childhood Behavior Disorder. Am. J. Psychiat. **112:** 613–618, 1956.

13. KAWI, ALI A., and PASAMANICK, BENJAMIN. The Association of Factors of Pregnancy with the Development of Reading Disorders in Childhood. J.A.M.A. (In press.)

14. PASAMANICK, BENJAMIN, and KAWI, ALI A. A Study of the Association of Prenatal and Paranatal Factors with the Development of Tics in Children: A Preliminary Investigation. J. Pediat. **48:** 596–601, 1956.

15. RIDER, ROWLAND V.; TABACK, MATTHEW; and KNOBLOCH, HILDA. Association Between Premature Birth and Socioeconomic Status. A.J.P.H. **45:** 1022–1028, 1955.

16. PASAMANICK, BENJAMIN; KNOBLOCH, HILDA; and LILIENFELD, ABRAHAM M. Socioeconomic Status and Some Precursors of Neuropsychiatric Disorders. Am. J. Orthopsychiat. **26:** 594–601, 1956.

17. TOMPKINS, W. T., and WIEHL, D. G. Nutritional Deficiencies as Causal Factor in Toxemia and Premature Labor. Am. J. Obst. & Gynec. **62:** 898–919 (Oct.), 1951.

Problems in Bioclimatology

RENÉ J. DUBOS

Ideally, the bioclimatologist should have the characteristics of both the classical and the romantic type of scientist, for he must deal quantitatively with the measurable effects that the known forces of the physical environment exert on biological processes, and he must also cultivate an awareness of the fact that other undefined cosmic factors influence in obscure but profound ways the growth, behavior, and fate of all living things. I must acknowledge immediately that I have never worked in any aspect of bioclimatology, nor have I made a systematic survey of the relevant literature. But as a student of the etiology of disease, both in individuals and in complex populations, I have come to realize, like many others, that bioclimatological mechanisms often condition both the etiology and the manifestations of pathological processes. While this type of experience constitutes no justification for dogmatic statements on bioclimatological problems, it has led to more general questions regarding the effects that environmental forces exert on living things and particularly on man. These questions I shall now try to formulate.

Biological rhythms

As everyone knows, most biological phenomena exhibit rhythms which are linked to those of the physical world. There are many well documented examples of biological cycles characterized by daily, seasonal, annual, or longer periodicities, and some of them have been studied in the laboratory with exquisite precision. For example, the phototactic response of Euglena exhibits a rhythm with a 24 hour period which is independent of temperature, at least between 16°C. and 33°C. The fact that this endogenous rhythm is exhibited by a unicellular organism demonstrates that "biological clocks"* do not require the

---

* A critical review of the concept of "biological clocks" has recently been published by Brown, F. A., Jr., *Am. Scientist,* **47,** 147 (1959).

complexities of nervous organization.[1] Other phenomena like the emergence of insects into activity act as landmarks for the season of the year and may be more complex in their determinism.[2] Our colleague, Dr. Frank L. Horsfall, has told me that he shelters under his Long Island home a colony of termites which regularly emerge between March 15 and March 25 every year, independently of any climatic factor of which he is aware.

Clearly, these rhythms are the manifestations of built-in biological clocks and for this reason they appear at first sight to have no bearing on our symposium. After all, as pointed out by Dr. Konrad J. K. Buettner,[3] nearly all biological and meteorological factors have a yearly and a daily period and, therefore, any correlation between the two groups is but an expression of the fact that weather and life take place on a revolving and rotating earth. Nevertheless, the problem of cycles is one pertinent to our discussion because the biological clocks are not as immutably set as appears; instead, they rapidly change their timing in accordance with changes in the physical environment. Let me illustrate this statement with a specific example taken from a very recent publication.

TABLE 1. Time displacement of potassium urinary excretion.

Place	Date	Meq/3 hr. at indicated time*		
		0–3	9–12	21–24
U.S.A.	8/1	3.1	15.8	5.7
Japan	8/5	21.8	6.5	11.4
Korea	10/14	4.5	12.7	4.6

* Time is recorded as local time. (Data from E. B. Flink and R. P. Doe, 1959).

In man, the urinary excretion of 17 hydroxycorticosteroids exhibits a well-defined and fairly stable daily rhythm. Thus, measurements of these adrenal hormones made at very frequent intervals during a thirty-hour shift by air travel from Continental United States (Central Standard Time) to Japan and Korea, revealed that the urinary excretion remained synchronized with C.S.T. even after arrival in Asia.[4] Progressively, however, the timing of excretion changed and after 9 days it had become synchronized with Asian time. The rhythm of excretion of sodium and potassium exhibited a similar pattern. Likewise, other physiological phenomena have cyclical patterns which are under the influence of the environment. Thus, the diurnal temperature rhythm in man was observed to change following airplane flight from Ontario to England. In this case, it took three to four days for the Canadian temperature rhythm to fall in step with the European rhythm.[5] The problem of biological cycles certainly lends itself to experimental analysis since changes in rhythm can be produced at will in laboratory animals. For instance, it has been possible by inverting the light schedule of mice for two weeks to produce shifts in daily rhythm with regard to blood eosinophils, mitoses in pinnal epidermis of liver, hepatic nucleic acid metabolism, and blood levels of corticosterone.[6]

As is well known, the Hippocratic writings repeatedly and forcefully emphasized that the occurrence of many types of disease has a marked seasonal character. In our communities, every one is aware of the winter incidence of acute respiratory disease and the summer incidence of poliomyelitis among human beings. And our colleague, Dr. Richard Shope, never tires of discussing the striking autumn incidence of hog influenza and hog cholera among the swine herds in the Middle West. Less well known, but almost as pronounced, are the seasonal ebbs and flows in the clinical manifestation of metabolic disorders, for example diabetes and circulatory diseases.[7, 8]

A number of well known facts immediately come to mind to suggest mechanisms through which climatological factors could indirectly affect the incidence or severity of disease. Crowding, physical activity, availability of certain types of food, prevalence of parasites and their vectors, etc. etc., are all factors in the causation of disease which are profoundly conditioned by the physical environment. But in addition to these obvious determinants there are others less well recognized, which are probably more significant. This belief is based on the fact that the internal environment of man—as well as of animals—is more variable than was believed a generation ago.[9]

There is no doubt of course that the essential characteristics of the internal environment must remain within certain limits to be compatible with the maintenance of life. On the other hand, it is also true that some of the biochemical activities of tissues can undergo profound quantitative variations and that some of these changes exhibit a marked seasonal pattern. A striking illustration of these biochemical cycles was discovered by C. and G. Cori some 30 years ago.[10] In the course of their studies on sugar metabolism, the Coris became aware of a marked seasonal variation in the ketonuria of rats kept without food for 48 hours. During the summer months (from May to October) the excretion of acetone

TABLE 2. Seasonal ketonuria in fasting rats.*

| Month | Mg of acetone bodies per diem | |
	per 100 gm. wt.	per rat
Apr.		32
May		67
June	6.2	51
July		36
Sept.		12
Oct.		5
Nov.		7
Dec.	1.9	5
Jan.		12
Feb.		7
March		7

* Data from G. and C. Cori, 1927 (seasonal averages) and from Burn and Ling, 1928 (monthly averages).

bodies brought about by fasting proved consistently to be three times greater than during the winter months. The fact that the excretion of acetone bodies did not rise during the winter when the rats were placed in a room at a temperature comparable to that of the summer provides evidence that factors other than heat were responsible for the greatest fasting ketosis observed during the summer.

These findings have been confirmed and extended in England by Burn and Ling,[11] who found indeed that the difference in fasting ketonuria between the spring-summer season and the fall-winter season was even much greater than that observed by the Coris. With the strain of rats used in England, the difference was of the order of ten-fold. Furthermore, the amount of glycogen in the liver of rats after 24 hours' fat diet also proved to vary according to a seasonal pattern, being much higher in the winter than in the summer.

There have been suggestions that this seasonal change has an evolutionary basis, namely that animal tissues have developed mechanisms which enable them to withstand successfully long periods of starvation in the winter. According to this view, energy requirements during the winter would be more likely to be met by combustion of the fat stores whereas this metabolic mechanism would not play as essential a role during the summer.[9, 11, 12]

While the intimate biochemical processes involved in the shift from summer to winter metabolism need not be discussed here, it is of interest to point out that the summer ketosis was associated with a reduced capacity of the tissues to oxidize glucose, and was probably due to a reduced functional activity of the pancreas. It appears, in other words, that the seasonal patterns of physiological behavior can have their basis in seasonal variations of hormonal activity. There are, of course, many other examples of cycles involving hormonal activity—for example, those associated with menstruation or those resulting in the diurnal variation in output of adrenal corticosteroids mentioned above. What must be emphasized anew at this time is that these built-in cycles are influenced by variable climatologic factors. It has long been known that the size of the thyroid and of the adrenals is normally greater in the winter than in the summer in laboratory animals, and can be altered at will by changing the environmental temperature (for a recent example, see reference 13). We have seen also that the rhythm in secretion of adrenal corticosteroids progressively varies when the geographical environment is changed. In fact, the study of these effects constitutes a rapidly expanding field of animal physiology. Suffice it to mention here as examples the studies of human performance in high mountains[14, 15] and of the nutritional aspects of climatic stress.[16] Professor Alexander von Muralt has kindly provided me for this occasion with a list of papers dealing with the pathological effects of weather on man. From these studies it appears that objective tests are available for quantitative observations as shown by the fact that warm fronts are associated with a decrease, and cold fronts with an increase, in capillary resistance.[17] It can hardly be doubted therefore that disease states—which in final analysis are always the expression of physiological disturbances—can be affected by the complex of physical forces which make up the climatological environment. Moreover, this statement applies not only to metabolic disorders, but just as well to diseases caused by microbial agents.

Population fluctuations

In addition to diurnal and seasonal rhythms which are well documented, there are other biological cycles with longer periodicities. It has long been known, of course, that plant and animal populations in the wild undergo tremendous quantitative changes.[18] For example, the records of the Hudson Bay Company provide fascinating material to document the statement that there have occurred large fluctuations in the numbers of fur animals as well as of the rodents on which they feed.[19, 20] The analysis of historical records and of the findings in recent wild life surveys have led to the belief that many population changes are determined by climatic factors, and furthermore there has been a tendency to accept that some at least of these changes exhibit a cyclic character. While the evidence for a true periodicity is not always convincing, there seems to be little doubt that population fluctuations are often the expression of responses to changes in the physical environment.

Well documented information bearing on this problem has come from the study of tree rings in the North American continent. Comparison of the thickness of tree rings has revealed that marked changes have occurred in the rate of plant growth during the past 2,000 years, probably as a result of variations in temperature and in atmospheric precipitation. There is reason to believe that these changes have also played an important part in the life of the Pueblo Indians—affecting the location of their settlements and the size of their population.[21] It is worth mentioning here that, as repeatedly emphasized by Huntington, climatic changes have probably been influential also in determining the growth and decay of other civilizations all over the world.

Fairly accurate information derived from wild life surveys in our time has provided evidence that the climate conditions both the distribution and the abundance of several animal species—as illustrated by the history of rabbit populations in Australia.[22, 23] The European rabbit *Oryctolagus cuniculus* was introduced into Tasmania at the beginning of the 19th century and spread over much of the island. Very rapidly, color variants became established and they now exist with different frequencies in different areas—the black rabbits reaching a frequency of 20 percent in places of highest rainfall. This particular example is of special interest because it illustrates that climatic factors can operate through genetic mechanisms. A related example is provided by the well-known fact that animals living in colder climates are usually larger than those of related species living in warmer climates. In most situations considered in the present report, however, mechanisms other than genetic must be invoked since the biological responses to climatic changes occur so rapidly that they can hardly be due to genetic alterations.

In certain cases, the explanation appears rather straightforward, for example with regard to plankton which changes continuously in abundance and composition from season to season and from year to year. In 1925 the warm equatorial counter-current off Columbia and Ecuador (El Nino) shifted its course so strongly to the South (as it does once every seven years) that the population of plankton, fish, and water birds normally found off the Peruvian coast fled or died, being replaced by warm water species.[24] When the current from the Atlantic predominates on the English coast, it brings water rich in phosphate which favors one species of glassworm on which the herring feeds. In contrast, current from the Channel brings in water poor in phosphate, resulting in failure of the herring fishery. The "red tide" which swept immense numbers of dead fish into the Florida beaches in 1946 and again in 1952, as it does approximately once a decade, was caused by a microscopic flagellate which is always present in the waters off the Florida coast, but in numbers too small to be harmful: its population reaches toxic levels only when atmospheric circumstances bring about the local stagnation of low-salt brackish water in certain areas.

In contrast to these fairly simple situations, the biological findings remain unexplained in most cases. Over the past three decades Errington[25] has analyzed the wild life surveys in Iowa with regard to populations of the ruffed grouse, the snowshoe hare, and especially the muskrats. The results of his analysis leave no doubt that the numbers of these animals have fluctuated enormously during the period under consideration. Yet there is no indication that heat, humidity, water levels, and other obvious variables can account for population changes, for disease states, or for patterns of behavior of the animals. While the findings are not explainable in terms of the meteorological data customarily recorded by the Weather Bureau, it is not impossible according to Errington that the biological patterns are related to the intensity of ultraviolet or other radiation—perhaps indirectly through some effect on the qualitative characteristics of the food available to the animals.

Decreases in the numbers of wild animals are commonly associated with a variety of disease states—both of metabolic and infectious character.[25, 26] It is therefore of importance to inquire into the evidence that climatological factors can actually affect resistance to disease. In fact, as already mentioned, there is a widespread belief among lay persons and physicians alike that certain types of weather disturbances are associated with particular illnesses.

In this country, Petersen and Mills[7, 8] have long emphasized that the incidence and gravity of each type of pathological disorder can be correlated with either climate or weather. As illustration it will suffice to mention here two types of weather which appear to be potentially harmful to man. One is the frontal or disturbed weather, the other the Föhn or Chinook with descending subtropical air in the whole troposphere, each type apparently bringing in its train a specific set of clinical and physiological events. Most familiar is the conviction expressed in many folklores that pains from scars and from arthritis sharpen during weather of the frontal type. Few are the persons indeed who do not believe that:

> "A coming storm our shooting corns presage,
> Our aches will throb, our hollow tooth will rage."

There are many reports, on the other hand, that periods of Föhn in Switzerland and in Southern Germany are associated with increases in death rates, in automobile accidents, and in circulatory as well as mental disorders.[3]

In these special climatic situations, the pathological disorders seem to occur without any detectable change in any of the known geophysical surface elements. The patients may not even be aware of any bad weather in the usual sense. It would appear, therefore, that these weather disturbances operate through physical factors which are still obscure or even completely unrecognized. A few related observations made with microorganisms are worth mentioning at this time. Whereas the metabolism of bacteria and yeast seems to be attenuated during cyclonic periods, it is intensified during anticyclones. By recording automatically such activities as luminescence, motility, acid production, sporulation, etc., it was found that the changes occurred so rapidly ($\frac{1}{2}$–1 hour) that they could not be correlated with the usual daily weather curves.[27]

Geophysical factors involved in bioclimatology

It would be appropriate at this point to discuss in detail the specific components of climate which are known, or have been claimed, to exert biological effects. However, this aspect of the problem will be treated cursorily because of shortness of time and even more for lack of convincing knowledge.

Temperature and humidity are of course the two climatological factors which are best understood. At their simplest their biological effects are illustrated by the close connection that exists between air temperature and the tempo of a cricket's chirp. It is said that counting the number of chirps in 14 seconds and adding 40 will give the temperature within a couple of degrees. Likewise, the higher the temperature, the faster ants move. As example of more complex effects of temperature, one could quote the discovery by Dr. André Lwoff (reported by Dr. Albert Sabin) that a difference of 2°C. can bring about the selection of virulent or avirulent mutants of polioviruses.[28] On the other hand, temperature and humidity have also less direct consequences by reason of the physiological responses that they elicit in living things. In the case of man, his semitropical origin is reflected in the narrow range of atmospheric environment to which he is adapted in his native biological state. Any departure from this environment is likely to cause physiological disturbances. A temperature of 29.4°C. (85°F.), with moderate humidity and low air movement, seems best for human comfort in the absence of housing and clothing. In practice, these artificial acids supplement several physiological mechanisms which permit a fairly wide range of adaptive heat control. Thus, enormous changes in blood flow through the skin capillaries can occur within a few minutes and regulate heat loss upward or downward as needed. When increased blood flow proves inadequate for rapid cooling, the sweating mechanism comes into play and provides heat loss by evaporation. While the needs for temperature control are more prolonged, for example in cases of passage from one season or one country to another, the body can regulate its own heat production through changes in metabolic rates. Needless to say, these regulatory mechanisms are effective only within a limited range and, furthermore, any excessive demand on them will cause profound physiological disturbances. In fact, as already mentioned, there is an enormous amount of clinical evidence that weather changes are commonly associated with exacerbation of many disease states. As Hippocrates said 2,000 years ago, "It is changes that are chiefly responsible for diseases, especially the greatest changes, the violent alterations both in the seasons and in other things. But seasons which come on gradually are the safest, as are gradual changes of regimen and temperature."

Contrary to common belief, it has not yet been shown that pressure changes *per se* can affect either the comfort or the health of man—except of course in the special cases of life at great depths or high altitudes. It may be worth mentioning at this time, however, that very slight reductions in pressure have been shown to exert profound effects on insect behavior, effects which appear to be independent of oxygen tension. In the laboratory, as well as in the field, the feeding habits, rate of development, and locomotor activity of higher insects are appreciably increased by slightly lowered or falling pressures. These conditions also seem to be associated with the sudden occurrence of mass emergencies.[29]

Needless to say, there is no general statement that can serve to describe the multifarious biological effects of the various types of radiation. Their deleterious effects go from reversible lesions in the skin to the production of lethal hereditary defects. Their beneficial effects range all the way from the synthesis of vitamin D to the orientation provided by polarized light for the motion of insects. The use of artificial light to prolong and increase egg production denotes profound influences on the endocrine system, and this becomes manifest also in bird migrations and in many other complex biological processes.

Recently, experiments with cosmic rays and their secondaries have pointed to the existence of even more profound hormonal effects of radiation. Whereas no clear evidence has been obtained that ordinary cosmic rays have any biological activity, cosmic ray shower electrons (produced by cosmic ray particles that penetrate into heavy matter) were found to increase mutation rates in a fungus, to interfere with normal reproduction in rabbits, and to accelerate the rate of development of cancers in mice pretreated with 20-methylcholantrene.[30]

Among other climatological factors which have been recognized recently are the small ionized molecules of the air and the so-called "sferics" which stem from natural electric discharges. It has been claimed that positive space charges have deleterious effects whereas negative space charges have beneficial effects—as illustrated, for example, by enhancement of proliferation of tissue cells exposed *in vitro* to negative ions.[31] Even human patients have apparently benefitted from such treatment.[3] If these claims can be validated, they point to a neglected aspect of biophysics, namely the space charges of small ions.

Air pollution is a bioclimatological factor of increasing importance in the causation of disease. Air pollutants range in kind from pollens and other allergens to toxic gases and aerosols produced by industrial plants, automobile exhausts, and domestic fires. Free HCl and H_2SO_4, sulfur dioxide, nitrogen dioxide, ozone, hydrocarbons, and pulverized rubber from automobile tires are but a few of the air pollutants known to exert toxic effects on human, animal, plant, and microbial life.[32, 33] The disappearance of lichens from modern cities, and the tremendous toll exacted by chronic bronchitis in certain industrial areas, serve to illustrate the varied aspects and the magnitude of the problem. Ozone deserves to be singled out in this discussion because it is present in large concentration in the smogs over Los Angeles, Phoenix, and Tucson, as well as in the atmosphere reached by high altitude flying. Even short exposure to the concentrations of ozone encountered in these circumstances produces pulmonary oedema and increases the susceptibility of experimental animals to bacterial infections.[34-36] It is worth mentioning in this respect that in Switzerland the Föhn seems to bring down large amounts of ozone from the upper atmosphere, a peculiarity which has been claimed to account for some of the untoward physiological effects of this type of air current.[3]

Air conditioning

It is theoretically possible to control almost any factor of the indoor environment—temperature, humidity, pressure, radiation, space charge, size and composition of aerosol particles, etc. And it is obvious that air conditioning has already greatly contributed to general comfort, relief of allergic symptoms, and increase in working efficiency. At first sight, therefore, it would appear that control of the indoor environment is always desirable and that the only practical problems that it presents are those to be dealt with by architects and engineers. In reality, however, air conditioning has biological implications that transcend comfort and working efficiency, and that are still obscure.

While it is easy to appreciate the immediate direct effects of air conditioning, such as the sense of well-being and renewed vigor, it is difficult to predict its distant and indirect effects. Little is known, for example, concerning the responses of the mucous membranes and of the vascular bed to sudden and repeated shifts from the hot humid atmosphere of the street to the cool and dry environment indoors. Comfort of the moment may have to be paid for in the future in the form of new respiratory and circulatory disorders.

More studies are also needed with regard to the effect of air conditioning on the ability of the body to adapt to unpleasant and even dangerous environmental factors. To illustrate the range of these adaptive processes, it will suffice to mention again the physiological mechanisms used by the body to regulate its temperature, and to refer to the new finding that progressive exposure to low concentrations of ozone increases resistance to the toxic effects of this gas.[37]

Even more important perhaps is the fact that air conditioning may interfere with some of the diurnal and seasonal cycles discussed earlier in this report. One need only recall here the variations in endocrine activities that are brought about by changes in temperature or in exposure to light. Of interest also are the claims that an increased rate of growth appears to result from the removal of certain metabolic stresses.[38] No information is available concerning the effect of air conditioning on processes which are so obviously correlated with seasonal metabolic changes. Yet these problems will certainly become of increasing urgency as man achieves greater control over his physical environment and removes himself from the physicochemical conditions under which he has evolved as a physiological machine.

Conclusions

I have tried to illustrate in this essay some of the effects of climatological factors on different types of biological phenomena: on the regular endogenous rhythms which exhibit diurnal or seasonal periodicities; on the long range fluctuations in size and behavior of populations; on the immediate physiological disturbances which are caused by the vagaries of the weather. I have also tried to emphasize that the biological responses to the environment cannot be described merely in terms of immediate direct effects, but must be regarded as dynamic processes, conditioned by the adaptive powers of the organisms, and often resulting in long range cumulative alterations. More than anyone, I realize the superficiality of my knowledge in these fields. Nevertheless, I cannot help expressing my belief that living things, including man, respond not only to heat, humidity, light and other obvious climatic components which are readily perceived by the senses, but also to many other environmental factors not readily identified, and in part still unknown. Awareness of these complexities may not be helpful in solving practical problems. But it teaches humility to the overconfident biologist. In this spirit I had intended to close this essay with Hamlet's words:

> "There are more things in heaven and earth, Horatio,
> Than are dreamt of in your philosophy."

But the wise remarks of one of my critical colleagues now seem more apropos In his words: "A lack of correlation with known environmental factors does not prove that unknown factors are operating. Primitive man explains natural phenomena with magic; when we are confronted with the inexplicable we too often fall back on mysticism, in somewhat more sophisticated language. This is a matter of personal taste, and on this point I must confess to being rather more with Horatio than Hamlet. Horatio no doubt was limited in his philosophy, but Hamlet believed in ghosts."

REFERENCES

1. BRUCE, V. G., and C. S. PITTENDRIGH, *Proc. N.A.S.,* **42,** 676 (1956).
2. BROWN, F. A., JR., "Discussion on Biological Rhythms," at Federation of American Societies for Experimental Biology (1959).
3a. BUETTNER, K. J. K., "Physical Aspects of Human Bioclimatology," in *Compendium of Meteorology,* ed. T. F. Malone (Boston: American Meteorological Society, 1951), p. 1112.
3b. ———, *Fed. Proc.,* **16,** 631 (1957).
4. FLINK, E. B., and R. P. DOE, *Proc. Soc. Exp. Biol. and Med.,* **100,** 498 (1959).
5. BURTON, A. C., *Canad. M. A. J.,* **75,** 715 (1956).
6. HALBERG, F., C. P. BARNUM, R. H. SILBER, and J. J. BITTNER, *Proc. Soc. Exp. Biol. and Med.,* **97,** 897 (1958).
7a. MILLS, C. A., *Medical Climatology* (Springfield, Ill.: Charles C Thomas, 1939).
7b. ———, "Climate in Health and Disease," in *The Oxford Medicine,* ed. H. A. Christian (New York: Oxford University Press, 1949), **1,** p. 453.
8. PETERSEN, W. F., *The Patient and the Weather* (Ann Arbor: Edwards Bros., 1937).
9. SARGENT, F., II, *Meteorological Monographs,* **2,** 68 (1954); SARGENT, F., II, *Arch. Met. Geoph. Biokl.,* Serie B: Allgemeine und Biologische Klimatologie, Band II, p. 289.
10. CORI, G. T., and C. F. CORI, *J. Biol. Chem.,* **72,** 615 (1927).
11. BURN, J. H., and H. W. LING, *J. Physiol.,* **65,** 191 (1928).
12. HUGHES, E., *Seasonal Variation in Man* (London: H. K. Lewis and Co., Ltd., 1931).
13. MAQUSOOD, M., *Nature,* **167,** 323 (1951).
14. MONGE, M. C., *Meteorological Monographs,* **2,** 50 (1954).
15. VON MURALT, A., *Experimentia Supplementum,* **6,** 86 pp. (1957).
16. MITCHELL, H. H., and M. EDMAN, *Nutrition and Climatic Stress* (Springfield, Ill.: Charles C Thomas, 1951).
17. REGLI, J., and R. STÄMPFLI, *Helv. Physiol. Acta,* **5,** 40 (1947).
18. COLE, L. C., *Cold Spring Harbor Symp. Quant. Biol.,* **22,** 1 (1957).
19. ELTON, C., *Voles, Mice, and Lemmings, Problems in Population Dynamics* (Oxford: Oxford University Press, 1942).
20. PITELKA, F. A., *Cold Spring Harbor Symp. Quant. Biol.,* **22,** 237 (1957).
21. HUNTINGTON, E., *Civilization and Climate,* 3rd edition, (New Haven: Yale University Press, 1924).
22. BIRCH, L. C., *Cold Spring Harbor Symp. Quant. Biol.,* **22,** 203 (1957).
23. BARBER, H. N., *Nature,* **173,** 1227 (1954).
24. WELTY, C., *Sci. American,* **197,** 118 (1957).
25. ERRINGTON, P. L., *Cold Spring Harbor Symp. Quant. Biol.,* **22,** 287 (1957).
26. CHRISTIAN, J. J., *J. Mammal.,* **31,** 247 (1950).
27. BORTELS, H., *Zbl. Bakteriol., II,* **105,** 305 (1942); BORTELS, H., *Zbl. Bakteriol.,* **155,** 160 (1950); BORTELS, H., *Die Naturwissenschaften,* **38,** 165 (1951); BORTELS, H., *I. J. B. B.,* **3,** Part I, Section F (1959).
28. SABIN, A. B., and A. LWOFF, "The Relation between Reproductive Capacity of Polioviruses at Different Temperatures in Tissue Culture and Neurovirulence,"

presented at 96th Annual Meeting of National Academy of Sciences, Washington, D.C., April 1959.

29. WELLINGTON, W. C., *Canad. J. Res.,* **24,** Sect. D, 51 (1946).
30. DUELL, G., and B. DUELL, *Meteorological Monographs,* **2,** 61 (1954).
31. WORDEN, J. L., and J. R. THOMPSON, *Anat. Rec.,* **124,** 500 (1956).
32. HAAGEN-SMIT, A. J., *Science,* **128,** 869 (1958).
33. *Proceedings of National Conference on Air Pollution,* Public Health Service, Washington, D.C., November 18–20, 1958.
34. STOKINGER, H. E., in *Proceedings of the Air Pollution Research Planning Seminar,* Public Health Service, Cincinnati, December, 1956.
35. HEIMANN, H., L. O. EMIK, R. A. PRINDLE, and W. M. FISHER, *Progress in Air Pollution Medical Research,* Public Health Service (1958).
36. MILLER, S., and R. EHRLICH, *J. Inf. Dis.,* **103,** 145 (1958).
37. MENDENHALL, R. N., presented at Ohio Valley Section Society for Experimental Biology and Medicine, Columbus, Ohio, October 31, 1958.
38. HERRINGTON, L. P., *Meteorological Monographs,* **2,** 30 (1954).

THE
FETAL
ENVIRONMENT

Monie, in the first paper, is correct in stating that the human fetal environment is not as "safe" as was once thought. In terms of organic selection, the fetal environment is very likely the severest environment man encounters in his period of life—but this represents a professional bias of the editor.

SUPPLEMENTARY READINGS

CONEN, P. E., A. G. BELL, and N. ASPIN, Chromosomal Aberration in an Infant Following the Use of Diagnostic X-rays. 1963, *Pediatrics,* **31:** 72–79.

CSAPO, A. I., H. JAFFIN, T. KERENYI, C. E. R. DeMATTOS, M. B. DeSOUSA FILHO, Fetal Death in Utero. 1963, *American Journal of Obstetrics and Gynecology,* **87:** 892–905.

LUCEY, JEROLD F., and RICHARD E. BEHRMAN, Thalidomide: Effect upon Pregnancy in the Rhesus Monkey. 1963, *Science,* **139:** 1295–1296.

MATSUNAGA, EL, Intra-Uterine Selection by the ABO Incompatibility of Mother and Foetus. 1955, *American Journal of Human Genetics,* **7:** 66–71.

WARBURTON, DOROTHY, and F. CLARKE FRASER, Spontaneous Abortion Risks in Man: Data from Reproductive Histories Collected in a Medical Genetics Unit. 1964, *American Journal of Human Genetics,* **16:** 1–25.

Influence of the Environment on the Unborn*

IAN W. MONIE

Throughout our lives we are constantly reacting to the environment in which we live. Heat, light, atmospheric pressure, terrestial and extraterrestial radiation, gravity, microorganisms and the multitude of chemicals contained in food, water and air are continually acting upon us, determining our constitutions and our destinies. At one time it was felt that the mammalian fetus was relatively sheltered from the effects of such environmental factors but careful clinical and experimental studies have now shown this belief to be untenable.

While the mother does afford protection to the unborn in many ways—for example, by detoxifying noxious substances and by destroying microorganisms which would be harmful were they to reach the young—this is secondary to the preservation of her own organism. Where the agent is not harmful to the mother and protective reactions are absent, the effect on the embryo can be disastrous. Indeed, the majority of teratogenic (malformation-producing) agents or procedures belong to this category and are especially destructive in the early stages of gestation. Thus, rubella, if contracted by the mother during the first trimester, causes little maternal upset but may result in serious eye, ear and cardiovascular malformations in the embryo.[11] Again, maternal ingestion of thalidomide, a glutamic acid imide that once was supposed to be a harmless sedative, has recently been linked with a syndrome of phocomelia, cavernous angioma and duodenal stenosis in the offspring.[17]

* Presented as part of the Basic Science Session at the 92nd Annual Meeting of the California Medical Association, Los Angeles, March 23 to 27, 1963. From the Department of Anatomy, University of California Medical Center, San Francisco 94122.

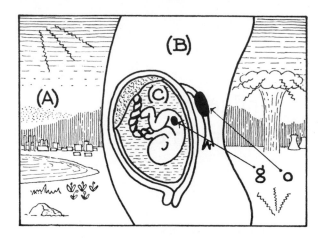

FIG. 1. The maternal and embryonic environments. (A) the *matroenvironment* consisting of the physical and chemical components, and the animal and plant life, in the surroundings of the mother. Radiation from outer space, the earth, and man-made sources is indicated by wavy lines; (B) the *macroenvironment* or maternal body; (C) the *microenvironment* composed of the placenta, membranes and amniotic fluid. (B) and (C) constitute the embryonic environment.

The maternal and embryonic environments

The unborn has to contend with three environments. The one with which it is in immediate contact, consisting of the amniotic fluid, the placenta and membranes, has been designated the *microenvironment* by Warkany.[7] The maternal body may be called the *macroenvironment,* and the surroundings of the mother, the *matroenvironment* (Figure 1). Substances inhaled or ingested by the mother from the matroenvironment may reach the embryo unchanged, or may produce changes in the macroenvironment or microenvironment which are ultimately experienced by the embryo. It is also possible for substances to pass from the macroenvironment and accumulate in the microenvironment in large enough amounts to cause embryonic damage. In the case of radiation the embryo may be directly affected, or it may be affected by the products of reaction with the macroenvironment.

Environment and genetic factors

Nineteenth century experimental embryologists clearly showed that environmental change could disturb development both in invertebrates and in lower vertebrates, and by the beginning of the present century considerable attention was being directed to abnormal intrauterine conditions as causes of malformation and abortion in man.[2,18] However, the importance of inherited factors in the normal and abnormal development of mammals was now appreciated and the significance of the environment gradually became subordinated to that of the germ-plasm; this concept generally prevailed until the early forties.

TABLE 1. Some factors which produce malformations.

	In Animals	In Man
Physical	Radiation, hypothermia	Radiation
Chemical:		
Hormones	Insulin, cortisone, androgen, estrogen, epinephrine	Sex hormones
Antigrowth factors ...	Nitrogen mustard, chlorambucil, azaserine, 6-mercaptopurine	?
Other	Trypan blue, quinine, hypoxia, salicylate, colchicine, iodine deficiency, antibiotics	Thalidomide
Nutritional:		
Deficiency	Vitamins A, B_{12}, D, E,* folic acid (PGA*), pantothenic acid,* nicotinic acid,* riboflavin*	Aminopterin†
Excess	Vitamin A	....
Other	Starvation	....
Micro-organismal	Hog cholera, influenza A, Newcastle virus	Rubella, syphilis, toxoplasmosis

* Vitamin antagonist employed alone or with deficient diet.
† A folic acid antagonist.

Nevertheless, during the period when genetic factors were considered of primary importance in the causation of congenital abnormalities, reports continued to appear on the influence of the environment on the unborn. It became evident, for example, that x-irradiation[13,14] or radium treatment of the mother during pregnancy could result in fetal death or deformity, and that lack of iodine in pregnant sows resulted in reduced litter-size.[27] Cleft palate[3] was frequently seen in whelps of captive lions unless the mothers were fed goat flesh and soft bone during pregnancy, while sows receiving a vitamin A-deficient diet produced piglets with eye defects[12] and other malformations. However, it was not until 1940 and the publication of a study by Warkany and Nelson[28] showing that pregnant rats fed a deficient diet (later shown to be riboflavin deficiency) produced young with skeletal and other abnormalities, that attention was again seriously directed to the influence of the environment on mammalian development. The teratogenic effect of rubella on the human fetus observed soon after this gave further impetus to the renewed interest in environmental factors; since then a host of teratogenic agents or procedures has been discovered (Table 1).

Today, however, it is generally agreed that the majority of congenital abnormalities result from the interplay of *both* genetic and environmental factors[9] although in certain instances one may play a much more important role than the other. Since there is no apparent structural difference between congenital abnormalities produced by genetic and by environmental factors, in many cases it is difficult to determine which is of primary or sole importance.

In addition to malformations resulting from environmental or genetic factors, or to a combination of these, it is now known that abnormality of chromosomal number is responsible for such conditions as Turner's and Klinefelter's syndromes, and for mongolism. What role, if any, environmental or genetic factors play in the determination of such chromosomal disturbance has not yet been determined.

Teratogenic agents—timing and specificity

It would appear that either an excess or an insufficiency of almost any chemical or physical agent can, in certain circumstances, result in defective embryonic development; thus, either maternal insufficiency[31] or excess[5] of vitamin A produces abnormal rat young when occurring at a particular stage of pregnancy.

The time of introduction of a teratogenic agent is especially important, the embryo usually being most sensitive when the principal body systems are being established; in man, this is between the third and eighth week, and in rats during the second week of gestation (parturition occurs on the 22nd or 23rd day). In the later stages of pregnancy the fetus is much less sensitive but by no means immune to environmental influence; thus, in man, toxoplasmosis can produce hydrocephaly, and syphilis a variety of malformations in the later stages of gestation. Also, in rats the giving of 6-aminonicotinamide (6-AN), a nicotinic acid antimetabolite, as late as the 19th day of gestation can produce hydrocephaly in the young.[4]

Generally, when a teratogenic agent is given very early in gestation it either does not disturb the conceptus or it destroys it entirely, while, if given late in pregnancy its effects may be greatly reduced or absent; there is consequently a critical time for each agent during which maximum damage to the conceptors will result, and this varies with the species involved. In the case of thalidomide, for example, it has been observed that the human embryo is most sensitive between the 27th and 43rd days after conception.[17]

While the time of introduction of the agent is undoubtedly of importance, there is generally mounting evidence that certain agents have a predilection for one or more systems or regions of the embryo.[30] This is suggested, for example, by the preponderance of limb damage in human fetuses by thalidomide, and by the frequent absence of the kidney in rat young from chlorambucil.[23] On the other hand, certain teratogenic factors, such as maternal folic or pteroylglutamic acid (PGA) deficiency,[10,25,26] are associated with a broad spectrum of malformations and are considered "universal" teratogens.

The employment of teratogens in experimental animals is exceedingly valuable for studying the pathogenesis of many congenital abnormalities, and different defects can be produced by varying the time of action of the same agent, or

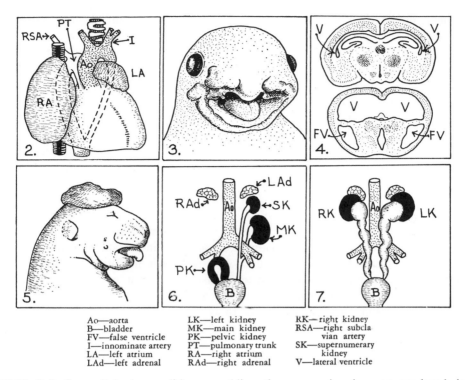

Ao—aorta
B—bladder
FV—false ventricle
I—innominate artery
LA—left atrium
LAd—left adrenal

LK—left kidney
MK—main kidney
PK—pelvic kidney
PT—pulmonary trunk
RA—right atrium
RAd—right adrenal

RK—right kidney
RSA—right subclavian artery
SK—supernumerary kidney
V—lateral ventricle

FIGS. 2–7. Congenital abnormalities resembling those occurring in man produced in rat young as a result of trypan blue (Figure 2), and folic acid (PGA) deficiency (Figures 3-7) during pregnancy; (2) Transposition of the great vessels and double aorta; (3) Facial defects and cleft palate; (4) Control and hydrocephalic brains from three-week-old rats; (5) Exencephaly, micrognathia, and glossoptis; (6) Pelvic and supernumerary kidneys; and (7) Bilateral hydronephrosis.

by using different agents (Figures 2 through 7). Thus, a transitory PGA-deficiency in rats from the 7th to 9th day of gestation produces many abnormalities of the brain and eye; from the 9th to 11th day, mainly cardiovascular abnormalities;[1,21] and from the 10th to 13th days, principally urogenital malformations.[22] However, if it is desired to study dextrocardia or transposition of the great vessels, trypan blue[8] is the agent of choice, as it provides a much higher incidence of these anomalies than maternal PGA-deficiency.

Human teratogens

Of the great number of agents or procedures recognized as teratogenic in mammals, only a few are definitely known to affect humans. Proven teratogenic agents in man are: rubella, sex hormones, aminopterin (4-amino PGA), toxoplasmosis, radiation and thalidomide (Table 1). Many other chemical substances, physical factors and microorganisms are suspect but absolute proof is lacking.

It is sometimes stated that experimentally produced congenital malformations are caused by dosages of teratogenic agents at levels much greater than ever experienced by man. In many instances this is probably true but the effects of combinations of small amounts of teratogens cannot be overlooked and work on this important aspect is now proceeding.[6] Preliminary results indicate that certain combinations of low dosages of teratogenic agents have an adjuvant effect on the production of malformations while others seem to show a protective effect. The problem, however, is complex and requires more detailed study.

Pathogenesis of malformations

The ability to produce abnormal embryos in animals by means of teratogenic agents has made it possible to obtain more accurate information on the genesis of many malformations. Thus, absence of a kidney is not always the result of primary renal agenesis but may be due to degeneration of the metanephros secondary to maldevelopment of the ureter or the Wolffian duct;[23] again, renal ectopia can result from retarded growth of the vertebral column.[22] Further, hydrocephaly may follow from retarded development of the cerebral cortex, and closure of the aqueduct result from secondary compression of the midbrain by the distended cerebral hemispheres.[24]

Any congenital abnormality must spring initially from disturbance of intracellular chemistry. Actively dividing cells are the most sensitive to teratogenic agents, although the phase when such sensitivity is maximal varies. Thus, radiation and radiomimetic substances such as chlorambucil cause fragmentation of chromosomes, the cell being most sensitive during the resting phase; colchicine, on the other hand, interferes with anaphase, so that mitosis is incomplete.

The mode of action of many teratogenic agents is uncertain although seemingly relevant facts are known is some instances. Thus, trypan blue, at one time used to treat mange in animals, is highly teratogenic and when injected into pregnant animals rapidly stains the maternal tissues; no similar coloration occurs in the embryo and it has been suggested that it may cross the placenta in a colorless form. However, when injected into pregnant rabbits, trypan blue alters the serum protein content of the maternal blood[16] and it is possible that this may lead, in turn, to abnormal placental transfer and subsequent fetal abnormality. In the case of PGA-deficiency the formation of nucleoproteins essential for growth and cell-division is probably disturbed; riboflavin deficiency, on the other hand, possibly may interfere with the oxidative processes in both the mother and the embryo.

The site of primary damage by a teratogenic agent conceivably may be either the placenta or the embryo; studies on the effect of maternal PGA-deficiency, however, have shown that embryonic death precedes placental change, and it is probable that this sequence is common to many teratogenic procedures.[15]

The teratogenic effects of antimetabolites generally can be counteracted by simultaneously supplying an adequate amount of the corresponding vitamin, yet in some instances an entirely different substance may also have an alleviating effect. Thus, in maternal vitamin A-deficiency in rats it has been observed that fetal damage can be reduced by thyroxine.[20] Also, recent studies, again in rats, have shown that thalidomide increases the sensitivity of hemoglobin to oxidation by nitrites and that this can be prevented by simultaneously giving pyridoxine and riboflavin.[19] In the future, it is possible that teratogenic side-effects of otherwise useful drugs may be prevented by prescribing with them antidotes to their undesired effects.

Testing for teratogenicity

The fact that thalidomide has produced severe malformations in man when no such effects were found in test animals has drawn attention to the difficulties of screening substances for possible teratogenicity in man. Species, and even strain, differences often result in decidedly different responses to the same agent and this undoubtedly is related to genetic make-up.

Even where a drug is non-teratogenic for the majority of humans, there is always the possibility of teratogenic effect in a few individuals on account of their genetic construction. This, however, is no different from drug sensitivity or post-vaccinal conditions which we are accustomed to anticipate in a small number of cases. New drugs, of course, must be intensively screened in a greater variety and number of test animals than before. This will help to reduce the chance of disaster in man. Also, we should not fail to check the old established drugs, the long-trusted components of the physician's armamentarium. In this regard, the demonstration of teratogenic action by salicylates[29] in rats should be kept in mind. In view of our present knowledge, avoiding all drugs in the early stages of pregnancy unless deemed absolutely necessary by the physician is obvious.

The quest for information on the causation of malformations also requires the detailed study of aborted human embryos. Too often normality or abnormality is determined by external inspection alone and, since a normal-looking embryo can have severe visceral abnormalities within, a diagnosis is of little value unless based on dissection, and possibly on histological and biochemical studies as well. Detailed examination of such material is time-consuming and requires special skills, but it must be undertaken and, wherever possible, the findings related to the maternal history. The establishment of centers to which human abortion material could be sent for special study would doubtless facilitate such an undertaking.

Lastly, while laboratory studies have an important part in the detection of teratogenic agents, an equally significant role is played by the practicing physician, for by astute observation and careful recording he can, as he has so often in the past, draw attention to actual or potential dangers and open the way to appropriate safeguards.

REFERENCES

1. BAIRD, C. D. C., NELSON, M. M., MONIE, I. W., and EVANS, H. M.: Congenital cardiovascular anomalies induced by PGA-deficiency in the rat, Circulation Res., 2:544–554, 1954.
2. BALLANTYNE, J. W.: Manual of Antenatal Pathology, Vol. II, William Wood & Co., New York, 1902.
3. BLAND-SUTTON, J.: The Story of a Surgeon, Methuen, London, 1930.
4. CHAMBERLAIN, J.: Effects of 6-Aminonicotinamide on rat embryogenesis, Ph.D. Thesis, University of California, 1962.
5. COHLAN, S. Q.: Congenital anomalies in the rat produced by excessive intake of vitamin A during pregnancy, Pediatrics, 13:556–567, 1954.
6. CHIN, E.: Combinations of teratogenic procedures in rat embryogenesis, Ph.D. Thesis, University of California, 1963.
7. EBERT, J. D.: First International Conference on Congenital Malformations, J. Chron. Dis., 13:91–132, 1961.
8. FOX, M. H., and GOSS, C. M.: Experimental production of a syndrome of congenital cardiovascular defects in rats, Anat. Rec., 124:189–207, 1956.
9. FRASER, F. C.: Causes of congenital malformations in human beings, J. Chron. Dis., 10:97–110, 1959.
10. GIROUD, A. J., and LEFEBVRES, J.: Anomalies provoquées chez le foetus en l'absence d'acide folique, Arch. franç. pediat., 8:648–656, 1951.
11. GREGG, N. M.: Congenital cataract following German measles in mother, Tr. Ophth. Soc. Australia, 3:35–46, 1942.
12. HALE, F.: Pigs born without eyeballs, J. Hered., 24: 105–106, 1933.
13. HANSON, F. B.: Effects of x-rays on the albino rat, Anat. Rec., 24:415, 1923.
14. JOB, T. T., LEIBOLD, G. J., and FITZMAURICE, H. A.: Biological effects of roentgen rays, Amer. J. Anat., 56:97–117, 1935.
15. JOHNSON, E. M., and NELSON, M. M.: Morphological changes in embryonic development resulting from transitory PGA-deficiency in early pregnancy, Anat. Rec., 133:294, 1959.
16. LANGMAN, J., and VAN DRUNEN, H.: The effect of trypan blue upon maternal protein metabolism and embryonic development, Anat. Rec., 133:513–526, 1959.
17. LENZ, W., and KNAPP, K.: Thalidomide embryopathy, Arch. Envir. Health, 5:100–105, 1962.
18. MALL, F. P.: In Keibel and Mall's Human Embryology, Vol. 1, J. B. Lippincott Co., Philadelphia, 1910.
19. METCALF, W. K.: Thalidomide, the nitrite sensitivity reaction and the vitamin B complex, Proc. Anat. Soc. Gt. Brit. and Ire., February 1963.
20. MILLEN, J. W., and WOOLLAM, D. H. M.: Thyroxine and hypervitaminosis, A. J. Anat., 93:566, 1959.
21. MONIE, I. W., NELSON, M. M., and EVANS, H. M.: Persistent right umbilical vein as a result of vitamin deficiency during gestation, Circulation Res., 2:187–190, 1957.
22. MONIE, I. W., NELSON, M. M., and EVANS, H. M.: Abnormalities of the urinary system of rat embryos resulting from transitory PGA-deficiency during gestation, Anat. Rec., 127:711–724, 1957.

23. MONIE, I. W.: Chlorambucil-induced abnormalities of the urogenital system of rat fetuses, Anat. Rec., 139:145–152, 1961.
24. MONIE, I. W., ARMSTRONG, R. M., and NELSON, M. M.: Hydrocephaly in rat young as a result of PGA-deficiency from the 8th to 10th day of gestation, Anat. Rec., 139:315, 1961.
25. NELSON, M. M., ASLING, C. W., and EVANS, H. M.: Production of multiple congenital abnormalities in young by maternal PGA-deficiency during gestation, J. Nutrition, 48:61–80, 1952.
26. NELSON, M. M., WRIGHT, H. V., ASLING, C. W., EVANS, H. M.: Multiple congenital abnormalities resulting from transitory PGA-deficiency during gestation in the rat, J. Nutrition, 56:349–370, 1955.
27. SMITH, G. E.: Fetal athyrosis. A study of the iodine requirements of the pregnant sow, J. Biol. Chem., 29:215–225, 1917.
28. WARKANY, J., and NELSON, R. C.: Appearance of skeletal abnormalities in the offspring of rats reared on a deficient diet, Science, 92:383–384, 1940.
29. WARKANY, J., and TAKACS, E.: Experimental production of congenital malformations in rats by salicylate poisoning, Am. J. Path., 35:315–331, 1959.
30. WILSON, J. G.: Experimental studies on congenital malformations, J. Chron. Dis., 10:111–130, 1959.
31. WILSON, J. G., and BARCH, S.: Fetal death and maldevelopment resulting from maternal vitamin A deficiency in the rat. Proc. Soc. Exp. Biol. & Med., 72:687–693, 1949.

Maternal Height and
the Prevalence of Stillbirths*

JACK B. BRESLER

In a series of investigations spanning many years, Baird and his co-workers in Aberdeen, Scotland, have developed the thesis that shorter women generally had poorer reproductive histories than taller women (Baird, 1949; Baird, 1952; Baird and Illsley, 1953; Baird, Hytten and Thomson, 1958). In Baird's papers there occur repeatedly a number of important and interrelated themes correlating maternal height with reproduction: (a) where ability to deliver a child through the vagina was taken as an index of poor reproductive performance, it was found that this inability was about four times greater for women under 5'1" than for women over 5'4", (b) the rate of caesarean operations was inversely related to maternal height, (c) premature labor is more common in shorter women, (d) taller women have pelvic brim areas large enough to accommodate a baby of any size, and (e) generally women with larger pelvic areas (correlated with taller maternal height) have better reproductive potentialities for mechanical reasons.

The purpose of this report is to provide data relating maternal height to stillbirths and abortion rates for an American population.

Methods

The population presented in this report is derived from a larger sample previously described in extensive detail (Bresler, 1961).

A few summary statements pertinent to the accumulation of the present sample are in order, however. The medical records of the Providence Lying-In Hospital, Providence, Rhode Island, were searched for family information on all

* This investigation was supported by a research grant RG-9426, Public Health Service.

white, Rh negative women who entered the hospital at least once from 1950 to 1958. The items collected which are of particular importance to the present study included the number of pregnancies, stillbirths, and abortions, age, height, and religion of mother, presence or absence of Anti-Rh titer reading for each trimester of each pregnancy.

Each woman or case met certain criteria before being included in this sample. In general the requirements were established in order to derive a sample of women with optimal capacities for the production of live born offspring. Women who were shown in previous studies to be poorer risks for the production of full-term live offspring were eliminated. At no time was maternal height a cause for the rejection or acceptance of a case. Accordingly, only women who were 18 to 34 years of age and who had not had more than four pregnancies at time of data collection were included. Fetal loss, from reasons still not completely understood, rises very rapidly with increasing age after 34 and with more than four pregnancies. Baird's papers provide information on these points. Furthermore the entire case of a woman was eliminated from study if she exhibited a positive Anti-Rh titer reading for any trimester of any pregnancy. These restrictions resulted in a sample of non-sensitized, white, urban women who, from the standpoint of age and parity, had excellent advantages for reproduction.

Data will be presented on the reproductive histories of these 272 women. The mean age of the women was 26.9 years and the mean number of pregnancies these women had was 2.44. In none of the classes or categories of Tables 1, 2, or 3 was there any significant divergence from the mean age or mean number of pregnancies.

Data. In Table 1, data are presented relating maternal height to the number of women who have ever had a spontaneous abortion or a stillbirth.

A 2×2 comparison was made for the number of women who had ever aborted with those who had never aborted. The other division was made for women under 5'6" compared with those 5'6" or over. The two-tailed X^2 test was used because there is not available from Baird's papers or other sources any

TABLE 1. Relation of maternal height to number of women who have ever had abortions or stillbirths.

	Height of women					
	Under 5'	5'0" to 5'2"	5'3" to 5'5"	5'6" to 5'8"	5'9" to 5'11"	Total
Number of women	9	65	131	57	10	272
Women ever abortion	1	14	25	11	1	52
Percent women ever abortion	11.1	21.5	19.8	19.3	10.0	19.1
Women ever stillbirth	1	5	6	0	0	12
Percent women ever stillbirth	11.1	7.7	4.6	0.0	0.0	4.4

TABLE 2. Religious distribution of women who have ever had a stillbirth. All women are under 5'6".

Religion of women	No.	Total	Ever stillbirth	Expected— based upon % total
		%		
Catholic	132	64.4	8	7.7
Protestant	58	28.4	3	3.4
Other	15	7.3	1	0.9
Total	205	100.0	12	12.0

TABLE 3. Height distribution for Catholic and Protestant women.

	Under 5'6"		5'6" and over		Total
	No.	%	No.	%	
Catholic	132	69.5	32	50.0	164
Protestant	58	30.5	32	50.0	90
Total	190	100.0	64	100.0	254

Test on distribution: d.f. $= 1$, $X^2 = 7.1$, $P < 0.01$. Correction made for continuity.

statement that maternal height and abortion rate are correlated. The X^2 is .03 and $.90 < P > .80$. It is reasonable to conclude that maternal height is not a factor in the abortion rate.

On the other hand Baird has established the stillbirth rate to be height dependent and it is this foreknowledge which permits the use of the one way Fisher exact probability test. The 2×2 analysis for the stillbirth rate was the same as indicated for the abortion rate. The exact probability is .03. The data on the average stillbirth rate per woman corroborate Baird's findings on average stillbirth rate per pregnancy.

Religion was the only ethnic group datum available and this distribution is indicated in Tables 2 and 3. Although the numbers in Table 2 are small, the observed frequency of women who have ever had a stillbirth is close to the expected values. In Table 3 the relationship of maternal height to religion is not on a random basis. This indicates that Protestant women are generally taller than the Catholic women.

Conclusion

Even after some very stringent limitations were made upon the sample selection, there does appear to be an inverse relationship between maternal height and the rate at which women have had a stillbirth. It is certainly understood that maternal height signifies or represents pelvic area with which it is correlated. Pelvic

area data is not available for this investigation but Bernard (1952) has previously presented data correlating maternal height and pelvic brim area.

The findings of Baird's investigation and the present study have a number of ramifications. It will be necessary, for example, for demographers to take careful note of the height of a woman when obtaining stillbirth data. It will never do to compare the stillbirth rate between an hypothetical upper class of a predominantly Protestant population with a lower class of a predominantly Catholic composition without correcting for height differences. Otherwise lower stillbirth rates which will almost certainly be found in the upper class strata may be ascribed exclusively to better environmental factors when in fact this class is significantly taller and inherently predisposed for anatomical reasons to a lower stillbirth rate.

REFERENCES

BAIRD, D. 1949 Social factors in obstetrics, Lancet, *1:* 1079–1083.
——— 1952 The cause and prevention of difficult labour. Amer. J. Obstet. Gynec., *63:* 1200–1212.
BAIRD, D., and R. ILLSLEY 1953 Environment and childbearing. Proc. Roy. Soc. Med., *46:* 53–59.
BAIRD, D., F. E. HYTTEN and A. M. THOMSON 1958 Age and human reproduction. J. Obstet. Gynec. Brit. Emp., *65:* 865–876.
BERNARD, R. M. 1952 The shape and size of the female pelvis. Trans. Edinburgh Obstet. Soc., *59:* 1–16.
BRESLER, J. B. 1961 Effect of ABO-Rh interaction on infant hemoglobin. Hum. Biol., *33:* 11–24.

Part 2

SOME ENVIRONMENTAL FACTORS DEVELOPED BY MAN

HUMAN POPULATIONS AND STRESS

One of the most pressing problems today is the ever-increasing number of people. The paper by Dorn is an excellent introduction to population growth. The papers by Deevey and Hoagland discuss some of the unhappy consequences of overcrowding.

SUPPLEMENTARY READINGS

CALHOUN, JOHN B., Population Density and Social Pathology. 1962, *Scientific American,* **206:** 139–148.

CHITTY, DENNIS, A Note on Shock Disease. 1959, *Ecology,* **40:** 728–731.

CHRISTIAN, JOHN J., Phenomena Associated with Population Density. *Proceedings of the National Academy of Sciences,* **47:** 428–449.

COLE, LAMONT C., Ecology and the Population Problem. 1955, *Science,* **122:** 831–832.

PETTERSSON, MAX, Increase of Settlement Size and Population Since the Inception of Agriculture. 1960, *Nature,* **186:** 870–872.

World Population Growth: An International Dilemma

HAROLD F. DORN*

During all but the most recent years of the centuries of his existence man must have lived, reproduced, and died as other animals do. His increase in number was governed by the three great regulators of the increase of all species of plants and animals—predators, disease, and starvation—or, in terms more applicable to human populations—war, pestilence, and famine. One of the most significant developments for the future of mankind during the first half of the 20th century has been his increasing ability to control pestilence and famine. Although he has not freed himself entirely from the force of these two regulators of population increase, he has gained sufficient control of them so that they no longer effectively govern his increase in number.

Simultaneously he has developed methods of increasing the effectiveness of war as a regulator of population increase, to the extent that he almost certainly could quickly wipe out a large proportion, if not all, of the human race. At the same time he has learned how to separate sexual gratification from reproduction by means of contraception and telegenesis (that is, reproduction by artificial insemination, particularly with spermatozoa preserved for relatively long periods of time), so that he can regulate population increase by voluntary control of fertility. Truly it can be said that man has the knowledge and the power to direct, at least in part, the course of his evolution.

This newly gained knowledge and power has not freed man from the inexorable effect of the biological laws that govern all living organisms. The evolutionary process has endowed most species with a reproductive potential that,

* The author is affiliated with the National Institutes of Health, Bethesda, Md., in the Biometrics Research Branch, National Heart Institute.

unchecked, would overpopulate the entire globe within a few generations. It has been estimated that the tapeworm, *Taenia,* may lay 120,000 eggs per day; an adult cod can lay as many as 4 million eggs per year; a frog may produce 10,000 eggs per spawning. Human ovaries are thought to contain approximately 200,000 ova at puberty, while a single ejaculation of human semen may contain 200 million spermatozoa.

This excessive reproductive potential is kept in check for species other than man by interspecies competition in the struggle for existence, by disease, and by limitation of the available food supply. The fact that man has learned how to control, to a large extent, the operation of these biological checks upon unrestrained increase in number has not freed him from the necessity of substituting for them less harsh but equally effective checks. The demonstration of his ability to do this cannot be long delayed.

Only fragmentary data are available to indicate the past rate of growth of the population of the world. Even today, the number of inhabitants is known only approximately. Regular censuses of populations did not exist prior to 1800, although registers were maintained for small population groups prior to that time. As late as a century ago, around 1860, only about one-fifth of the estimated population of the world was covered by a census enumeration once in a 10-year

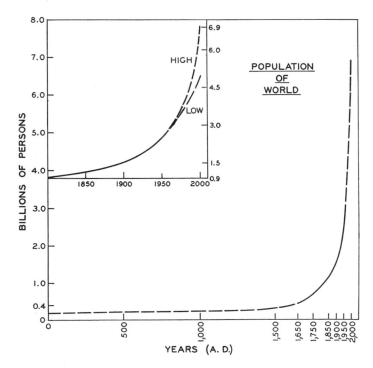

FIG. 1. Estimated population of the world, A.D. 1 to A.D. 2000.

period (*1*). The commonly accepted estimates of the population of the world prior to 1800 are only informed guesses. Nevertheless, it is possible to piece together a consistent series of estimates of the world's population during the past two centuries, supplemented by a few rough guesses of the number of persons alive at selected earlier periods. The most generally accepted estimates are presented in Figure 1.

These reveal a spectacular spurt during recent decades in the increase of the world's population that must be unparalleled during the preceding millennia of human existence. Furthermore, the rate of increase shows no sign of diminishing (Table 1). The period of time required for the population of the world to double has sharply decreased during the past three centuries and now is about 35 years.

TABLE 1. The number of years required to double the population of the world. [From United Nations data (*9, 14*)]

Year (A.D.)	Population (billions)	Number of years to double
1	0.25(?)	1650(?)
1650	0.50	200
1850	1.1	80
1930	2.0	45
1975	4.0	35
2010	8.0*	?

* A projection of United Nations estimates.

Only a very rough approximation can be made of the length of time required for the population of the world to reach one-quarter of a billion persons, the estimated number at the beginning of the Christian era. The present subgroups of *Homo sapiens* may have existed for as long as 100,000 years. The exact date is not necessary, since for present purposes the evidence is sufficient to indicate that probably 50,000 to 100,000 years were required for *Homo sapiens* to increase in number until he reached a global total of one-quarter of a billion persons. This number was reached approximately 2000 years ago.

By 1620, the year the Pilgrims landed on Plymouth Rock, the population of the world had doubled in number. Two hundred years later, shortly before the Civil War, another 500 million persons had been added. Since that time, additional half billions of persons have been added during increasingly shorter intervals of time. The sixth half billion, just added, required slightly less than 11 years, as compared to 200 years for the second half billion. The present rate of growth implies that only 6 to 7 years will be required to add the eighth half billion to the world's population. The change in rate of growth just described has taken place since the first settlers came to New England.

Implications

The accelerating rate of increase in the growth of the population of the world has come about so unobtrusively that most persons are unaware of its implications. There is a small group who are so aroused by this indifference that, like modern Paul Reveres, they attempt to awaken the public with cries of "the population bomb!" or "the population explosion!"

These persons are called alarmists by those who counter with the assertion that similar warnings, such as "standing-room only" and "mankind at the cross-roads," have been issued periodically since Malthus wrote his essay on population, about 200 years ago. Nevertheless, says this group, the level of living and the health of the average person has continued to improve, and there is no reason to believe that advances in technology will not be able to make possible a slowly rising level of living for an increasing world population for the indefinite future. Furthermore, the rate of population increase almost certainly will slow down as the standard of education and living rises and as urbanization increases.

A third group of persons has attempted to estimate the maximum population that could be supported by the world's physical resources provided existing technological knowledge is fully utilized. Many of these calculations have been based on estimates of the quantity of food that could be produced and a hypothetical average daily calorie consumption per person.

As might be expected, the range of the various estimates of the maximum world population that could be supported without a lowering of the present level of living is very wide. One of the lowest, 2.8 billion, made by Pearson and Harper in 1945 on the assumption of an Asiatic standard of consumption, already has been surpassed (2). Several others, ranging from 5 to 7 billion, almost certainly will be exceeded by the end of this century. Perhaps the most carefully prepared estimate as well as the largest—that of 50 billions, prepared by Harrison Brown—would be reached in about 150 years if the present rate of growth should continue (3).

I believe it is worth while to prepare estimates of the maximum population that can be supported and to revise these as new information becomes available, even though most of the estimates made in the past already have been, or soon will be, demonstrated to be incorrect (in most instances too small), since this constitutes a rational effort to comprehend the implications of the increase in population. At the same time it should be recognized that estimates of the world's carrying capacity made in this manner are rather unrealistic and are primarily useful only as very general guidelines.

In the first place, these calculations have assumed that the earth's resources and skills are a single reservoir available to all. In reality this is untrue. The U.S. government attempts to restrict production of certain agricultural crops by paying farmers not to grow them. Simultaneously, in Asia and Africa, large numbers of persons are inadequately fed and poorly clothed. Except in a very general sense there is no world population problem; there are population problems varying in nature and degree among the several nations of the world. No single solution is applicable to all.

Since the world is not a single political unity, the increases in production actually achieved during any period of time tend to be considerably less than those theoretically possible. Knowledge, technical skill, and capital are concentrated in areas with the highest level of living, whereas the most rapid increase in population is taking place in areas where such skills and capital are relatively scarce or practically nonexistent.

Just as the world is not a single unit from the point of view of needs and the availability of resources, skills and knowledge to meet these needs, so it also is not a single unit with respect to population increase. Due to political barriers that now exist throughout the entire world, overpopulation, however defined, will become a serious problem in specific countries long before it would be a world problem if there were no barriers to population redistribution. I shall return to this point later, after discussing briefly existing forecasts or projections of the total population of the world.

Most demographers believe that, under present conditions, the future population of areas such as countries or continents, or even of the entire world, cannot be predicted for more than a few decades with even a moderate degree of certainty. This represents a marked change from the view held by many only 30 years ago.

In 1930 a prominent demographer wrote, "The population of the United States ten, twenty, even fifty years hence, can be predicted with a greater degree of assurance than any other economic or social fact, provided the immigration laws are unchanged" (4). Nineteen years later, a well-known economist replied that "it is disheartening to have to assert that the best population forecasts deserve little credence even for 5 years ahead, and none at all for 20–50 years ahead." (5).

Although both of these statements represent rather extreme views, they do indicate the change that has taken place during the past two decades in the attitude toward the reliability of population forecasts. Some of the reasons for this have been discussed in detail elsewhere and will not be repeated here (6).

It will be sufficient to point out that knowledge of methods of voluntarily controlling fertility now is so widespread, especially among persons of European ancestry, that sharp changes in the spacing, as well as in the number, of children born during the reproductive period may occur in a relatively short period of time. Furthermore, the birth rate may increase as well as decrease.

Forecasting population growth

The two principal methods that have been used in recent years to make population forecasts are (i) the extrapolation of mathematical curves fitted to the past trend of population increase and (ii) the projection of the population by the "component" or "analytical" method, based on specific hypotheses concerning the future trend in fertility, mortality, and migration.

The most frequently used mathematical function has been the logistic curve which was originally suggested by Verhulst in 1838 but which remained unnoticed until it was rediscovered by Pearl and Reed about 40 years ago (7). At first it was thought by some demographers that the logistic curve represented a rational law of population change. However, it has proved to be as unreliable as other methods of preparing population forecasts and is no longer regarded as having any unique value for estimating future population trends.

A recent illustration of the use of mathematical functions to project the future world population is the forecast prepared by von Foerster, Mora, and Amiot (8). In view of the comments that subsequently were published in this journal, an extensive discussion of this article does not seem to be required. It will be sufficient to point out that this forecast probably will set a record, for the entire class of forecasts prepared by the use of mathematical functions, for the short length of time required to demonstrate its unreliability.

The method of projecting or forecasting population growth most frequently used by demographers, whenever the necessary data are available, is the "component" or "analytical" method. Separate estimates are prepared of the future trend of fertility, mortality, and migration. From the total population as distributed by age and sex on a specified date, the future population that would result from the hypothetical combination of fertility, mortality, and migration is computed. Usually, several estimates of the future population are prepared in order to include what the authors believe to be the most likely range of values.

Such estimates generally are claimed by their authors to be not forecasts of the most probable future population but merely indications of the population that would result from the hypothetical assumptions concerning the future trend in fertility, mortality, and migration. However, the projections of fertility, mortality, and migration usually are chosen to include what the authors believe will be the range of likely possibilities. This objective is achieved by making "high," "medium," and "low" assumptions concerning the future trend in population growth. Following the practice of most of the authors of such estimates, I shall refer to these numbers as population projections.

The most authoritative projections of the population of the world are those made by the United Nations (9, 10) (Table 2). Even though the most recent of these projections were published in 1958, only 3 years ago, it now seems likely that the population of the world will exceed the high projection before the year 2000. By the end of 1961 the world's population at least equaled the high projection for that date.

Although the United Nations' projections appear to be too conservative in that even the highest will be an underestimate of the population only 40 years from now, some of the numerical increases in population implied by these projections will create problems that may be beyond the ability of the nations involved to solve. For example, the estimated increase in the population of Asia

TABLE 2. Estimated population of the world for A.D. 1900, 1950, 1975, and 2000. [From United Nations data (9), rounded to three significant digits]

Area	Estimated population (millions)		Projected future population (millions)			
			Low assumptions		High assumptions	
	1900	1950	1975	2000	1975	2000
World	1550	2500	3590	4880	3860	6900
Africa	120	199	295	420	331	663
North America	81	168	232	274	240	326
Latin America	63	163	282	445	304	651
Asia	857	1380	2040	2890	2210	4250
Europe including U.S.S.R.	423	574	724	824	751	987
Oceania	6	13	20	27	21	30

from A.D. 1950 to 2000 will be roughly equal to the population of the entire world in 1958! The population of Latin America 40 years hence may very likely be four times that in 1950. The absolute increase in population in Latin America during the last half of the century may equal the total increase in the population of *Homo sapiens* during all the millennia from his origin until about 1650, when the first colonists were settling New England.

Increases in population of this magnitude stagger the imagination. Present trends indicate that they may be succeeded by even larger increases during comparable periods of time. The increase in the rate of growth of the world's population, shown by the data in Table 1, is still continuing. This rate is now estimated to be about 2 percent per year, sufficient to double the world's population every 35 years. It requires only very simple arithmetic to show that a continuation of this rate of growth for even 10 or 15 decades would result in an increase in population that would make the globe resemble an anthill.

But as was pointed out above, the world is not a single unit economically, politically, or demographically. Long before the population of the entire world reaches a size that could not be supported at current levels of living, the increase in population in specific nations and regions will give rise to problems that will affect the health and welfare of the rest of the world. The events of the past few years have graphically demonstrated the rapidity with which the political and economic problems of even a small and weak nation can directly affect the welfare of the largest and most powerful nations. Rather than speculate about the maximum population the world can support and the length of time before this number will be reached, it will be more instructive to examine the demographic changes that are taking place in different regions of the world and to comment briefly on their implications.

Decline in mortality

The major cause of the recent spurt in population increase is a world-wide decline in mortality. Although the birth rate increased in some countries—for example, the United States—during and after World War II, such increases have not been sufficiently widespread to account for more than a small part of the increase in the total population of the world. Moreover, the increase in population prior to World War II occurred in spite of a widespread decline in the birth rate among persons of European origin.

Accurate statistics do not exist, but the best available estimates suggest that the expectation of life at birth in Greece, Rome, Egypt, and the Eastern Mediterranean region probably did not exceed 30 years at the beginning of the Christian era. By 1900 it had increased to about 40 to 50 years in North America and in

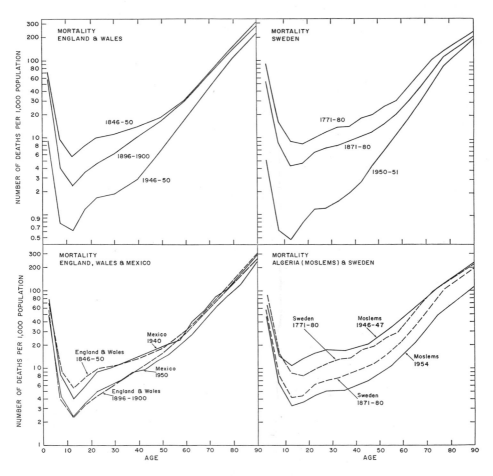

FIG. 2. Age-specific death rates per 1000 per year for Sweden, England and Wales, Mexico, and the Moslem population of Algeria for various time periods from 1771 to 1954.

most countries of northwestern Europe. At present, it has reached 68 to 70 years in many of these countries.

By 1940, only a small minority of the world's population had achieved an expectation of life at birth comparable to that of the population of North America and northwest Europe. Most of the population of the world had an expectation of life no greater than that which prevailed in western Europe during the Middle Ages. Within the past two decades, the possibility of achieving a 20th-century death rate has been opened to these masses of the world's population. An indication of the result can be seen from the data in Fig. 2.

In 1940, the death rate in Mexico was similar to that in England and Wales nearly 100 years earlier. It decreased as much during the following decade as did the death rate in England and Wales during the 50-year period from 1850 to 1900.

In 1946–47 the death rate of the Moslem population of Algeria was higher than that of the population of Sweden in the period 1771–80, the earliest date for which reliable mortality statistics are available for an entire nation. During the following 8 years, the drop in the death rate in Algeria considerably exceeded that in Sweden during the century from 1771 to 1871 (*11*).

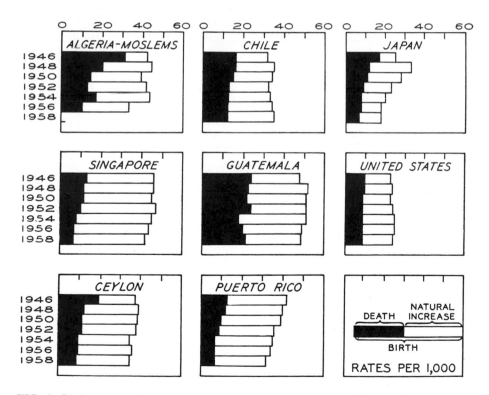

FIG. 3. Birth rate, death rate, and rate of natural increase per 1000 for selected countries for the period 1946–58.

The precipitous decline in mortality in Mexico and in the Moslem population of Algeria is illustrative of what has taken place during the past 15 years in Latin America, Africa, and Asia, where nearly three out of every four persons in the world now live. Throughout most of this area the birth rate has changed very little, remaining near a level of 40 per 1000 per year, as can be seen from Fig. 3, which shows the birth rate, death rate, and rate of natural increase for selected countries.

Even in countries such as Puerto Rico and Japan where the birth rate has declined substantially, the rate of natural increase has changed very little, owing to the sharp decrease in mortality. A more typical situation is represented by Singapore, Ceylon, Guatemala, and Chile, where the crude rate of natural increase has risen. There has been a general tendency for death rates to decline universally and for high birth rates to remain high, with the result that those countries with the highest rates of increase are experiencing an acceleration in their rates of growth.

Regional levels

The absolute level of fertility and mortality and the effect of changes in them upon the increase of population in different regions of the world can be only approximately indicated. The United Nations estimates that only about 33 percent of the deaths and 42 percent of the births are registered (*12*). The percentage

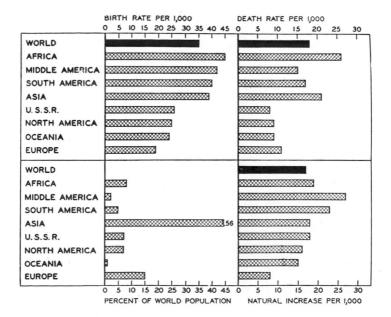

FIG. 4. Percentage of the 1958 world population, birth rate, death rate, and rate of natural increase, per 1000, for the period 1954–58 for various regions of the world.

registered ranges from about 8 to 10 percent in tropical and southern Africa and Eastern Asia to 98 to 100 percent in North America and Europe. Nevertheless, the statistical staff of the United Nations, by a judicious combination of the available fragmentary data, has been able to prepare estimates of fertility and mortality for different regions of the world that are generally accepted as a reasonably correct representation of the actual but unknown figures. The estimated birth rate, death rate, and crude rate of natural increase (the birth rate minus the death rate) for eight regions of the world for the period 1954–58 are shown in Fig. 4.

The birth rates of the countries of Africa, Asia, Middle America, and South America average nearly 40 per 1000 and probably are as high as they were 500 to 1000 years ago. In the rest of the world—Europe, North America, Oceania, and the Soviet Union—the birth rate is slightly more than half as high, or about 20 to 25 per 1000. The death rate for the former regions, although still definitely higher, is rapidly approaching that for people of European origin, with the result that the highest rates of natural increase are found in the regions with the highest birth rates. The most rapid rate of population growth at present is taking place in Middle and South America, where the population will double about every 26 years if the present rate continues.

These regional differences in fertility and mortality are intensifying the existing imbalance of population with land area and natural resources. No matter how this imbalance is measured, that it exists is readily apparent. Two rather crude measures are presented in Figs. 4 and 5, which show the percentage distribution of the world's population living in each region and the number of persons per square kilometer.

An important effect of the decline in mortality rates often is overlooked—namely, the increase in effective fertility. An estimated 97 out of every 100

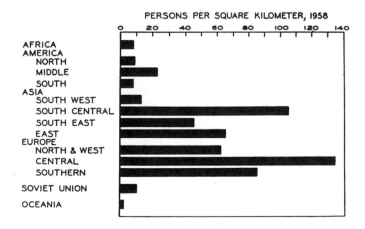

FIG. 5. Number of persons per square kilometer in various regions of the world in 1958.

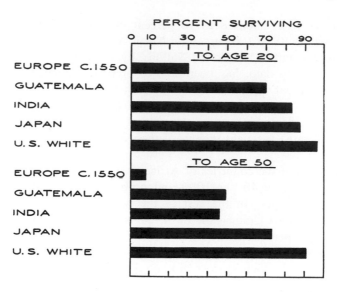

FIG. 6. Percentage of newborn females who would survive to the end of the reproductive period according to mortality rates in Europe around A.D. 1500 and in selected
countries around 1950.

newborn white females subject to the mortality rates prevailing in the United
States during 1950 would survive to age 20, slightly past the beginning of the
usual childbearing age, and 91 would survive to the end of the childbearing
period (Fig. 6). These estimates are more than 3 and 11 times, respectively,
the corresponding estimated proportions for white females that survived to these
ages about four centuries ago.

In contrast, about 70 percent of the newborn females in Guatemala would
survive to age 20, and only half would live to the end of the childbearing
period if subject to the death rates prevailing in that country in 1950. If the
death rate in Guatemala should fall to the level of that in the United States in
1950—a realistic possibility—the number of newborn females who would survive to the beginning of the childbearing period would increase by 36 percent;
the number surviving to the end of the childbearing period would increase by
85 percent. A corresponding decrease in the birth rate would be required to
prevent this increase in survivorship from resulting in a rapid acceleration in
the existing rate of population growth, which already is excessive. In other
words, this decrease in the death rate would require a decrease in the birth rate
of more than 40 percent merely to maintain the status quo.

As can be seen from Fig. 3, the birth rate in countries with high fertility
has shown little or no tendency to decrease in recent years. Japan is the exception. There, the birth rate dropped by 46 percent from 1948 to 1958—an amount
more than enough to counterbalance the decrease in the death rate, with the
result that there was a decrease in the absolute number of births. As yet there

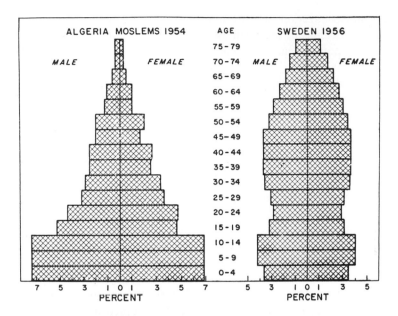

FIG. 7. Percentage distribution by age of the population of Sweden in 1956 and the Moslem population of Algeria in 1954.

is very little evidence that other countries with a correspondingly high birth rate are likely to duplicate this in the near future.

Another effect of a rapid rate of natural increase is demonstrated by Fig. 7. About 43 percent of the Moslem population of Algeria is under 15 years of age; the corresponding percentage in Sweden is 24, or slightly more than half this number. Percentages in the neighborhood of 40 percent are characteristic of the populations of the countries of Africa, Latin America, and Asia.

This high proportion of young people constitutes a huge fertility potential for 30 years into the future that can be counterbalanced only by a sharp decline in the birth rate, gives rise to serious educational problems, and causes a heavy drain on the capital formation that is necessary to improve the level of living of the entire population. A graphic illustration of this may be found in the recently published 5-year plan for India for 1961–66, which estimates that it will be necessary to provide educational facilities and teachers for 20 million additional children during this 5-year period (*13*).

Historical pattern in western Europe

Some persons, although agreeing that the current rate of increase of the majority of the world's population cannot continue indefinitely without giving rise to grave political, social, and economic problems, point out that a similar situation existed in northwestern and central Europe during the 18th and 19th centuries.

Increasing industrialization and urbanization, coupled with a rising standard of living, led to a decline in the birth rate, with a consequent drop in the rate of increase of the population. Why should not the rest of the world follow this pattern?

There is small likelihood that the two-thirds of the world's population which has not yet passed through the demographic revolution from high fertility and mortality rates to low fertility and mortality rates can repeat the history of western European peoples prior to the development of serious political and economic problems. A brief review of the circumstances that led to the virtual domination of the world at the end of the 19th century by persons of European origin will indicate some of the reasons for this opinion.

Around A.D. 1500 the population of Europe probably did not exceed 100 million persons (perhaps 15 to 20 percent of the population of the world) and occupied about 7 percent of the land area of the earth. Four hundred years later, around 1900, the descendants of this population numbered nearly 550 million, constituted about one-third of the world's population, and occupied or controlled five-sixths of the land area of the world. They had seized and peopled two great continents, North and South America, and one smaller continent, Australia, with its adjacent islands; had partially peopled and entirely controlled a third great continent, Africa; and dominated southern Asia and the neighboring islands.

The English-, French-, and Spanish-speaking peoples were the leaders in this expansion, with lesser roles being played by the Dutch and Portuguese. The Belgians and Germans participated only toward the end of this period of expansion. Among these, the English-speaking people held the dominant position at the end of the era, around 1900.

The number of English-speaking persons around 1500, at the start of this period of expansion, is not known, but it probably did not exceed 4 or 5 million. By 1900 these people numbered about 129 million and occupied and controlled one-third of the land area of the earth and, with the non-English-speaking inhabitants of this territory, they made up some 30 percent of the population of the world.

This period was characterized by an unprecedented increase in population, a several-fold expansion of the land base for this population, and a hitherto undreamed of multiplication of capital in the form of precious metals, goods, and commodities. Most important of all, the augmentation in capital and usable land took place more rapidly than the growth in population.

A situation equally favorable for a rapid improvement in the level of living associated with a sharp increase in population does not appear likely to arise for the people who now inhabit Latin America, Africa, and Asia. The last great frontier of the world has been closed. Although there are many thinly populated areas in the world, their existence is testimony to the fact that, until now, these have been regarded as undesirable living places. The expansion of population to the remaining open areas would require large expenditures of capital for irrigation, drainage, transportation facilities, control of insects and parasites, and other purposes—capital that the rapidly increasing populations which will need these areas do not possess.

In addition, this land is not freely available for settlement. The entire land surface of the world is crisscrossed by national boundaries. International migration now is controlled by political considerations; for the majority of the population of the world, migration, both in and out of a country, is restricted.

The horn of plenty, formerly filled with free natural resources, has been emptied. No rapid accumulation of capital in the form of precious metals, goods, and commodities, such as characterized the great 400-year boom enjoyed by the peoples of western-European origin, is possible for the people of Africa, Asia, and Latin America.

Last, but not least, is the sheer arithmetic of the current increase in population. The number of persons in the world is so large that even a small rate of natural increase will result in an almost astronomical increment over a period of time of infinitesimal duration compared to the duration of the past history of the human race. As was pointed out above, continuation of the present rate of increase would result in a population of 50 billion persons in another 150 years. A population of this magnitude is so foreign to our experience that it is difficult to comprehend its implications.

Just as Thomas Malthus, at the end of the 18th century, could not foresee the effect upon the peoples of western Europe of the exploration of the last great frontier of this earth, so we today cannot clearly foresee the final effect of an unprecedented rapid increase of population within closed frontiers. What seems to be least uncertain in a future full of uncertainty is that the demographic history of the next 400 years will not be like that of the past 400 years.

World problem

The results of human reproduction are no longer solely the concern of the two individuals involved, or of the larger family, or even of the nation of which they are citizens. A stage has been reached in the demographic development of the world when the rate of human reproduction in any part of the globe may directly or indirectly affect the health and welfare of the rest of the human race. It is in this sense that there is a world population problem.

One or two illustrations may make this point more clear. During the past decade, six out of every ten persons added to the population of the world live in Asia; another two out of every ten live in Latin America and Africa. It seems inevitable that the breaking up of the world domination by northwest Europeans and their descendants, which already is well advanced, will continue, and that the center of power and influence will shift toward the demographic center of the world.

The present distribution of population increase enhances the existing imbalance between the distribution of the world's population and the distribution
of wealth, available and utilized resources, and the use of nonhuman energy.
Probably for the first time in human history there is a universal aspiration for
a rapid improvement in the standard of living and a growing impatience with
conditions that appear to stand in the way of its attainment. Millions of persons
in Asia, Africa, and Latin America now are aware of the standard of living
enjoyed by Europeans and North Americans. They are demanding the opportunity to attain the same standard, and they resist the idea that they must be
permanently content with less.

A continuation of the present high rate of human multiplication will act as a
brake on the already painfully slow improvement in the level of living, thus
increasing political unrest and possibly bringing about eventual changes in government. As recent events have graphically demonstrated, such political changes
may greatly affect the welfare of even the wealthiest nations.

The capital and technological skills that many of the nations of Africa, Asia,
and Latin America require to produce enough food for a rapidly growing population and simultaneously to perceptibly raise per capita income exceed their existing national resources and ability. An immediate supply of capital in the amounts
required is available only from the wealthier nations. The principle of public
support for social welfare plans is now widely accepted in national affairs. The
desirability of extending this principle to the international level for the primary
purpose of supporting the economic development of the less advanced nations
has not yet been generally accepted by the wealthier and more advanced countries. Even if this principle should be accepted, it is not as yet clear how long
the wealthier nations would be willing to support the uncontrolled breeding of
the populations receiving this assistance. The general acceptance of a foreign-
aid program of the extent required by the countries with a rapidly growing
population will only postpone for a few decades the inevitable reckoning with
the results of uncontrolled human multiplication.

The future may witness a dramatic increase in man's ability to control his
environment, provided he rapidly develops cultural substitutes for those harsh
but effective governors of his high reproductive potential—disease and famine—
that he has so recently learned to control. Man has been able to modify or
control many natural phenomena, but he has not yet discovered how to evade the
consequences of biological laws. No species has ever been able to multiply without limit. There are two biological checks upon a rapid increase in number—a
high mortality and a low fertility. Unlike other biological organisms, man can
choose which of these checks shall be applied, but one of them must be. Whether
man can use his scientific knowledge to guide his future evolution more wisely
than the blind forces of nature, only the future can reveal. The answer will not
be long postponed.

REFERENCES

1. *Demographic Yearbook* (United Nations, New York, 1955), p. 1.
2. F. A. PEARSON and F. A. HARPER, *The World's Hunger* (Cornell Univ. Press, Ithaca, N.Y., 1945).
3. H. BROWN, *The Challenge of Man's Future* (Viking, New York, 1954).
4. O. E. BAKER, "Population trends in relation to land utilization," *Proc. Intern. Conf. Agr. Economists, 2nd Conf.* (1930), p. 284.
5. J. S. DAVIS, *J. Farm Economics* (Nov. 1949).
6. H. F. DORN, *J. Am. Statist. Assoc.* **45,** 311 (1950).
7. R. PEARL and L. J. REED, *Proc. Natl. Acad. Sci. U.S.* **6,** 275 (1920).
8. H. VON FOERSTER, P. M. MORA, L. W. AMIOT, *Science* **132,** 1291 (1960).
9. "The future growth of world population," *U.N. Publ. No. ST/SOA/Ser. A/28* (1958).
10. "The past and future growth of world population—a long-range view," *U.N. Population Bull. No. 1* (1951), pp. 1–12.
11. Although registration of deaths among the Moslem population of Algeria is incomplete, it is believed that the general impression conveyed by Fig. 2 is essentially correct.
12. *Demographic Yearbook* (United Nations, New York, 1956), p. 14.
13. New York *Times* (5 Aug. 1961).
14. "The determinants and consequences of population trends," *U.N. Publ. No. ST/SOA/Ser. A/17* (1953).

The Hare and the Haruspex:
A Cautionary Tale.*

EDWARD S. DEEVEY

Fifteen thousand years ago, when some of our more sensible ancestors had retired to paint pictures in caves in the south of France, the Scandinavian peninsula lay buried under a glacier. Even as recently as the seventh millennium B.C., when the arts and vices of civilization were already flourishing in the towns of Mesopotamia, the part of the earth's crust that is now Scandinavia was still depressed by the weight of half a mile of ice. Although the country has been rebounding at a great rate ever since, many Scandinavians remain depressed today. One reason may be that the Ice Age, as any Eskimo knows, is not yet over. The Scandinavian Airlines tourist who comes and goes like a swallow in the opalescent summer rarely glimpses the wintry or Pleistocene side of Nordic character, which accounts for its toughness, but which also results in some of the world's highest rates of alcoholism and suicide.

Perhaps because it was colonized so recently, the land the Norse called *Midgard* has always been treated as such—as middle ground, that is—by some of its inhabitants; as a good place to be *from,* on the way to some such place as *Asgard,* the abode of the gods. Rome, Byzantium, Normandy, and Britain were all chosen in their turn as earthly versions of *Asgard.* For a while, in the later Stone Age, the earliest emigrants could simply retrace their fathers' footsteps back to Europe, for the Danish Sounds were dry then, and dry land in the southern North Sea made Britain a peninsula before Scandinavia became one. By Roman and Viking times, given access to long ships, emigration continued to be almost as easy as it was fashionable. If one looks at a map of the land of the midnight sun (and remembers what happens when the sun goes

* This article was first published in The Yale Review for Winter 1960, copyright Yale University Press. It is reprinted here with permission.

down), it is easy to picture history as a series of glacial pulsations, or Gothic spurts, extruding adventurous Northmen toward successive seats of power, and milder winters. Nowadays, possibly because the northern weather is improving, the emigrants are less warlike than they used to be, and Visigoths and Vikings have tended to give way to movie actresses and physicists. The last of the great landwasters, Gustavus Adolphus, died more than three hundred years ago. It was only a few years before his time—in 1579 to be exact—that the animal kingdom seems to have caught the idea and carried it on, for that is the first year in which the now-famous lemmings are known to have been on the march.

Biologists, of whom I am one, have been taking a lively interest in lemmings lately. These rat-sized hyperborean field mice were unknown in the ancient world, and even the sagas are strangely silent about them. They really began to draw attention only in Queen Victoria's time, and especially in England, when the notion somehow got about that Plato's Atlantis lay on the Dogger Bank, under the North Sea. The lemmings' efforts to emigrate from Norway were then explained as vain attempts to recover a lost homeland, now occupied by such thoroughly English creatures as the haddock and the sprat. The fact that Swedish lemmings march in the wrong direction, toward the Baltic, tends to undermine this theory, but science has not come up with a better explanation until very recently. Biologists always hesitate to impute human motives to animals, but they are beginning to learn from psychologists, for whom attributing animal motives to humans is part of the day's work. What is now suspected is that the lemmings are driven by some of the same Scandinavian compulsions that drove the Goths. At home, according to this view, they become depressed and irritable during the long, dark winters under the snow. When home becomes intolerable, they emigrate, and their behavior is then described by the old Norse word, *berserk*.

A lemming migration is one of the great eruptions of nature, and its reverberations, like fallout, are of more than local concern. Biologists like to picture nature in the abstract as a sort of irregular lattice, or Mondrian construction, composed of feeding relations, whose seemingly random placement is actually so tightly organized that every strut depends on all the others. The lemmings' place in this picture is that of a strut more easily fretted than most, because, like other vegetarians that nourish a variety of carnivores, they are more fed upon than feeding. As Caruso's vocal cords, suitably vibrated, could shatter glassware, the whole of animate creation sometimes seems to pulsate with the supply of lemmings. In normal years they live obscurely, if dangerously, in the mountains of Scandinavia, and on the Arctic tundra generally. Periodically, despite the efficient efforts of their enemies—which include such mainstays of the fur industry as the marten and the white fox—their reproductive prowess gets the upper hand, and the tundra fairly teems with them. At such times, about every four years somewhere in Norway, though any given district is afflicted less frequently, the balance of nature goes entirely awry, and the Mondrian composition seems to degenerate into parody. Sea birds give up fishing and flock far inland to gorge on lemmings, while the more local hawks and owls hatch and feed families that are several times larger than usual. Foxes, on the shores of the Arctic Ocean, have been known to hunt for lemmings fifty miles out on the pack ice. The reindeer, which ordinarily subsist on reindeer moss, acquire a taste for lemmings just as cattle use salt. Eventually, faced with such troubles (but not necessarily *because* of them—I'm coming to that), lemmings are seized with the classic, or rather Gothic, obsession, and millions of them desert the tundra for the lowlands.

The repercussions then begin in earnest. As the clumsy animals attempt to swim the lakes and rivers, the predatory circle widens to include the trout and salmon, which understandably lose interest in dry flies. The forested lowlands, already occupied by other kinds of rodents as well as by farmers and their dogs and cats, are not good lemming country—the winters are too warm, for one thing—but while the lemmings press on as though aware of this, they show no sign of losing their disastrous appetites. When the crops are gone, though seldom before, exorcism by a Latin formula is said to have some slight effect in abating the plague. Finally, the vanguard may actually reach the sea, and, having nowhere else to go, plunge in—sometimes meeting another army trying to come ashore from a nearby island. A steamer, coming up Trondheim Fjord in November 1868, took fifteen minutes to pass through a shoal of them, but they were swimming *across* the fjord, not down it to the sea. The landward part of their wake is a path of destruction, strewn with dead lemmings, and an epidemic focus of lemming fever—which is not something the lemmings *have,* but a kind of tularemia that people get from handling the carcasses. As the Norwegians take up this unenviable chore their thoughts rarely turn to Mondrian or any other artist; the better-read among them may wonder, however, who buried the six hundred members of the Light Brigade.

American lemmings migrate too, but their outbreaks are observed less often, because no cities lie in their path. Knowledgeable bird-watchers are kept posted, nevertheless, by invasions of snowy owls, which leave the tundra when the lemming tide has passed its flood, and appear in such unlikely places as Charleston, the Azores, and Yugoslavia. Every four years or so, therefore, the lemmings affect the practice of taxidermy, and the economics of the glass-eye industry, as the handsome but unhappy birds fall trophy to amateur marksmen while vainly quartering the fields of France and New England. Closer to the center of the disturbance, the cities of western Norway see lemmings before they see owls, and they are not unknown as far away from the mountains as Stockholm, though spring fever is reported to be commoner than lemming fever along the Baltic beaches of Sweden. Oslo is ordinarily too far south, but was visited in 1862, in 1876, in 1890, and again in 1910. The 1862 migration, coinciding with the Battle of Antietam, may have been the greatest of the century, and one of its episodes was touching, if not prophetic. The Norwegian naturalist Robert

Collett saw them, he said, "running up the high granite stairs in the vestibule of the University" (of Oslo). Evidently they were begging to be investigated by professors. The Norwegian savants were busy, however, and scorned the impertinent intrusion. In 1862 the discoverer of the death wish, Sigmund Freud, was a six-year-old boy in far-away Freiburg, and if he ever saw a lemming or shot a snowy owl his biographers have repressed it.

That the lemmings are neurotically sick animals, at least during migration, has not escaped the notice of close, or even of casual, observers. For one thing, they wander abroad in the daytime, as small mammals rarely do. For another, when crossed or cornered they show a most unmouselike degree of fight; as Collett said, "they viciously drive their sharp teeth into the foot, or the stick advanced toward them, and allow themselves to be lifted high up by their teeth." Descriptions of the last snarling stages of the march to the sea recall the South Ferry terminal at rush hour, or a hundred-car smashup on a California turnpike. In his authoritative and starkly titled book, *Voles, Mice, and Lemmings,* the English biologist, Charles Elton, summed up "this great cosmic oscillation" as "a rather tragic procession of refugees, with all the obsessed behaviour of the unwanted stranger in a populous land, going blindly on to various deaths." Offhand, however, neurosis does not seem to explain very much of this, any more than shellshock is a cause of war, and, in trying to understand the upheaval, the experts have tended to set the psychopathic symptoms to one side while looking for something more basic.

That something, presumably, would be some property of the lemmings' environment—food, predators, disease, or weather, or perhaps all working together—that periodically relaxes its hold on the mournful numbers. Find the cause of the overcrowding, so the thinking has run, and you will find why the lemmings leave home. But this thinking, though doubtless correct, has been slow to answer the question, because it tends to divert attention from the actors to the scenery. The oldest Norse references to lemmings confuse them with locusts, and the farmer whose fields are devastated can hardly be expected to count the pests' legs and divide by four. More detached students know that mammals do not drop from the sky, but in their own way they too have been misled by the locust analogy, supposing that lemmings swarm, as locusts do, because of something done *to* them by their surroundings. The discovery that the migrations are cyclical, made only a few years ago by Elton, strengthened the assumption that some environmental regularity, probably a weather cycle, must set the tune, to which the lemmings, their predators, and their diseases respond in harmonics. Close listeners to nature's symphony soon reported, however, that it sounded atonal to them, more like Berg's opera *Wozzeck,* say, than like Beethoven's Sixth. Cycles of heavenly conjunctions were also looked into, but while the tides are pulled by the sun and moon, and the seasons are undeniably correlated with the zodiac, nothing in astrology reasonably corresponds to a four-year cycle.

If the lemmings' quadrennial fault lies, not in their stars, but in themselves, it is easy to see why the fact has been missed for so long. One reason, of course, is that most of their home life takes place under several feet of snow, in uncomfortable regions where even Scandinavians pass little time outdoors. The main trouble has been, though, as a quick review of thirty years' work will show, that the lemmings' path is thickly sown with false clues. Among these the snowy owls and white foxes rank as the reddest of herrings. The idea that the abundance of prey is controlled by the abundance of predators is a piece of folklore that is hard to uproot, because, like other superstitions, it is sometimes true. The farmers and gamekeepers of Norway have acted on it with sublime confidence for more than a hundred years, backed by a state system of bounty payments, and hawks, foxes, and other predators are now much scarcer there than they are in primeval Westchester County, for example. The result has been that while the grouse-shooting is no better than it used to be, the lemmings (and the field mice in the lowlands, where varmints are persecuted most actively) have continued to fluctuate with unabated vigor. A pile of fox brushes, augmented mainly every fourth year remains as a monument to a mistaken theory, but their owners may take some gloomy pride in having furnished a splendid mass of statistics.

An even more seductive body of data exists in the account books of the Arctic fur trade, some of which go back to Revolutionary days. They give a remarkable picture of feast or famine, most kinds of skins being listed as thousands of times more plentiful in good years than in lean. Those that belonged to the smaller predators, such as the white fox and the ermine, rise and fall in numbers with the hauntingly familiar four-year rhythm, and the trappers' diaries (which make better reading than the bookkeepers' ledgers) show that their authors placed the blame squarely, or cyclically, on lemmings. Farther south there are periodic surges among such forest-dwellers as the marten and the red fox, whose fluctuating food supply is field mice. Lynx pelts, known to the trade under various euphemisms for "cat," show a still more beautiful cycle of ten years' length, which certainly matches the abundance of showshoe hares, the lynxes' principal prey. The ten-year pulse of lynxes was extricated, after a brief but noisy academic scuffle, from the coils of the eleven-year sunspot cycle, and by the mid-'thirties the theory of mammal populations had settled down about like this: the prey begin to increase, and so do their slower-breeding predators; at peak abundance the predators nearly exterminate the prey, and then starve to death, so clearing the way for the prey to start the cycle over again.

The simple elegance of this idea made it enormously appealing, not least to mathematicians, who reduced it to equations and found it to have an astonishing amount of what they call *generality*. In physics, for instance, it is the "theory of coupled oscillations"; as "servomechanism theory" it underlies many triumphs of engineering, such as remote control by radar; in economics, it explains the tendency for the prices of linked products, such as corn and hogs, to chase each other in perpetually balanced imbalance. Regardless of the price of hogs, or furs, however, some killjoys soon declared that the formulae seemed not to apply to rodents. Some populations of snowshoe hares, for example, were found to oscillate on islands where lynxes, or predators of any sort, were scarcer than mathematicians. Besides, the equations require the coupled numbers of predator and prey to rise and fall smoothly, like tides, whereas the normal pattern of mammal cycles is one of gradual crescendo, followed abruptly by a crashing silence. A Russian biologist, G. F. Gause, was therefore led to redesign the theory in more sophisticated form. The predator, he said, need not be a fur-bearing animal; it can be an infectious disease. When the prey is scarce, the chance of infection is small, especially if the prey, or host, has survived an epidemic and is immune. As the hosts become more numerous, the infection spreads faster, or becomes more virulent, until the ensuing epidemic causes the crash.

In this new, agar-plated guise the theory was not only longer, lower, and more powerful; it was testable without recourse to the fur statistics, the study of which had come to resemble numerology. Made newly aware of lemming fever and tularemia, pathologists shed their white coats for parkas, and took their tubes and sterilizers into the field. The first reports were painfully disappointing: wild rodents, including lemmings, harbored no lack of interesting diseases, but the abundance of microbes had no connection with that of their hosts. Worse, the animals seemed to enjoy their ill health, even when their numbers were greatest, and when they died there was no sign of an epidemic. Not of infectious disease, anyway; but there was one malady, prevalent among snowshoe hares, that certainly was not infectious, but that just as certainly caused a lot of hares to drop dead, not only in live-traps, but also in the woods when no one was around. Long and occasionally sad experience with laboratory rabbits suggested a name, shock disease, for this benign but fatal ailment, the symptoms of which were reminiscent of apoplexy, or of insulin shock. The diagnosis, if that is what it was, amounted to saying that the hares were scared to death, not by lynxes (for the bodies hardly ever showed claw-marks), but, presumably, by each other. Having made this unhelpful pronouncement, most of the pathologists went home. The Second World War was on by that time, and for a while no one remembered what Collett had said about the lemmings: "Life quickly leaves them, and they die from the slightest injury . . . It is constantly stated by eyewitnesses, that they can die from their great excitement."

These Delphic remarks turned out to contain a real clue, which had been concealed in plain sight, like the purloined letter. An inquest on Minnesota snowshoe hares was completed in 1939, and its clinical language describes a grievous affliction. In the plainer words of a later writer,

> This syndrome was characterized primarily by fatty degeneration and atrophy of the liver with a coincident striking decrease in liver glycogen and a hypoglycemia preceding death. Petechial or ecchymotic brain hemorrhages, and congestion and

hemorrhage of the adrenals, thyroid, and kidneys were frequent findings in a smaller number of animals. The hares characteristically died in convulsive seizures with sudden onset, running movements, hind-leg extension, retraction of the head and neck, and sudden leaps with clonic seizures upon alighting. Other animals were typically lethargic or comatose.

For connoisseurs of hemorrhages this leaves no doubt that the hares were sick, but it does leave open the question of how they got that way. Well-trained in the school of Pasteur, or perhaps of Paul de Kruif, the investigators had been looking hard for germs, and were slow to take the hint of an atrophied liver, implying that shock might be a social disease, like alcoholism. As such, it could be contagious, like a hair-do, without being infectious. It might, in fact, be contracted in the same way that Chevrolets catch petechial tail fins from Cadillacs, through the virus of galloping, convulsive anxiety. A disorder of this sort, increasing in virulence with the means of mass communication, would be just the coupled oscillator needed to make Gause's theory work. So theatrical an idea had never occurred to Gause, though, and before it could make much progress the shooting outside the windows had to stop. About ten years later, when the news burst on the world that hares are mad in March, it lacked some of the now-it-can-be-told immediacy of the Smyth Report on atomic energy, but it fitted neatly into the bulky dossier on shock disease that had been quietly accumulating in the meantime.

As a matter of fact, for most of those ten years shock disease was a military secret, as ghastly in some of its implications as the Manhattan Project. Armies are not supposed to react like frightened rabbits, but the simple truth, that civilians in uniform can suffer and die from shock disease, was horrifyingly evident in Korea. As was revealed after the war, hundreds of American captives, live-trapped while away from home and mother, had turned lethargic or comatose, or died in convulsive seizures with sudden onset. Their baffled buddies gave it the unsympathetic name of "give-up-itis."

Military interest in rodents was whipped up long before 1939, of course, but its basis, during more ingenuous ages, was not the rodents' psyches. Rats have fought successfully, if impartially, in most of mankind's wars, but the Second World War was probably the first in which large numbers of rodents were deliberately kept on active duty while others were systematically slaughtered. To explain this curious evenhandedness, and at the risk of considerable oversimplification, we may divide military rodents (including rabbits, which are not rodents, but lagomorphs, according to purists) into two platoons, or squadrons. First, there are wild, or Army-type rodents, which not only nibble at stores but carry various diseases; they are executed when captured. Then there are domestic, cabined, or Navy-type rodents; during the war these were mainly watched by Navy psychologists in an effort to understand the military mind. The story of the first kind was superbly told by the late Hans Zinsser in *Rats, Lice, and History,* a runaway best-seller in the years between World Wars. Conceivably as a result, there were no outbreaks of louse-born typhus in the Second World War, but, in the course of their vigil, wildlife men continued to run into pathologists at Army messes around the world. The yarn of the Navy's rats has never been publicized, however (except, obliquely, in such studies of mass anxiety as William H. Whyte's *The Organization Man*).

The kind of nautical problem the psychologists had in mind was not the desertion of sinking ships, but the behavior of men under tension. The crowding of anxious but idle seamen in submarines, for instance, had had some fairly unmartial effects, which needed looking into. As subjects, when mariners were unavailable, the psychologists naturally used rats, which can be frustrated into states of high anxiety that simulate combat neurosis. So now, to recapitulate, there were *three* kinds of rodent experts in the Pacific theatre—zoologists, pathologists, and psychologists—and when they met, as they often did at the island bases, something was bound to happen. What emerged was a fresh view of rats, with which some of the lonelier islands were infested. These were no ordinary rats, but a special breed, like the Pitcairn Islanders, a sort of stranded landing-party. They were descendants of seagoing ancestors, marooned when the whalers had left; but, as the only wild mammals on the islands, they had reverted to Army type. It was soon noticed that when they entered messhalls and BOQ's they solved intellectual problems with great acumen, along with some anxiety-based bravado. Outdoors, on the other hand, their populations went up and down, and when abundant they terrorized the nesting seabirds or ran in droves through the copra plantations. Often, too, they simply dropped dead of shock. In short, they were rats, but whereas in confinement they behaved like psychologists, when at liberty they acted remarkably like lemmings.

If islanded feral rats contributed to the lemming problem, biologists could take wry pleasure in the fact, for most of the rats' contributions to insular existence—to the extinction of hundreds of kinds of interesting land birds, for instance—have been a lot less positive. Then, too, a back-to-nature movement led by psychologists promised to be an exhilarating experience, especially if it included an id-hunt through Polynesia. I have to admit, though, that it didn't work out quite that way, and my account of events in the Pacific theatre may be more plausible than accurate. The published facts are scanty, and my own duty as a Navy biologist was spent amid barnacles, not rodents, on the Eastern Sea Frontier. My first-hand knowledge of Pacific islands, in fact, is confined to Catalina, where rats are visible only on very clear days. What I *am* sure of is that startling things were learned in many countries, during the war years, about the capabilities of many kinds of animals besides rats. When these were added up it was not incredible that rodents might suffer the diseases of suburbia; some students would not have been surprised, by then, if bunnies were found to say "boo" to each other in Russian.

Bees, for example, were proved to be able to tell other bees, by means of a patterned dance like a polonaise, the direction and the distance from the hive at which food could be found, as well as the kind of flower to look for and the number of worker-bees needed to do the job. For compass directions they report the azimuth of the sun, but what they perceive is not the sun itself, but the arrangement of polarized light that the sun makes around the sky.

Navigating birds, on the other hand, take bearings on the sun directly, or on the stars, but when visual cues fail they fall back on an internal chronometer, conceivably their heart-beat, to reach their destination anyway.

Prairie-dogs in their towns pass socially accepted facts, such as the invisible boundaries between their neighborhoods, from one generation to the next; they do it by imitating each other, not by instinct, and European chickadees do the same with their trick, invented about 1940, of following milkmen on their routes and beating housewives to the bottled cream.

Ravens and jackdaws can count up to six or seven, and show that they can form an abstract concept of number by responding, correctly, whether the number is cued by spots on cards, by bells or buzzers, or by different spoken commands.

A Swedish bird called the nutcracker remembers precisely where it buried its nuts in the fall, then digs them up, in late March, say, confidently and without errors through two feet of snow.

For its sexual display, an Australian species called the satin bowerbird not only constructs a bower, or bachelor apartment, decorating it with flowers and *objets d'art,* as do other members of its family, but makes paint out of charcoal or fruit-juice and paints the walls of its bower, using a pledget of chewed bark for a daub.

Bats avoid obstacles in total darkness, and probably catch flying insects too, by uttering short, loud screams and guiding themselves by the echoes; the pitch is much too high for human ears to hear, but some kinds of moths can hear the bats coming and take evasive action.

Made groggy by facts like these, most of them reported between 1946 and 1950, biologists began to feel like the White Queen, who "sometimes managed to believe as many as six impossible things before breakfast." Still, no one had yet spent a winter watching rodents under the snow, and the epicene behavior of bowerbirds was not seen, then or since, as having any direct bearing on mammalian neurosis. If anything, the intellectual feats of birds and bees made it harder to understand how rodents could get into such sorry states; one might have credited them with more sense. Until new revelations from the Navy's rats laid bare their inmost conflicts, the point was arguable, at least, that anxiety is a sort of hothouse bloom, forced in psychologists' laboratories, and could not survive a northern winter.

As a footnote in a recent article makes clear, the United States Navy takes no definite stand on rodents. "The opinions or assertions contained herein," it says (referring to a report on crowded mice), "are the private ones of the writer, and are not to be construed as official or reflecting the views of the Navy Depart-

ment or naval service at large." This disavowal is a little surprising, in that its author, John J. Christian, as head of the animal laboratories of the Naval Medical
Research Institute at Bethesda, Maryland, can be considered the commander of
the Navy's rodents. Ten years ago, though, when he wrote what may be thought
of as the Smyth Report on population cycles, his opinions were temporarily freed
from protocol. An endocrinologist and Navy lieutenant (j.g.), Christian had
left the Fleet and gone back to studying mice at the Wyeth Institute, in Philadelphia. His luminous essay was published where anyone at large could read
it, in the August 1950 issue of the *Journal of Mammalogy,* under the title "The
Adreno-Pituitary System and Population Cycles in Mammals." In it Christian
said, in part:

> We now have a working hypothesis for the die-off terminating a cycle. Exhaus-
> tion of the adreno-pituitary system resulting from increased stresses inherent in a
> high population, especially in winter, plus the late winter demands of the repro-
> ductive system, due to increased light or other factors, precipitates population-wide
> death with the symptoms of adrenal insufficiency and hypoglycemic convulsions.

Dedicated readers of the *Journal* remembered the snowshoe hares' congested
adrenals, and did not need to be reminded that shock is a glandular disorder.
They also knew their scientific Greek, and easily translated *hypoglycemia* as
"lack of sugar in the blood"; but what they found new and fascinating was
Christian's clinical evidence—much of it reported by a young Viennese internist
named Hans Selye—tending to show that rodents might die, of all things, from
a surfeit of sexuality. Most people had thought of rabbits as adequately equipped
for reproduction, but that is not the point, as Christian developed it: what does
them in is not breeding, exactly, but concupiscence. Keyed up by the stresses of
crowded existence—he instanced poor and insufficient food, increased exertion,
and fighting—animals that have struggled through a tough winter are in no shape
to stand the lust that rises like sap in the spring. Their endocrine glands, which
make the clashing hormones, burn sugar like a schoolgirl making fudge, and the
rodents, not being maple trees, have to borrow sugar from their livers. Cirrhosis
lies that way, of course, but death from hypertension usually comes first.

In medical jargon, though the testy author of *Modern English Usage* would
protest, the name for this state of endocrine strain is *stress.* As the physical
embodiment of a mental state, anxiety, it is worth the respectful attention of all
who believe, with mammalogists, that life can be sweet without necessarily
caramelizing the liver. Despite its technicality, the subject is uncommonly rewarding. It is not only that seeing a lemming as a stressed animal goes far toward
clearing up a famous mystery. And, although the how and why of psychosomatic
ailments in wild rodents are undeniably important to tame men, the problems of
gray flannel suits are not my main concern. The real attraction of stress, at least
for a biologist, consists simply in the way it works: it turns out to contain a whole
array of built-in servomechanisms. That is, the coupled oscillation of hosts and

diseases, which Gause thought underlie the fluctuating balance of nature, is mimicked inside the body, and may be said to be controlled, by mutual interaction between the glands. Biologists are impressed by abstract resemblances of this sort, which, after all, are their version of *generality*. In explaining stress by means of some fairly garish metaphors, therefore, I find it soothing to remember that what is called "imagery" in some circles is "model-making" in others.

As it happens, the master himself is no slouch at imagery. Selye's recent book, *The Stress of Life,* is notable, among other things, for its skillful use of the didactic, or Sunday-supplement, analogy. Without plagiarizing his exposition, though, it is possible to speak of vital needs as payable in sugar, for which the liver acts as a bank. Routine withdrawals are smoothly handled by hormones from the pancreas and from the adrenal medulla, which act as paying tellers; but the top-level decisions (such as whether to grow or to reproduce) are reserved for the bank's officers, the adrenal cortex and pituitary glands. Stress, in Selye's view, amounts to an administrative flap among the hormones, and shock results when the management overdraws the bank.

If the banking model is gently dissected, it reveals its first and most important servomechanism: a remarkably bureaucratic hookup between the adrenal cortex, acting as cashier's office, and the pituitary, as board of directors. Injury and infection are common forms of stress, and in directing controlled inflammation to combat them the cortex draws cashier's checks on the liver. If the stress persists, a hormone called cortisone sends a worried message to the pituitary. Preoccupied with the big picture, the pituitary delegates a vice-presidential type, ACTH or adrenocorticotropic hormone, whose role is literally to buck up the adrenal cortex. As students of Parkinson would predict, the cortex, bucked, takes on more personnel, and expands its activities, including that of summoning more ACTH. The viciousness of the impending spiral ought to be obvious, and ordinarily it is; but while withdrawals continue, the amount of sugar in circulation is deceptively constant (the work of another servomechanism), and there is no device, short of autopsy, for taking inventory at the bank. If the pituitary is conned by persisting stress into throwing more support to ACTH, the big deals begin to suffer retrenchment. A cutback of ovarian hormone, for instance, may allow the cortex to treat a well-started foetus as an inflammation to be healed over. Likewise, the glandular sources of virility and of maternity, though unequally prodigal of sugar, are equally likely to dry up. Leaving hypertension aside (because it involves another commodity, salt, which needn't be gone into just now), the fatal symptom can be hypoglycemia. A tiny extra stress, such as a loud noise (or, as Christian would have it, the sight of a lady rabbit), corresponds to an unannounced visit by the bank examiner: the adrenal medulla is startled into sending a jolt of adrenalin to the muscles, the blood is drained of sugar, and the brain is suddenly starved. This, incidentally, is why shock looks like hyperinsulinism. An overactive pancreas, like a panicky adrenal, resembles an untrustworthy teller with his hand in the till.

Haruspicy, or divination by inspection of the entrails of domestic animals, is supposed to have been extinct for two thousand years, and no one knows what the Etruscan soothsayers made of a ravaged liver. Selye would snort, no doubt, at being called a modern haruspex, but the omens of public dread are at least as visceral as those of any other calamity, and there are some sound Latin precedents—such as the geese whose gabbling saved Rome—for the view that emotion is communicable to and by animals. More recently, thoughtful veterinarians have begun to notice that neurotic pets tend to have neurotic owners, and a report from the Philadelphia Zoo blames "social pressures," on the rise for the last two decades, for a tenfold increase of arteriosclerosis among the inmates. If Selye seems to be playing down anxiety—the word is not even listed in the index of his book—I can think of two possible reasons, both interesting if not entirely convincing. Anxiety is an ugly word, of course, and using it can easily generate more of it, just as calling a man an insomniac can keep him awake all night; Selye, as a good physician, may well have hesitated to stress it in a popular book about stress. More important, probably, is the fact that Selye, like any internist, begins and ends his work with bodily symptoms, and only grudgingly admits the existence of mind. A curious piece of shoptalk, which he quotes approvingly and in full from a San Francisco medical man (not a psychiatrist), suggests that some of his professional colleagues, like too many novelists, have read Freud without understanding him:

> The dissociation of the ego and the id has many forms. I had an American housewife with dermatomyositis [an inflammation of skin and muscles] [the brackets are Selye's] who had been taught how to play the piano when she was little, and had continued for the entertainment of the children, but didn't get very far. When she started on large doses of ACTH she was suddenly able to play the most difficult works of Beethoven and Chopin—and the children of the neighbors would gather in the garden to hear her play. Here was a dissociation of the ego and the id that was doing good. But she also became a little psychotic, and so her dosage of ACTH had to be lowered, and with every 10 units of ACTH one sonata disappeared. It had ended up with the same old music poorly performed.

The false note here, of course, is that business about "the dissociation of the ego and the id." Whatever the id may be, it is not considered innately musical, and *my* professional colleagues would count it a triumph to be able to teach it anything, even "Chopsticks." Still, we may take the anecdote as showing *some* kind of mental effect of stress; what the psychologist sees as rather more to the point is the obverse of this: moods and emotions cannot be injected hypodermically, but their cost is paid in sugar, and their action on the cortex is precisely that of ACTH. Christian finds, for instance, that crowding mice in cages enlarges their adrenals, but fortunately, in experiments of this sort, it is not always necessary to kill the animals to learn the answer. A microscope sample of blood reveals a useful clue to endocrine tension: college students at exam time show a shortage of the same type of white cell that is also scarce in the blood of crowded mice. (The skittish blood cells are called *eosinophils;* I mention this because the word is sure to turn up in detective stories before long.) The fact that tranquillizing drugs do their work by blocking various hormones opens up another line of evidence, as well as a fertile field for quackery. But the surest sign that anxiety is stress—and its most lurid property—is its ability to visit itself on the unborn. The maker of this appalling discovery, William R. Thompson of Wesleyan University, tells us nothing of the sins of his rats' fathers, but his report shows all too clearly that the offspring of frustrated mothers, part of whose pregnancy was spent in problem boxes with no exit, carried the emotional disturbance thoughout their own lives. Nestling birds can learn the parents' alarm call while still inside the egg (as the nearly-forgotten author of *Green Mansions* was among the first to notice), but the mammalian uterus is more soundproof, and the only reasonable explanation of Thompson's results is that the aroused maternal hormones perverted the silver cord, and made it a pipeline to a forbidden supply of sugar.

Circumspectly, now, so as to forestall any harumphs from the naval service at large, we may return to Christian's crowded mice. In outward demeanor the ordinary house mouse, *Mus musculus,* is the least military of rodents, but his dissembling is part of the commando tradition, and he would not have got where he is today without a lot of ruthless infighting. Nowadays house mice spend little time outdoors if they can help it, but in more rustic times they often scourged the countryside, like Marion's men, and the tenth-century Bishop of Bingen (who perished in the Mouse Tower) learned to his cost that country mice can be pushed too far. Recently, at some of our leading universities (Oslo, strange to say, has still not been heard from), mouse-watching has proved informative, if not exactly edifying, and I cull a few tidbits from the notes of some shocked colleagues:

The first thing to notice is that the old murine spirit of mass emigration is not yet dead, despite the effeteness of modern urban living. Not long ago an outbreak was observed—provoked, in fact—at the University of Wisconsin, where the scientists had set up a mouse tower, or substitute patch of tundra, in a junkroom in the basement of the zoology building, and set traps (not enough, as it turned out) in the neighboring offices and laboratories. Nothing happened for a while, except that the food—half a pound of it a day—kept disappearing. Then, in Browning's words, "the muttering grew to a grumbling; and the grumbling grew to a mighty rumbling"; and the experiment, though publishable, became unpopular; the room was simply overstuffed with mice, like a sofa in a neglected summer cottage.

Chastened, yet encouraged by this experience, the zoologists fell back on emigration-proof pens, where they could keep tab on the mice. Taking census whenever they cleaned the cages (which was pretty often, at someone's pointed insistence), they noticed that the numbers went up and down, but, as there were no seasons or predators and food was always abundant, the fluctuations made little sense at first. Gradually, though, when one of the observers, Charles Southwick, thought to count the tiffs as well as the mice, the shiny outlines of a servomechanism came into sight: as each wave of numbers crested and broke, the scuffles averaged more than one per mouse-hour, and hardly any young mice survived to the age of weaning. Putting the matter this way lays the blame, unchivalrously, on the mothers, and in fact, as the tension mounted, their nest-building became slovenly and some of them failed to nurse their litters, or even ate them (proper mouse food, remember, was always plentiful). But the males were equally responsible, though for different hormonal reasons. Like chickens with their peck-order, the buck mice were more concerned for status than for posterity, and the endocrine cost of supremacy was sexual impotence. In one of the pens two evenly-matched pretenders played mouse-in-the-manger with the females, and suppressed all reproduction until they died.

While the Wisconsin mice were either suffering from stress or practicing a peculiarly savage form of moral restraint, mice at other centers were also made unhappy, or at least infertile, by being given plenty of food, space, and sexual access. It came as no great surprise, then, when the adrenals of Christian's mice were found to swell, as he had predicted eight years before, in proportion to the numbers of their social companions. The really arresting experiment, which dilutes the inhumanity of some of the others, shows that rodents—rats, at any rate—*prefer* to be crowded and anxious. At the National Institutes of Health, in Bethesda, John C. Calhoun allowed litter-mates to grow up in one large pen, where every rat had an individual food hopper. From the start, when eating, they huddled like a farrow at a single hopper; later, though free to roam, eat, and nest in four intercommunicating pens, these rats and their descendants spent most of their time in one of the four, and as I write this they are still there, paying for their sociability in lowered fertility and shortened lives. For his part, my friend Calhoun coined a phrase that deserves to outlive his rats, and is still musing on *pathological togetherness*.

At this point in the argument, explaining the lemmings' periodic dementia should be anticlimactically easy. I seem to have overstated the case, in fact, for it seems less Gothic than *gothick,* like some of the more unnecessary behavior described by the brothers Grimm. The cycle starts where population problems always do, with the lemmings' awesome power of procreation. Nubile at the age of thirty-five days, averaging seven or eight young at a cast, a female lemming may have worries, but barrenness is not one of them, and four litters is par for a summer's dalliance. Lemming life is more austere in winter, but not much. As long as food is plentiful under the snow, the winter sport of pullulation and fighting continue as at a disreputable ski resort. The wonder is—until we remember the owls and foxes above and the weasels *in* the runways—that it takes as long as four years for the numbers to become critical, like the mass of an atomic bomb. When the Thing goes off, then, it is the younger lemmings that emigrate, in search of a patch of tundra that is slightly more private than the beach at Coney Island; though less overtly anxious to begin with, presumably, their state of mind on reaching downtown Oslo is another matter entirely. The older, better-established residents, or those with stouter livers, stay home and die of shock—having first passed on the family disease to the next generation. Before the epidemic of stress has run its course, it spreads to the predators, too (though *this* form of lemming fever is caught, ironically, from *not* eating lemmings). The snowy owl that died at Fayal, Azores, in 1928 may or may not have known that it had really reached Atlantis, but in being shot by an anxious man it provided a textbook, or postgraduate, example of a coupled oscillation.

If all this is true, and I think it is, the Norse clergymen who exorcized the lemmings in Latin were clearly on the right track, and what the Scandinavians need is a qualified haruspex. Before they hire one, though (I am not a candidate), or resort to spraying the tundra with tranquillizers (which would be expensive), there is one tiny reservation: there is not a scrap of *direct* evidence that the lemming suffers from stress. Come to think of it, no one has yet spent a winter watching lemmings under the snow. (Some Californian zoologists lived for several winters in Alaska, trying valiantly to do just that, but the runways are pretty small for Californians, and for most of the time there was trouble finding *any* lemmings.) Except for some circumstantial lesions of the skin, which could be psychosomatic, like shingles (and which ruin the lemming's pelt), the case for contagious anxiety therefore rests on a passel of tormented rodents, but not as yet on *Lemmus lemmus*. That animal has baffled a lot of people, and I could be mistaken too. But if I am, or at least if the lemmings' adrenals are not periodically congested, I will eat a small population of them, suitably seasoned with Miltown. Fortunately, lemmings are reported to taste like squirrels, but better; in Lapland, in fact, with men who know rodents best, it's lemmings, two to one.

Cybernetics of
Population Control

HUDSON HOAGLAND

There is an ambivalence about many scientific discoveries, and it is ironical that our best humanitarian motives in medicine and public health are primarily responsible for the grave dangers of the population explosion. I would like to consider some of the ways in which nature deals with overcrowding in other animal societies, since this may shed some light on our own population problems.

In multiplying cultures of microorganisms, the growth rate accelerates exponentially; but as toxic metabolic products such as acids or alcohols accumulate, the rate declines and the curve describing numbers of organisms as a function of time ultimately flattens off.

Insect populations are regulated in various ways. The fruit fly, *Drosophila,* above certain population densities, decreases its egg laying in an amount proportional to the density. In flour beetles, below a fixed number of grams of flour per beetle, cannibalism occurs in some species and egg production drops off; in one species, crowding results in females puncturing and destroying some of the eggs they have produced. Frequency of copulation also declines with crowding. There are some species of flour beetles with glands that produce a gas, the release of which is increased with crowding. This gas is lethal to larvae and acts as an antaphrodisiac at high densities of population. Flour contaminated with beetle excrement inhibits egg production of another species; mixing this contaminated flour with fresh flour decreases the rate of population growth, despite the ample food supply.

Among mammals other than man, it was long thought that food and predators were the controlling factors in limiting populations. It was thought, for example, that the four-year cycles of buildup and decline of lemming populations, terminating in their suicidal migrations, were due to an increase in predators accompanying population growth which ultimately caused the panic and decline.

But the migrations and deaths appear now not to be caused by the predators. Rather, the predators appear to multiply in response to the multiplying prey. While the lemming cycles have not been studied as systematically as those of other species, it seems likely that these four-year fluctuations in population densities are determined by factors now known to regulate cycles in other species.

Minnesota jack rabbit populations rise and fall through cycles of several years' duration. There is a build-up followed by a dying off. It was observed that when the animals died off there was usually plenty of food—they didn't starve. There was no evidence of excessive predators. Furthermore, the bodies showed no sign of any specific epidemic that killed them. To quote from a 1939 study of the dead animals: "This syndrome was characterized primarily by fatty degeneration and atrophy of the liver with a coincident striking decrease in liver glycogen and a hypoglycemia preceding death. Petechial or ecchymotic brain hemorrhages and congestion and hemorrhage of the adrenals, thyroid, and kidneys were frequent findings in a smaller number of animals. The hares characteristically died in convulsive seizures with sudden onset, running movements, hindleg extension, retraction of the head and neck, and sudden leaps with clonic seizures upon alighting. Other animals were typically lethargic or comatose." The adrenals were hypertrophied in some cases and atrophied in others. Such signs—liver disease, hypertension, atherosclerosis and adrenal deterioration—are typical of the acute stress syndrome that results from overactivity of the pituitary-adrenal axis.

Studies of rodents showed that, after the severe stress of winter crowding in burrows when population densities were high, there was much fighting among the males, sex drives were at a low ebb, the young were often eaten, and the females produced premature births. There was also increased susceptibility to nonspecific infections—another byproduct of excessive production of adrenal corticoids. After such a colony has been depleted in numbers through effects of the stress syndrome, the colony then tends to build up again, and so it goes through repeated cycles of growth and decline.

A pair of deer were put on a small island of about 150 acres in Chesapeake Bay about forty years ago. The deer were kept well supplied with food. It was found that the colony grew until it reached a density of about one deer per acre. Then the animals began to die off despite adequate food and care. Examination of the dead animals again showed marked evidence of the adrenal stress syndrome. In studies of crowding in the Philadelphia zoo, it was found that in some species of animals there was a tenfold increase in atherosclerosis under conditions of severe crowding, and there were many other symptoms characteristic of stress. John Christian of the Naval Medical Research Institute made population studies in relation to crowding of mice. In his 1950 paper in the *Journal of Mammalogy,* "The Adrenopituitary System and Population Cycles in Mammals," he wrote: "We now have a working hypothesis for the die-off terminating a cycle. Exhaustion of the adrenopituitary system resulting from increased stresses inherent in a high population, especially in winter, plus the late winter demands of the reproductive system, due to increased light or other factors, precipitates population-wide death with the symptoms of adrenal insufficiency and hypoglycemic convulsions."

Overcrowding in rat colonies

John Calhoun of the National Institutes of Health, investigating rats kept at critical levels of crowding, found high infant mortality, high abortion rates, and failure of mothers to build nests. The rats showed evidence of the stress syndrome, and Calhoun speaks of "pathological togetherness." He has reviewed this work in "Population Density and Social Pathology" (*Scientific American,* February 1962), a summary of which follows.

Calhoun confined wild Norway rats in a one-quarter acre enclosure with plenty of food and water. At the end of 27 months the population stabilized itself at 150 adults. One would expect from the very low adult mortality rate in uncrowded conditions a population of 5,000, not 150 rats. But infant mortality was extremely high. The stress from social interaction disrupted maternal behavior so that only a few of the young survived. Calhoun later studied groups of domesticated white rats confined indoors in observation rooms under better controlled conditions. Six different populations were examined. Each group was allowed to increase to twice the number that his earlier experience indicated could occupy the space allotted with only moderate stress. Pathological behavior was most marked in the females. Pregnancies were often not full term. There were many abortions and many maternal deaths. The mothers often could not nurse or care for their young. Among the males there was much sexual deviation, cannibalism, and other abnormal behavior ranging from frenetic overactivity to pathological withdrawal in which some males emerged from their nests only to eat and drink. Patterns of social behavior were thus badly deranged at twice normal crowding.

The experiments took place in four interconnecting pens, each six by six feet in area. Each was a complete dwelling unit with a drinking fountain, a food hopper, and an elevated artificial burrow containing five nest boxes. There was comfortable space for 12 adult rats in each pen. The setup should thus have been able to support 48 rats comfortably. At the stabilized number of 80 to 100—double the comfortable population—which they were allowed to reach by breeding, an even distribution would have been 20 to 25 adults in each pen. But the rats did not dispose themselves in this way.

Biasing factors were introduced in the following fashion. Ramps were arranged enabling the animals to get from one pen to another and so to traverse the entire four pens in the room. However, the two end pens, numbers 1 and 4, each had only one ramp, which connected them with pens 2 and 3, respectively, while the middle pens had two ramps each, i.e., ramps connecting pen 2 with pen 3 and with pen 1, and ramps connecting pen 3 with pen 2 and pen 4. This arrangement immediately skewed the probabilities in favor of a higher density in the two middle pens, since pens 2 and 3 could be reached by two ramps whereas pens 1 and 4 by only one ramp each. But with the passage of time strange aspects of the behavior of the group skewed the distribution in an unexpected way, and also resulted in an unexpected arrangement of the sex ratios. The females distributed themselves about equally in the four pens, but the male population was concentrated almost overwhelmingly in the middle pens. One reason for this was the status struggle among the males. Shortly after six months of age, each male enters into a round-robin of fights and eventually fixes his position in the social hierarchy. Such fights took place in all of the pens, but in the end pens it became possible for a single dominant male to take over the area as his territory.

Calhoun describes how this came about. The subordinate males in all pens adopted the habit of arising early. This enabled them to eat and drink in peace. Rats generally eat in the course of their normal wanderings, and the subordinate residents of the end pens, having been defeated by the dominant male in these pens, were likely to feed in one of the middle pens where they had not had as yet to fight for status. When, after feeding, they wanted to return to their original quarters, they found it very difficult to do so. By this time the dominant male in the end pen would have awakened and he would engage the subordinates in fights as they tried to come down the single ramp to the pen. For a while the subordinate would continue his efforts to return to what had been his home pen, but after a succession of defeats he would become so conditioned that he would not even make the attempt. In essence, Calhoun points out that the dominant male established his territory of domination in the end pens and his control over a harem of females—not by driving the other males out but by preventing their return over the one ramp leading to the end pen. While the dominant male in an end pen slept a good part of the time, he made his sleeping quarters at the base of the ramp. He was therefore on perpetual guard, awakening as soon as another male appeared at the head of the ramp. He usually only had to open his eyes for the invader to wheel around and return to the adjoining pen. Since there were two ramps for pens 2 and 3, no one male could thus dominate both of them. The dominant males in pens 1 or 4 would sleep calmly through all the comings and goings of his harem. Seemingly he did not even hear them. His condition during his waking hours reflected his dominant status. He would move about in a casual and deliberate fashion, occasionally inspecting the burrow and nests of his harem. But he would rarely enter a burrow, as some other males did in the middle pens, merely to ferret out the females. A dominant male might tolerate other males in his domain, provided they were phlegmatic and made themselves scarce. Most of the time these subordinate males would hide in the burrows with the adult females, and only come out onto the floor to eat and drink. These subordinate males never tried to engage in sex activity with the females.

In the end pens, where population density was thus kept low, the mortality rate among infants and females was also low. Of the various social environments that developed, the breed pens—as the end pens were called—were the only healthy ones. The harem females generally made good mothers and protected their pups from harm. The pregnancy rates of the females in the middle pens were the same as those in the end pens, but a very much lower percentage of their pregnancies terminated in live births. In one series of experiments 99 percent of the young born in pens 2 and 3 perished before weaning.

The females that lived in the densely populated middle pens became progressively less adapted to building adequate nests. Normally, this is an undertaking that involves repeated periods of sustained activity with the searching out of appropriate materials, such as the strips of paper which were made available to them, and transporting the strips to a nest which they arrange in a cup-like form. In the crowded middle pens, however, the females began merely to pile the strips in heaps, sometimes trampling them into a pad, showing little signs of cup formation. Later they would bring fewer and fewer strips to the nesting site, and in the midst of transporting a bit of material would drop it and engage in some other activity, occasioned by contact and interaction with other rats met on the way. In the extreme disruption of their behavior during the later months of the population's history, they would build no nests at all, but would bear their litters on the sawdust in the burrow box. The females also lost the ability to transport their litters from one place to another—a thing they would normally do with skill. If they tried to move a litter, they would drop individuals and scatter them about on the floor. The infants thus abandoned throughout the pens were seldom nursed. They would die where they were dropped and were thereupon eaten by the adults. In the middle pens, when a female would come into heat, she would be relentlessly pursued by all of the males until she was exhausted. This caused the death of 25 percent of the females in a relatively short time in the crowded pens; in contrast, only 15 percent of the adult males died over the same time in the middle pens. In the end brood pens, however, this sort of thing didn't happen. The females in these pens would retire to bear their young in nests they made in a normal fashion, and were protected from the excessive attention of the other males by the dominant male.

In the middle pens, a great deal of fighting among the males went on, with now one and now another assuming the dominant position. In contrast, in the end brood pens, one male predominated and peace generally reigned. These dominant males took care of the females and of the juveniles, never bothering them in any way.

Among the subordinate males there was much abnormal behavior. For instance, there was a group of homosexuals. They were really pansexual animals, and apparently could not discriminate between sex partners. They made sexual advances to males, juveniles, and females that were not in estrus. They were frequently attacked by their more dominant associates, but they very rarely contended for status.

Another type of male emerged in the crowded pens. This was essentially a very passive type that moved a good deal like a somnambulist. These rats ignored the others of both sexes. and all the other rats ignored them. Even when the females were in estrus, these passive animals made no advances to them, and only very rarely did other males approach them for any kind of play. They were healthy, attractive, and sleek, but were simply zombies in their conduct.

The strangest of all the abnormal male types was what Calhoun called the probers. These animals, which always lived in the middle pens, took no part at all in the status struggle. Nevertheless they were the most active of all the males, and persisted in their activities in spite of attacks by the dominant animals. In addition to being hyperactive, the probers were hypersexual, and in time many of them became cannibalistic. They were always chasing females about, entering their nests, having intercourse with them in the nest, a thing that the normal rats would never do. These probers conducted their pursuits of estrus females in a very abnormal manner, abandoning all the courtship ritual that is characteristic of normal mating rats.

These experiments of John Calhoun show the development of serious pathology in a society which is directly attributable to overcrowding at only twice the number of rats per unit area required for a healthy society.

Stress in human populations

A question of immediate interest is to what extent the stress syndrome may be a factor in reducing the growth rate of human populations. As far as I know, there are no adequate data to answer this question. Studies from a number of laboratories including our own have demonstrated that the human pituitary adrenal system responds under stress in a way similar to that of other mammals. There is indirect evidence that inmates of concentration camps experienced acute forms of the stress syndrome that may have accounted for many deaths. Concentration camps are more appropriately compared with highly congested animal populations than are city slums, since even in very crowded cities, the poor do have some mobility. They can escape from their immediate congestion on streets and associate with other segments of the population. The incidence of street gangs and juvenile delinquency is especially characteristic of overcrowded city areas and constitutes a form of social pathology. Several studies have also indicated a higher incidence of schizophrenia and of other psychotic and neurotic behavior in congested urban areas than in more spacious environments, but other factors may be involved here. The increased incidence of atherosclerosis and other cardiovascular pathology associated with urban living and its competitive stresses may also be enhanced by crowding, although direct evidence for this is lacking. In underdeveloped countries with high birth rates and recently lowered death rates, producing population growth of two to four percent per year, any growth-retarding effect of the stress syndrome is masked by the use of health measures that are enhancing life expectancies.

V. C. Wynne-Edwards has published an important book called *Animal Dispersion in Relation to Social Behavior* (New York: Hafner Press, 1962). He points out that in nature, a failure in food supplies results in a local emergency of overpopulation, which, especially among highly mobile flying animals such as insects and birds, can be immediately relieved by emigration. The social hierarchy and code of behavior of the animals are devices to force out the surplus. The exiles may be condemned to perish or, under other circumstances, may set up new populations in other places. In the cold boreal and arctic regions, most of the new species are birds. Many birds are adapted to exploit intermittent or undependable food crops and are to a large extent nomadic in their search for regions where supplies are temporarily plentiful. Two distinct biological functions appear to be served by emigration. One is that of a safety valve to give immediate relief to overpopulation, and the other is a pioneering function to expand and replenish the range of the species as a whole, and provide for gene exchange. Emigration of the safety valve kind is associated with stress and with quickly deteriorating economic conditions (locusts). On the other hand, providing pioneers is something that can be afforded only when conditions are good. In more variable environments, both functions tend to become important and to be exercised on a large scale. The individuals expelled are in either case usually the junior fraction of the hierarchy.

In this connection I am reminded of human colonizing activities—the Greek city-states that sent young people off to colonize the Mediterranean area—Italy, Sicily, Africa, and the lands around the Aegean and the Black Sea. The younger sons of families in Britain, Portugal, Spain, and France established colonies in the western hemisphere and relieved population pressures at home. Like many animal colonies, Australia was originally colonized by a group very low in the British pecking order, i.e. prisoners. In 1670, Ireland had a population of about a million people. By 1845 this had increased to eight million. The Irish were heavily dependent upon only one crop—the potato, which was grown on small plots of land sufficient to feed a family. Over a period of six years (1848 to 1854) a blight destroyed the potato crop. About a million people starved and another million emigrated. Agriculture reforms were introduced: the small plots were consolidated for purposes of diverse crop farming and primogeniture was established. But the population continued to fall, and it is now about four million— half of what it was before the potato famine. Reasons for this decline were continued emigration and a change in habits to very late marriages and often no marriage at all. The eldest son maintains the farm and cares for his parents, usually not marrying while they are alive. The result is that population growth in Ireland is low despite the influence of the Catholic Church. But today, human emigration on a significant scale has ceased everywhere. The frontier is no more and there are few areas that welcome immigrants in our world of intensified nationalisms.

Wynne-Edwards points out that the same general social machinery that controls safety-valve emigrations is involved in regulating seasonal redispersions of animals, such as the annual two-way migrations of birds. Many studies, other than those already mentioned, of mortality promoted by stress have been made. The white stork has been intensively studied. Nestling mortality is often very heavy under crowded conditions and individual chicks may be deliberately killed and sometimes eaten by one of their parents, usually the father. This is most likely to happen where the parents are beginners or young adults, and presumably of lower social status in the pecking hierarchy. The killing off of the young under prolific breeding conditions is characteristic of a great many birds and mammals, and is a direct result of social stress. The killing of the young and cannibalism are known to occur quite widely in mammals; for instance, in rodents, lions, and also in primitive man. Cases of cannibalism are found in fish, spider crabs, and spiders and of fratricide in various insect larvae. *In all cases experimentally investigated, the mortality is found to be dependent on population density and to cease below a certain critical population density.*

Mortality from predation has also been examined. This appears to be density-dependent to the extent that the prey cooperates by making its surplus members especially vulnerable to predators. The density-dependent elements in predation thus seem to arise on the part of the prey and not on that of the predators. Because of lowered resistance to infective agents following prolonged stress, disease as a form of predation may effectively reduce excessive population. In this case a surplus of individuals predisposed to injury by their dominant fellows naturally experiences a variable amount of uncontrolled mortality; this tends to fall most heavily on the young, which are as yet unprotected by acquired immunity from bacterial and viral infections. But social stress can lead to casualties at all ages, both through direct and mortal combat and through stress-induced disease. The victim of severe stress is likely to develop physiological disorders affecting many organs, especially the lymphatic apparatus, including the spleen and thymus, and also the nervous system, circulatory, digestive, and generative organs, and the endocrine glands, especially the adrenal cortex, which serves an intermediary role between the stressor and the organs responding to adrenal cortical hormones. Social stress is sometimes partly physical, as when the exercise of pecking order rights leads to the infliction of wounds or to withholding food and shelter. But, as Wynne-Edwards points out, it may be largely mental, just as we find that man, in his simpler-minded states, may die from the conviction that he has been bewitched. Cases are known of birds, mammals, and amphibians similarly dying from nonspecific injuries apparently induced by social stress.

The population explosion

What about man? What can we do about the world population explosion? We could, of course, do nothing and just wait for the stress syndrome or a new virus to do its work. It has been said that until recently our politicians had washed their hands of the population problem but are now wringing their hands over it. We can leave the "solution" to some trigger-happy dictator with a suitable stockpile of nuclear weapons, or perhaps we can finally decide on an optimal population for the world and, by education and social pressure, try to see that it is not exceeded. At the present average growth rate of two percent per year, there will be one square yard of earth per person in 600 years. Population growth depends only on the difference between birth rate and death rate. Man is the only animal that can direct its own evolution. Which of these two variables will he manipulate?

Prejudice, indifference, and hostility are the major blocks to population limitation. We know many methods of birth control: coitus interruptus, jellies, douches, diaphragms, condoms, surgical procedures, and "the pill," and ongoing research will give us more and better methods. None of these are of value if people refuse their use. For the very poor and illiterate, the cost and the difficulties of using contraceptives demand massive financial, social, and educational government aid. Prudery and politics, myth, superstition, and tradition, have so far rendered birth control ineffective in countries most in need of it.

Grenville Clark in a recent paper has argued that the population explosion probably cannot be controlled until the world has acquired universal and complete disarmament under world law, at which time a substantial part of the $120 billion now being spent on weaponry might, if we are wise enough, be used to raise the living standards of have-not peoples. He bases this view on the often demonstrated fact that birth control procedures are used exclusively only by literate and prosperous people with hope and ambition for bettering their own lots and those of their children. The take-off point for family planning and limitation requires a critical level of education and prosperity not now found in the very poor countries.

A still more gloomy view might be that if we do not manage to disarm in a decade or so we shall probably solve the population problem by nuclear extermination. In any case, the two major problems of our time—nuclear war and the population explosion—are closely linked together. Physics and the medical sciences have given all of mankind these two worldwide challenges never dreamed of by previous generations. Only by fundamental changes in our ways of thinking can these problems be solved.

RADIATION
AND
HUMAN LIFE

We must now regard radiation as one of the major environmental factors affecting human health and evolution. Three sources of radiation—geological contributions, nuclear bomb explosions, and medical use of x-rays—are discussed in this volume. The paper by Gentry, Parkhurst and Bulin in a previous section, "The Land and Disease Patterns," is pertinent to this problem. The paper by Radford and Hunt in the next section, "The Air We Breathe," indicates that cigarettes may represent an additional source of radiation.

SUPPLEMENTARY READINGS

BRAESTRUP, CARL B., and RICHARD T. MOONEY, X-ray Emission from Television Sets. 1959, *Science,* **130:** 1071–1074.

GOULD, A. R., A Cumulative Deposition of Fall-Out Within Buildings. 1962, *Nature,* **193:** 1152–1153.

HARLOW, HARRY F., and LOUIS E. MOON, The Effects of Repeated Doses of Total-Body X Radiation on Motivation and Learning in Rhesus Monkeys. 1956, *The Journal of Comparative and Physiological Psychology,* **49:** 60–65.

HUNT, EDWARD L., and DONALD J. KIMELDORF, Evidence for Direct Stimulation of the Mammalian Nervous System with Ionizing Radiation. 1962, *Science,* **137:** 857–859.

LEWIS, E. B., Leukemia and Ionizing Radiation. 1957, *Science,* **125:** 965–972.

MERTEN, D., and O. SUSCHNY, Some Factors Influencing the Food-Chain Transport of Radioactive Materials into Cow's Milk. 1961, *Nature,* **189:** 806–808.

SHIELDS, LORA M., and PHILIP V. WELLS, Effects of Nuclear Testing on Desert Vegetation, 1962, *Science,* **135:** 38–40.

Biological Aspects
of Nuclear Weapons*

CYRIL L. COMAR

There has naturally been great public interest about the effects of radiation on the human population, past, present, and future, mainly because nuclear weapons now make it possible for practically every organism living on earth to be exposed to detectable radiation from a single event controlled by man. Lack of knowledge, misunderstandings, a new mysterious force abroad in the world, personal involvement, radioactive contamination of milk and babies—all have led to a degree of emotional controversy.

It is attempted here to present an up-to-date and balanced view of the important biological radiation problems of the day. For the purposes of clarity and not evasion it is necessary to oversimplify, restrict the discussion to the most important matters, and omit details. Hopefully, this discussion will further an understanding of the difficult problems of present-day affairs on a basis both national (should we ban nuclear tests?) and personal (should I change my dietary habits?).

Some generalities

It must be crystal clear to all sane and thoughtful people that nuclear warfare is not the means for attainment of national or ideological goals. The category of the sane and thoughtful would include all people from extreme Left to Right, the general public, military leaders, and government officials. Also included are all peoples of other countries, especially those of Russia. From news impressions, one cannot be sure that the Red Chinese have reached this degree of under-

---

* A lecture delivered January 11, 1962, as one of a series of Cornell University Lectures on *Nuclear Peril and Disarmament*.

standing as yet, but it is to be hoped they would by the time they are capable of producing and conveying nuclear weapons. Our primary objective then must be to avoid war, but at the same time to preserve our political systems of individual rights and freedom. How best this can be accomplished is the crucial issue, and strategy is a matter to be much debated, although not here. Personally I feel that simply to display moral indignation about the seriousness and necessity of avoiding nuclear warfare provides our government leaders with little that they do not already fully appreciate.

There seems to be public consternation and confusion because reputable scientists have expressed differing views about the effects of nuclear weapons. Unfortunately, in a sense, the public seems to regard scientists as god-like in their pronouncements. Perhaps this is due to the advertising approach, where science is used to promote sales. Actually, we should be proud that anyone in this country can state his view and have his ideas represented widely, and we would not want it any other way. Also, disagreement among scientists is the rule rather than the exception, because such disagreement emphasizes the gaps in our knowledge, and very often stimulates needed research.

This places a burden on the public, the need to evaluate and judge. There is a keyword that can help, namely "credentials." From whence, and by what authority does a man obtain his information; what are his "credentials"? A reputable scientist, speaking in his own field, deserves careful attention—a scientist speaking out of his field should be given one vote, just as anyone else.

We must be especially careful about opinions and numbers presented only in part and selected to support specific points of view—for example, to prepare public opinion for nuclear war, one could in truth predict the continued existence of mankind regardless of any foreseeable dissemination of nuclear debris; in the opposite direction, one could predict, even from weapons testing carried out to date, what appears to be vast numbers of individual genetic deaths, and a vast amount of individual human suffering accumulated over thousands of years.

The credentials for viewpoints expressed here arise from a consensus gained by personal contact with various National and International Committees, reports of which are listed. Within recent years there has been developing general agreement as to the levels of radiation exposure resulting from past nuclear tests and the order of magnitude of effects expected. Disagreement arises primarily on moral issues and on the uncertainties in the necessary balancing of potential biological cost against potential benefit from a given course of action. All are keenly aware of the need for intensive research.

The nuclear weapon and fallout

When a nuclear weapon is detonated, tremendous quantities of heat are produced within a small period of time—thousandths of a second—and within a relatively small quantity of matter. As a result, all materials within the immediate vicinity of the device are completely vaporized, and raised to temperatures approaching those of the sun. The high temperature gives rise to what is known as the "fireball," which expands rapidly, heating material within the environment as it expands, and which then starts to rise. As the fireball rises, violent winds are produced which can suck large quantities of soil or water into the hot fireball and molten particles can condense onto this material. These heavy dirt particles or droplets, with their attached radioactive contamination, may return rapidly to earth and are called "local fallout." The extent and nature of fallout may vary considerably. For example, an airburst in which the explosion occurs at an appreciable distance above the earth's surface, so that dirt or water are not sucked into the cloud, produces little or no local fallout; this may be an important consideration if the strategy of an attack is to use large weapons to produce damage by fire. A land-surface explosion, on the other hand, produces a cloud heavily loaded with debris, containing relatively great numbers of the large particles raised by the surface winds. Under such conditions, it is estimated that about 80 percent of the total debris deposits as local fallout.

For purposes of discussion, then, fallout can be classified either as local or as world-wide. Local fallout, sometimes called "close-in" fallout, is defined as that which is deposited within 24 hours after detonation. Human beings have not been exposed to local fallout except for accidents such as involved the Marshall Islanders and the 23 Japanese fishermen. World-wide fallout can be classified into two categories—either as "tropospheric" or "intermediate" fallout, which is deposited within the first 30 to 60 days; or as "stratospheric" or "delayed" fallout, which may take many months or years for deposition. The radioactive iodine in our milk during October 1961, was an example of intermediate fallout from the Russian 1961 tests. Our present body burdens of radioactive strontium result mainly from stratospheric fallout from the tests prior to 1959.

Local fallout is distinguished by its settling speed and high radiation intensity, consisting of visible particles heavy enough to fall through the air. The particles are transported by winds as they settle; with light winds, they will settle close to the site of explosion and make an intense radioactive area; with heavy winds, they will be spread over larger areas, to give relatively lower radiation intensities. Local fallout is of critical importance in warfare, but of little interest from the standpoint of testing, because it is limited to the test site. The important thing about local fallout is that external radiation is the major hazard, and that the radiation intensity decreases rapidly with time, because the local fallout as produced contains considerable short-lived radioactive materials. As a rule of thumb, it is estimated that, for every seven-fold increase in time, the radiation intensity decreases by a factor of 10. For example, if the radiation intensity were 4000 units at one hour after the explosion, it would be 400 units after seven hours, and 40 units after 49 hours.

World-wide fallout is important both in warfare and in weapons testing. In contrast to warfare, about which we hope always to have to speculate, world-wide contamination is now with us. The earth and all living things on it are now contaminated to a degree with radioactive materials from past tests, and we must have an understanding of the levels of such contamination and the effects that such levels might produce in order to evaluate the biological cost of any further testing. It should also be noted that, as a result of warfare, those countries not involved will, however, be subject to world-wide fallout from the nuclear weapons used; also, areas in the warring countries that escape local fallout will be subject to world-wide fallout.

The fission products and radioactive contamination

To understand the implications of world-wide fallout which is important primarily after entrance into the body, we must consider the specific radioactive elements that are produced and their behavior. The terms radioactive elements, radio-isotopes, and radionuclides are used loosely to designate forms of elements that are unstable and give off ionizing radiation. From an atomic explosion, there can result contamination with the fissile material itself, such as uranium or plutonium, and with the so-called fission products. The primary and secondary fission products consist of about 200 radioactive species of elements. In addition, there is the possibility that some radioactive materials may be produced by activation with the neutrons from the weapons, just as in the process used for production of radioisotopes in a nuclear reactor. From the biological standpoint, perhaps the most important activation product is the radionuclide carbon 14, arising from reaction of neutrons with nitrogen atoms of the atmosphere. Of the 200 or so radioactive species produced by the weapons, only a few are of biological importance. This is because a radioactive material must possess several characteristics to varying degrees, or otherwise it cannot be potentially harmful to the human population.

First, the radionuclide must be produced by the explosion in appreciable amounts.

The second characteristic that governs the biological hazard is the so-called physical half-life of the given radioactive material, this being the time required for one-half of any given amount to disappear by radioactive decay. For world-wide fallout, which is relatively slow in coming to earth, radionuclides with half-lives of less than days or weeks are of little significance.

Another important characteristic that governs the biological hazard is the efficiency with which the particular radioactive material is transferred from the atmosphere through the food chain to the human diet. This transfer occurs primarily by two routes: contamination can stick to surfaces of plants which are eaten directly by man or eaten by animals with the passage of the radioactive elements into milk and meat; another pathway is incorporation into the soil for uptake by plants through their roots and subsequent entry into the diet of man. Knowledge of these pathways is of utmost importance for future assessments because contamination by surface adsorption is governed by the *rate of fallout,* whereas contamination through the soil is governed by the *cumulative amounts* of radioactivity deposited. The rate tends to decrease relatively rapidly after cessation of nuclear explosions, whereas the cumulative total builds up from all previous tests and decreases only by radionuclides becoming physically unavailable and by physical decay. Metabolic barriers may prevent the radioactive material from reaching locations in the body where it may cause damage, depending on the behavior of the substance in the food chain or man's system. For example, although the rare earths are common fission products, their absorption from the intestinal tract is so small in man and animals that they are of little importance as a hazard to man. Similarly, any unfission uranium or plutonium would likewise be poorly absorbed.

A final important factor that governs hazard is the length of time that a material is retained in the body. Thus, for example, strontium 90, which deposits in bone like calcium and is removed relatively slowly, would be potentially more hazardous than cesium 137, which deposits in soft tissues, like potassium, and is removed fairly rapidly.

Thus, it appears that, of all the radioactive materials produced, only a few are limiting as a potential hazard; these are strontium 90, which is a bone-seeker and could eventually lead to leukemia and bone cancer, and cesium 137 and carbon 14, which would be of interest primarily from the standpoint of genetic effects. Under certain conditions, iodine 131 could be of potential hazard from tropospheric fallout, but because of its eight-day half-life, it does not present a long-term problem.

The human population is exposed to world-wide fallout mainly by radioactive contamination of food and water, the radioactivity then being eaten and built into the body where it serves as a source of internal irradiation. Thus, from world-wide fallout the radiation for the most part will be long-term, that is, delivered over the lifetime of the individual.

During the last 10–12 years, considerable research has been done on the metabolic behavior and movement of fission products through the food chain to end up in the body of man. Suffice it to say that our knowledge of this area is reasonably adequate, coming from extensive experimental studies, collections and analyses of foodstuffs, and collections and analyses of thousands of human bones. Thus, there is reliable information on amounts of radionuclides present in the human population from the weapons tests completed in 1958.

Biological effects of radiation

The term radiation refers to the transport of energy without a material carrier, such as radiation of light rays from sun to earth, from desk lamp to desk. The type of radiation we are concerned with is of a special kind, called ionizing radiation, which has relatively large amounts of energy and has characteristic effects on biological materials. For example, if one drinks a cup of hot tea, a certain amount of thermal energy is transferred to the body as the tea cools down and reaches body temperature; that same amount of energy, delivered in the form of ionizing radiation, would end a person's tea-drinking days forever.

To discuss radiation it is necessary to deal with amounts, and therefore some sort of unit is needed. To keep matters as uncomplicated as possible, only one unit will be used, the Roentgen, named after the discoverer of the X-ray. The roentgen is based on ionization produced and can be taken to represent radiation dose absorbed in tissue. This is convenient because biological effects depend primarily on the amount of energy that is dissipated in the tissue and are governed closely by the amount of ionization. As far as we are concerned, it is important only to know what the unit means in terms of the effects of interest. For example, few of us remember what a volt is, but although we don't worry about shock from an electric train (6–10 volts), we would not change a tube in a plugged-in radio while sitting in a bathtub; and we know full well what would happen if we tangled with a high-voltage line (over 10,000 volts). To illustrate the practical meaning of the roentgen unit, consider two examples: Whole body exposure of man to a dose of about one roentgen produces no observable biochemical or clinical effect; about 400 roentgens will kill about half the individuals exposed. Later, more specific effects will be mentioned.

The whole question of biological effects is extremely complicated and space does not permit full discussion. To understand the problems posed by radiation from nuclear weapons it is essential, however, to mention three general principles.

I. Radiation effects can be classified as either genetic or somatic. The genetic effects of radiation are those which affect offspring conceived after the exposure of individuals. The effects of radiation upon the exposed individuals themselves, such as the production of leukemia or bone tumors, or the shortening of lifespan—these are called somatic effects.

II. A given radiation exposure, delivered over a long period of time, produces less biological effect than when delivered over a short period of time. For example, a man exposed to a single dose of 600 roentgens of radiation over a lifetime would show effects that were scarcely, if at all, observable. This behavior comes about because of the body's capacity to recover in part from the radiation, if given time. There is recent evidence that the genetic response may also be decreased when a given radiation dosage is spread over a long period of time. Thus, if a linear extrapolation to low dose rates is made, the predicted effects will always be in error on the side of safety. This principle is of especial importance in the evaluation of effects from world-wide contamination that is built into our bodies and delivers its radiation dose over a lifetime.

III. Is there a level of radiation exposure below which no harm is caused? This is called the "threshold" question. In many studies of the effects of drugs and chemical agents, in addition to radiation, one usually gives increasing doses of the agent and measures the effect. For many substances one finds that the effect as measured is zero until a certain dose, which is called the threshold, is reached. Theoretically, any dose lower than threshold would be expected to cause no effect. It must be emphasized, however, that such behavior is entirely dependent upon the sensitivity of the methods for detecting the effect. For example, as more sensitive methods become available, the threshold dose might well be lowered, even approach zero. Where the population of the world is exposed by dissemination of radioactivity from nuclear weapons, then tremendous numbers of individuals are involved which certainly increases the sensitivity of observation. There is general agreement that genetic effects show a non-threshold behavior curve—that is, that there is no radiation dose below which genetic effects would not be observed. There is no agreement as to whether somatic effects are threshold or non-threshold in behavior. Until there is definite evidence, we must be prudent and err on the side of safety by assuming that any amount of radiation wil produce some measure of harm.

Our next task is to see what are the best estimates of how much harm results from given exposures to radiation. It is convenient to classify radiation effects either as high-level, above 50 roentgens, or low-level with especial interest below about one roentgen. Evaluation of high-level radiation effects is not particularly difficult since experiments can be done with animals, and observations are available from human beings, either accidentally exposed or treated medically.

Evaluation of the effects of radiation at low levels, especially when the exposure is over long periods of time, is much more difficult. There is no direct evidence on the effects of radiation under conditions of low-level, long-term exposure. The reason is simply that, under these conditions, experimental studies are practically impossible, requiring vast numbers of experimental animals (millions), long periods of time (decades), and sensitive criteria of damage.

The most useful approach to evaluation of low-level, long-term exposures is to consider the background radiation to which mankind has always been exposed, and simply to assume that additional exposure to radiation at about the same level as background will produce about the same harm, and always to recognize that the more we increase our exposure over background, the more uncertain are we about the effects. Essentially, this means that if any amount of radiation produces harm, then the radiation from our natural environment, background radiation, must have been producing harm to mankind through the centuries, and perhaps can serve as our best yardstick.

Since the beginning of time man has been exposed to external radiation from cosmic rays and from naturally-occurring radioactive materials such as uranium, thorium and potassium 40 in the ground, air and structures in which he lives and works. Man has also been exposed to internal radiation from radionuclides that occur universally in the body, for example, potassium 40, carbon 14, and members of the radium and thorium families. It is estimated that the typical radiation dosage from such natural sources is about one-tenth of a roentgen per year, amounting then to about seven roentgens over a standard 70-year lifetime.

It must be pointed out that, in some areas of the world, in parts of India and Brazil, for example, the natural radiation exposure may be up to ten times higher than this. Population studies are being done to see if any effects can be detected. Such studies are most difficult, however, because one needs to have controlled populations for comparison: populations that have the same standard and way of living, the same nutritional plane, the same medical care, the same degree of inbreeding. As yet, in these areas there is no evidence that the backgrounds ten times higher than average are deleterious, but this does not mean that there are no affected individuals. It does mean that the number of individuals affected is too small to be detected.

Let us now consider the relationship between radiation exposure and harm to the population. For reasons of clarity, the discussion is limited to the two situations most likely to be encountered—an exposure similar to that of background resulting from world-wide fallout, and a single exposure at high levels as from local fallout. The two most important radiation effects are the production of leukemia and genetic defects; others are of much less concern.

Biological effects from world-wide fallout

Nuclear testing was stopped in the fall of 1958 and, with the exception of the French tests which did not contribute significantly to environmental contamination, there was no testing until the Russian series of 1961. There are reliable data on the present levels of radioactivity in the human population that have resulted from the tests through 1958. If one adds up all of the dosages from the radioactive materials, including carbon 14, it appears that the population exposure from world-wide fallout is about five one-thousandths of a roentgen per year—in other words, about five percent of background.

In the Western countries, exposure for medical purposes is about equal to that from background and therefore amounts to about 50% of total exposure. The medical profession is doing all it can to keep exposure to a minimum and it must be remembered that the individual who receives medical exposure expects to benefit from it. Fallout and miscellaneous peacetime uses such as from watches and luminous buttons, etc., power reactors and radioisotope usage, television, each contribute some two to three percent of total exposure.

Consequences expressed in numbers have been conservatively estimated and presented only to provide some idea of the magnitudes involved. It is emphasized that uncertainties are large.

The natural incidence of genetic defects in the world population is about four percent, which means that each year there are about three million genetic disabilities of which perhaps one million are due to background radiation. Testing through 1958 may have added as few as 2500 or as many as 100,000 cases over subsequent years. Genetic defects may be of all kinds: The innocuous defect such as the early death of an embryo that passes unnoticed; varying degrees of impaired vigor and fertility; and the worst type of defect that causes suffering but does not interfere with reproduction.

Out of a world population of three billion the natural incidence of leukemia is about 150,000 cases per year, of which some 1500 cases per year are estimated to result from background radiation. Testing through 1958 has probably added a further 75; the number will decrease with time, since leukemia incidence falls off at four to seven years after radiation exposure. Bone tumors are less frequent in occurrence than leukemia, and less liable to production by radiation.

For those not accustomed to thinking in terms of population statistics two examples are cited for comparison. In the United States alone, about 40,000 people a year are killed on the highways—a biological cost we accept for transportation. In peacetime military pursuits there are about 1400 accidental deaths per year—a biological cost for preparedness. These figures are not quoted to justify any unnecessary additions to individual suffering, but merely to emphasize that normally we do not have personal anxiety about such risks.

From a moral standpoint, we as individuals or as a nation would not want to undertake any action that would unnecessarily cause even one instance of human suffering in the world population. Realistically, we know that man has always been faced with the protection of his well-being from natural and man-made changes in his environment and circumstances. Each step forward, for example, the use of fire, electricity, transportation, medical practice, has been a great boon to humanity, while at the same time causing individual hardship that in no sense of the word is preventable. Man developed and needs fire and heat, but individuals die from fires and boiler explosions. In medical practice, uncounted lives are saved by antibiotics, but individuals have allergies and die from antibiotics. This point certainly needs no further belaboring. Even the controlled peaceful uses of atomic energy will produce some radiation exposure, and therefore by our standards will have some biological cost. But everyone, I am sure, would agree that these biological costs are far outweighed by the benefits to mankind.

As far as nuclear testing is concerned there is no question but that it has contributed in a small way to world-wide radiation exposure, and that we should therefore take the position that further production of uncontrolled radioactive contamination should not be undertaken unless this be unequivocally justifiable. In point of fact, it would seem that the decision to undertake further atmospheric testing by this country should be based primarily upon the military, political, propaganda or disarmament benefits to be obtained. At the present stage of affairs, it appears in actuality that the biological effects of further testing would be of minor consideration.

There is interest, of course, in what one might expect from the 1961 Russian series of tests. Through 1958 there had been put into the atmosphere about 100 megaton equivalents of fission products, and this produced roughly a five percent increase of radiation exposure over background. From what we know of the 1961 Russian tests, which put up about 25 megatons of fission, it is anticipated that the increase from them would be considerably less than another five percent. One may well wonder, if we are not worried about the tests up through 1958, about the Russian tests in 1961, or about another series by the United States, whether there is a point at which we should worry. The answer is, of course, yes, but settling on a given level is difficult because each country will have its own concept of benefit *vs.* cost. It is certainly to be hoped that national self-interest, if nothing else, will dictate control on an international basis.

Biological effects of high radiation exposure

What is expected to happen when populations are exposed to high levels of radiation delivered over short times? Practically all persons exposed to more than 800 to 1000 roentgens will die. About fifty percent of persons exposed to 400 roentgens will die. If pregnant women were exposed to as little as 30 roentgens there would be expected a high percentage of malformations of the newborn, depending upon the age of the unborn child at exposure.

In regard to fertility, the radiation effects are similar for both men and women. About 150 roentgens would induce brief, temporary subfertility; 250 roentgens might induce temporary sterility for one or two years; and 500–600 roentgens might well produce permanent sterility.

In regard to leukemia, it is estimated that each 100 roentgens of radiation will cause about 100 cases of leukemia per million people per year; the normal incidence is 50 cases per million people per year.

In human beings, genetic effects are difficult to evaluate since no direct observations are easily available. Social conditions interact with biological phenomena; for instance, medical care maintains genetically handicapped individuals who may reproduce themselves and transmit deleterious genes, and public health has reduced infant mortality, one of the major selective agents. Can genetic radiation damage lead to the extinction of the human species? Based on present knowledge of radiation and population genetics this is most unlikely; the levels of radiation needed to cause genetic extinction would produce obliteration of humanity by direct damage.

Some present-day problems

Since human exposure to world-wide fallout is primarily by food, a matter of primary interest is whether there is control of the food that we can buy and whether any upper limits have been set for contamination which, when exceeded, would be reason for concern and action. Levels of radioactivity are being watched very carefully by Federal agencies, especially the Public Health Service, and the categorical statement may be made that, if one can buy a food on the market, it may be eaten and enjoyed. The Government has established a body known as the Federal Radiation Council which is setting guide-lines in regard to levels of radioactive contamination in food. For example, this body has indicated that a daily intake, averaged annually, of 0 to 20 micromicrocuries of strontium 90 requires no consideration; if the intake should fall between 20 and 200 micromicrocuries, then quantitative surveillance and some routine control might be necessary; at intakes between 200 and 2000, action would be called for. (The micromicrocurie is a unit for amounts of radioactivity.)

In 1959 and 1960, when strontium 90 levels were at their highest from the tests carried out prior to and including 1958, the average dietary intake in the United States was about 15 micromicrocuries of strontium 90. It has now fallen to about nine. Next spring, we can expect to see the effects of the Russian tests and it is estimated that the new levels will be about the same as those reached following the cessation of testing in 1958.

There has been considerable publicity about radioactive iodine in milk during September and October of 1961, the main point being that the thyroids of children appear to be especially sensitive. So far the levels observed have warranted no action.

The question is often asked as to whether we should modify our diet or food technology to decrease somehow the intake of radioactive contamination, with suggestions being made to supplement diets with stable calcium which theoretically reduces strontium retention, or to give iodine drops to block thyroid uptake, or perhaps to reduce milk intake. The answer at present is categorically no. The chance of doing harm by individual and perhaps misguided modification of diets far outweighs the chance of doing any good. Paradoxically, for example, even though milk is the single largest source of strontium 90 in the diet, reducing the milk intake tends to increase the body burden of strontium to be developed. This is because milk calcium contains less Sr^{90} than does plant calcium, since the cow uses calcium more effectively than it does strontium. If the diet were to contain no milk, then the body would get all its calcium from plant sources, which are more highly contaminated. If it were not for milk, our bodies would contain three to five times more strontium 90 than at present.

Another question often raised is whether or not consideration is being given to the decontamination of land and of foodstuffs. Such decontamination measures, or as they are now called, remedial measures, are under intensive scientific investigation. Again it must be emphasized that remedial measures should be taken only when declared necessary by responsible authorities. They are mentioned here as a matter of information, since none is practical and in any event such measures would only be considered under conditions of serious accident or warfare. Remedial measures being investigated for decontamination of land are as follows:

1. Removal of recently-contaminated grass or crops;
2. Scraping off several inches of surface soil;
3. Leaching with large quantities of solvents that would move strontium down the soil profile;

4. Liming of acid soils to reduce the strontium content or the strontium-to-calcium ratio in the crop;
5. Deep ploughing to reduce the uptake of radioactive contamination by shallow-rooted grasses;
6. Using deep-rooted plants;
7. Using land for plants with low ratio of calcium-to-calories or for fiber.

Plant foods could be reduced in contamination by removing the bran from cereal products and by washing or skinning fruits and vegetables. Remedial measures for animals would consist of avoidance of surface-contaminated herbage and supplying uncontaminated calcium.

Considerable attention is being given to removal of strontium 90 and cesium 137 from milk by use of ion exchange resins. The procedure is technically feasible but as yet could not be used on a large scale without greatly increasing the cost and requiring considerable installation time and capital investment. It is emphasized that there would be greater probabilities of harm from nutritional and health problems created by attempts to decontaminate milk on a large scale, than from present levels of radioactivity. Any food problems with iodine 131 can best be handled by storage for appropriate times before use, as for example the use of canned milk.

Changes in man's diet, as already indicated, might include use of uncontaminated calcium and reservation of less contaminated food for segments of the population at greatest risk, such as children and pregnant women.

Nuclear warfare

Since there is no way of knowing the scale and pattern of attack, only non-educated guesses are possible. No attempt will be made to draw a word picture of the chaos that would ensue; none of us has a vivid enough imagination. It must be emphasized that our frames of reference would be changed completely. Previously established acceptable levels of radiation would have no meaning whatsoever. The hungry man who has to decide between starvation as against increasing his chances of developing cancer in 10 or 20 years will make that decision during the split second between the time his hand touches the food and his mouth opens to receive it.

Within close range of a surface explosion, blast and heat would be the major destructive forces and any survivors would also be at risk from external radiation. Intense fallout would cover up to hundreds of square miles nearby and persons not sheltered would be exposed to most hazardous intensities of radiation. Outside this area, there would be another zone up to thousands of square miles where a proportion of those not sheltered would be at serious risk. In areas untouched by "local fallout" the risk from radiation would be slight.

Large weapons, if used, would probably be exploded at high altitudes and this would increase the areas of fire damage (perhaps to a 50-mile radius for

100 megatons), but would decrease the areas subject to local fallout. Under these conditions, future food production would not be complicated by radioactive contamination although other ecological factors might become important. For example, there could be unchecked fires over large areas of forests and grass-lands followed by spring thaws that would erode denuded slopes and flood the valleys; intensification of plant and animal disease might be expected.

If weapons were exploded so as to maximize local fallout, then future food production would depend on how much arable land was left reasonably un-contaminated. The fact that we have as much as a million or so square miles of agricultural land makes it difficult to conceive of any attack that would leave us without sufficient usable land. The major short-term problems would most likely be those of logistics and transport. Theoretical studies on the basis of attacks that were credible in past months and years indicate that life and food production would go on. For example, the latest study with which I am familiar indicated that an attack of about 1400 megatons would leave 70 percent of our cropland usable and 90 percent of our livestock alive. But the capability for destruction increases with time and predictions are meaningless.

Could then the North American man survive a nuclear attack? Certainly individuals would. Whether the survival would be 5 or 95 percent would depend on what the enemy can do and wants to do, and to a lesser degree on defensive preparedness. Whether the North American man could be well-adjusted and happy, I leave to the psychologists; whether he would again assume world leadership, I leave to the geopoliticians.

Let us now consider the situation in the areas of the world that receive world-wide fallout only. If we assume, as a point of departure, that a total of 20,000 megatons would be used in the war, and that this would involve 10,000 megatons of fission, we can estimate what the mean population exposure might be. It is recalled that previous weapon tests of 100 megatons of fission gave a radiation exposure equivalent to about five percent of natural background. This means that 10,000 megatons would increase the radiation exposure to about five times that of background, assuming the same pattern of detonations as in past tests. The exposure in the Southern hemisphere would be much less. Thus, life in the rest of the world would, to all intents and purposes, go on as usual as far as radiation damage is concerned. The greater the number of megatons, however, the greater the load of distress and suffering that individuals and all human societies would have to support.

Another generality

It has been argued that nations disappear from the world or from world leadership for one of two reasons: (*a*) the fight to achieve supremacy, or (*b*) the desire for an easy life. I have not noted any great urge to fight for supremacy. There does seem to be a desire for the easy life. . . . schooling with frills, easy programs and long vacations; spectator sports, bright youngsters who don't get to college, dull ones who do; the drive to shorten the work week, etc. These examples are not cited in criticism of any group or to belittle our great national achievements. Rather, the point is made that we have a tremendous and literally untapped reserve of creative manpower which, when coupled with productive efficiency, should permit us to accomplish whatever is needed. If we want to badly enough, we can make the sacrifices and put forth the effort to mount simultaneously a deterrent, a peace offensive, a coexistence offensive, a world leadership offensive, a space offensive, a health and education offensive, a civil defensive—whatever it's going to take to keep us out of nuclear war and to allow us to fulfill the responsibilities of world leadership.

Summary

1. Any use of nuclear energy or radiation involves a biological cost which must always be weighed against the benefits expected.

2. Controlled peacetime use of nuclear energy yields benefits far in excess of biological costs.

3. The biological cost of past weapons tests of about 100–150 megatons of fission is small enough so that individuals need have no anxiety about personal or family well-being.

4. The factor of biological cost is minor in reaching decisions about resumption of atmospheric weapons tests; other factors—military, strategic, political, propaganda—are much more important.

5. Full scale nuclear warfare means mutual destruction, certainly of highly organized social systems, although all life would most probably not be obliterated in the countries attacked, and the rest of the world might go essentially unscathed. Recognition of these facts by rational men is the hope for prevention of nuclear war.

REFERENCES

1. *The Effects of Nuclear Weapons,* by Samuel Glasstone, Editor. U.S. Atomic Energy Commission. Washington, D.C. 1957.
2. Hearings before the Special Subcommittee on Radiation of the Joint Committee on Atomic Energy. 85th Congress. First session on "The nature of radioactive fallout and its effects on man." Part 1, May 27–June 3. Part 2, June 4–7. Washington, D.C. 1957.
3. Report of the United Nations Scientific Committee on the Effects of Atomic Radiation. General Assembly: 13th session. Supplement No. 17 (A/3838). New York. 1958.
4. The Biological Effects of Atomic Radiation. Summary Reports. National Academy of Sciences—National Research Council. Washington, D.C. 1956.

5. The Biological Effects of Atomic Radiation. Summary Reports. National Academy of Sciences—National Research Council. Washington, D.C. 1960.
6. The Hazards to Man of Nuclear and Allied Radiations. Second Report to Medical Research Council. London. 1960.
7. Background Material for the Development of Radiation Protection Standards. Federal Radiation Council, Staff Report. No. 1, May 1960.
8. Background Material for the Development of Radiation Protection Standards. Federal Radiation Council, Staff Report. No. 2, September 1961.
9. *Radiation, Genes, and Man,* by BRUCE WALLACE and TH. DOBZHANSKY. Holt, Rinehart, and Winston, New York. 1959.
10. Radioactivity in Foods. C. L. COMAR. *J. Amer. Med. Assoc., 171,* 119, 1959.

Leukemia, Multiple Myeloma, and Aplastic Anemia in American Radiologists*

E. B. LEWIS

It has never been excluded that the excessive number of deaths from leukemia in American radiologists (*1–3*) is largely or wholly an artifact of diagnosis. For example, leukemia might have the same probability of occurrence in a radiologist as in a member of the general male population, but have a higher probability of being accurately diagnosed in a radiologist owing to such factors as his more ready access to medical facilities. A way of testing such a possibility became evident when Court Brown and Doll (*4*) discovered that one form of the disease, namely, chronic lymphatic leukemia (CLL), is apparently either not induced by ionizing radiation, or is much less readily induced than are the forms of this disease in which other types of cells are affected. Their finding was based on leukemia deaths arising in a group of adult British males who had received x-ray therapy for an arthritic condition (ankylosing spondylitis). Among 28 such deaths only one was reported as due to CLL; yet, as will be discussed below, this type of leukemia is one of the commonest forms of the disease in adult white males. More recently, Pochin (*5*) cites only one death reported as being due to lymphatic leukemia (subchronic) among 17 deaths from leukemia arising in a group of adults who had received radioiodine therapy for hyperthyroidism.

Evidently, if radiation (or some other agent acting in a similar manner) is responsible for a rise in the death rates for leukemia in a given population, the death rate for chronic lymphatic leukemia in that population should rise little, if at all. On the other hand, if diagnosis is responsible, the death rate for CLL

* Reprinted from *Science*, December 13, 1963, Vol. 142, No. 3598, pages 1492–1494. Copyright © 1963 by the American Association for the Advancement of Science.

should rise proportionately, since diagnosis ought not to affect classification by histological cell type differentially.

This report presents the principal findings of a study designed to answer three interrelated questions. (i) Do excessive numbers of deaths from leukemia continue to occur in American radiologists in recent years? (ii) If so, does the number of deaths from CLL occur in accord with expectation based on radiation or on diagnosis as the responsible factor? (iii) Do excessive numbers of deaths occur in this group from diseases related to leukemia?

To assess the significance of an observed number of deaths from a given cause it is first necessary to determine the composition, with respect to age and size, of the living population that produces such deaths, and then to compute the number of deaths expected in that population had it been subject to the mortality of some standard reference population. The living population of radiologists chosen for study is restricted to those physicians who are listed in the biennial editions of the *Directory of Medical Specialists* (DMS) (6) as being certified by the American Board of Radiology. Punched cards showing name, year of Board-certification, and year of birth were prepared for all such individuals residing in the continental United States and having entries in the 1950 and 1960 editions of these directories (7). Similar cards, showing also year of death, were prepared for Board-certified radiologists who were known to have died in the study period and whose names appeared in one or more of the DMS editions spanning the years 1948 to 1960, inclusive. The resulting deck of cards, after elimination of duplicates and of cards bearing female names, provided the basic data for computing the composition, with respect to age, of the living male population as of July 1 of each year of the 14-year period, and for each year of age from 35 to 74, inclusive (8). The results, by 5-year age groups, for representative years, 1950, 1955, and 1960, are shown in Table 1. The estimated num-

TABLE 1. The percentage composition, according to age, of the population of male radiologists for selected years. The estimated total number of living radiologists between the ages of 35 and 74, inclusive, for these years were: (1950) 2542.0; (1955) 3353.0; (1960) 4571.5 (8).

Age	1 July 1950	1 July 1955	1 July 1960
35–39	27.0	22.8	26.8
40–44	21.2	24.3	19.9
45–49	15.6	17.8	18.6
50–54	11.3	12.1	13.3
55–59	10.3	8.4	8.8
60–64	7.4	6.9	5.6
65–69	5.0	4.8	4.3
70–74	2.2	2.8	2.8

ber of male radiologists aged 35 to 74 years, inclusive, increased from 2167 in 1948 to 4713.5 in 1961; for the entire 14-year period the number of man years at risk at these ages was 47,348.

The U.S. white male population was the standard chosen for the present study. It is the ultimate population from which the radiologists are drawn and it is the only relevant population for which sufficient data are available to calculate the death rates for the rather rare diseases which are under study here.

Death rates for leukemia and related diseases categories in the U.S. white male population were computed for each 5-year age group between 35 and 74, inclusive, and for as many years of the study period as the data permitted (9) (Fig. 1).

The population of deceased radiologists was identified by two methods: by scanning the death notices in the *Journal of the American Medical Association* for any reference to radiology, and by matching all the names of radiologists entered in the 1950 or 1954 DMS editions with all such names in the 1960 edition (10). The first method yielded the names of 426 individuals who were listed as Board-certified radiologists in one or more of the DMS editions from 1948 to 1960, inclusive, and whose deaths could be substantiated by means of death certificate sources as having occurred between the ages of 35 and 74, inclusive. The second method yielded the names of two more such individuals; for one, the name appeared in the death notices of the Journal without mention of radiology; for the other, no death notice could be found but a death certificate was located.

Certified copies of death certificates were obtained for all but three of the 428 deaths located in the population under study (11). Selection of the main cause of death from the group of causes usually listed on the death certificate was then made by following the international rules for coding the cause of death (12).

In Table 2, the observed number of deaths for which the main cause was leukemia or a related disease is compared with the corresponding expected numbers calculated by applying the death rates (with respect to specific age and year of death) in the U.S. white male population for the disease category in question to the number of living radiologists at risk (13). Also shown are values of the "mortality ratio," defined in the usual way as the ratio of the observed number of deaths from a given cause to the number which could have been expected had the population at risk been subject to the mortality experience of the standard (14).

It is evident that the observed 12 deaths from leukemia greatly exceeds the expected number of 4.02. The probability of observing 12 or more deaths under these circumstances can be obtained from the Poisson distribution and has a value of 0.001. The mortality ratio for leukemia is 3.0 (12 : 4.02); however, the limits for such a ratio are wide. The 95 percent Poisson confidence limits

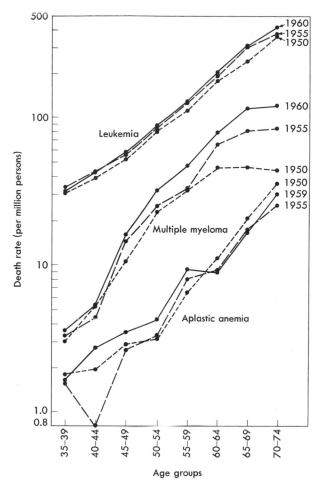

FIG. 1. Death rates, with respect to specific age and cause, in the U.S. white male population (deaths per million living persons per year) for selected years of the study period (semi-log plot) (9). Death rates for aplastic anemia for each stage group below age 50, and for multiple myeloma for each group below age 40, are based upon 20, or fewer, deaths.

for the 12 observed deaths are 6.2 and 21.0 deaths; it follows that the true mortality ratio for leukemia is not likely to be lower than 1.5 (6.2 : 4.02) nor higher than 5.2 (21.0 : 4.02).

It becomes important, as already noted, to compare observed and expected numbers of deaths from chronic lymphatic leukemia in the present study population. On the basis of the death rates for lymphatic leukemia in the U.S. white male population for the years 1949 (15), 1951, and 1956 (9), the only years for which data are available, roughly 4.4 deaths among the 12 leukemia deaths

TABLE 2. Mortality among radiologists: deaths attributed to cancers of the lymphatic and blood-forming tissues and from aplastic anemia. Only deaths occurring between the ages of 35 and 74, inclusive, in the 14-year period, 1948 to 1961, are included (*12–14, 18*).

International code rubric	Principal disease	Number of deaths		P^*	Mortality ratio (M.R.)	95% Confidence M.R.
		Observed	Expected			
200	Lymphosarcoma	4†	2.4	> .05	1.7	0.5 to 4.3
201	Hodgkin's disease	1	1.6	> .05	0.6	0.02 to 3.5
202, 205	Lymphoblastoma	1	0.38	> .05	2.6	0.07 to 14.6
203	Multiple myeloma	5	1.01	.004	5.0	1.6 to 11.6
204	Leukemia	12	4.02	.001	3.0	1.5 to 5.2
292.4	Aplastic anemia	4	0.23	.0001	17.0	4.7 to 44.5

* Probability that the observed number of deaths, or a larger number, would occur by chance.
† Includes two deaths from lymphosarcoma, one from reticulum cell sarcoma, and one from malignant lymphoma.

in the population under study are expected to be of the lymphatic type (*16*). Although death rates for CLL as such are not tabulated, it is known from studies of MacMahon and Clarke (*17*) that among adult white males (in Brooklyn) the vast majority of cases of lymphatic leukemia are of the chronic rather than of the acute type. Among the 12 deaths from leukemia in the present study, only one was reported as being due to the lymphatic type and this case was further specified (on the death certificate) to be acute rather than chronic. The failure of any of these 12 deaths to be ascribed to CLL suggests that radiation exposure rather than diagnosis is the principal factor responsible for the excessive number of deaths from leukemia in this population (*18*). It is, of course, possible that some other factor (or factors) which acts in the same manner as radiation, is responsible.

For certain lymphomas such as Hodgkin's disease, lymphosarcoma, and lymphoblastoma, the observed numbers of deaths in the population under study occur in reasonable agreement with the expected numbers (Table 2). On the other hand, for both multiple myeloma and aplastic anemia the observed numbers of deaths exceed the expected numbers at levels which, statistically, are highly significant (*19*).

The excessive number of deaths from aplastic anemia in radiologists (4 observed as opposed to 0.2 expected) parallels a similar finding in the study of Court Brown and Doll (*4*); namely, that an excessive number of deaths from aplastic anemia (12 observed as opposed to 0.3 expected) occurred among patients receiving large doses of x-rays to the spine. Although aplastic anemia is not classified as a cancer (*12*), some cases of the disease are believed to be identical with aleukemic leukemia—a form of leukemia in which there is an excessive number of white cells in the bone marrow but not in the peripheral blood. Upon review of the 12 deaths ascribed to aplastic anemia in their series, Court Brown and Doll concluded that one-half had been certain or probable cases of aleukemic leukemia.

The excessive number of deaths from multiple myeloma (5 observed as opposed to 1.01 expected) in the population under study has no parallel in other studies of irradiated adults with one exception (20). That there may be a real association between radiation and an increased risk of multiple myeloma is supported by the similarity of this disease to aleukemic leukemia. Thus, multiple myeloma is characterized by an excessive proliferation of immature plasma cells in the bone marrow without an excessive count of these cells in the peripheral blood; hence, it is sometimes classified as an aleukemic phase of plasma cell leukemia (21).

It is important to consider why, if radiation increases the risk of multiple myeloma, other studies of irradiated groups have not detected such an increase. Reports of multiple myeloma being a cause of death in individuals under the age of 30 are so rare (22) that only studies of adult individuals are likely to yield significant numbers of cases of this disease. Studies of atom-bomb survivors (23) fail to mention multiple myeloma.

However, deaths from this disease are so rarely reported in Japan (24), that few or no deaths would be expected among such survivors even if their death rate from this disease were many times the normal Japanese rate. The failure of Court Brown and Doll (4) to mention this disease in their series of spondylitic patients may or may not represent a real discrepancy with the present findings; it can be inferred that roughly only four or five deaths from multiple myeloma would be expected in their spondylitic series if the age-specific death rates for this disease had increased to the same proportionate extent as did the age-specific death rates for leukemia in that series (25).

Although an association between radiation exposure and increased risk of multiple myeloma is suggested by the present study, it is not established. Additional studies are needed of the incidence of multiple myeloma in other groups of irradiated adults, such as hyperthyroid patients who have received radioiodine therapy (5). It would also be of value to conduct retrospective studies, along the lines of the ingenious ones of Faber and of Stewart *et al.* (26); that is, the histories of exposure to radiation experienced by multiple myeloma patients would be compared with such histories obtained from various "control" groups such as CLL patients (27).

REFERENCES

1. H. C. MARCH, *Radiology* **43**, 275 (1944); *Am. J. Med. Sci.* **220**, 282 (1950); *ibid.* **242**, 137 (7961).
2. L. I. DUBLIN and M. SPIEGELMAN, *J. Am. Med. Assoc.* **137**, 1519 (1948).
3. E. B. LEWIS, *Science* **125**, 965 (1957); R. SELTSER and P. E. SARTWELL, *Am. J. Public Health* **49**, 1610 (1959).

4. W. M. COURT BROWN and R. DOLL, *Leukemia and Aplastic Anemia in Patients Irradiated for Ankylosing Spondylitis,* Medical Research Council (Brit.) Special Rept. Series No. 295 (H. M. Stationery Office, London, 1957).

5. E. E. POCHIN, *Brit. Med. J.* **II,** 1545 (1960).

6. *Directory of Medical Specialists* (Marquis, Chicago, 1950–1960).

7. When year of birth was not stated, it was readily found in the case of every male radiologist by reference to editions of the *American Medical Directory* (American Medical Association, Chicago).

8. Dates of births were punched to the nearest half-year for the deceased group. For the living population it was necessary to assume that a birth was equally likely to have occurred in the first as in the second half of a year. This accounts for the presence of "half-individuals" (Table 1). Any errors due to wrong assignment to sex are likely to be negligible since only 2.8 percent of the names of Board-certified radiologists in the 1950 and 1960 editions of the *Directory of Medical Specialists* are estimated to be of females.

9. Death rates were computed by dividing the number of deaths in each 5-year age group (obtained from *Vital Statistics of the United States,* U.S. Govt. Printing Office, Washington, D.C. 1948–59) by the latest mid-year census estimates of the living population of U.S. white males (obtained from *Current Population Reports,* Series P-25, Nos. 98, 246, and 265, U.S. Bureau of the Census, Washington, D.C.). The National Vital Statistics Division of the U.S. Public Health Service kindly provided the following unpublished data: deaths of U.S. white males (by 5-year age groups) from leukemia for 1960–1961, from multiple myeloma for 1949–1961, from aplastic anemia for 1950 and for 1953–1959; and deaths of U.S. white males (by 10-year age groups) from lymphatic leukemia for 1951 and 1956.

10. A third method was used, but yielded no additional names. This involved checking the death notices in unpublished annual bulletins of the American College of Radiology, the majority of whose members are Board-certified radiologists. It remains possible that a few deaths occurred that were not detected by any of the three methods.

11. In two cases, death certificates were unobtainable because the place of death could not be traced; in the third case, death occurred outside the U.S. Among the 425 death certificates obtained, four were for deaths occurring outside the continental U.S.; in none of these four cases, however, was death ascribed to causes under discussion in this report.

12. *Manual of the International Statistical Classification of Disease, Injuries and Causes of Death.* Fifth, Sixth and Seventh Revisions. (World Health Organization, Geneva, 1938, 1948, 1955).

13. In this computation the terms of an 8×14 matrix of white male death rates (eight 5-year age groups for 14 years of the study period) were identically multiplied by the terms of a similar matrix of the numbers of living radiologists, and then summed over all 112 products. Death rates were calculated for leukemia for the years 1948–1961 inclusive and for multiple myeloma for the years 1949–1961, inclusive. For all other diseases shown in Table 2, the necessary data were lacking for 1948 and for 1960–1961. For these two time periods, death rates for such diseases were assumed to be the same as the corresponding rates for 1949 and for 1959, respectively. The over-all systematic error introduced by using such

substituted rates in computing the expected number of deaths of radiologists is believed to be, at the most, a 3 percent under- or over-estimation of the true expected numbers.

14. The value of the mortality ratio for deaths from all causes in the present study population is 0.8. This agrees well with Dublin and Spiegelman's (2) findings for the years 1938–1942, that the class of full-time medical specialists, and the sub-classes thereof, including radiologists, each enjoyed lower death rates from all causes of death combined than did the class of all physicians (or of all white males). (See also reference 3.) For the present study population, it should be remembered that the value of the mortality ratio for any given cause of death is expected to be less than 1.0 if the radiologists were to enjoy as low a mortality rate for that cause as they do for all causes of death combined.

15. A. G. GILLIAM, *Blood* **8,** 698 (1953).

16. In this computation the 1949 rates were applied to the years 1948–1949, the 1951 rates to the years 1950–1954 and the 1956 rates to the years 1955–1961.

17. B. MacMAHON and D. W. CLARKE, *Blood* **11,** 871 (1956).

18. For four additional deaths in the study population, the death certificates reported leukemia as a contributory rather than as the underlying or main cause of death; among these four, one was listed as lymphatic (chronicity unspecified) and the other as CLL. With these four deaths added to the 12 valid deaths, the ratio stands at one death with mention of CLL to 15 deaths without mention of this type. For still another death in the study population, the Journal death notice listed the cause as "myelogenous leukemia"; however, a certified copy of the death certificate failed to mention leukemia and ascribed death to another cause.

19. An analysis (in preparation) of the distribution of deaths in the study population from leukemia, multiple myeloma, and aplastic anemia by age at death and year of death shows (i) that the observed number of deaths in each age group tends to exceed the expected number to the same proportionate extent that the observed total number of deaths in all age groups exceeds the corresponding expected total number, and (ii) that there is no tendency for the death rates for leukemia and multiple myeloma to decline during the 14-year period; however, for aplastic anemia, all four observed deaths occurred between 1948 and 1953, inclusive.

20. W. POHL [*Med. Klin. Munich* **55,** 1839 (1960)] reports three cases of multiple myeloma among German medical technicians with long histories of occupational exposure to radiation; however, the statistical significance of such a finding cannot be assessed because no information was provided on composition, in terms of size and age, of the living population of technicians from which the three cases were drawn.

21. I. SNAPPER, L. B. TURNER, H. L. MOSCOVITZ, *Multiple Myeloma* (Grune and Stratton, New York, 1953).

22. B. MacMAHON and D. W. CLARKE, *J. Chronic Diseases* **4,** 508 (1956).

23. R. HEYSSEL, A. B. BRILL, L. A. WOODBURY, E. T. NISHIMURA, T. GHOSE, T. HOSHINO, M. YAMASAKI, *Technical Report 02-59, ABCC* (National Academy of Sciences—National Research Council, Washington, D.C., 1959).

24. *Deaths from Multiple Myeloma (Plasmocytoma) in Selected Countries by Sex and Age,* Epidemiology and Vital Statistics Rept. No. 8 (World Health Organization, Geneva, 1955), p. 24.

25. In this computation it was assumed that for each 5-year age group in which leukemia deaths occurred in the Court Brown and Doll study, the ratio of leukemia deaths to multiple myeloma deaths would be the same as the corresponding ratios for British males for the years 1950–1952, the only years for which published data (see reference *24*) are available.

26. M. FABER, in *Transactions of the 6th Congress of the European Society of Haematology* (Karger, New York, 1957), p. S-211; A. STEWART, W. PENNYBACKER, R. BARBER, *Brit. Med. J.* **II,** 882 (1962).

27. I thank R. Giesen, M. Hershey and S. Hillyard and especially my wife for technical assistance. I thank F. Lawler for writing the programs used to calculate the age composition of, and the expected numbers of deaths in, the study population. This work was supported in part by an institutional grant from the American Cancer Society (IN-39).

THE AIR
WE BREATHE

*There is a popular expression that "the only thing
free is air." This is not true any more in some parts of the
world. Air pollution has increased to levels whereby
special equipment is needed to purify the air. The first
two papers in this section describe some of the
detrimental effects of air contamination.*

*It also appeared sensible to include the problems of
smoking in this section.*

*Let us imagine, therefore, the "typical" American
driving to work. He is smoking a "typical"
air-contaminating cigarette in a "typical" traffic congestion
of air-contaminating automobiles, on his way to work
at a "typical" air-contaminating factory. He is a
bad insurance risk.*

SUPPLEMENTARY READINGS

ANDERSON, A. E. JR., J. A. HERNANDEZ, PHILLIPPA ECKERT, ALVAN G. FORAKER, Emphysema in Lung Macrosections Correlated with Smoking Habits. 1964, *Science,* **144:** 1025–1026.

CANNON, HELEN L., and JESSIE M. BOWLES, Contamination of Vegetation by Tetraethyl Lead. 1962, *Science,* **137:** 765–766.

DAMON, A., Constitution and Smoking. 1961, *Science,* **134:** 339–340.

EISENBUD, MERRIL, and HENRY G. PETROW, Radioactivity in the Atmospheric Effluents of Power Plants That Use Fossil Fuels. 1964, *Science,* **144:** 288–289.

HAMMOND, E. CUYLER, The Effects of Smoking. 1962, *Scientific American,* **207:** 39–51.

MIDDLETON, JOHN T., and ARIE J. HAAGEN-SMIT, The Occurrence, Distribution, and Significance of Photochemical Air Pollution in the United States, Canada, and Mexico. 1961, *Journal of the Air Pollution Control Association,* **11:** 129–134.

Air Conservation

A. J. HAAGEN-SMIT*

Our confidence in the abundance of the four principal elements of our forefathers has been severely shaken in recent times. We have learned that the increasing population will have less and less room in which to grow its crops and keep its cattle. Coal, oil, and gas reserves have definite time limits, and we might have had to face a major war over water rights had our ancestors not been wise enough to create a United States of America. Finally, our supposedly infinite supply of air has turned out to be limited, too. With the advent of atomic energy, many of these problems can be solved, but the universal use of atomic energy will make the problem of keeping our air fit to breathe even more difficult. Now we are concerned with constituents present in concentrations of a few parts per million. The future, and part of the present, generation must worry about the removal of pollutants present in quantities smaller by a factor of many powers of ten. In this more efficient cleaning process, the theoretical knowledge and technical skill required will be far greater than the knowledge and skill available today.

Perhaps we should even be grateful that in recent years air pollution disasters and near disasters have developed on such a scale that they have attracted the attention of the whole world. Such an episode occurred in London, when, during a black fog period in 1952, some 4000 excess deaths were recorded. Other disasters drawing world-wide attention were those in Donora, Pennsylvania, Poza Rica, Mexico, and the Meuse Valley in Belgium (1). In each of these incidents dozens of people met their death by suffocation.

In recent years, the smog conditions developing in Los Angeles and in other cities on the Pacific Coast have greatly inspired a more intensified effort to clean

* Dr. Haagen-Smit is professor of biochemistry at California Institute of Technology, Pasadena.

the air all over our country (2). Keeping the air clean is expensive. In the Los Angeles area alone it is estimated that several hundred million dollars have been spent already to curtail some emissions, and many more will have to be spent before the smog will again be unnoticeable. At the present time the air-pollution-control authorities, working against a 4 percent increase in population, are doing somewhat better than holding the line. Over the whole nation the expense will be staggering and will probably run into billions of dollars.

It is understandable that there has been a great deal of resistance to the installation of costly control equipment which often does not contribute in a direct manner to profits. Some of the objections have been removed in recent years, and it is now generally conceded that damage from air pollution is large and that recovery measures often pay for themselves and in some cases may even make profits. Corrosion due to the emission of various chemicals is a source of tremendous expense to the public. Recovery methods will reduce this corrosion and will also lower the cleaning bills for the outside, as well as the inside, of our houses. But even if no direct profit is made, the many intangibles make it worth while to improve working conditions. The standard of living of the workers is raised, and possible adverse effects on their health are eliminated. This contributes to an increased efficiency on the part of the worker. It also raises the value of the industrial property and of the surounding real estate. In many cases, management has gone much further than merely curing existing air pollution problems. At the present time, climatological and topographical conditions are examined carefully in selecting the site for new industry, and in the construction of new buildings the installation of air-pollution-control equipment is considered beforehand, rather than at a time when public relations have suffered a severe setback.

The old slogan, "Prosperity is measured by the number of smoking stacks," is no longer true. Today, prosperity can be gaged by the number of strange-looking bulges protruding from the roofs of the factories. These bulges are dust- and fume-collectors and indicate that the community and its industry have progressed to a standard of living and social consciousness that does not permit objectionable emissions to spread over other peoples' property. Many modern factories and offices have installed in the air-conditioning system air-purification systems as well, since experience has shown that clean air is healthier and leads to less absenteeism and, in addition, keeps cleaning and redecorating costs at a minimum. Scientific laboratories, too, have found that the protection from plant damage, from interference in the sensitive enzyme systems, and from destruction of oxidant-sensitive organic compounds which can be obtained by air purification is worth while.

Less satisfactory, from a hygienic point of view, is the way many of us spend our day undergoing fumigations with tobacco smoke and engine exhaust—a combination which for many years has been under suspicion where its effects on health are concerned.

One of the most common forms of air pollution is that caused by smoke. A cross-country trip by airplane should convince anyone that smoke is a problem in every great city from Los Angeles to New York. Large streamers, extending for scores of miles, have their origin in open burning dumps, lumberyards, steel mills, foundries, and power plants, to name only a few of the multitude of sources. This is an old problem; some 200 years ago laws were passed in England to regulate the burning of certain types of coal. Even today, combustion is still a major source of air pollution.

At first sight this problem of controlling the emission of smoke appears quite simple—just wash it out! But we have only to think how tobacco smoke from a Turkish pipe bubbles, seemingly undisturbed, through water, to realize that perhaps this problem is not so easily solved after all. Large particles of soot and dust can readily be removed in settling chambers, or in cyclones, where gravitational or centrifugal forces are used to separate the particles by weight. Other methods consist in filtering out the dust through cloth made of cotton, woven plastics, or even glass fibers, in structures known as baghouses. For very fine

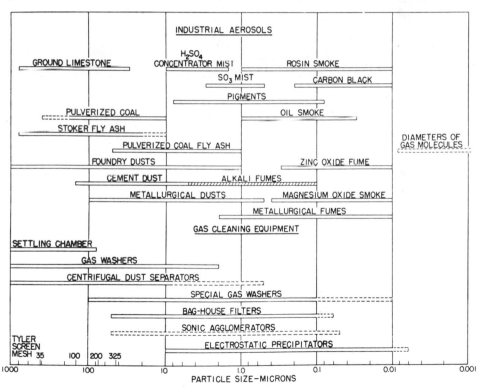

FIG. 1. Particle size chart illustrating relative size of well-known particulates and the effective range of various control methods. [H. P. Munger, "The spectrum of particle size and its relation to air pollution," in L. C. McCabe, *Air Pollution* (2, chap. 16)]

dust, of the order of from 0.5 to 1.0 micron, we have to apply processes whereby the electrically charged particle is removed by electrostatic forces by passage between electrodes kept at a potential difference of 15,000 to 40,000 volts. A comparison of particle size of effluents and the means of their recovery is shown in Fig. 1. By catching the particles of a size close to the wavelength of light, an important fraction of the dust responsible for the scattering of light is removed, and therefore the probability of visible plume formation is substantially decreased. The process is attractive to industry because of the low cost of maintenance and the negligible drop in pressure, and it is commonly used in open-hearth furnaces in steel mills and in coal-burning plants (Fig. 2). Recently its use was extended in Los Angeles to the control of stack emissions from oil-fired boilers in power plants. Each one of these dust-collection processes has found wide application in industry, but even today systematic studies to increase their efficiency would be most welcome.

The dust present in fuel is not the only agent responsible for an objectionable plume from smokestacks. Virtually all other constituents of flue gas—water, carbon monoxide, and oxides of sulfur and nitrogen—play some role. It is interesting to watch this plume formation take place in a long glass tube through which the hot stack gases are led. As soon as the gases cool below the dewpoint range, we see a deposition of metal salts, largely in the form of sulfates, along the side of the tube. Next we find a region of droplets, containing insoluble dust embedded in an acid solution of metal salts. Finally, on further cooling, the bulk of the water, containing some sulfuric acid and sulfur dioxide, condenses. When the gas stream, cooled to outside temperature, leaves the experimental stack, it escapes largely as a plume of water vapor containing trace amounts of sulfuric acid, and nearly all the sulfur dioxide and nitrogen oxide, in gaseous form. In this passage very little sulfur dioxide has been converted to sulfuric acid. The dew point of the outlet is close to that of the outside temperature, and only slight heating is required to cause the visible plume to disappear. This practice is followed in many installations where weather conditions are conducive to plume formation.

We expect that phenomena similar to those observed in the glass tubes take place when the gases are released from the stack, with the droplet size adjusting itself to the outside temperature and humidity. This is an important factor in the variability of plume density observed in otherwise identical combustion con-

---

FIG. 2. Before the installation of smoke-control equipment, the normal operation of the open-hearth furnaces at Kaiser Steel Corporation's Fontana, California, plant produced smoke which was released directly into the atmosphere. These two pictures, taken within minutes of each other, graphically demonstrate the effectiveness of the electrostatic precipitator on top of the building. (Left, above) Picture taken with all the units temporarily shut off. (Left, below) Picture taken a few minutes later with the equipment back in operation, showing clear sky. [Kaiser Steel Corporation]

ditions. The formation of droplets by condensation is not the end of plume formation, for both sulfur and nitrogen oxides, as well as metal salts, participate in a series of reactions leading to a gradual oxidation of sulfur dioxide into sulfuric acid, and of nitric oxide into higher oxides and nitric acid.

Laboratory investigations by Johnstone and Coughanowr (3) have shown that oxidation of sulfur dioxide takes place slowly by photochemical action. These authors estimated that about 1 percent would be oxidized per hour in intense sunlight. This would indicate that in an atmosphere containing 0.1 to 1.0 part per million of sulfur dioxide, about 100 hours of sunlight would be required to decrease visibility to about 1 mile. In continuation of these experiments it was found that oxidation occurs much faster in water solution under the influence of metal salts. Such conditions could conceivably occur in droplets present in the stack plume. The suggestion has been made that it is this reaction which is responsible for the haziness observed at considerable distance from industrial establishments. Evidence that such oxidations do take place when the gases have left the stack is found in an interesting pollution balance made at one time by the Los Angeles County Air Pollution Control District (4). The amount of emission of sulfur dioxide from all sources—refinery operations, oil burning, and gasoline consumption—is well known. We also know the area in which this emission is dispersed, as well as the height of the inversion layer which limits its upward movement. From these data we are able to calculate the expected sulfur dioxide concentration and compare this with the actual observed average concentration. We find, in making up this balance, that about half of the sulfur dioxide is lacking, as is shown in Table 1. This missing sulfur dioxide is found mostly as

TABLE 1. Comparison of measured and calculated concentrations of pollutants in downtown Los Angeles (4, p. 41).

Pollutant	Clear day* (parts per million by vol.)		Day of intense smog† (parts per million by vol.)	
	Measured	Calculated	Measured	Calculated
Carbon monoxide	3.5	3.5‡	23.0	23.0‡
Oxides of nitrogen	0.08	0.10	0.4	0.6
Sulfur dioxide	0.05	0.08	0.3	0.5
Total hydrocarbons§	0.2	0.40	1.1‖	2.6
Aldehydes	0.07	0.02	0.4	0.1
Organic acids	0.07	0.03	0.4‖	0.2

* Visibility, 7 miles.
† Visibility, less than 1 mile.
‡ The method defines the calculated value as the same as the measured value for CO.
§ Calculated as hexane.
‖ Preliminary values.

calcium and ammonium sulfates in dust settling over the country. Free sulfuric acid, except in close proximity to the stack, is virtually absent.

Research work on the effects of stack gas constituents on plants and animals is still an important field of environmental hygiene. Only recently some interesting data were revealed on the synergistic effects of aerosols and oxides of sulfur on physiological responses such as flow resistance in the respiratory system (5). This specific air pollution problem illustrates how much work has to be done before we can really understand the phenomena connected with the emission of dust and fumes. Some of this work is in the field of engineering, and other aspects deal with inorganic, physical, physicochemical, and photochemical processes. Finally, we have problems in physiology and pathology of plants and animals, as well as legal and economic problems.

Los Angeles smog

Notwithstanding its many facets, this control problem is simple compared with a more recently discovered air pollution problem which threatens to affect all metropolitan areas. It is an oxidized hydrocarbon type of pollution, better known as Los Angeles smog, from its place of discovery (Fig. 3).

FIG. 3. Dense smog over Los Angeles Civic Center. Note how the buildings project above the base of the inversion layer, while pollution remains below. [Los Angeles County Air Pollution Control District]

FIG. 4. Severe damage on the under side of spinach leaves caused by Los Angeles smog. [Los Angeles County Air Pollution Control District]

During the war years, Los Angeles was suddenly surprised to find itself engulfed in an eye-irritating cloud of chlorine-like odor. This incident lasted about a year and was generally attributed to the emissions from a synthetic-rubber plant. After the control of these emissions, complaints stopped, only to be resumed after the war. The rubber plant could not be blamed this time, for it was closed, nor could sulfur dioxide and soot be blamed for the severe eye irritation. As a matter of fact Los Angeles is a very clean city in this respect, with a dustfall of only 20 to 30 tons per month per square mile, as compared with several times this quantity in other industrial cities. There is no resemblance at all to the problems of cities in the eastern part of the United States, where coal is the major source of energy and where, consequently, soot blackens all buildings. The eye-irritating clouds in Los Angeles are accompanied by complaints from farmers about crop damage (Fig. 4) and, strangely enough from rubber manufacturers, who observed that their products cracked more heavily in this area than in other sections of the country (Fig. 5). Control of dusts and sulfur dioxide did not help, for the phenomena are due to an effect quite different from the more old-fashioned, reducing type of air pollution. Los Angeles smog, contrary to this type of pollution, is typified by its strong oxidizing action (6, 7).

For practical measurement of the typical oxidizing effect of Los Angeles smog, liberation of iodine from potassium iodide, oxidation of phenolphthalin to phenolphthalein, and many other oxidation-reduction reactions can be used. For an explanation of the effect of oxidizing smog on living tissue, its demonstrated action on amino acids such as cysteine, tryptophan, and histidine, as well as on glutathione and lysozyme, is significant and might well account for the irritating symptoms. The measured oxidant action is caused by an excess of oxidizing over reducing components in the polluted air. In Los Angeles smog

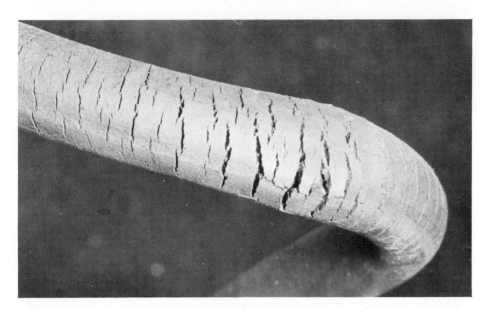

FIG. 5. Severe rubber cracking observed in Los Angeles area. [J. W. Haagen-Smit]

the concentration of sulfur dioxide, a reducing substance, is low, and its effects are usually negligible. In other areas, the presence of the oxidizing pollutants may well have escaped attention because of the masking effect of an excessive amount of reducing substances. It is quite possible that the oxidizing pollutants which characterize Los Angeles smog are of more frequent occurrence than was originally suspected.

The concentration of the oxidant varies during the day, increasing toward noon and decreasing to virtual absence during the evening and night hours. The time of increased concentration of the oxidant is invariably correlated with eye irritation and haze. The type of damage to plants from oxidizing pollutants is readily distinguishable from damage from other types of pollutants, such as sulfur dioxide or fluoride. Sensitive plants—spinach, sugar beets, alfalfa, endive, oats, and pinto beans—are used extensively to gage the spread of the pollution (Fig. 6). A major part of the oxidant consists of ozone, which is directly responsible for the excessive rubber cracking observed in the Los Angeles area. Spectrographic, as well as chemical, methods have definitely established the presence of ozone concentrations 20 to 30 times higher than those found in unpolluted air, where the normal concentration amounts to 1 to 3 parts per hundred million.

A simple and inexpensive method of measuring ozone involves the use of bent pieces of antiozodant-free rubber as indicators (Fig. 7) (8). The time necessary for the appearance of the cracks is directly related to the ozone content of the air. At night, and on smog-free days, it may take as long as an hour for the first cracks to appear; on a smoggy day, cracks are often evident in a matter

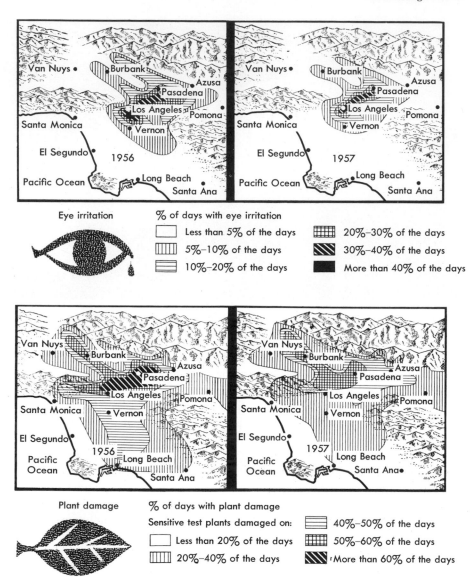

FIG. 6. The effect of air pollution control in the Los Angeles area for the period 1956–57. The intensity of eye irritation (top) has decreased, as has the area over which eye irritation is observed. Reported plant damage (bottom), too, has been less severe. [Los Angeles County Air Pollution Control District]

FIG. 7. Ozone in air is measured by its effect on rubber under strain. The degree of cracking indicates the concentration. [Los Angeles County Air Pollution Control District]

of a few minutes, under the conditions of the test. During heavy smog periods the total oxidant concentration is higher than can be accounted for on the basis of the presence of ozone alone when determined by spectrographic methods. This excess oxidant, corrected for the action of oxides of nitrogen, consists mainly of peroxidic material formed by the atmospheric oxidation of organic material. These organic peroxides are held to be responsible for eye irritation and plant damage resulting from smog. In the atmosphere over a city it is to be expected that the reactive ozone will enter into reactions with a number of other pollutants. Among the most prevalent of these groups are olefins, present in gasoline; fumigation experiments with gasoline fractions, and also with pure olefins which have been allowed to react with ozone, led to a reproduction of the typical plant-damage symptoms and to eye irritation, haze formation, and typical smog odor, as well. These experiments strongly indicated that the irritating materials were intermediate oxidation products of hydrocarbon oxidation and are of peroxidic nature, since the usual end products—aldehydes, ketones, and organic acids—are inactive in the concentration range used.

Most organic compounds are relatively stable against oxidation, when completely pure, but the presence of peroxides speeds the auto-oxidation considerably through a chain reaction initiated by hydrogen removal from the hydrocarbon chain. This effect can be accomplished also through the action of light on either the hydrocarbon or the oxygen molecule. In the latter case, the excited oxygen may remove hydrogen. Most hydrocarbons do not have absorption bands in the wavelength region of sunlight for a direct photochemical reaction. Similar reactions can be accomplished in a roundabout way by having a substance present which accepts the light energy and subsequently transfers it to the compound to be oxidized. In nature we find such substances in chlorophyll and other photochemically active pigments. In polluted atmospheres nitrogen dioxide functions as an oxidation catalyst in this way. Strong absorption of light by nitrogen dioxide occurs from the near ultraviolet through the blue part of the spectrum, and, upon irradiation, nitrogen dioxide splits into atomic oxygen and nitric oxide. Fumigation experiments with gasoline or olefin in the presence of oxides of nitrogen resulted in eye irritation and the same type of plant damage that was previously obtained with ozone acting on the olefins directly. In this case, too, we are able to calculate the concentration of hydrocarbon which should be present in a certain area and compare this with the actually observed concentration, just as we have done with the sulfur oxides. We find that the hydrocarbon concentration in the air is less than it had been calculated to be; on the other hand, the concentrations of the oxidation products—aldehydes and acids—are considerably higher than had been calculated, as is shown in Table 1. All these observed facts are in harmony with an explanation of Los Angeles smog as an oxidation phenomenon of organic material.

Formation of ozone

When all the typical symptoms of smog had been reproduced, the problem remained of accounting for the relatively high ozone content in the polluted atmosphere. It is now well established that the generation of ozone is intimately connected with the same photochemical reaction of organic material and oxides of nitrogen which causes eye irritation and plant damage. The formation of ozone is apparently a general phenomenon and is observed with many types of hydrocarbons, as well as with alcohols, ketones, aldehydes, and acids. The production of ozone has been attributed to the intermediate formation of peroxide radicals. This hypothesis is supported by the behavior of a model substance, biacetyl, upon irradiation. Years of photochemical research have shown that this diketone dissociates predominantly into acetyl radicals, which are further decomposed into methyl radicals and carbon monoxide. In most of these photochemical experiments the presence of oxygen is rigorously excluded to avoid complication. When oxygen is admitted, the free radicals will form peroxy radicals, and these apparently react with more oxygen to yield ozone:

$$\underset{\underset{\displaystyle O}{\|}}{H_3C-C} \xoverset{\displaystyle O\ \ \ O}{\underset{\displaystyle\vdots}{\underset{\|\ \vdots\ \|}{C}}-CH_3} \xrightarrow{h\nu} \underset{\underset{\displaystyle O}{\|}}{H_3C-\overset{\displaystyle .}{C}} \xrightarrow{O_2} \underset{\underset{\displaystyle O}{\|}}{H_3C-COO} \xrightarrow{O_2} \underset{\underset{\displaystyle O}{\|}}{H_3C-\overset{\displaystyle .}{CO}} + O_3$$

This rather surprising result can readily be verified by a simple lecture experiment in which a drop of biacetyl is introduced into a Pyrex flask. Next, a small piece of rubber with the ends tied together to form a loop is suspended in the flask. After exposure for an hour to sunlight, the rubber is heavily cracked, due to ozone attack. The rubber used should not contain antiozodants, of course. Infrared investigations have confirmed the chemical analysis and indicate that we are really dealing with ozone. Another well-known instance of radical formation is the irradiation of alkyl nitrites whereby an alkyl radical and nitric oxide are formed. When irradiation is carried out in air or oxygen, the alkyl radical forms a peroxide radical and ozone formation can readily be established. This reaction is similar to that postulated in the formation of smog of the Los Angeles type. The starting products in that case are nitrogen dioxide and hydrocarbons or their derivatives. We may visualize, first, a light-activated dissociation of nitrogen dioxide to nitric oxide and atomic oxygen, followed by a reaction of the atomic oxygen with a molecule of oxygen to form ozone. Atomic oxygen may also abstract a hydrogen from a hydrocarbon, with formation of an alkyl radical. This, in turn, can form ozone, as shown previously in the case of biacetyl. Also, reactions between nitric oxide and alkyl and alkylperoxy radicals may take place. Representatives of such combinations have been found in

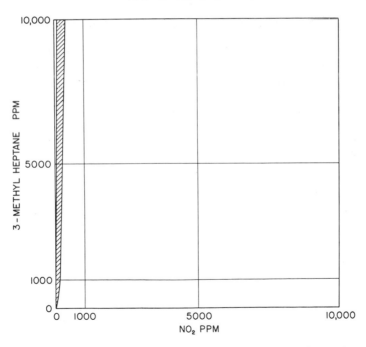

FIG. 8. Area of ozone formation with 3-methylheptane and NO_2. Ozone formation takes place only at concentrations indicated by shaded area (10,000 parts per million, volume for volume, is equivalent to 1 percent). [A. J. Haagen-Smit and M. M. Fox, *Air Repair* (7)]

long-path infrared studies conducted by workers at the Franklin Institute (9). Especially interesting is the formation of a peracylnitrite, a direct combination product of the photochemically produced nitric oxide and peroxy radical. This compound appears in smog atmospheres as well as in irradiation of synthetic mixtures of hydrocarbons and nitrogen oxides. It is postulated that these types of compounds play an important role as intermediates in the reoxidation of the nitric oxide to nitrogen dioxide.

A systematic study of the area of concentrations of hydrocarbon and oxides of nitrogen where ozone formation takes place showed that the reaction is limited to quite low concentrations of the reactants, as is shown in Fig. 8. Experiments of this type have focused attention on the circumstances peculiar to the problem of air pollution—that is, the extreme dilution. A chemist referring loosely to slow and fast reactions has in mind the conditions in laboratory synthesis, where concentration of about 10 percent are most commonly used. In atmospheric reactions the concentrations are in the order of 0.00001 percent—about one millionth as much. As a result, reactions which under the usual laboratory conditions are considered fast become very slow. For example, when a bimolecular reaction with participants in the concentration range of 10 percent (100,000 parts per million) requires 0.0036 second to go halfway to completion, it takes 10^6 times as long, or a whole hour, to reach the same point with a concentration of 0.1 part per million. Under the latter circumstances, not only can ozone survive attack by reducing agents but even free radicals have a far better chance of survival. It took many years to unravel relatively simple reactions such as the photodecomposition of acetone, biacetyl, and other compounds. In the air these reactions are complicated by the presence of oxygen, water, carbon dioxide, and an almost infinite variety of organic compounds from the evaporation and combustion of gasoline and from the burning of trash in its various forms.

Theoretical investigations

The field of atmospheric reactions is now being actively studied by a number of physical chemists and provides an interesting example of the way in which a practical problem has stimulated a number of theoretical investigations. Such study has familiarized a large group of physical chemists with the exciting field of extreme dilution, in which research should prove to be far less disturbed and complicated than research at higher concentrations, where molecules collide all too frequently. In addition, the practical aspects of air-pollution photochemistry have made available the instrumentation necessary to study these phenomena from a theoretical point of view. The purely theoretical physicist and chemist would have difficulty in obtaining the millions of dollars which have gone into the development of these instruments. It is gratifying to find that, as a by-product of the study of an unpleasant problem such as air pollution, a significant contribution to fundamental problems in chemistry could be made.

Automobile exhaust fumes

These remarkable reactions have now been confirmed in at least four different laboratories and provide a firm basis for control measures. We know which compounds contribute to these reactions and we know their sources, and now the Air Pollution Control District has only to control hydrocarbons, their oxidation products, and the oxides of nitrogen. Unfortunately, the necessary control equipment cannot be ordered because it still has to be invented. After hydrocarbons at refineries have been recovered, the major remaining source of hydrocarbons is the exhaust of automobiles, which amounts to 1200 tons per day. Direct and catalytic afterburners and deceleration devices are now being developed, but even after a successful device has been produced it will take many years before such devices will be installed on all the cars in the Los Angeles area. Pressing air pollution considerations can now be added to the many other arguments for streamlining our transit systems.

There are other difficulties. The major contributor to the oxides of nitrogen is, again, the automobile, and, apart from injection of water into the cylinders and the combustion of very rich fuel mixtures, no means are yet available for reducing the oxides of nitrogen. Several engineering laboratories are now searching for ways to reduce the nitrogen dioxide content of exhaust gases from gas, oil, and gasoline combustion through studies on the variable combustion conditions which can be obtained through boiler modification or changes in engine design. Often the question has come up, "Can't we do one or the other—hydrocarbon control or nitrogen dioxide control?" The answer, I believe, is "No." Most of the smog reactions are directly dependent on the product of the concentration of both hydrocarbons and oxides of nitrogen.

The private automobile is a major offender in both respects, and there is no reasonable basis for hope that control devices in the hands of the average car owner will give anywhere near the performance they give in an automobile-testing laboratory. Also, changes in gasoline composition could not be expected to have a drastic effect on smog-producing hydrocarbons in the exhaust. The steady increase in population tends to neutralize any control effort, and it is therefore evident that emissions must be controlled wherever possible. Besides being an objectionable factor in the photochemical reactions, the nitrogen oxides are objectionable in their own right and are quite toxic even in low concentrations. Fortunately we have not yet reached anywhere near the lower alert limit of 5.0 parts per million, but the concentration of this pollutant is steadily increasing, and since it appears in all combustions, the increase is practically proportional to the increase in population. Especially in areas of heavy traffic the concentration might at times surpass the safe limits, or, rather, what we now believe are safe limits. Oxides of nitrogen are rather unpleasant compounds. In concentrations of only 25 parts per million they act like war gases such as phosgene and cause lung edema. It is quite possible that, at far lower doses, objectionable damage might occur.

Cigarette and cigar smoke

Oxides of nitrogen are prominent in a quite different form of air pollution. Cigarette and cigar smoke contains from 300 to 1500 parts per million of oxides of nitrogen, which is completely removed by inhalation, through adsorption in the lungs. No attention has been given to this agent as a causative factor of respiratory ailments in smokers. Its strong toxic action should be an inducement to study more intensely the volatile components of tobacco smoke than has been done in the past, when most attention has been given to nonvolatile tars containing carcinogenic hydrocarbons.

Air pollution control administrations have a difficult task in surviving the years of waiting for engineering to catch up with the demands of the community. Programs for meeting emergency conditions have somewhat contributed to better feelings on the part of the public. It is understandable that most people not accustomed to smelling or inhaling a concoction of ozone, oxides of nitrogen, ozonides, and substances $x, y,$ and z begin to be a little worried. In recent years the medical profession in Los Angeles has set certain levels below which a catastrophe would be unlikely to occur. This is admittedly a very difficult decision to make and it has pointed to a serious deficiency in our knowledge of environmental hygiene.

Pollution levels

In studies of the health effects of air contaminants it becomes evident that there is a great difference between the industrial and general population levels. The industrial group generally represents a selected group of healthy individuals from which the extrasensitive has been removed, because the working conditions do not agree with them. For the whole population such a selection does not take place to any large degree, and we are dealing with the oversensitives—the sick, the young, and the very old. Public health officers have a most difficult task in establishing pollution levels for such a heterogeneous group, and it is a foregone conclusion that when levels are finally adopted there will be those who will maintain that they are too high, while others will charge persecution of industry because the levels are set too low. Animal experiments, and even experiments with human beings, while indicating some level of toxicity or annoyance, cannot give the answer for a general population. In urban areas we are dealing with several million people, and many would call the death of one or two persons per million, or some 20 for a town the size of Los Angeles, a disaster. The impossibility of approaching this accuracy of prediction in an experimental human, or even animal, colony is evident, for we would have to experiment with a few million individuals to get a statistically valid answer.

We come, therefore, to the conclusion that the only person able to give answers with any certainty about the result of some large-scale fumigation is the epidemiologist gathering data on death rates and general health status. It is, of course, unfortunate that this kind of study comes too late to prevent the disaster;

on the other hand, these studies furnish extremely valuable data on ways to prevent recurrence of the same series of events. It is for this reason that the study, such as that by workers at Harvard, of pretoxic effects, consisting in physiological responses warning of the danger ahead, is one of the most promising approaches to the study of pollution levels. These studies deal with the combined and synergistic effects of aerosols and sulfur dioxide. The physiological changes noted are greater flow resistance in the respiratory system, as reported by Amdur and Mead (*10*). The effects found at lower concentration do not necessarily represent toxic symptoms but may have to be regarded in the same class as sneezing, coughing, or blinking of the eye—therefore as warning signs and pretoxic symptoms.

Air pollution disaster can be prevented. Even nuisance effects can be minimized by planning at the right time. Such planning requires some basic information which can be furnished by the meteorologists. A study must be made of wind trajectories, for the progress of a package of air loaded with pollutants over the area should be known. Also needed are data on the change in concentration in a pollution cloud as it moves across a given area. This change comes about through turbulence and chemical reactions. As in the case in Los Angeles, relatively harmless gases may react to form irritants while moving across the basin. We like to know how long it takes for the pollutants to react sufficiently to give us maximum irritation.

When all these facts, plus the size and nature of the emission, are known, we can begin to think of plotting the trajectories and the isopollution lines for different substances. This kind of calculation has been described by Frenkiel (*11*) for a hypothetical case in the Los Angeles area. The calculation, which, practically, can be made only by means of electronic calculating machines, shows the fanning out of the emission from a single point of origin and its gradual dilution (Fig. 9). When we are dealing with a diffuse source such as the automobile, we can divide the area into a number of smaller areas for which traffic density, and therefore pollution, are known (Fig. 10). By calculating and integrating each one of these contributions, we arrive at the effect of a multiple source of pollution such as the automobile. This method, more than any other, shows clearly the contribution made by different sources, often miles away, to the pollution at a particular spot. Anyone enveloped by the expanding cloud will experience nuisance effects, regardless of whether or not he is in the exact center. On the basis of this concept, it is possible to express quite clearly how strongly the individual contribution from different sources may vary from one location to another, although both are in the same general area. Almost everyone is aware of this fact. Nevertheless it is quite common to refer loosely to minor and major sources, completely losing sight of the fact that in certain neighborhoods a local nuisance may have a greater effect than larger sources located far away. A great deal of friction could be avoided by recognizing this simple fact, and Frenkiel's "relative contribution charts" for different locations could be of great help in objectively settling some of the hot arguments (Fig. 11). A prerequisite for

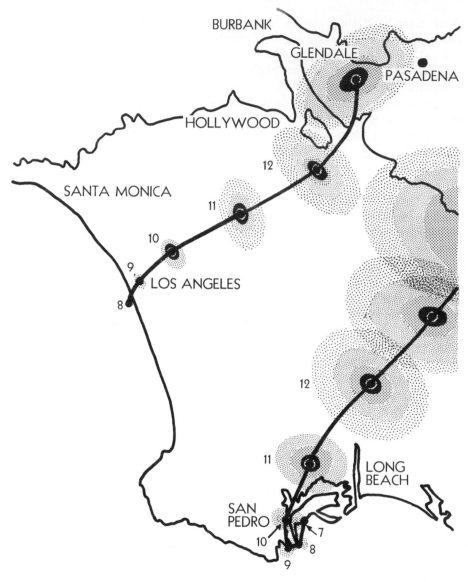

FIG. 9. Hypothetical dispersion of smoke puffs released at two points of the Los Angeles basin at 7 A.M. and 8 A.M., respectively. [F. N. Frenkiel (*11*)]

FIG. 11. Relative contributions of the three principal pollution sources to the mean concentration at California Institute of Technology. The effects of topographical features and inversion are taken into account in the mathematical model of Los Angeles County. The relative proportions of the "important" pollutants emitted by the three principal sources are based on recent studies in Los Angeles County. [F. N. Frenkiel (*11*)]

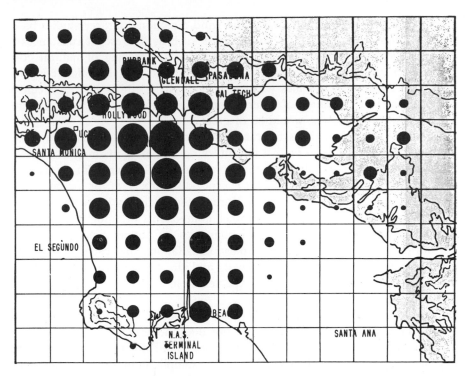

FIG. 10. Geographical distribution of traffic in the Los Angeles area. Area of circles is proportional to the number of vehicles; each square represents 16 square miles. [F. N. Frenkiel (*11*)]

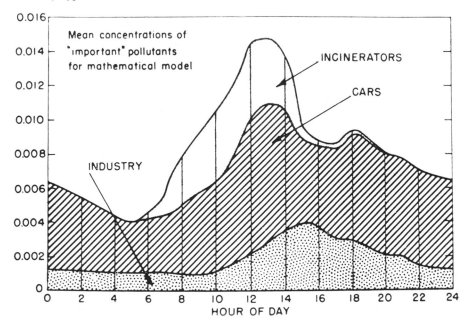

such calculations is reliable information on wind directions. Tracer studies based on the addition of easily identifiable materials such as fluorescent substances to the stack gases may be helpful. Much cheaper is the tracing of natural components specific to some of the sources. Aerial photography also offers considerable promise, especially at times when plumes 10 to 20 miles in length can be observed. Closer cooperation of other organizations, such as the Air Force and military and civilian groups, would be of great help.

Application of the methods for the calculation of pollutant distribution and movement would allow us to predict the future development of smog at a certain location and to predict what the elimination of certain sources will do as compared with the removal of others. This is especially important for a complicated case such as we find in Los Angeles. Here, most of the hydrocarbon material is emitted by the automobile, but the other components of smog, the oxides of nitrogen, are produced in nearly equal quantities by automobiles and installations burning gas or oil. The stationary installations are usually large, the trail of oxides of nitrogen is well defined, and the concentration of oxides of nitrogen may be higher than could be expected from a pollution cloud from such a diffuse source as the automobile.

Climatological conditions, and therefore air pollution moved by the wind currents, do not respect legal boundaries, nor does the pollution suddenly stop at the shore line, beyond which it is somewhat more difficult to maintain observation posts. In the Los Angeles area basin, for example, pollution from the southern industrial area can reach the Los Angeles Civic Center by either a land or a sea route. Federal and state testing programs have drawn attention to these wind movements, which cause pollutants to drift as far as islands 50 miles off the Pacific coast. These pollutants can readily be seen from the air and are quite different in appearance from low-lying clouds, due to their lack of structure and often to their characteristic yellowish-brown, off-white color, caused by refraction rather than by any color of specific chemicals.

Earlier in this article I have discussed more or less regularly occurring, or chronic, air pollution problems. There is, however, a more acute type of pollution which occurs when, through accidents such as explosions of tanks of toxic chemicals or through explosion of enemy bombs, large areas may become dangerous. In such circumstances it is of great importance to have the ability and the machinery to push a button on a computer which tells the health authorities in only a few minutes the area to which the poisonous cloud is drifting and what its concentration will be.

Conclusion

Air pollution problems are as varied as the activities of people themselves. We have looked in some detail at only two types of pollution. It has been my intent to make it clear that the problems met in air conservation are extremely complex and need the cooperative assistance of many scientific and technical disciplines. There is hardly any field of human endeavor that is not touched. The student of environmental hygiene has, as his laboratory, hundreds of square miles; as his chemicals, about everything a population emits to the air—in other words, a mixture representing a sizable portion of the inorganic and organic chemicals. His accomplishments have to be attuned to a population so varied in reactions and responses that an "average" person has no meaning in his problem. Entering into and often interfering with the normal occupations of the community, he has to be endowed with diplomatic and legal talents. The increased importance of his job in protecting the cleanliness of the air is felt in many quarters, and several universities and federal agencies have started courses in practical and theoretical aspects of air pollution control. Needed, too, are engineering studies to lead to the improvement of existing methods and to the invention of more efficient and economical processes to deal with old and new problems in air pollution.

REFERENCES

1. P. DRINKER, *Harben Lectures* (1956); "Air pollution and the public health," *J. Roy. Inst. Public Health and Hyg.* (July, Aug., Sept. 1957).
2. L. C. McCABE, *Air Pollution* (McGraw-Hill, New York, 1952).
3. H. F. JOHNSTONE and D. R. COUGHANOWR, "Absorption of SO_2 from air and oxidation in drops containing catalysts," *Ind. Eng. Chem.* **50**, 1169 (1958).
4. *Los Angeles County Air Pollution Control District, 2nd Tech. and Admin. Rept. on Air Pollution Control in Los Angeles County* (1950–51).
5. M. O. AMDUR, *Ind. Hyg. Quart.* **18**, 149 (1957).
6. A. J. HAAGEN-SMIT, C. E. BRADLEY, M. M. FOX, *Ind. Eng. Chem.* **45**, 2086 (1953); A. J. HAAGEN-SMIT and M. M. FOX, *S.A.E. Trans.* **63**, 575 (1955).
7. A. J. HAAGEN-SMIT and M. M. FOX, *Air Repair* **4**, 105 (1954).
8. C. E. BRADLEY and A. J. HAAGEN-SMIT, *Rubber Chem. and Technol.* **24**, 750 (1957).
9. E. R. STEPHENS, *J. Franklin Inst.* **263**, 349 (1957); E. R. STEPHENS, W. E. SCOTT, P. L. HANST, R. C. DOERR, *J. Air Pollution Control Assoc.* **6**, 159 (1956).
10. M. O. AMDUR and J. MEAD, *Am. J. Physiol.* **192**, 364 (1958).
11. F. N. FRENKIEL, *Sci. Monthly* **82**, 196 (1956).

Effect of Synthetic Smog on Spontaneous Activity of Mice

ROBERT D. BOCHE AND
J. J. QUILLIGAN, JR.

Since Stewart's pioneering experiments on the measurement of the activity of rats and mice with revolving wheels and kymographs, numerous investigators have studied the factors which influence the behavior of rats in this type of apparatus (1). Attempts have been made to calibrate or improve the wheels, or invent new means of measurement, such as tambour-mounted or tilting cages, photoelectric or magnetic devices, and a variety of mazes, most of which measure different quantities (2). Furthermore, many environmental and biological factors affect activity, yet relatively little is known about the motivation involved, despite several investigations of this phase of the problem (3).

Some of the factors which tend to complicate the use of these techniques are age, sex, diurnal cycle, oestrus cycle, visible light (5), heredity (6), and hunger and dietary deficiencies (7). Drugs with both stimulating and depressing effects on activity are known (8). Whole-body radiation also exerts some influence, though activity is not especially responsive to this kind of insult (9). Tobacco smoke is also claimed to have some effects (10). Although other air pollutants have not been systematically studied, one of Stewart's original observations is of interest in this connection. During the course of his experiments on the effects of barometric pressure and alcohol on the activity of rats, he observed a decrease on several occasions which he attributed to the escape of gas in his laboratory. While he does not indicate whether the poisoning seriously affected his animals in other ways, he was apparently the first to observe the effect of an air pollutant on voluntary activity (1).

The experiments described in this report were performed in the expectation that biological methods which measure the voluntary behavior of the experimental animal would provide sensitive indicators of environmental factors such as air pollution and infectious agents, since relatively small sensory impulses may be amplified by the neuromuscular system of the animal into large changes in behavior (4).

For the purpose of studying these effects, we have employed two modified 100 ft³ refrigerators. The chambers are similar and are provided with activated charcoal filtered air pulled by an exhaust blower on the roof. The temperature is approximately the same in both chambers. A mixture of ozone and gasoline vapor in air is forced into the exposure chamber. (The technique is similar to that described by Kotin and Falk, *11*.) This smog is analyzed daily for total oxidant with phenolphthalein (*12*) and for ozone by absorption in neutral potassium iodide (*13*).

The mice used for the present study were young adult C57BL/6 males; they were caged individually, and they had free access to laboratory chow. The rotating wheels, 6¾ inches in diameter, were lined with a plastic film in which fine carborundum powder is embedded for traction. Rotation is recorded remotely by electric counters activated by microswitches.

After approximately 3 weeks in the wheel cages, the mice stabilized their activity. The cages were then placed in the chambers, one in smog, the other in purified air. At intervals of 24 hours, the cages were exchanged between chambers, the smogged mouse being placed in filtered air, the filtered air mouse in smog. This process was repeated for a total of 6 days in light smog and 6 days in heavy smog; there was a 1-week interval in the filtered air chamber between the two periods of exposure to smog.

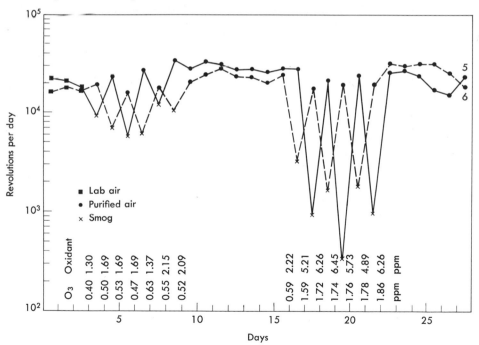

FIG. 1. Spontaneous wheel turning activity of two C57 Black male mice in different environments. The total oxidant and ozone determinations are shown at the bottom of the graph for each day of exposure to synthetic air pollutant mixture.

Figure 1 is a semilogarithmic plot of the daily activity records of two individual mice throughout one experiment. The smog concentrations in parts per million (ppm) for each exposure day are shown at the bottom. The regular manner in which low concentrations of smog diminish the wheel-turning is obvious and significant ($P = <.001$), by analysis of variance, as is the greater inhibition which occurred after the smog concentration was increased. The ozone concentration in the first series of exposures corresponds to a first-stage alert in Los Angeles (0.5 ppm), although the total oxidant values are somewhat higher. These experiments are easily repeatable with different kinds of wheels. Thus far, we have shown reduced activity in smog with a total of 14 mice. Furthermore, a decrease in activity is noted for at least 3 weeks when the mice remain in the smog chamber. The activity techniques, though little used for the study of disease, may be sensitive indicators of subclinical disturbances (*14*).

REFERENCES

1. C. C. Stewart, *Am. J. Physiol.* **1,** 40 (1898). For a comprehensive discussion of activity see N. L. Munn, *Handbook of Psychological Research on the Rat* (Houghton Mifflin, Boston, Mass., 1950), Chap. 3.
2. J. S. Szymanski, *Arch. ges. Physiol. Pflüger's* **158,** 343 (1914); B. F. Skinner, *J. Gen. Physiol.* **9,** 3 (1933); O. L. Lacey, *Am. J. Psychol.* **57,** 412 (1944); B. A. Campbell, *J. Comp. and Physiol. Psychol.* **47,** 90 (1954); J. T. Eayers, *Brit. J. Animal Behavior* **2,** 20 (1954); P. N. Strong, Jr., *J. Comp. and Physiol. Psychol.* **50,** 596 (1957); W. G. Mitchell, *Science* **130,** 455 (1959).
3. G. Wald and B. Jackson, *Proc. Natl. Acad. Sci. U.S.* **30,** 255 (1944); J. P. Seward and A. C. Pereboom, *J. Comp. and Physiol. Psychol.* **48,** 272 (1955); W. R. Hill, *ibid.* **49,** 15 (1956).
4. J. R. Platt, *Am. Scientist* **44,** 180 (1956).
5. C. P. Richter, *Comp. Psychol. Monographs* **1,** 2 (1922), *Quart. Rev. Biol.* **2,** 307 (1927); J. McV. Hunt and H. Schlosberg, *J. Comp. Psychol.* **28,** 285 (1939); D. C. Jones, D. J. Kimeldorf, P. L. Rubadeau, T. J. Castanera, *Am. J. Physiol.* **172,** 109 (1953).
6. E. A. Rundquist, *J. Comp. Psychol.* **16,** 415 (1933); E. G. Brody, *Comp. Psychol. Monographs* **17,** No. 5 (1942); W. R. Thompson, *J. Heredity* **47,** 147 (1956); A. M. Mordkoff and J. L. Fuller, *ibid.* **50,** 6 (1959).
7. P. S. Siegel and M. Steinberg, *J. Comp. and Physiol. Psychol.* **42,** 413 (1949); J. F. Hall, *ibid.* **49,** 339 (1956); J. A. F. Stevenson and R. H. Rixon, *Yale J. Biol. Med.* **29,** 575 (1957).
8. L. V. Searle and C. W. Brown, *Psychol. Bull.* **34,** 558 (1937); M. R. Jones, *J. Comp. Psychol.* **35,** 1 (1943); M L. Tainter, *ibid.* **36,** 143 (1943).
9. R. W. Leary and T. C. Ruch, *J. Comp. and Physiol. Psychol.* **48,** 336 (1956); P. E. Fields, *ibid.* **50,** 386 (1957)

10. H. E. FIELD, *Univ. Calif. Publs. Physiol.* **5,** 189 (1926).
11. P. KOTIN and H. FALK, *Proc. 3rd Natl. Air Pollution Symposium, Pasadena, Calif.* (1955).
12. L. C. McCABE, *Ind. Eng. Chem.* **45,** 111A (1953).
13. A. LADENBURG and R. QUASIG, *Ber. deut. chem. Ges.* **34,** 1184 (1901).
14. We are indebted to Dr. Keith J. Hayes for helpful discussions. This work was supported by research grant RG4657 from the U.S. Public Health Service.

Smoking and Death Rates—
A Riddle in Cause and Effect*

E. CUYLER HAMMOND

The fact that tobacco smoke contains one of the deadliest and fastest-acting poisons known is sufficient to raise suspicion that smoking may be a harmful habit. A person who inhales the smoke from two packs of ordinary cigarettes absorbs an amount of nicotine which would kill him in short order if administered in a single dose. In addition, tobacco smoke contains an appreciable quantity of carbon monoxide, small amounts of other poisons (including arsenic, hydrogen sulfide, and hydrogen cyanide) and numerous polycyclic hydrocarbons, at least one of which is a known carcinogen [1]. Why so many of us get pleasure from partaking of such a mixture is something of a mystery.

The chemical analysis of tobacco smoke, while suggestive, does not in itself prove anything about the long-term effects of smoking. Some chemicals which are highly toxic in large doses are harmless or even beneficial in small doses. Other substances may be practically harmless in a single large dose but cause serious damage after prolonged exposure to relatively small doses. Furthermore, there are some factors which seem to have little or no effect on healthy individuals but which have deleterious effects on patients suffering from certain diseases.

As scientists, I think we would all agree that the ideal way to determine the long-term effects of smoking would be to set up a well-controlled experiment on human beings. It should start when the subjects are in their teens and continue until the last one dies of old age. Unfortunately, this is a bit impractical for numerous reasons. For example, it would be quite impossible for the investigator to maintain the same degree of control over human subjects as over

* A Sigma Xi National Lecture, 1957–58.

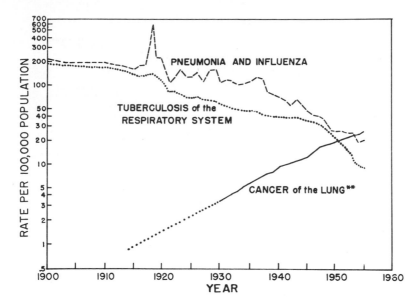

FIG. 1. Trends in death rates for selected respiratory diseases among white males in the United States, 1900–1955. The death rates are standardized for age on the 1940 United States population. (National Office of Vital Statistics, Bureau of the Census.)

laboratory animals. For these reasons, many studies have been made to ascertain what happens to people who of their own volition have smoked for many years.

Perhaps the least satisfactory has been the study of time trend associations. As shown on Figure 1, a tremendous increase has occurred in the reported death rate from lung cancer. In this country, the age standardized rate for white males rose from about 0.7 per 100,000 in 1914 to 28.4 per 100,000 in 1956. This led to the hypothesis that a corresponding increase must have occurred in one or more factors responsible for lung cancer, probably some substance inhaled into the lungs, Concurrently, a decrease occurred in three other lung diseases: tuberculosis, influenza, and pneumonia.

Coal soot, dust from asphalt highways, motor vehicle exhaust fumes, fumes from fuel oil, and cigarette smoke have been suspect in relation to lung cancer because: 1) they are inhaled into the lungs, and 2) they contain substances capable of producing cancer under some experimental conditions. All except coal have increased in this country during the same time that the lung cancer death rate has been rising. (See Figure 2.) Does this prove that one or more of these agents is a causative factor in the production of lung cancer? If so, then one should also conclude that cigarette smoking prevents pneumonia. Not only has the decline in pneumonia paralleled the rise in cigarette smoking but it has been shown that cigarette smoke will kill pneumococci *in vitro* as well as various bacteria in the mouth of a smoker [2].

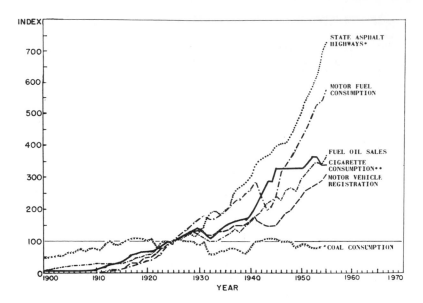

FIG. 2. Trends in selected environmental factors in the United States in 1900 through 1955 (1924–1926 = 100). The state asphalt highways indicate the high-type bituminous roads under state control. (United States Bureau of Agricultural Economics, United States Bureau of Public Roads, United States Bureau of Mines.)

During the German invasion of Norway in World War II, a remarkable drop occurred in the death rate from circulatory diseases, the rate rising again soon after the war [3]. (See Figure 3.) One might suppose that this was due to a temporary alteration in one or more environmental factors. Three factors often mentioned in connection with circulatory diseases are diet, smoking, and "anxiety" or "nervous tension." Diet and cigarette consumption were severely restricted in Norway during the war years. Therefore, it is possible that either one or both of these restrictions were responsible for the temporary decline in the death rate. On the other hand, there was very likely an increase in "anxiety" under the conditions imposed by the Nazis. This might be taken as an indication that "anxiety" is not a factor of prime importance in circulatory disease deaths.

The difficulty with all such time trend association studies is that a vast number of things in the human environment have changed with time. Indeed, change seems to be more the rule than the exception. Therefore, parallel time trends, while sometimes suggestive, are far from definitive.

The same sort of difficulty arises when comparisons are made between different geographic areas. For example, the age standardized death rate from lung cancer is higher in urban areas than in rural areas. Some investigators have taken this as an indication that air pollution is a factor of prime importance in lung cancer. However, it has been found that cigarette smoking is considerably more

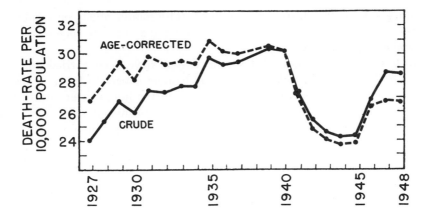

FIG. 3. Mortality from circulatory diseases in Norway 1927–1948. Standard population: population of Norway in 1940. (This figure is reprinted by permission of the *Lancet*. See Reference 3.)

common among city dwellers than among farmers [4]. Innumerable other differences between urban and rural life could be mentioned, so there would be no reason to single out air pollution and cigarette smoking were it not for outside evidence which points suspicion in their direction. Among other things, diagnostic facilities tend to be somewhat better in cities than in rural areas and this may partly account for the difference in the reported lung cancer death rate. This explanation could not account for the fact that the total deaths and the death rate from most diseases, including coronary artery disease, are higher in urban than in rural areas.

Another fact of interest is that death rates from both lung cancer and coronary artery disease are much higher among males than among females. The majority of deaths from these diseases occur in persons over the age of 55. In a representative sample of the United States population studied by the Bureau of the Census several years ago, it was found that in age group 55 and over, 7.2 percent of the men but only 0.6 percent of the women were smoking a pack or more of cigarettes a day [4]. I need hardly say that males and females differ in several ways besides their smoking habits.

Retrospective studies

I will now turn to a type of investigation which is far more definitive than those previously mentioned. It is usually called the "retrospective" or "historic" method of studying the association between a disease and antecedent factors. The design is generally about as follows:

The investigator first selects a group of subjects who are ill or have died of a particular disease. He then selects one or more other groups of subjects who do not have the disease in question. Information about past habits, exposures, etc., is obtained either by questioning the subjects themselves or by questioning their relatives.

No less than 20 studies of this general type have been carried out in this country and abroad on smoking in relation to lung cancer.* In every instance, a far higher proportion of smokers was found in the lung cancer group than in the control group. When type of smoking was considered, cigarette smoking seemed more highly associated with lung cancer than cigar or pipe smoking.

Several studies of the same general type have shown a high degree of association between smoking habits and cancer of the mouth and cancer of the larynx and a moderately high degree of association between smoking and cancer of the bladder. In the case of mouth cancer, cigar and pipe smoking seemed to be particularly involved. An association has also been found between tobacco chewing and the occurrence of mouth cancer.

At least three independent retrospective studies have shown an association between smoking habits and coronary artery disease [5, 6, 7]. That is, a higher proportion of smokers was found among patients with coronary artery disease than among persons in the control groups. Retrospective studies have also shown an extremely high degree of association between smoking habits and Buerger's disease [8] (a circulatory disease of the extremities) and a high degree of association between smoking and peptic ulcers [9].

This method of study as usually carried out has been severely criticized by a number of authors, myself included. What disturbs me most is that the subjects in the so-called experimental group are not questioned until after they become ill. This raises the possibility that responses to questions pertaining to past habits may be biased on account of the illness. This possibility was minimized in one of the studies by questioning all of the subjects before a final diagnosis had been made [10].

The other major difficulty lies in the selection of subjects, particularly those in the control group. For example, there is a possibility that people who smoke are more likely (or are less likely) to be hospitalized than are people who do not smoke. This factor might bias the results of a retrospective study in which the control group consists of hospital patients with diseases other than the disease under investigation. This particular difficulty was avoided in one of the studies on smoking and lung cancer by using two different control groups: *a*) hospital patients with diseases other than lung cancer, and *b*) a representative sample of the population of the area in which the hospital was located [11]. It turned out that the highest percentage of smokers was found in the lung cancer group, the next highest percentage in the hospital control group, and the lowest percentage in the general population control group. This suggests that smoking

---

* Space does not permit giving reference to all of the many studies on smoking in relation to cancer.

is associated not only with lung cancer but also with the probability of being hospitalized for other diseases.

Several other criticisms of the method may be valid in certain instances but probably do not apply to the particular studies under consideration here.

If the results of a study are erroneous due to some flaw in the design, then the same error is apt to occur again if the study is repeated in identically the same way. The numerous retrospective studies on lung cancer were conducted in many different ways. This is particularly true as to the ways in which the subjects were selected. In several of the studies, factors such as occupation, place of residence, and drinking habits were taken into consideration. Because of these variations in design, it seems most unlikely that all 20 of them could be wrong when all 20 yielded essentially the same results.

A study of very different design was carried out by Raymond Pearl [12] on smoking in relation to the over-all death rate. His data were obtained by questioning members of selected families about all the members of their family group, both living and dead. Among men in the middle age group he found the death rate to be about twice as high for heavy smokers as for non-smokers. This difference disappeared in the old age groups. The method used by Pearl has also been criticized.

Prospective studies

Because of questions which had been raised as to the validity of the retrospective method, two prospective studies on smoking in relation to death rates were started in 1951; one by Doll and Hill [13] in England and the other by Hammond and Horn [14] in this country. I will first describe our study.

As previously mentioned, what worried me most about the retrospective method was the possibility of bias resulting from questioning people who are ill. In order to avoid this difficulty, we decided to obtain information on the smoking habits of a very large number of presumably well persons and then follow them for a number of years. After designing and pretesting a smoking questionnaire, we recruited and trained some 22,000 American Cancer Society volunteers as researchers for the study. Each volunteer was asked to get a questionnaire filled out by about 10 white men between the ages of 50 and 69 whom she knew well and would be able to trace. They were told not to enroll a man who was seriously ill or if they knew he had lung cancer. Once a year thereafter, they reported on the status of each man as "alive" or "dead" or "don't know." A copy or abstract of the death certificate was obtained on each death reported. Further medical information was obtained whenever cancer was mentioned on a death certificate. The study area included 394 counties in nine states.

Between January and June of 1952, satisfactory smoking questionnaires were obtained from 189,854 men; 187,783 of them were traced by the volunteers through October 1955 and 11,870 deaths were reported.

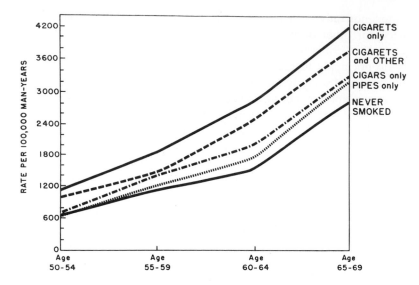

FIG. 4. Total death rates by type of smoking (lifetime history) and by age at start of study. (This figure and figures 5–7 and 9–11 are reprinted by permission of the *Journal of the American Medical Association*. See Reference 14.)

Total death rates. Figure 4 shows the age specific death rates per 100,000 man-years by type of smoking. Note that men with a history of regular cigarette-smoking-only had the highest death rates. Men who had never smoked had the lowest death rates. The others fell in between.

In order to summarize these findings, we computed the number of deaths which would have occurred in each smoking category if their age specific death rates had been exactly the same as for men who never smoked. (See Figure 5.) This will be referred to as the "expected" number of deaths. The expected number of deaths divided by the observed number of deaths is called the mortality ratio. By this definition, the mortality ratio for men who never smoked is 1.00.

Among men with a history of cigarette-smoking-only, 4406 deaths were observed during the course of the study compared with just 2623 expected. Thus the mortality ratio (4406 ÷ 2623) was 1.68. In other words, the death rate of these cigarette smokers was 68 percent higher than the death rate of men who never smoked, age being taken into consideration. Men who smoked cigarettes but also smoked cigars or pipes had a mortality ratio of 1.43. For cigar smokers the mortality ratio was 1.22 and for pipe smokers the mortality ratio was 1.12.

It is not certain why the death rate of cigar and pipe smokers was lower than the death rate of cigarette smokers. However, it is reasonable to suppose that tobacco smoke is more likely to have an effect upon a person who inhales the smoke than upon a person who does not inhale the smoke. The preliminary

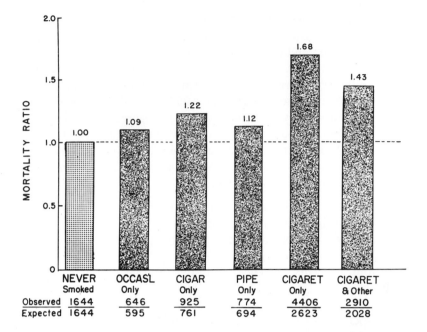

FIG. 5. Mortality ratios for total deaths by type of smoking.

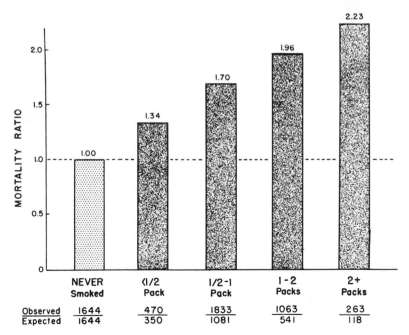

FIG. 6. Mortality ratios for total number of deaths by current amount (1952) of cigarette smoking.

results of a study I am now conducting seem to indicate that the great majority of cigarette smokers inhale while cigar and pipe smokers seldom inhale. Men who smoke both cigars and cigarettes seem to inhale less than men who smoke only cigarettes.

Men with a history of regular-cigarette-smoking-only were classified by their current amount of cigarette smoking in 1952. As shown in Figure 6, the death rate increased steadily with the amount of cigarette smoking. For those who smoked less than one half a pack of cigarettes a day, the death rate was just 34 percent higher than for men who never smoked. For those who smoked two packs or more of cigarettes a day, the death rate was 123 percent higher than for men who never smoked.

Death rates by broad categories of causes. Having found a high degree of association between cigarette smoking and the total death rate, we next sought to determine what diseases were involved. For this purpose, we first divided the deaths into just five broad categories as shown in Figure 7.

Deaths from accidents, violence, and suicide appeared to be unrelated to smoking habits.

Deaths from pulmonary diseases other than lung cancer showed a high degree of association with smoking habits, the mortality ratio for cigarette smokers being 2.85. Only 338 out of the 11,870 deaths in the study were classified in this category which included 124 deaths attributed to pneumonia or

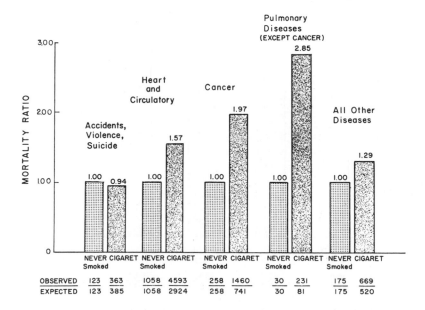

FIG. 7. Mortality ratios by major causes of death. Ratios for cigarette smokers are compared with those for men who never smoked.

influenza, 41 to pulmonary tuberculosis, 76 to asthma, and 97 to other lung diseases such as bronchitis an pneumoconiosis. While all of these seemed to be associated with cigarette smoking, pneumonia and influenza showed the highest degree of association with a mortality ratio of 3.90.

1460 cigarette smokers died of cancer compared with an expected total of only 741, had their age specific death rates been the same as for men who never smoked. The mortality ratio was 1.97.

The deaths of 4593 cigarette smokers were attributed to diseases of the heart and circulatory system as compared with 2924 expected, the mortality ratio being 1.57.

Deaths due to all other causes combined showed some association with cigarette smoking as indicated by a mortality ratio of 1.29.

Cancer. The cancer deaths were classified according to primary site; that is, the location where the disease presumably started. This cannot always be ascertained with certainty since cancer tends to spread to many parts of the body.

Lung cancer showed by far the highest degree of association with cigarette smoking, the mortality ratio being 10.73. I will have more to say about this in a moment.

The next highest association was for a group of adjacent sites all of which are directly exposed to tobacco smoke or saliva and bronchial secretions containing material from tobacco smoke. These sites are lip, mouth, tongue, larynx, pharynx, and esophagus. The mortality ratio of cigarette smokers for cancer of these sites combined was 5.06. The data indicated that pipe and cigar smoking may be as important or more important than cigarette smoking in respect to cancer of several of these sites.

Cigarette smokers had a mortality ratio of 1.77 for cancer of the genito-urinary system. This category includes cancer of the bladder, kidney, and prostate. In most of these cases, cancer was present at the time of death in two or more of these sites as well as in other parts of the body. Evidence as to the exact spot where the disease started was far from conclusive in many instances. However, cancer of the bladder appeared to be more highly associated with cigarette smoking than was cancer of any other site in this group, the mortality ratio for bladder cancer being 2.17.

Cancer of the digestive system was associated with cigarette smoking to the degree indicated by a mortality ratio of 1.35. Deaths attributed to primary cancer of the liver showed a particularly high degree of association with smoking. However, cancer arising in the lung or other organs very frequently metastasizes to the liver and is sometimes mistaken for primary cancer of the liver. Therefore, we are uncertain whether this association is real or whether it resulted from confusion in primary site in some instances. Cancer of the rectum showed no association with smoking habits. Cancer of the colon showed a negative association and cancer of the stomach and cancer of the pancreas showed positive associations with cigarette smoking, but these were not statistically significant.

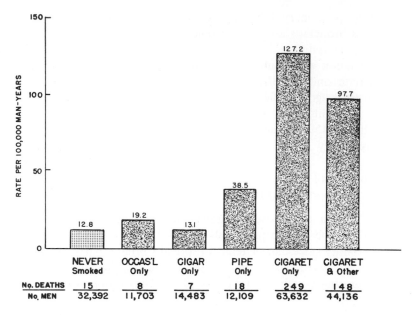

FIG. 8. Age-standardized death rates due to carcinoma of lung (all reported) by type of smoking as classified from lifetime history.

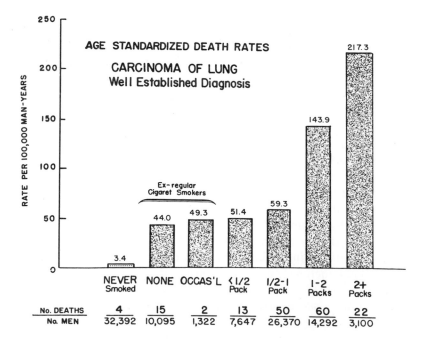

FIG. 9. Age-standardized death rates due to well-established cases of bronchogenic carcinoma (exclusive of adenocarcinoma) by current amount of cigarette smoking.

Cancer of the lymphatic and hematopoietic system includes leukemia, Hodgkin's disease, lymphosarcoma, reticulosarcoma, and a few other similar diseases. Leukemia showed no association with smoking habits. The others mentioned appeared to be associated with cigarette smoking, but not to a statistically significant degree.

Cancer of sites other than those already mentioned showed no association with smoking habits.

Lung cancer: 448 deaths were attributed to primary cancer of the lung. Figure 8 shows the age standardized death rates per 100,000 man years by smoking categories. I should mention that a minor category has been omitted (i.e., men who smoked cigars and pipes but not cigarettes) to save space on the chart, so the total adds up to only 445 deaths instead of 448. Note the low rate of 12.8 per 100,000 man years for men who never smoked and the high rate of 127.2 per 100,000 man years for men with a history of cigarette smoking only.

Most pathologists will accept a diagnosis of cancer as being proved only when it has been confirmed by microscopic examination of a specimen of the tumor. One type of cancer, called adenocarcinoma, was considered separately because some investigators are of the opinion that it has a different etiology from other types of lung cancer. Out of 32,392 men who never smoked, only 4 died with a well-established diagnosis of lung cancer (excluding adenocarcinoma) during the course of the study. Out of 63,632 men with a history of cigarette-smoking-only, 162 died with this diagnosis.

Figure 9 shows age standardized death rates by amount of cigarette smoking for the well-established cases of lung cancer, excluding adenocarcinoma. Note the very high rate for men who smoked two or more packs a day.

Those of us who are ex-very-heavy-cigarette-smokers have something of a personal interest in the lung cancer death rate of men who stopped smoking cigarettes. (See Figure 10.) Men currently smoking a pack or more of cigarettes a day in 1952 had a lung cancer death rate (well-established cases) of 157.1 per 100,000 per year. Those who had previously smoked at this level but had given it up for 1 to 10 years had a rate of 77.6, and those who had given it up for 10 years or longer had a rate of only 60.5.

Because of the hypothesis that air pollution associated with urbanization may be a causative factor in lung cancer, we divided the subjects into those living in rural areas and those living in cities of various sizes. Holding smoking habits constant, the lung cancer death rate was found to be somewhat higher in cities than in rural areas. However, this difference was very small as compared with the difference between non-smokers and cigarette smokers. In all areas, the lung cancer death rate was very low among men who had never smoked regularly and high among regular cigarette smokers.

Coronary artery disease. Coronary artery disease kills far more Americans than any other single cause of death. It is the only form of heart disease which appeared to be significantly associated with cigarette smoking.

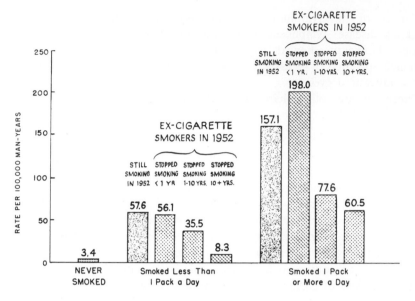

FIG. 10. Age-standardized death rates due to well-established cases of bronchogenic carcinoma (exclusive of adenocarcinoma). Rates for men who have stopped smoking are compared with those of men who never smoked and those for men still smoking in 1952.

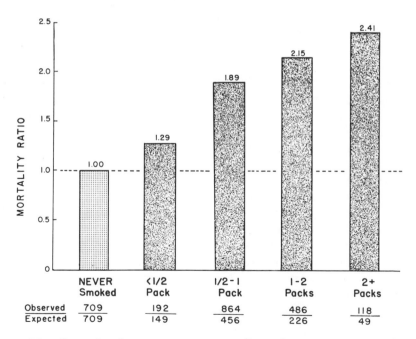

FIG. 11. Mortality ratios due to coronary artery disease by current amount of cigarette smoking.

Figure 11 shows the relationship between coronary artery disease deaths and the amount of cigarette smoking. Note the steady increase in the mortality ratio with amount of cigarette smoking. The coronary artery disease death rate of men smoking two packs or more of cigarettes a day was nearly two and a half times as high as the rate for men who never smoked. Men who had given up cigarette smoking for a number of years had lower death rates from coronary artery diseases than did men who were currently smoking cigarettes at the start of the study. No association was found between pipe smoking and coronary artery disease and only a moderate degree of association was found between cigar smoking and coronary artery disease.

Other diseases.   Fifty-one men in the study died of gastric ulcers and every one of them was a smoker; 46 had a history of regular cigarette smoking and the other 5 smoked only cigars or pipes. Duodenal ulcer death rates were also considerably higher among cigarette smokers than among non-smokers. Non-syphilitic aortic aneurism deaths were highly associated with cigarette smoking. General arteriosclerosis and cerebral vascular lesions were associated with cigarette smoking but to a far lesser degree. Cirrhosis of the liver was the only other disease showing an appreciable association with cigarette smoking (except for a few diseases where the number of deaths was too small for statistically stable rates).

The Doll and Hill prospective study.   The prospective study of Doll and Hill [13] was similar in design to our study except that the subjects were all British physicians and information on smoking habits was obtained by mail questionnaires. It is still in progress. Since the number of subjects was smaller, not enough deaths have yet occurred for the authors to make such a detailed analysis by causes of death. However, their first published results were essentially the same as ours in respect to lung cancer. They also found an association between smoking habits and death rates from peptic ulcers, bronchitis, pulmonary tuberculosis, and coronary artery disease.

Summary of evidence from retrospective and prospective studies

Considering all of the evidence, it can hardly be doubted that an extremely high degree of association exists between cigarette smoking and lung cancer. While fewer studies have been made on other diseases, it is virtually certain that an association exists between cigarette smoking and coronary artery disease, Buerger's disease, cancer of certain sites directly exposed to tobacco smoke, cancer of the bladder, peptic ulcers, and certain respiratory diseases. Although the mortality ratio (cigarette smokers compared with non-smokers) is several times as high for lung cancer as for coronary artery disease, the very large number of excess deaths from coronary artery disease in cigarette smokers was perhaps the most important finding of our prospective study. This would be true regardless of the explanation.

The associations we found between cigarette smoking and diseases other than those mentioned above are less well established for two reasons: *a*) the findings have not yet been confirmed by other investigators, and *b*) in some instances the observed association may have resulted from misdiagnosis (e.g., death being attributed to primary cancer of the liver when in fact it was due to primary cancer of the lung with metastasis to the liver).

Other types of evidence

As previously noted, a high degree of association has been found between smoking habits and death rates from gastric and duodenal ulcers. Clinical evidence suggests an explanation. Several investigators have reported on the result of treatment for peptic ulcers [15, 16]. They found that the disease recurred far more frequently among patients who failed to stop smoking when advised to do so than among patients who did stop smoking. The findings in these studies may perhaps be open to question since controls were inadequate. However, they have recently been confirmed by a very well controlled clinical experiment [9]. There is also some evidence from animal experiments on the subject. Toon, Cross, and Wangensteen [17] administered small doses of histamine to two groups of dogs. One group was directly exposed to cigarette smoke by means of a tube inserted in the trachea and the other group was not exposed to cigarette smoke. Peptic ulcers occurred in both groups of dogs, but the proportion developing the disease was far higher in the exposed group than in the control group. There is evidence that the effect was due to nicotine in the smoke.

There is some clinical evidence that cigarette smoking may increase the probability of the recurrence of pulmonary tuberculosis in patients in whom this disease has been brought under control [18].

An extremely high association was found between cigarette smoking and cancer of sites directly exposed to tobacco smoke or material from the smoke. A well-known carcinogenic agent, 3,4-benzpyrene has been identified in very small quantities in tobacco smoke and no less than six independent investigators have produced cancer on the skins of mice and rabbits with material condensed from tobacco smoke. While some investigators have had negative results from such experiments, the finding now seems to have been amply confirmed. Cancer has also been produced on the skin of rabbits with material distilled from tobacco [19]. Wynder and Wright [20] have chemically fractionated cigarette smoke condensate and report that most of the material capable of producing cancer when smeared on the skin of a mouse is contained in one small fraction of neutral tar.

It is well established that long and heavy exposure to dust containing uranium, nickel, or chromates can cause human lung cancer in man [21]. This shows that the disease can be caused by more than one substance inhaled into the lungs.

It has been shown experimentally in animals: (1) that tobacco smoke tends to inhibit ciliary action in the trachea and bronchial tubes, and (2) that material from cigarette smoke tends to accumulate in spots where cilia have been destroyed or ciliary action inhibited [22]. Detailed microscopic studies of the bronchial tubes of men indicate that a number of histologic changes such as are usually produced by carcinogenic materials are encountered more frequently among cigarette smokers than among non-smokers [23, 24]. These changes included marked basal cell hyperplasia, stratification, squamous metaplasia, and a lesion called "carcinoma-*in-situ*" or "atypism" depending upon the views of the pathologist.

While cancer produced by a carcinogenic agent most frequently occurs at the site of application, this is not necessarily the case. For example, it is known that cancer of the bladder can be caused by long exposure to a chemical used in the aniline dye industry [25]. This may be of significance in respect to the finding that death rates from cancer of the bladder are higher among smokers than among non-smokers. Perhaps it also explains the relatively low association found between smoking and cancer of some other internal organs; but this is far from certain.

There is an enormous literature on the acute effects of smoking as well as the acute effects of two important components of cigarette smoke, nicotine and carbon monoxide. A number of these effects involve the circulatory system directly or indirectly. They may be summarized briefly as follows:

Smoking has a stimulating effect on the central nervous system and autonomic ganglia, induces secretion of the antidiuretic hormone from the posterior lobe of the pituitary gland, and increases blood sugar [1]. It has been demonstrated that smoking causes constriction of the peripheral blood vessels, increases the blood pressure, increases the pulse rate, and produces marked changes in the electrocardiograms and ballistocardiograms of some patients with coronary artery disease. In addition, Eisen and Hammond [26] have shown that cigarette smoking produces an increase in red blood cell counts and in packed cell volume. Preliminary experiments conducted by the same investigators seem to indicate that cigarette smoking results in a decrease in the clotting time of the blood; but this has not yet been established with certainty. All of these acute effects of smoking have been found in experiments on human beings.

A number of investigators have exposed mice to cigarette smoke to study the effect, if any, on the occurrence of lung tumors in these animals. Considering the purpose of these experiments, the highly toxic effects of cigarette smoke on mice have been a source of annoyance. In some preliminary experiments, I first tried a high exposure and most of the animals went into convulsions and died in a few minutes. If the exposure is somewhat lower, the initial effect is not so severe but the death rate is high from causes other than cancer, particularly in the first month or two of the experiment [27]. At relatively low exposures there seems to be little if any effect on the occurrence of lung tumors, although one investigator [27] obtained results which he thought were significant and another investigator [28] obtained results which were suggestive. These experiments may or may not have meaning concerning the occurrence of lung cancer in man. However, they certainly show that exposure to cigarette smoke can cause an increase in the death rate of mice. Perhaps this has some bearing on the finding of a very high total death rate among heavy cigarette smokers.

One group of investigators has reported that mice exposed to cigarette smoke show greatly increased activity along with poor gain in weight and a high death rate [29]. The way they describe the increased activity is reminiscent of what might be ascribed to "nervous tension" if observed in men. Considering the known effects of nicotine on the nervous system, the possibility of such a connection does not seem altogether unreasonable.

Discussion

As previously described, an association between smoking habits and certain diseases has been reported by many different investigators and can now be considered as established beyond reasonable doubt. There is evidence that smoking may be associated with a number of other diseases, but this will remain in doubt until independently verified. The following discussion will be confined to those diseases for which an association with smoking has been proved or at least reasonably well established.

The finding of an association between smoking and death rates from a particular disease might be accounted for by any one of the following hypotheses:

(1) Smoking is a direct cause of the disease. That is to say, exposure to tobacco smoke is capable of producing the disease in susceptible individuals. (This permits the possibility that one or more other factors may also be capable of producing the disease.)

(2) Smoking increases the susceptibility of the individual to the effect of some other agent which is a direct cause of the disease.

(3) Smoking has a deleterious effect upon individuals who have the disease and increases the probability of their dying of the disease.

(4) Some "third factor" increases the probability that the individual will smoke and also either increases the probability that the individual will develop the disease or has a deleterious effect upon people with the disease.

(5) Smoking is associated with some "third factor" which either increases the probability that the individual will develop the disease or has a deleterious effect on people with the disease; but the association between smoking and the "third factor" is not due (or not entirely due) to a causal relationship between the two.

(6) The disease is a cause of smoking or increases the amount of smoking in individuals who have already taken up the habit.

The six hypotheses listed above are not mutually exclusive. Conceivably, they could occur in any combination. The assumed "third factor" could be a combination of several factors. Furthermore, a number of other more complex hypotheses are conceivable, but most of them amount to about the same thing as one or some combination of these six. For example, smoking may increase the probability of occurrence of some "third factor" which in turn is a cause of the disease. In terms of the end result, this is no different from hypothesis Number 1.

Our problem is to decide which of the six hypotheses provides the most reasonable explanation for the observed association between smoking habits and each of the diseases involved.

Let us start with cancer of sites having the heaviest and most direct exposure to tobacco smoke products (i.e., mouth, tongue, and lip). Particularly in cigar and pipe smokers, these tissues are exposed to condensed tobacco smoke products as well as to the smoke. The conditions of exposure are quite similar to conditions established in experiments in which tobacco smoke condensates have been painted on the skin of mice and rabbits. The similarity includes dosage, method of application, length of exposure time in terms of the normal life expectancy of the species, and the cell type (squamous) of the surface layer of the tissue. Furthermore, the cancer produced in the experimental animals is of the same histologic type (i.e., epidermoid carcinoma) as cancer of the lip, tongue, and mouth occurring in human beings. It is true that different species of animals as well as different inbred strains of the same species vary greatly in susceptibility to certain of the known carcinogenic compounds. However, when an agent has been shown to be carcinogenic for rabbits as well as for several different inbred strains of mice, there is reason to suppose that it is probably carcinogenic for other species, including man. Thus, the experimental evidence supports the hypothesis that the smoking of pipes, cigars, and cigarettes is a direct cause of cancer of the sites under consideration (i.e., it supports hypothesis Number 1).

So far as I know, there is no evidence whatsoever in support of any of the other five hypotheses outlined above. Of course, one can imagine that the use of tobacco in all forms is highly associated with some "third factor" which causes cancer of the mouth, tongue, or lip; but no one has yet suggested any "third factor" which seems to meet these specifications.

The esophagus is exposed to material condensed or dissolved from tobacco smoke and the pharynx and larynx may be somewhat exposed to condensed material as well as to tobacco smoke. It is uncertain whether cancer of these sites is as highly associated with cigar and pipe smoking as with cigarette smoking. However, the evidence strongly suggests that hypothesis Number 1 is the correct explanation for the association between smoking and cancer of the esophagus, the pharynx and the larynx.

Lung cancer shows an extremely high degree of association with amount of cigarette smoking but far less (if any) association with pipe and cigar smoking. Evidence that cigarette smokers almost always inhale while pipe and cigar smokers seldom inhale seems to be a reasonable explanation for this difference. What is commonly called lung cancer is almost exclusively cancer arising in the epithelium of the bronchial tubes (i.e., bronchogenic carcinoma). The surface layer of this tissue (i.e., ciliated columnar cells interspersed with goblet cells) is very different from the skin of a mouse or rabbit. Among smokers who inhale, the bronchial epithelium is exposed to tobacco smoke but is not heavily exposed to condensed material, which drips from a pipe stem or appears on the end of a cigar. For these reasons, the experimental production of cancer on the skin of animals smeared with tobacco smoke condensates does not in itself provide very strong evidence that cigarette smoking is a direct cause of lung cancer. However, it does provide some measure of support for that hypothesis.

Histologic evidence that tissue changes such as marked basal cell hyperplasia, squamous metaplasia, and "atypism" (or "carcinoma-*in-situ*") occur much more frequently in the bronchial epithelium of smokers than of non-smokers gives strong support to the direct causal hypothesis. Experimental evidence that exposure to cigarette smoke inhibits ciliary action in the bronchial tubes supports the direct causal hypothesis. It also supports the hypothesis that exposure to tobacco smoke creates a situation in which the bronchial tubes are more susceptible to the carcinogenic effects of any other carcinogenic agent inhaled into the lungs (i.e., air pollutants of various sorts and some types of industrial dusts and vapor). The fact that the lung cancer death rate of ex-cigarette smokers was found to be lower than that of men who continued to smoke is regarded by some as being very strong evidence that cigarette smoking is either a direct cause of lung cancer or increases susceptibility to lung cancer produced by some other agent. Other evidence, such as the sex difference, the urban-rural difference, and the time trends in lung cancer death rates and cigarette consumption is consistent with the causal hypothesis.

Considering time relationships, the hypothesis that lung cancer causes people to smoke is quite untenable. The hypothesis that some "third factor" is responsible for both lung cancer and smoking is hardly more tenable. For example, one might have postulated that the association between lung cancer and cigarette smoking resulted from an association between smoking and certain occupational hazards or general environmental factors such as air pollution associated with urbanization. This has been ruled out by studies in which occupation and place of residence were taken into consideration. It has been suggested that there may be some hereditary factor which results in both lung cancer and a strong desire to smoke cigarettes. This is an ingenious idea. However, if it is true, one must assume that a genetic factor of this sort appeared and became widely spread throughout the populations of many countries during the last fifty years. This seems a bit unlikely. Anyone with a good imagination can think of other such conceivable mutual causation hypotheses, but no one has yet presented any evidence in support of any of them.

With so much evidence all pointing in the same direction, and no evidence pointing in any other direction, I can only arrive at one conclusion. In my opinion, cigarette smoking is a major factor in the causation of lung cancer.

The association between smoking and cancer of the bladder is small as compared with the association between cigarette smoking and cancer of sites directly exposed to the smoke. What evidence exists on the subject suggests that there may be causal relationship. However, in my opinion there is not sufficient evidence to draw any definite conclusion at the present time.

While peptic ulcers seldom cause death, they do cause a great deal of suffering. Clinical trials indicate that smoking has a deleterious effect on people with peptic ulcers. The controls used in at least one study of the subject seem to rule out the possibility that the effect is due to some "third factor." This clinical evidence provides a reasonable explanation of why death rates from this disease are far higher among smokers than among non-smokers. It is conceivable that there is a three-way connection between smoking, nervous tension, and peptic ulcers. However, this is not incompatible with the evidence of a bad effect of smoking on patients with the disease. Whether smoking increases the probability that an individual will develop peptic ulcers is an open question.

Buerger's disease causes so few deaths that no evidence was obtained on the subject from the two prospective studies. However, numerous clinical studies have provided convincing evidence that: (*a*) the disease seldom if ever occurs in a non-smoker, and (*b*) that smoking has a very bad effect on patients with the disease. The evidence that smoking has an influence on this particular circulatory disease gives some measure of support to the hypothesis that smoking may have an effect related to some other circulatory diseases.

The degree of association between cigarette smoking and coronary artery disease (as measured by mortality ratios) is relatively small as compared with the degree of association between cigarette smoking and lung cancer. Unlike lung cancer, coronary artery disease is now the most common cause of death in the United States, even among non-smokers. The association between cigarette smoking and coronary artery disease death rates accounted for over half of the excess deaths associated with cigarette smoking in our study.

There is no evidence at present that smoking has an influence on the occurrence of atherosclerosis of the coronary arteries. While this condition is regarded as the major factor leading to coronary occlusion and coronary thrombosis, it is extremely common in American men of all ages (particularly those in the old age groups) and does not necessarily produce clinical symptoms. This being the case, it is evident that some other factor(s) have an influence on the occurrence of thrombosis in coronary arteries affected by atherosclerosis. Furthermore, coronary thrombosis does not necessarily cause death; many patients recover almost completely and live for many years after an attack.

The known acute effects of smoking on the heart rate, the blood pressure, the circulation, and the blood suggest that smoking may increase the probability of a blood clot (i.e., thrombus) forming in a coronary artery already affected by atherosclerosis. It seems equally likely, or perhaps more likely, that cigarette smoking has a deleterious effect upon patients with coronary artery disease. This is suggested by the acute effects of smoking as outlined above; by the known effects of smoking on the electrocardiograms and ballistocardiograms of some patients suffering from coronary artery disease; and by the apparent effects of smoking on the lungs. At any given moment, there are a large number of men in the population who have had an attack of coronary artery disease (including undiagnosed cases as well as those which have been diagnosed). There is a great deal of evidence that any added strain on the heart is likely to precipitate death in such individuals. For example, almost any severe lung condition seems to result in an increase in the reported death rate from coronary artery disease. This has been shown by the increase in reported coronary artery disease deaths during influenza epidemics [30] and at the time of the great London fog of 1952 [31]. In this regard, the association found between cigarette smoking and death rates from infectious diseases of the lungs may well be related etiologically to the association between cigarette smoking and coronary artery disease death rates.

It is conceivable that an association exists between cigarette smoking and some "third factor" which has a causal relationship to coronary artery disease. For example, one might postulate that either diet or an abnormally low heart rate or nervous tension is a "third factor" of this sort. Since smoking seems to affect the appetite perhaps it leads to an alteration in diet which in turn leads to coronary artery disease. Perhaps some people with chronically low heart rates smoke to obtain temporary relief from this condition and it is possible that this condition predisposes the individual to coronary artery disease. Conceivably, nervous tension leads to heavy cigarette smoking and also has a deleterious effect on people with coronary artery disease. There could be a complex mutually causative relationship between these several factors. For example, there is as much reason to suppose that cigarette smoking causes nervous tension as to believe that nervous tension causes cigarette smoking. Perhaps they are mutually causative as in an autocatalytic type of reaction.

While any one of these hypotheses may be correct, in my opinion the sum total of evidence points to the conclusion that cigarette smoking increases the probability of death from coronary artery disease. Even if this is not the case, such a large number of deaths are involved in the association between cigarette smoking and coronary artery disease that the subject deserves the most careful consideration and further study.

Summary

An association has been found between smoking habits and death rates from a number of different diseases, prominent among them being lung cancer, cancer of other tissues directly exposed to tobacco smoke, coronary artery disease, and peptic ulcers. The fact that a disease is associated with some factor in the environment does not necessarily mean that the factor causes the disease. Possible interpretations of the observed associations are discussed in the light of evidence from experimental, clinical, and pathological studies.

REFERENCES

1. "The Biological Effects of Tobacco," edited by ERNEST L. WYNDER. Little, Brown and Company (Boston) 1955.
2. E. C. HAMMOND. Lung Cancer and Common Inhalants, *Cancer 7*, 1100–1108 (November 1954).
3. A. J. STROM, and R. A. JENSEN. Mortality from Circulatory Diseases in Norway 1940–1945, *Lancet 1*, 126 (1951).
4. W. HAENSZEL, M. B. SHIMKIN, and H. P. MILLER. Tobacco Smoking Patterns in the United States, Public Health Monograph #45 (1956), United States Department of Health, Education and Welfare, Public Health Service.
5. S. DOLGOFF, R. SCHREK, G. P. BALLARD, and L. A. BAKER. Tobacco Smoking as an Etiologic Factor in Disease; II; Coronary Disease and Hypertension, *Angiology, 3*, 323–324 (August 1952).
6. J. P. ENGLISH, F. A. WILLIAMS, and J. BERKSON. Tobacco and Coronary Disease, *J. Amer. Med. Assn., 115*, 1327 (1940).
7. M. P. GERTLER and P. D. WHITE. Coronary Heart Disease in Young Adults, Harvard University Press, Cambridge (1954).
8. R. H. GOETZ. Smoking and Thromboangiitis Obliterans, *Clin. Proceedings, 1*, 190 (1942).
9. R. DOLL, F. A. JONES, and F. PYGOTT. Effect of Smoking on the Production and Maintenance of Gastric and Duodenal Ulcers, *Lancet, 1*, 657, March 29, 1958.
10. M. LEVIN. Etiology of Lung Cancer: Present Status, *New York State J. Med., 54*, 769 (1954).
11. R. DOLL and A. B. HILL. A Study of the Etiology of Carcinoma of the Lung, *Brit. Med. J., 2*, 1271–1286 (1952).
12. RAYMOND PEARL. Tobacco Smoking and Longevity, *Science, 87*, 216 (1938).
13. R. DOLL and A. B. HILL. Lung Cancer and Other Causes of Death in Relation to Smoking, *Brit. Med. J., 2*, 1071–1081 (November 10, 1956).
14. E. C. HAMMOND and D. HORN. Smoking and Death Rates—Report on 44 Months of Follow-up of 187,783 Men, *J. Amer. Med. Assn., 166*, 1159–1172 (March 8, 1958), *166*, 1294–1308 (March 15, 1958).
15. I. GRAY. Tobacco Smoking and Gastric Symptoms, *Ann. Intern. Med., 3*, 267 (1929).
16. R. C. BATTERMAN and I. EHRENFELD. The Influence of Smoking upon the Management of the Peptic Ulcer Patient, *Gastroenterology, 12*, 575 (1949).
17. R. W. TOON, F. S. CROSS, and O. H. WANGENSTEEN. Effect of Inhaled Cigarette Smoke on the Production of Peptic Ulcer in the Dog, *Proc. Exper. Biology Med., 77*, 866–969 (August 1951).
18. C. R. LOWE. An Association between Smoking and Respiratory Tuberculosis, *Brit. Med. J., 2*, 1081 (1956).
19. A. ROFFO. Sobre los Filtros en el Tabaquisino el Narquite y el Algodon como Filtro del Alquitran de Tabaco, *Bol. Inst. de Med. Exp. Para el Estud. y Trad. de Cancer, 16*, 255–268 (1939).
20. E. L. WYNDER and G. F. WRIGHT. A study of Tobacco Carcinogenesis. I. The Primary Fractions, *Cancer, 10*, 255 (March-April 1957).

21. "Pulmonary Carcinoma: Pathogenesis, Diagnosis, and Treatment," edited by EDGAR MAYER and H. C. MAIER, New York University Press, J. B. Lippincott, New York.
22. A. C. HILDING. On Cigarette Smoking, Bronchial Carcinoma and Ciliary Action. III. Accumulation of Cigarette Tar Upon Artificially Produced Deciliated Islands in the Respiratory Epithelium, *Ann. Otol. Rhin. & Laryng., 65,* 116–130 (1956).
23. O. AUERBACH, J. B. GERE, J. B. FORMAN, T. G. PETRICK, H. J. SMOLIN, G. E. MEUHSAM, D. Y. KASSOUNY, and A. P. STOUT. Changes in the Bronchial Epithelium in Relation to Smoking and Cancer of the Lung, A Report of Progress, *New England J. Med., 256,* 97 (January 17, 1957).
24. S. C. CHANG, Microscopic Properties of Whole Mounts and Sections of Human Bronchial Epithelium of Smokers and Non-Smokers, *Cancer, 10,* 1246 (November-December 1957).
25. W. C. HUEPER. Occupational Tumors and Allied Diseases, Charles C Thomas Company, Springfield, Illinois (1942).
26. M. E. EISEN, and E. C. HAMMOND. The Effect of Smoking on Packed Cell Volume, Red Blood Cell Counts, Haemoglobin and Platelet Counts, *Canadian Med. Assn. J., 75,* 520 (1956).
27. J. M. ESSENBERG. Cigarette Smoke and the Incidence of Primary Neoplasm of the Lung in the Albino Mouse, *Science, 116,* 561–564 (1952).
28. J. A. CAMPBELL. The Effects of Exhaust Gases from Internal Combustion Engines and of Tobacco Smoke upon Mice with Special Reference to Incidence of Tumors of the Lung. *Brit. J. Exper. Path., 17,* 146–158 (1936).
29. J. M. ESSENBERG, M. HOROWITZ, and E. GAFFNEY. The Incidence of Lung Tumors in Albino Mice Exposed to the Smoke from Cigarettes Low in Nicotine Content, *Western J. Surg. Obstr. Gynec., 63,* 265–267 (May 1955).
30. S. D. COLLINS and J. LEHMAN. "Excess Deaths from Influenza and Pneumonia and from Important Chronic Diseases during Epidemic Periods, 1918–51." Public Health Monograph 10 (1953), U.S. Dept. Health, Education & Welfare, Public Health Service.
31. Mortality and Morbidity during the London Fog of December 1952, Ministry of Health Report #95, H.M. Stationery Office (1954).

Polonium-210:
A Volatile Radioelement
in Cigarettes

EDWARD P. RADFORD
AND VILMA R. HUNT

Although it is well known that ionizing radiation is carcinogenic in man (*1*), there has been no evidence that radioisotopes in cigarettes are implicated in the production of lung cancer. Measurements of potassium-40 and radium isotopes have been made in tobacco (*2, 3*) but these elements are not volatile at the temperature of a burning cigarette—600°C. to 800°C. (*4*)—and therefore cannot deliver any significant radiation dose. Turner and Radley (*3*) measured total alpha-particle activity in raw tobacco and cigarette ashes, and concluded that the dose derived from radon and its daughter products would be less than 1 percent of that of the normal background to the bronchial epithelium. Our studies were undertaken to reevaluate the concentration of alpha-emitting radioelements in cigarettes. In our experiments we have found in tobacco significant amounts of Po^{210}, which we believe to be in equilibrium with its parent Pb^{210}. A substantial part of this polonium appears in cigarette smoke, and on the basis of certain assumptions we calculate that polonium may constitute a significant initiator of neoplasia in the bronchial epithelium of a person who smokes cigarettes.

The methods we have used for separating radium isotopes and Po^{210} have been described previously (*5*). Briefly, the sample is treated with hot concentrated HCl (wet-ashing), the polonium is plated on silver, and the radium isotopes are then coprecipitated with lead sulfate and barium sulfate. We have not found it necessary to modify our routine procedure in separating polonium or radium from cigarettes, although with digestion by hot concentrated HCl, solution of cigarettes or ash is incomplete and a considerable amount of undigested material remains. Nevertheless, we have recovered nearly 100 percent of polonium added to cigarettes during digestion, the same recovery as that for teeth and bones (5). Polonium samples were counted in gasflow proportional counters with background counts of alpha particles in the range of 0.5 to 1.5 count/hr. We have confirmed that the radioactivity plated on silver with the initial separation is Po^{210} by observing its decay, which has closely conformed to the Po^{210} half-life of 138 days.

This report deals only with the polonium content of cigarettes and cigarette smoke. The cigarettes we used were four of the regular-sized American brands purchased in local stores. The smoke from cigarettes puffed artificially was obtained by drawing air through cigarettes connected to a filter holder. This holder contained a fiberglass prefilter (6) backed by a Millipore HA filter that retains 100 percent of the particles in the size range of tobacco-smoke particles (7). The fiberglass prefilter actually collected nearly all of the smoke and was used to prevent rapid clogging of the HA filter. From the filter holder, gas from the smoking cigarette was led through a trap containing 50 ml of 0.5 normal HCl, then to a rotameter connected to a vacuum line. When the cigarette was smoked artificially it was in a nearly vertical position. The vacuum line was clamped off between puffs, and during each puff the flow rate was maintained at 15 ml/sec for 2 to 3 seconds. The puffs were carried out every 50 seconds for 6 minutes (or eight puffs); this puffing pattern was the average of that, observed without their knowledge, for a number of smokers in our laboratory, and is similar to that reported by Hilding (8). It resulted in consumption of about 60 to 70 percent

TABLE 1. Polonium content of American cigarettes and smoke from cigarettes artificially puffed. Figures in parentheses are number of analyses.

	Po^{210} content (pc)				Recovery* (%)	Po^{210} in main-stream smoke (pc)	Ratio of main-stream to total smoke (%)
Whole cigarette	Ash	Butt	Total smoke	Total in ash, butt, and smoke			
			Brand A, nonfilter				
0.43(4)	0.031(2)	0.13(2)	0.19(2)	0.35	81	0.10(3)	52
			Brand B, nonfilter				
0.48(5)	0.053(2)	0.12(2)	0.26(2)	0.43	90	0.12(2)	46
			Brand C, filter				
0.39(4)	0.035(2)	0.094(2)	0.19(2)	0.32	82	0.088(2)	47
			Brand D, filter				
0.40(4)	0.033(2)	0.15(2)	0.17(2)	0.35	88	0.070(3)	41

* Ratio of total in ash, butt, and smoke to total in whole cigarette.

of the cigarette, or somewhat less than that observed in cigarettes smoked by human subjects. Side stream smoke (smoke not drawn through the cigarette) was captured by placing a liter bottle over the burning cigarette. Air and smoke in the bottle were continuously drawn through the same filter system as the mainstream smoke, but the tube from the bottle was clamped only during puffing, when the tube from the cigarette was open. In this way both side stream and mainstream smoke were trapped together on the filters.

In these artificial smoking experiments, the following portions of the cigarette and smoke were analyzed for polonium: the ash and butt of the cigarette; smoke condensate on the fiberglass and HA filters; condensate that formed on the tubing and metal parts of the filter holder and on the walls of the liter bottle, all of which were carefully wiped after the cigarette was smoked; and the HCl trap through which the filtered air had been drawn. Blank analyses on filters, trap solution, and wipings of the tubing, filter holder, and bottle showed no polonium activity with the exception of the fiberglass filters, which had approximately 0.015 pc of Po^{210}. The HA filter and HCl trap showed little or no polonium after smoking, and in the results the content observed on the fiberglass (usually about 90 percent of the total) was combined with that from the condensate and HA filter.

Table 1 shows the polonium content of whole cigarettes of four brands. Also given are the contents of the ash, butt, and total smoke when all of the smoke, including the side stream, was trapped. Included in Table 1 are the results for mainstream smoke alone collected in different experiments. Table 1 indicates that only about half the polonium in the total smoke was in the mainstream when cigarettes were puffed by our technique. When all the smoke was captured, about 80 percent of the polonium disappearing in the smoking process could be accounted for. These results suggest that most of the volatile polonium is rapidly adsorbed on the smoke particles, although a small part could be gaseous and escape our trapping procedure, including the HCl trap. Because of the nature of the smoking pattern that was used, we believe that the mainstream smoke is probably low in these experiments, compared to actual smoking conditions. For example, the higher concentrations in the butt of brand D, Table 1, indicate that these cigarettes were not as completely smoked as the others. For this reason no significance can be attached to differences in mainstream content between filter and nonfilter brands. When cigarettes were smoked by human subjects the polonium content of the butt and ash was lower than that of the artificially smoked cigarettes, and the proportion of polonium lost from the cigarette was higher for filter cigarettes. We suspect that the amount of polonium absorbed by an individual may be dependent on the mode of puffing as well as on the fraction of total smoke inhaled.

The alpha-emitting isotopes we have investigated all occur naturally, and presumably have always been present in tobacco. Absorption of Pb^{210}, the parent of Po^{210}, by the plant roots may be supplemented by foliar absorption from "natural fallout" from decay of Rn^{222} in the atmosphere (*9*). From analysis of 5-year-old cigarettes, we conclude that the amount of polonium in fresh whole cigarettes (Table 1) is in equilibrium with the Pb^{210} parent. With respect to radium and polonium content, tobacco appears to be typical of plants generally, as judged by the total alpha-particle activity found in plants by Mayneord *et al.* (*10*). The radiation hazard from Po^{210} arises primarily because polonium is known to be completely volatile above 500°C. (*11*), or well below the temperature of a burning cigarette. In addition, polonium binds rapidly and strongly to surfaces, and hence attaches readily to smoke particles. Finally, its intermediate half-life of 138 days assures ample time for translocation of particles to the bronchi to take place.

The basic question which arises from our measurements concerns the radiation dose to the bronchial epithelium from Po^{210} present in tobacco smoke. To put the following calculations in perspective we estimate that the background dose to the bronchial epithelium is approximately 200 mrem per year, or about 5 rem per 25 years—similar to estimates by Chamberlain and Dyson (*12*) and Shapiro (*13*). In this estimate we have used a relative biological effectiveness (RBE) of 10 for alpha particles, in accord with recommendations of the International Commission for Radiation Protection (*14*).

The radiation dose delivered by polonium inhaled from cigarettes can be analyzed for two conditions. The first condition defines approximately the minimum radiation dose to be expected; in this case the dose arises from particles carried across the bronchial epithelium in the process of excretion by mucus flow up the bronchial tree. The smoke particles are assumed to be deposited by diffusion, largely on the alveolar epithelium, from where they are phagocytosed and carried up the bronchial epithelium (*15*). In this case we estimate that the minimum dose delivered by these particles for an individual smoking two packages of cigarettes a day for 25 years would be about 36 rem (*16*) or seven times the background exposure. This estimate does not take account of the radiation dose arising from Pb^{210} absorption in smoke, either from the beta particles emitted by Pb^{210} and Bi^{210}, or from the polonium daughter which would arise in the lungs from lead absorption. In addition, this calculation neglects the slowing effect of smoke on ciliary action (*17*), which would prolong the exposure time and increase the dose. For these reasons we believe that this estimate is probably conservative, and the dose could be 100 rem or more from this process.

The second condition defines the dose which might arise if local concentration of polonium occurs in various regions of the bronchial tree. The radiation dose delivered by local concentrations of polonium from particles in the bronchial epithelium wall itself, depends on the fraction of particles accumulated in these regions, and on the mean residence time occurring in such cases. There is no quantitative basis on which to estimate these two factors in human lungs, but it is likely from our preliminary measurements of polonium in the bronchial epithelium of lungs of smokers, that these local doses may range from several hundred rem to more than 1000 rem, in the case of an individual smoking two packs a day over a 25-year period. For example, in a 73-year old male who died of cardiac failure, who had smoked "one or more" packs of cigarettes per day for many years, the polonium content in the epithelium of a secondary bifurcation of the right lower lobe was 0.033 pc/cm², compared with 0.003 pc/cm² in the right main stem bronchus. This man had not smoked after hospital admission for smoke inhalation 10 days prior to death, and he had evidence of bronchial pneumonia at autopsy, so it is probable that equilibrium concentration of polonium in the epithelium at the time he was smoking was substantially higher. Even so, a level of 0.033 pc/cm² would give a dose of 165 rem in 25 years. This figure is a minimum value even for this region of epithelium, and higher values could also be present in heavier smokers. Further research and testing will be required to determine these local doses, particularly through the use of quantitative radiographs.

With regard to the amount of polonium absorbed into the circulation from tobacco smoke, compared to polonium absorbed from other sources, it is of interest that the urine of nonsmokers contains very little polonium (a mean of 0.011 pc per 24 hours for four subjects). On the other hand, three smokers who smoked an average of two packages of cigarettes a day were found to have an average polonium excretion of 0.065 pc per 24 hours, a nearly sixfold difference. These results suggest that the polonium content of the soft tissues of the body may be significantly elevated in smokers.

A comparison of death rates of lung cancer in smokers may be made to the well-known bronchial cancer incidence in miners exposed to radon daughters (*18*). We calculate the lung-cancer death rate in these miners to be 3 percent per year; their radiation exposure to the bronchial epithelium would be about 20,000 rem in the 17-year induction period (*19*). The radiation dose necessary to account for the lung-cancer death rate in males smoking 40 cigarettes a day or more—about 0.205 percent per year (*20*)—would, on this basis, be about 1300 rem over a 25-year period. A dose of this magnitude from polonium is probable only in localized areas of the bronchial tree, but the causes of lung cancer may not be identical in the two cases (particularly in the Schneeberg miners whose deaths occurred before cigarette smoking was widespread) because of the presence of strong cocarcinogens in cigarette smoke (*21*). Because of the well-known synergistic action of ionizing radiation and cigarette-smoke extracts, or other chemical agents, in experimental cancer production (*22*), the presence of these chemical promoters might lead to cancer from radiation doses at least an order of magnitude less than the figure of 1300 rem. A dose of 100 to 200 rem to the bronchial epithelium may be highly significant, therefore, and even doses at the lower estimate of 36 rem may not be negligible if the dose-response curve for cancer induction is linear for alpha-emitting substances.

This general comparison is independent of the relative biological effectiveness chosen for alpha particles.

We support the view that other chemical factors, particularly cocarcinogens, as well as physiological effects, such as alterations of ciliary activity by cigarette smoke, probably play an important part in the genesis of bronchial cancer in smokers. Our present conclusion is that Po^{210} inhaled in cigarette smoke may act as an important initiator in the production of bronchogenic carcinoma.

REFERENCES

1. J. FURTH and E. LORENZ, in *Radiation Biology,* A. HOLLAENDER, Ed. (McGraw-Hill, New York, 1954), vol. 1, p. 1145.
2. F. W. SPIERS and R. D. PASSEY, *Lancet* **1953-II,** 1259 (1953).
3. R. C. TURNER and J. M. RADLEY, *ibid.* **1960-I,** 1197 (1960).
4. E. S. HARLOW, *Science* **123,** 226 (1956).
5. E. P. RADFORD, JR., V. R. HUNT, D. SHERRY, *Radiation Res.* **19,** 298 (1963).
6. AP Prefilter, Millipore Filter Corp., Bedford, Mass.
7. W. J. MEGAW and R. D. WIFFEN, *Air Water Pollution* **7,** 501 (1963).
8. A. C. HILDING, *New Engl. J. Med.* **254,** 775 (1956).
9. C. R. HILL, *Nature* **187,** 211 (1960).
10. W. V. MAYNEORD, R. C. TURNER, J. M. RADLEY, *ibid.,* p. 208.
11. K. W. BAGNALL, *Advan. Inorg. Chem. Radiochem.* **4,** 197 (1962).
12. A. C. CHAMBERLAIN and E. D. DYSON, *Brit. J. Radiol.* **29,** 317 (1956).
13. J. SHAPIRO, *Arch. Environ. Health* **14,** 169 (1956).
14. Report of ICRP Committee II on Permissible Dose for Internal Radiation (1959), *Health Phys.* **3,** 1 (1960).
15. C. W. LABELLE and H. BRIEGER, *Arch. Environ. Health* **1,** 423 (1960).
16. Dose calculated on the basis of retention of 3.3×10^4 pc of Po^{210} in 25 years, a volume of the bronchial epithelium of 3 ml, and a mean transit time of the mucus sheet of 36 hours. This figure is from analysis of human bronchial mucus flow by Dr. Bernard Altshuler of New York University. We are indebted to Dr. Altshuler for making his calculations available to us.
17. H. L. FALK, H. M. TREMER, P. KOTIN, *J. Natl. Cancer Inst.* **23,** 999 (1959).
18. H. SIKL, *Acta, Unio Intern. Contra Cancrum* **6,** 1366 (1950); S. PELLER, *Human Biol.* **11,** 130 (1939).
19. A. PIRCHAN and H. SIKL, *Am. J. Cancer* **16,** 681 (1932).
20. E. C. HAMMOND, "Smoking in relation to mortality and morbidity," paper read at the meeting of the American Medical Association, Portland, Ore., 4 December 1963.
21. E. L. WYNDER, *Acta Med. Scand. Suppl.* **369,** 63 (1960); F. J. C. ROE, M. H. SALAMAN, J. COHEN, *Brit. J. Cancer* **13,** 623 (1959).
22. J. C. MOTTRAM, *Am. J. Cancer* **32,** 76 (1938); P. SHUBIK, A. R. GOLDFARB, A. C. RITCHIE, H. LISCO, *Nature* **171,** 934 (1953); F. G. BOCK and G. E. MOORE, *J. Natl. Cancer Inst.* **22,** 401 (1959).

23. Analytical work was done by Clement Nelson and Virginia Gilmore. Human lung tissue was obtained by John B. Little through the courtesy of J. Hallgrimsson of the Massachusetts General Hospital. We are indebted to Jacob Shapiro and Robley D. Evans for valuable discussions. Supported by contract AT(30-1)-3170 with the U.S. Atomic Energy Commission; the Higgins Fund, Harvard University; grant OH-00103-02 from the Division of Occupational Health, U.S. Public Health Service; and an institutional grant from the Rockefeller Foundation. Initial work performed while one of us (V.R.H.) was a scholar of the Radcliffe Institute for Independent Study.

MAN IN SPACE

As man travels into space, he encounters environments that are both alien and familiar. The observations made on the first United States manned space flight represent a suitable introduction to the space environment.

It is startling to learn in the paper by Siegel and his associates that a fair number of earth's plants and animals could survive on Mars.

SUPPLEMENTARY READINGS

CLAUS, GEORGE, and BARTHOLOMEW NAGY, A Microbiological Examination of Some Carbonaceous Chondrites. 1961, *Nature,* 594–596.

FITCH, FRANK W., and EDWARD ANDERS, Organized Element: Possible Identification in Orgueil Meteorite. 1963, *Science,* **140:** 1097–1099.

LOVELL, BERNARD, The Challenge of Space Research. 1962, *Nature,* **195:** 935–939.

REA, D. G., Evidence for Life on Mars. 1963, *Nature,* **200:** 114–116.

SALISBURY, JOHN W., Natural Resources of the Moon. 1962, *Nature,* **195:** 423–427.

STRUGHOLD, HUBERTUS, An Introduction to Astrobiology. 1960, *Astronautics,* Dec. Issue: 85–90.

The Mercury-Atlas-6
Space Flight[*]

JOHN H. GLENN, JR.
AND JOHN A. O'KEEFE

Glenn's observations

Luminous particles. Coming out of the night on the first orbit, at the first glint of sunlight on the capsule, I was looking inside the capsule to check some instruments for probably 15 or 20 seconds. When I glanced back out the window, my initial reaction was that the capsule (spacecraft) had tumbled and that I was looking off into a star field and was not able to see the horizon. I could see nothing but luminous specks about the size of the stars outside. I realized, however they were not stars. I was still in the attitude that I had before. The specks were luminous particles that were all around the capsule. There was a large field of spots that were about the color of a very bright firefly, a light yellowish-green color. They appeared to vary in size from maybe just pinhead size up to possibly ⅜ of an inch. I would say that most of the particles were similar to first-magnitude stars; they were pretty bright, very luminous. However, they varied in size, so there would be varying magnitudes represented. They were floating in space at approximately my speed. I appeared to be moving through them very slowly, at a speed of maybe 3 to 5 miles an hour. They did not center on the capsule, as though the capsule was their origin. I thought first of the lost Air Force needles that are some place in space, but they were not anything that looked like that at all.

---

* This article is republished, with the addition of orbital parameters, a map and an addendum, from appendixes C and D of *Results of the First United States Manned Orbital Space Flight, February 20, 1962,* published for the Manned Spacecraft Center, National Aeronautics and Space Administration, by the U.S. Government Printing Office, Washington, D.C. Glenn's observations are taken verbatim from the transcript of his debriefing session on Grand Turk Island, 21 February. A section on ultraviolet photography has been omitted from O'Keefe's comments. Some minor editorial changes have been made.

The other possibility that came to my mind immediately was that snow or little frozen water particles were being created from the peroxide decomposition. I don't believe that's what it was, however, because the particles through which I was moving were evenly distributed and not more dense closer to the capsule.

As I looked out to the side of the capsule, the density of the field to the side of the capsule appeared to be about the same as directly behind the capsule. The distance between these particles would average, I would estimate, some 8 to 10 feet apart. Occasionally, one or two of them would come swirling up around the capsule and across the window, drifting very, very slowly, and then would gradually move off back in the direction I was looking. This was surprising, too, because it showed we probably did have a very small flow field set up around the capsule or they would not have changed their direction of motion as they did. I do not recall observing any vertical or lateral motion other than that of the particles that swirled around close to the spacecraft. It appeared to me that I was moving straight through a cloud of them at a very slow speed. I observed these luminous objects for approximately 4 minutes before the sun came up to a position where it was sufficiently above the horizon that all the background area then was lighted and I no longer could see them.

After passing out of them, I described them as best I could on the tape recorder and reported them to the Cape. I had two more chances to observe them, at each sunrise; it was exactly the same each time. At the first rays of the sun above the horizon, the particles would appear. To get better observation of these particles and to make sure they were not emanating from the capsule, I turned the capsule around during the second sunrise. When I turned around toward the sunrise, I could see only 10 percent as many particles as I could see when facing back toward the west. Still, I could see a few of them coming toward me. This proved rather conclusively, to me at least, that I was moving through a field of something and that these things were not emanating, at least not at that moment, from the capsule. To check whether this might be snowflakes from the condensation from the thrusters, I intentionally blipped the thrusters to see if I was making a pattern of these particles. I could observe steam coming out of the pitchdown thruster in good shape, and this didn't result in any observation of anything that looked like the particles. I had three good looks at them, and they appeared identical each time. I think the density of the particles was identical on all three passes.

I would estimate that there were thousands of them. It was similar to looking out across a field on a very dark night and seeing thousands of fireflies. Unlike fireflies, however, they had a steady glow. Once in a while, one or two of them would come drifting up around the corner of the capsule and change course right in front of me. I think this was from flow of some kind, or perhaps the particles were ionized and were being attracted or repelled. It was not due to collisions, because I saw some of them change course right in front of me without colliding with any other particles or the spacecraft. If any particles got in near enough to the capsule and got into the shade, they seemed to lose their luminous quality. And when occasionally I would see one up very close, it looked white, like a little cottony piece of something, or like a snowflake. That's about the only description of them I have. There was no doubt about their being there, because I observed them three different times for an extended period of time. I tried to get pictures of them, but it looks like there wasn't sufficient light emanating from them to register on the color film.

The high layer

I had no trouble seeing the horizon on the nightside. Above the horizon, some 6 to 8 degrees, there was a layer that I would estimate to be roughly $1\frac{1}{2}$ to 2 degrees wide. I first noticed it as I was watching the stars going down. I noticed that as they came down close to the horizon they became relatively dim for a few seconds, then brightened up again, and then went out of sight below the horizon. As I looked more carefully, I could see a band, parallel to the horizon, that was a different color than the clouds below. It was not the same white color as moonlight on clouds at night. It was a tannish color or buff white, in comparison to the clouds, and not very bright. This band went clear across the horizon. I observed this layer on all three passes through the nightside. The intensity was reasonably constant through the night. It was more visible when the moon was up, but during that short period when the moon was not up, I could still see this layer very dimly. I wouldn't say for sure that you could actually observe the specific layer during that time, but you could see the dimming of the stars. But, when the moon was up, you very definitely could see the layer, though it did not have sharp edges. It looked like a dim haze layer, such as I have seen occasionally while flying. As stars would move into this layer, they would gradually dim; dim to a maximum near the center, and gradually brighten up as they came out of it. So, there was a gradient as they moved through it; it was not a sharp discontinuity.

Nightside observations of the earth. Over Australia, they had the lights of Perth on, and I could see them well. It was like flying at high altitude at night over a small town. The Perth area was spread out and was very visible, and then there was a smaller area south of Perth that had a smaller group of lights but they were much brighter in intensity—very luminous. Inland, there was a series of about four or five towns that you could see in a row, lined up pretty much east and west, that were very visible. It was very clear; there was no cloud cover in that area at that time.

Knowing where Perth was, I traced a very slight demarcation between the land and the sea, but that's the only time I observed a coastline on the nightside. Over the area around Woomera, there was nothing but clouds. I saw nothing but clouds at night from there clear up across the Pacific until we got up east of Hawaii. There was solid cloud cover all the way.

In the bright moonlight you could see vertical development at night. Most of the areas looked like big sheets of stratus clouds, but you could tell where there were areas of vertical development by the shadows, or lighter and darker areas on the clouds.

Out in that area at night, fronts could not be defined. You could see frontal patterns on the dayside. In the North Atlantic you could see streams of clouds, pick out frontal areas pretty much like those in the pictures from earlier Mercury flights.

With the moonlight, you are able to pick up a good drift indication, using the clouds. However, I don't think it's as accurate as the drift indications during the day. The drift indication is sufficient that you can at least tell what direction you're going at night, within about 10 or 15 degrees. In the daylight, over the same type clouds, you probably could pick up your drift down to maybe a couple of degrees.

The horizon was dark before the moon would come up, which wasn't very long. However, you can see the horizon silhouetted against the stars. It can be seen very clearly. After the moon comes up, there is enough light shining on the clouds that the earth is whiter than the dark background of space. Well, before the moon comes up, looking down is just like looking into the Black Hole at Calcutta.

There were a couple of large storms in the Indian Ocean. The Weather Bureau scientists were interested in whether lightning could be seen or not. This is no problem; you can see lightning zipping around in these storms all over the place. There was a great big storm north of track over the Indian Ocean; there was a smaller one just south of track, and you could see lightning flashing in both of them, especially in the one in the north—it was very active. It was flashing around, and you could see a cell going and another cell going and then horizontal lightning back and forth.

On that area, I got out the airglow filter and tried it. I could not see anything through it. This, however, may have been because I was not well enough dark adapted. This is a problem. If we're going to make observations like this, we're going to have to figure out some way to get better night-adapted in advance of the time when we want to make observations. There just was not sufficient time. By the time I got well night-adapted, we were coming back to daylight again.

Dayside observations. Clouds can be seen very clearly on the daylight side. You can see the different types—vertical developments, stratus clouds, little puffy cumulus clouds, and altocumulus clouds. There is no problem identifying cloud types. You're quite a distance away from them, so you're probably not doing it as accurately as you could looking up from the ground, but you can certainly identify the different types and see the weather patterns.

The cloud area covered most of the area up across Mexico, with high cirrus almost to New Orleans. I could see New Orleans; Charleston and Savannah were also visible.

You can see cities the size of Savannah and Charleston very clearly. I think the best view I had of any area during the flight was the clear desert region around El Paso on the second pass. There were clouds north of Charleston and Savannah, so I could not see the Norfolk area and on farther north. I did not see the Dallas area that we had planned to observe because it was covered by clouds, but at El Paso I could see the colors of the desert and the irrigated areas north of El Paso. You can see the pattern of the irrigated areas much better than I had thought we would be able to. I don't think that I could see the smallest irrigated areas; it was probably the ones that are blocked in by the larger irrigated areas, both around El Paso and at El Centro, which I observed after retrofire.

The western part of Africa was clear. That is a desert region where I mainly saw dust storms. By the time we got to the region where I might have been able to see cities in Africa, the land was covered by clouds. I was surprised at what a large percentage of the track was covered by clouds on this particular day. There was very little land area which could be observed on the daylight side. The eastern part of the United States and an occasional glimpse of land up across Mexico and over the desert area in Western Africa was all that could be seen.

I saw what I assume was the Gulf Stream. The water can be seen to have different colors. Another thing that I observed was the wake of a ship as I came over recovery area G at the beginning of the third orbit. I had pitched down to below retroattitude. I was not really thinking about looking for a ship. I was looking down at the water, and I saw a little V. I quickly broke out the chart and checked my position. I was right at area G, the time checked out perfectly for that area. So I think I probably saw the wake from a recovery ship; when I looked back out and tried to locate it again, the little V had gone under a cloud and I didn't see it again. The little V was heading west at that time. It would be interesting to see if the carrier in area G was fired up and heading west at the time.

I would have liked to put the glasses on and see what I could pick out on the ground. Without the glasses, I think you identify the smaller objects by their surroundings. For instance, you see the outline of a valley where there are farms, and the pattern of the valley and its rivers and perhaps a town. You can see something that crosses a river, and you just assume that it's a bridge. As far as being able to look down and see it and say "that is a bridge," I think you are only assuming that it's a bridge more than really observing it. Ground colors show up just like they do from a high-altitude airplane; there's no difference. A lot of the things you can identify just as from a high-flying airplane. You see by color variations the deep green woods and the lighter green fields and the cloud areas.

I could see Cape Canaveral clearly, and I took a picture which shows the whole Florida Peninsula; you see across the interior of the Gulf.

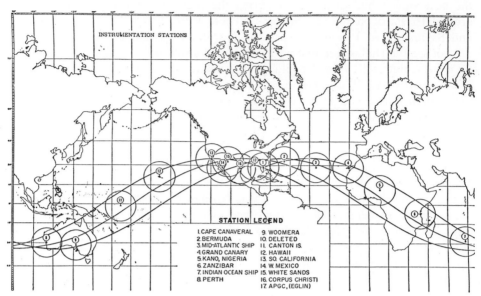

Map of orbital paths and ground stations.

TABLE 1. Parameters for the first United States manned space flight, 20 February, 1962.

Orbit parameters

Perigee altitude (statute miles)	100.03
Perigee altitude (nautical miles)	86.92
Apogee altitude (statute miles)	162.17
Apogee altitude (nautical miles)	140.92
Period (minutes, seconds)	88:29
Inclination angle (degrees)	32.54

Maximum conditions

Altitude (statute miles)	162.17
Altitude (nautical miles)	140.92
Space-fixed velocity (feet per second)	25,732.0
Earth-fixed velocity (feet per second)	24,415.0

Landing point

Latitude	21°26'N
Longitude	68°41'W

Sunset and sunrise horizon observations. At sunset, the flattening of the sun was not as pronounced as I thought it might be. The sun was perfectly round as it approached the horizon. It retained its symmetry all the way down, until just the last sliver of sun was visible. The horizon on each side of the sun is extremely bright, and when the sun got down to where it was just the same level as the bright horizon, it apparently spread out, perhaps as much as 10 degrees each side of the area you were looking at. Perhaps it was just that there was already a bright area there and the roundness that had been sticking up above it came down to where, finally, the last little sliver just matched the bright horizon area and probably added some to it.

I did not see the sunrise directly, only through the periscope. You cannot see that much through the scope. The sun comes up so small in the scope that all you see is the first shaft of light. The band of light at the horizon looks the same at sunrise as at sunset.

The white line of the horizon is extremely bright as the sun sets, of course. The color is very much like the arc lights they use around the pad.

As the sun goes down a little bit more, the bottom layer becomes a bright orange and it fades into red, then on into the darker colors, and finally off into blues and black as you get further up toward space. One thing that was very surprising to me, though, was how far out on the horizon each side of that area the light extends. The lighted area must go out some 60 degrees. I think this is confirmed by the pictures I took.

I think you can probably see a little more of this sunset band with the eye than with a camera. I was surprised when I looked at the pictures to see how narrow-looking it is. I think you probably can pick up a little broader band of light with the eye than you do with the camera. Maybe we need more sensitive color film.

JOHN H. GLENN, JR.

O'Keefe's comments

This paper discusses the preliminary attempts to explain the observations made by astronaut Glenn during the MA-6 flight. Analysis of Glenn's observations is continuing and is not yet complete. This paper is intended only to indicate the direction which the analysis is taking, not to provide the final explanations. The theories presented are mine, not the astronaut's. In some cases, final verification of these theories must await further Mercury flights.

Three principal points are to be considered in the field of space science as a result of the MA-6 flight. They are (i) the luminous particles (the Glenn effect), which are probably the result of the flaking off of paint, or possibly the condensation of moisture from the spacecraft heat exchanger; (ii) a luminous band seen around the sky and possibly due to airglow or aurora but probably due to reflections of the horizon between the windows of the spacecraft; and

(iii) the flattened appearance of the sun at sunset (this is not attested by the visual observations but appears fairly clear in the photographs).

Luminous particles.   Glenn observed a field of small, luminous objects surrounding his spacecraft at sunrise on all three orbits. He compares them to fireflies, especially in color, remarking that they were very luminous and variable in size.

Some of these particles came close to the spacecraft so that they got into the shade, as evidenced by a marked loss in brightness and a change in color from yellow-green to white. The change in color is comprehensible as being due to passage from illumination by direct sunlight to illumination by bluish light scattered from the twilight all along the horizon. Passage into the shadow is a clear indication that the particles involved were genuinely close at hand. It indicates that the particles were within the range of stereoscopic vision, so that Glenn's distance estimates are meaningful. It follows that his estimates of relative velocity are also meaningful: these estimates were 3 to 5 miles per hour—that is, 1.3 to 2.2 meters per second relative to the spacecraft. Glenn stated that the overall impression was that the spacecraft was moving through a field of these particles at a speed of 3 to 5 miles per hour.

This observation indicates that the luminous objects were undoubtedly associated with the spacecraft in their motion. The spacecraft velocity was approximately 8000 meters per second; the velocity of the particles was identical with that of the spacecraft in all three coordinates within about 1 part in 4000. Rough estimates show that this implies that the orbital inclination was the same for the particles as for the spacecraft within ± 0.01 degree. The eccentricity was the same within ± 0.0002. In particular, the spacecraft was at that time descending toward perigee at the rate of approximately 50 meters per second. The particles were descending at the same rate within ± 2 meters per second. Thus, from considerations of velocity alone, there is a very convincing demonstration that the particles were associated with the spacecraft.

In addition, it should be noted that the height at that time was 160 kilometers. It was thus at least twice the height of the noctilucent clouds (which apparently consist of ice particles and must therefore be considered). At this level, the atmosphere has a density of the order of 10^{-10} gram per cubic centimeter; it is completely unable to retard the fall of any visible object. Hence, there is no reason to expect any layer of particles to be sustained at this level. Anything at this height must be in orbit.

Size of the field.   An important consideration is the fact that the field of particles could not have been of very great extent. If, for example, we suppose that there were two or three of these "very luminous" particles within 3 meters of the window (the spacing being estimated by Glenn at 6 to 10 feet, or 2 to 3 meters), then in the next 3 meters there should have been 12 particles, averaging one-fourth as bright, so that the contribution to the total illumination from the second 3-meter group would have been the same as that from the first 3-meter group, and so on. Had the field extended to a distance of "several miles"—that is, say 10 kilometers—the total light would have been some 3000 times that of the individual nearby particles, and Glenn would have spoken of an intensely luminous fog. Since he saw the particles for times of about 4 minutes, during which he traveled about 1920 kilometers, the field, if a part of the environment, would have been of this length, and the particles would have covered the sky solidly in this direction, so that it would have looked like a cloud or a snowfield. This sort of calculation is well known in astronomy, under the name of Olber's paradox. It establishes with certainty that the particles did not extend far in any direction from the spacecraft. The fact that Glenn did not see a local concentration around the spacecraft means that there was no large increase in density within the range of stereoscopic vision, but it does not conflict with the idea that the field extended, at most, a few hundred meters in any direction.

Size and brightness. With respect to the brightness of the particles, conversations with Glenn have established that the most significant brightness estimate is the comparison with fireflies. T. J. Spilman, of the Smithsonian Institution, states that the available measures of light of *Photinus pyralis,* the common firefly of the eastern United States, indicate from 1/50 to 1/400 candle when the light is turned on. At a distance of 1 meter, a candle has a brightness of about -14; the firefly at 2 meters would be 200 to 1600 times fainter, or would have a brightness between about -8.3 and -6. At distances of the order of 20 meters, it would have a brightness between -3.3 and -1, comparable to that of planets or the brightest stars.

The full moon (brightness -12.6) is plainly visible on several of the photographs taken in orbits. The particles may possibly also be visible; but if so, they are not more than 1/10 the brightness of the full moon, and hence are not brighter than about -10. Of course occasionally a large particle may have come close, but the run of the mine must have been of brightness -10 or fainter.

A white object 1 centimeter in diameter, at a distance of 2 meters in direct sunlight would be of about -13.9 magnitude; if of pinhead size (2 mm in diameter) it would be -10.4. If we allow a reduction to 1 millimeter on account of the known fact that bright objects seem larger than they are, we find a brightness of -9, which is of the same order as that of the firefly at the same distance.

Probable cause of motion. The next question is, what is the agency which is causing the particles to move with respect to the spacecraft? The possibilities are electrical, magnetic, and gravitational fields; light pressure; and aerodynamic drag. Of these, the electrical forces can be discarded for mass motion over a large area, since we are in the lower F-region of the ionosphere and space is essentially a conductor. The magnetic fields can be divided into terrestrial and spacecraft fields. The spacecraft field is certainly too small, at reasonable distances, to account for the acceleration, and the terrestrial field cannot accelerate a dipole, because the field gradient is too small. Gravitational fields will act in almost precisely the same way on the spacecraft as on the particles. The acceleration will be in one direction for particles below the spacecraft and in the other direction for those above it; thus the gravitational fields will make the particles seem to go around the spacecraft with a steady motion rather than to move past it.

Light pressure and drag have similar effects at sunrise, but at heights of the order of 160 kilometers, drag is about 1 dyne per square centimeter, while radiation pressure is less by many orders of magnitude. Hence, the most probable source of the acceleration is aerodynamic drag.

Nature of the particles.   Important information about the nature of the particles is furnished by their behavior under the influence of drag forces. At sunrise, the spacecraft was a little above its minimum altitude of 160 kilometers. At this height, the density of the air is roughly 1.3×10^{-12} gram per cubic centimeter; the spacecraft velocity is about 8×10^5 centimeters per second; the drag pressure is thus about 1 dyne per square centimeter. Since Glenn states that he appeared to be moving slowly through a relatively stationary group of particles, it is evident that the particles could not have been greatly accelerated while they were in the near vicinity of the spacecraft. In comparison, a snowflake with a diameter of 1 millimeter and the usual density of 0.1 will be subjected to a force of about 0.01 gram per square centimeter of frontal area. It will thus be accelerated at the rate of 100 centimeters per second per second, and its velocity will exceed the velocities estimated for the particles after only 2 seconds, when it has gone 2 meters. We cannot escape from the problem by supposing the snowflakes to be much larger—say, 1 centimeter in diameter—because, though occasional particles may have been as large as this, the majority must have been smaller, since they did not give strong photographic images. Glenn tells us that their average separation was only about 6 to 10 feet, so that at any given moment one of the particles would be expected to be within a few meters of the spacecraft window, and hence brighter than the full moon.

A few particles, which came close to the window and could be examined in detail, appeared large and cottony. These were very probably snowflakes. They were seen to accelerate perceptibly in the airstream.

We are now in a position to attempt to decide what the particles were composed of. It is clear at once that we are not dealing with any sort of gas fluorescence or gas discharge, such as might be produced by the motion of the spacecraft through the ionosphere, because the lights were not visible until sunrise. They were, therefore, shining by reflected light. Solid or liquid particles are more efficient than gases in reflecting light, by factors of millions; hence the particles must be assumed to have been solid or liquid. Their sizes were probably in the millimeter range, as judged from their apparent brightness. Their densities must have been much higher than 0.1. The highest density one could reasonably assume would be about 3; in that case the particles would be accelerated at 3 centimeters per second per second, and would reach a velocity of 2 meters per second after a time of 1 minute, when they would be 50 meters away, and their velocities would be difficult to estimate accurately.

Possible sources of particles. It can be shown at this point that the particles could not have come from the sustainer (the launch vehicle), which was over 100 kilometers away at the first sighting and about 300 kilometers away at the third sighting. If accelerated over this distance at the lowest reasonable rate—namely, 3 centimeters per second per second—they would have passed the spacecraft at 135 meters per second, a velocity which cannot be reconciled with the observations. Any small particles observed at this altitude moving with low relative velocity must have been released from the spacecraft itself, and not very long before they were observed.

Another significant item is the total mass. With a separation of the order of 3 meters (10 feet), as reported by Glenn, there would be about 1 particle per 30 cubic meters; the particles apparently weighed about 3 milligrams each. If a 100-meter cube were filled with such particles, there would be about 30,000, with a total weight of about 1 kilogram. If we assume them to be 1-centimeter snowflakes, of mass 100 milligrams each, the total weight would be 30 kilograms. Since Glenn reports the field as extending widely, it is clear that the denser, smaller particles are more probable.

Among the materials known to have come off the spacecraft, only three appear to have had sufficient volume: (i) a considerable amount of paint and other materials in the area between the heat shield and the pressure vessel: (ii) water from the hydrogen peroxide thrusters; (iii) water from the cooling system.

Of these possibilities, the second can be discarded at once—first, because Glenn himself directly studied this possibility in flight by watching the output of the pitchdown thruster. He noted at that time that the jet of steam, which was visible, was entirely unlike the observed particles. In the second place, the velocity imparted to the steam as a necessary part of the thruster operation would have taken the steam away immediately.

The water from the cooling system may well have been responsible for a few of the large snowflakes which Glenn described. This water, after being used to cool the spacecraft, is released through a hole, about 2.5 centimeters across, into the space between the spacecraft bulkhead and the heat shield. This space is approximately 10 centimeters in depth and extends over the back of the heat shield, which is about 2 meters in diameter. The volume is thus roughly 3×10^5 cubic centimeters, or 300 liters. From this space, the water emerges through ten or more holes, each about 1 centimeter in diameter, spaced around the heat shield.

This system appears likely to produce snowflakes. During tests, the clogging of the 2.5-centimeter pipe by ice was a common occurrence. On the MA-6 flight this condition was indicated, by warning lights. It seems likely that vapor which got through the 2.5-centimeter pipe to the space back of the bulkhead would expand against the low pressure inside the bulkhead and cool. Ice crystals would form, but these might not leave the spacecraft for some time, because of the smallness of the ports relative to the size of the space. This situation, where a low gas pressure may be sustained for a considerable period, is very helpful in explaining the growth of snowflakes as large as 1 centimeter in diameter. It is hard to see how such flakes could grow in empty space.

As a result of the relatively low temperatures, the large size of the pipes, and the cooling and condensation back of the bulkhead, the gas pressure at the ports would be expected to be very low, so that the snowflakes would emerge with low velocities, as described by Glenn. It is easy to imagine a flake formed in this way drifting down past the spacecraft window slowly, in the manner described. As long as it was back of the heat shield, it would not encounter the airstream; but eventually, as described by Glenn, it would drift up into the airstream and then start moving up to the rear. Such particles would look like white cottony snowflakes because they were cottony snowflakes. Their color in direct sunlight would be different from their color in the shadow for the same reason that shadows at sunset are sometimes blue (*1*): the light that gets into the shadow is the light from the long twilight arc on the earth, and this is predominantly blue.

The total quantity of water available from this source is about 1 kilogram per hour. In view of the very short time that it could remain in the vicinity of the spacecraft and the relatively large total amount required to fill a reasonably large area around the spacecraft, it appears somewhat unlikely that ice was the material of the particles, though the possibility that dense ice crystals were involved cannot be entirely excluded.

Another possibility is that the particles were of solid material such as paint. Millimeter-size particles of this type would have densities of the order of 3 and masses of the order of 3 milligrams. Within a sphere of 10-meter radius, with the spacecraft at the center, there would be 140 such particles, with a total mass of about ½ gram. Within a sphere of 100-meter radius there would be particles with a total mass of about ½ kilogram. Let us suppose that particles of this type are liberated primarily at sunrise, possibly because of some cracking or stretching of the spacecraft skin that occurs at that time. In that case, liberation of not much more than 1½ kilograms of material during the whole flight would have been required for a particle-cloud of the size observed, especially if the density was somewhat less in the outer portions of the cloud. This figure is perhaps not inconsistent with the amount of material which could have flaked off. It is necessary to emphasize the extremely tenuous character of these figures, which depend on estimates of the cloud size, since the mass of material required varies with the cube of the diameter of the cloud.

To sum up, it appears that the Glenn effect is due to small solid particles, mostly about 1 millimeter in diameter, but with a few larger bodies in addition. The brightness of the majority of the particles was about −9 at a distance of 2 meters. They were probably at least as dense as water; higher densities are more likely. They were certainly not a part of the space environment but were something put in orbit as a result of the MA-6 flight. They were almost as certainly related to the spacecraft, not to the sustainer. There are two reasonable possibilities: (i) ice from the cooling system or (ii) paint or other heavy material which flaked off the spacecraft under the low pressures of the space environment.

Of these, the paint is the more probable because its higher density explains the orbital behavior better, and because we can understand why paint might be liberated only at sunrise, while ice would be liberated throughout the flight (thus, very large quantities of ice would be needed, as compared to the required amounts of paint).

In short, the most probable explanation of the Glenn effect is that it arose from millimeter-size flakes of material liberated at or near sunrise by the spacecraft.

The luminous band.   Glenn reports a luminous band on all three revolutions, at a height of 7 to 8 degrees above the horizon, tan-to-buff in color, and more luminous when the moon (then full) was up. He also states that the band was faintly and uncertainly visible when the moon was down; at such times he saw the horizon clearly silhouetted against the stars.

After the flight it was noted that many photographs of the twilight showed a luminous band parallel to the horizon. Photographs of the sky in full daylight showed a faint luminous zone extending all the way up from the horizon. The faintness of the band on daylight photographs was probably due to the automatic reduction of the exposure in strong light.

The focal length of the camera lens was 50 millimeters. The photographs were enlarged about 6.8 times for study; the scale was then about 0.17 degrees per millimeter. The height of the band seen on the enlargements was about 75 millimeters, corresponding to 12.6 degrees.

The band seen on the photographs had not been noted in the spacecraft. It was therefore thought at first to be perhaps a camera effect. However, the circular form of a camera lens makes it difficult to explain a band parallel to the horizon.

The most probable explanation of the luminous band seen on the photographs is that it results from multiple reflections within the spacecraft window system. The spacecraft has an inner and an outer window, which are inclined with respect to one another. The angle of inclination was found, by measuring the blueprints, to be about 6 degrees. Light passing through the outer window and reflected by the inner one back to the outer window, and then back again into the spacecraft, would have been turned through an angle of about 12 degrees, in a direction away from the top of the spacecraft, which in flight points near the horizon. This probably accounts for what was seen in the photographs. The existence of these reflections has been directly verified in the Mercury procedures trainer at the Mercury Control Center. It was further found, in spacecraft No. 18, that one of the reflections (there were two) was a light tan in color, like the band observed by Glenn.

Since it is a spacecraft phenomenon, the luminous band produced by reflection must also have been present in the night sky, especially after moonrise. It may have been the band observed by Glenn. The color which he remarked on may have resulted from an antireflectant coating which had been applied to the windows.

(*Addendum*. This supposition does not explain the disappearance of stars as they reach the level of the luminous band. However, let us note Glenn's comments on stars disappearing during the time between sunset and moonrise. During that time, the bright planet Venus set. It is possible that what Glenn saw was the disappearance of the reflection of Venus as it reached the level of the reflection of the horizon.)

If the band is not due to reflection, it may be possible to attribute it to some auroral phenomenon. There is a line in the auroral spectrum at 5577 angstroms. This line is known from rocket measurements to stop at 100 kilometers. A height of 100 kilometers would appear, at the spacecraft height of 250 kilometers, as a false horizon at an angular altitude of about 3 degrees. It would be green in color and would be more difficult to see after moonrise. In height and color it does not agree with the luminous band.

There are, in addition, two auroral red lines, at 6300 and 6464 angstroms, respectively, which are known to come from a height greater than any so far reached by rockets sent to observe them. From theory we estimate that they ought to be at a height of about 240 kilometers. These might be reconcilable with the observed luminous band, though they ought not to be easier to see after moonrise. They would explain the tan-to-buff color observed. On the other hand, these lines are much fainter than the line at 5577 angstroms, so it is hard to understand why they would be observed while it was missed.

On the whole, the balance of probability is that the luminous band was due to reflection in the spacecraft window. The outstanding reason for connecting the two is the belief that the inclined windows would have given a ghost image.

Glenn reports that the sunset appeared to be normal until the last moment, when the sun appeared to spread out about 10 degrees on either side, and to merge with the twilight band. Glenn specifically states that he did not see the sun as a narrow, flat object.

On the other hand, three consecutive photographs of the setting sun can be well interpreted in terms of the theoretically predicted sausage shape. In two of these there is some slight spreading of the image, evidently partly photographic and partly due to motion, and in the third the motion is considerable. All, however, appear to indicate a solar image of about $\frac{1}{2}$ degree in its greatest dimension, as required by theory, rather than a much shorter image, as would have been the case if the sun, setting, had looked as it does from the ground.

REFERENCE

1. M. MINNAERT, *Nature of Light and Color in the Open Air*, H. M. KREMER-PRIEST, Trans., K. E. BRIAN JAY, Ed. (Dover, New York, 1954), p. 136.

Martian Biology:
The Experimentalist's Approach

S. M. SIEGEL, L. A. HALPERN, C. GIUMARRO, G. RENWICK AND G. DAVIS

Recently, Salisbury, in a provocative article,[1] has constructed a speculative pic-ture of possible Martian life-forms, and of possible biogeochemical cycles in which such forms might participate.

We are in general agreement with the concepts which Salisbury has presented; as experimentalists, however, we question his reservations about the use of simulated environments. Speculation or even sound theorization notwithstanding, the sole model for life now available to us is life on Earth. Because statistical factors influence evolution, one would expect even identical planets to exhibit appreciable divergences in life-forms. Nevertheless, Earth and Mars might contain local environments in which convergent forms could arise. Thus, Salisbury suggests that the higher terrestrial plant, rather than the lower forms traditionally postulated in astronomical circles, is a good model for explaining some of the phenomena which have been held to indicate the presence of life on Mars. On the other hand, he distinguishes higher plants as plants which "universally require oxygen." This distinction suggests a divergence between the terrestrial model and its Martian counterpart which we believe may not exist.

Higher plants at low oxygen pressures

Mature air-grown plants, including *Coleus,* marigold and *Alyssum,* can survive many days under near-anaerobic conditions in spite of their aerobic history.[2] Lettuce, tomato, cucumber, bean, marigold, *Zinnia,* rye, corn, *Ageratum, Dian-*

* Union Carbide Research Institute, Tarrytown, N.Y. Reprinted from *Nature,* Vol. 197, No. 4865, pp. 329–331, January 26, 1963.

TABLE 1. Germination percentage after 3–6 days.

Kind of seed	Argon (or nitrogen)	2% oxygen + 98% argon	5% oxygen + 95% argon	Air
Lettuce	0	78	78	98
Marigold	0	33	—	57
Zinnia	0	22	—	57
Celosia	22	81	—	89
Alyssum	0	21	—	80
Portulaca	0	50	—	55
Carrot	0	50	—	32
Onion	0	65	—	69
Cucumber	17	88	96	100
Bean	0	—	60	53
Coleus	0	—	54	91
Tomato	0	—	33	91
Dianthus	7	—	50	82
Ageratum	—	—	33	84
Cabbage	0	9	71	95
Turnip	0	16	21	90
Beet	0	—	40	50
Rye	40	50	95	95
Barley	—	—	28	80
Corn	29	—	—	80
Rice	17	24	24	23

thus, Celosia, rice, turnip, broccoli and other common plants germinate well and produce sizable seedlings in an atmosphere containing 5 percent oxygen or less (ref. 3, Table 1). Several of these plants—notably cucumber, rye, corn, rice and *Celosia*—produce some seeds which are facultative anaerobes.

If our results with more than 30 higher plant species are at all representative, they indicate that, among terrestrial plants, many (perhaps most) require little oxygen; some (perhaps many) might qualify as microphilic aerobes; and a sizable minority, perhaps 10 percent, can function anaerobically.

Low oxygen-low temperature interaction

Many terrestrial plants are hardy enough to survive freezing and to grow during the more moderate phases of the extreme diurnal temperature cycles reported for Mars. The south tropical latitudes of Mars are notably mild.[4,5] Furthermore, we have found that cultivation of seeds in atmospheres containing little oxygen enhances the resistance of the seedlings to freezing and lowers the minimum temperature required for germination. Three-week-old cucumber seedlings grown from seed in air or in an atmosphere of 2 percent oxygen and 98 percent argon were cooled to $-10°C$., kept at that temperature for 1 h, and then allowed to

FIG. 1. Left: freeze-resistant cucumber seedlings grown for 3 weeks in an atmosphere of 2 percent oxygen plus 98 percent argon. Right: air-grown 3-week-old cucumber seedlings damaged by freezing (−10°C.). Both groups had been kept at −10°C. for 1 h and allowed to thaw for 1 h before being photographed.

thaw. As the air-grown seedlings thawed, they collapsed, presumably because of mechanical damage by ice crystals (Fig. 1, right). In contrast, the sturdy seedlings grown in an atmosphere of 2 percent oxygen were not damaged (Fig. 1, left). At temperatures below 10°C., cucumber seeds will germinate in air to an extent no greater than 10 percent in 10 days. If, however, the seeds are incubated in an argon atmosphere (containing only 0.005 percent oxygen) 50–90 percent germinate in 20 days at 6°–7°C., and subsequent shoot extension at a rate of 10 mm a day has been noted. Even under aerobic conditions, germination of cucumber seeds exposed daily to temperatures of −7°C. for 8 h and 23°C. for 16 h was about 30 percent in 2–3 days and 50 percent in 4 days. Cucumber is not noted for its resistance to cold.

Hardier species can germinate when exposed daily to temperatures of −7°C. for 16 h and 23°C. for 8 h. For the common 'rock garden' species, *Dianthus* and *Ageratum,* germination is 10 percent in 3–4 days in these temperature conditions. Germination for these species was doubled or tripled when the daily freezing period was shortened to 8 h.

We have already reported[6] the germination of winter rye and the development of green winter rye seedlings under a synthetic atmosphere which simulates in most respects the atmosphere believed to exist on Mars,[5] using a temperature-cycle of $+20°C$. (day) and $-10°$. (night). In one respect our synthetic atmosphere differs considerably from the real Martian atmosphere in that we added 1–2 percent by weight of water in the soil, which results in a substantial partial pressure of water in the enclosed atmosphere. The best available information indicates a much lower (perhaps 2 orders of magnitude) average water content in the Martian atmosphere than is present under our conditions. However, it must be borne in mind that astronomical observations of the Martian atmosphere as a whole would not, in all probability, reveal the presence of localized bodies of water, or of microclimates at the surface of Mars which are much higher in water content than for the total Martian atmosphere.

Xerophytes

Xerophytes are also markedly conditioned by their gaseous environment. Only a few specimens, of *Euphorbia clandestina* and *Gymnocalycium friederickii,* were tested, but the results were none the less striking.

In this experiment, specimens were grown in 16–1. jars either in air or in a synthetic atmosphere of volume composition as follows: oxygen 0.09 percent; carbon dioxide, 0.24 percent; argon, 1.39 percent; and nitrogen, 98.28 percent.

This gas mixture was used at a total pressure of 0.1 atmosphere (after De Vaucouleurs,[5] who provides a good general treatise on aereography). The plants were placed in a 1 : 1 mixture of potting soil and 'Perl-lome' ('Perl-lome,' a product of Certified Industrial Products, Inc., Hillside, New Jersey, is a derivative of perlite. De Vaucouleurs suggests that a felsitic rhyolite covers the Martian surface, and perlite is such a volcanic mineral). The water content of the soil and 'Perl-lome' mixture was about 1–2 percent by weight.

After about a month at 25°C., the jars were transferred to an unheated greenhouse. Temperatures were recorded and observations on plant conditions were made during January, February and March 1962. The mean daily maxima for these months were $+5°C.$, $-2°C.$ and $+8°C.$, respectively. The mean nightly minima were $-9°C.$, $-12°C.$ and 0°C.

By the end of February the four *Euphorbia* specimens grown in air were dead, but the four grown in the synthetic atmosphere were normal in appearance —green and erect by contrast with the yellow, shrivelled group grown in air. At the end of March, only one of the plants in the synthetic atmosphere appeared normal. The remaining three were no longer erect, although they retained green coloration and were not desiccated. Six *Gymnocalycium* plants were grown in each atmosphere. Three of those grown in air survived through February, and all those grown in the synthetic atmosphere still appeared normal at the end of

TABLE 2. Changes in weight and size of xerophytes under experimental atmospheric conditions.

Height (cm)			Diameter (cm)			Fresh weight (g)			Dry wt. (g)
Initial	Final	Change	Initial	Final	Change	Initial	Final	Change	
Euphorbia*, grown in air									
11.4	10.1	−1.3	1.0	0.5	−0.5	12.0	5.4	−6.6	4.7
Euphorbia*, grown in synthetic atmosphere									
11.6	11.9	+0.3	1.0	1.1	+0.1	12.0	12.5	+0.5	5.5
Gymnocalycium†, grown in air									
						13.9	5.2	−8.7	2.2
Gymnocalycium†, grown in synthetic atmosphere									
						14.5	6.3	−8.2	1.7

* Four specimens in each atmosphere.
† Six specimens in each atmosphere.

February. During March, the remaining plants grown in air died, while only one of those grown in the synthetic atmosphere died.

After 3 months of cold, the plants were examined and analysed. The *Euphorbia* plants grown in air had lost height, diameter and fresh weight (Table 2). Plants grown in the synthetic atmosphere showed a gain in these measurements, and all had retained some green coloration, even though only one out of four was scored as 'normal.' All the *Gymnocalycium* plants lost weight, regardless of the atmosphere in which they were grown.

Comparative chemical and biochemical tests made on *Euphorbia* plants grown in the two atmospheres revealed an interesting pattern of similarities and differences. Spectrophotometric determination of chlorophylls[7] in acetone extracts of the leaves (which form an apical whorl) showed that none were present in the group of dead plants that had been grown in air. Chlorophylls *a* and *b* were present in the usual 3 : 1 ratio in extracts from plants grown in the synthetic atmosphere. Longitudinal sections (3–5 mm) from the aerial portions of the plants were tested by immersion in several common reagents. Tissues from the two groups were similarly treated. Marked differences were observed in peroxidase activity and in the results of non-carbohydrate aldehyde determinations. (A mixture of 10^{-3} M pyrogallol and 10^{-3} M hydrogen peroxide in phosphate buffer (*p*H 4.5) was used as the peroxidase developer.) Even sharper were the distinctions in the results of tests for reducing sugar, starch, phosphorylase activity (tissues were immersed in 1 percent glucose-1-phosphate at *p*H 6.6 for 1 h at 25°C., then stained with KI_3 [after S. Siegel, *Bot. Gaz.,* **114,** 139 {1952}], and indole; all results were negative for the air-grown group and positive for the test group. Determinations of element composition for the two groups reflected no striking differences. [The determinations were made by Micro-Tech Laboratories, Skokie, Ill.])

TABLE 3. Germination of seeds in water vapour in air at 25°C.

Kind of seed	Germination after 13 days (percent)	Root-length after 13 days (mm)
Phlox	52	7.3
Cucumber	37	7.7
Marigold	18	1.0
Portulaca	63	4.9
Alyssum	26	8.3
Turnip	88	16.5
Carrot	40	18.3
Celosia	100	18.2
Rye	100	30.5

TABLE 4. Germination of rye in experimental atmosphere in water vapour at 25°C.

Incubation time (days)	No. Germinated	Germinated (percent)	Longest roots (mm)
1	6	4.5	1
4	45	33.8	5
5	100	75.3	15

Germination without liquid water

Xerophytism is a relative condition, and it seems reasonable to suppose that plants other than typical desert forms may be able to adapt to dry conditions. The seed, generally a rich source of hydrophilic colloids, is well known for its imbibitional powers. Accordingly, some experiments were carried out in which dry seeds were supported in closed jars, in air at a pressure of 75–125 mm of mercury, above a source of liquid water. Germination was slow as compared with usual rates, but the results (Table 3) show that a number of species can germinate and produce seedlings without difficulty under such conditions. When winter rye was placed in the synthetic atmosphere at a total pressure of 75 mm of mercury, 150 mm above a source of liquid water, germination was reasonably prompt and considerable root growth was noted after several days (Table 4).

Other factors

In our laboratory we are also investigating the effects of substratum and of ultra-violet radiation on plant growth under conditions of low temperature and low oxygen supply. We have observed that remarkably high levels of ultra-violet radiation are sometimes needed to suppress the growth of higher plants (energy of 10^8 ergs/cm^2 is only marginally effective as an inhibitor of growth in bean embryos).

Animal forms

Most of our investigative efforts have been concerned with the flowering plant. Other plants also show promising behaviour at low oxygen-levels. The fungus *Alternaria* and gametophytes of the fern *Pteridium* have been grown in an atmosphere of 5 percent oxygen and 95 percent argon.

Among animal forms, the ciliate *Colpoda* grows in hay-infusion cultures prepared and maintained under the synthetic atmosphere. HeLa cells, which can grow for 4 days under strictly anaerobic conditions more rapidly than in air, are being examined for adaptability (including clonal selection) to anaerobic culture of indefinite duration at low temperature in media of high osmotic concentration. *Planaria* have thus far shown rigidly aerobic behaviour, but they have been maintained for as long as 23 days in 5 percent oxygen and 95 percent argon and 16 days in 2 percent oxygen and 98 percent argon, as compared with 93 days in air.

The most striking results have been obtained with the common brine shrimp, *Artemia salina*. In sea-water (salinity 3 percent) or diluted sea-water (salinity 1 percent) in both liquid and agar media, active, viable *Nauplius* larvæ have been hatched in approximately equal percentages in air, in air reduced to 0.03 atmosphere, and in the synthetic gas mixture of 0.1 atmospheres. Typical values for hatching, based on findings with several hundred eggs per trial range from 35 to 45 percent in 2 days.

It seems likely that marine organisms could adapt to the requirements of existence in a variety of synthetic environments—existence in a medium which is 'dry' in the physiological sense and has a depressed freezing point.[8] If, as in the case of *Artemia,* such organisms were also facultative anaerobes or near anaerobes, their prospects for survival would be good indeed.

Members of other invertebrate phyla also possess unusual ranges of tolerance to low pressure, low oxygen, and low temperature. The small black ant, *Monomorium minutum,* retains general activity and positive phototaxy after more than 15 h in 1 percent oxygen and 99 percent argon. The nematode *Cephalobus* remains active indefinitely under anaerobic conditions or at total pressure of 0.03 atmosphere and shows remarkable tolerances to freezing and to salinity well in excess of that of sea-water.

Conclusions

Our results show that complex terrestrial organisms can survive and grow under conditions which constitute an extreme departure in one or more respects from the normal terrestrial environment. Of particular importance was the finding that tolerance of plants to low temperatures could be conditioned in a favourable manner by synthetic atmospheres low in oxygen. It would be reasonable to expect other combinations of stress factors to give rise to unusual and exciting biological responses.

While it is impossible to project these findings on to present-day attempts to anticipate the nature of life elsewhere in the solar system, it is reasonable to conclude that the 'plasticity' of organisms as we recognize them is far greater than the teachings of modern biology indicate. Thus, whatever environments may be encountered during future explorations of the solar system there is every prospect that those which are not too extreme relative to Earth, for example, those expected on Mars may well support forms of life that we could recognize readily.

REFERENCES

1. SALISBURY, F. B., *Science, 136,* 17 (1962); this article contains an excellent bibliography.
2. SIEGEL, S. M., *Physiol. Plantarum, 14,* 554 (1961).
3. SIEGEL, S. M., and HALPERN, L. A., *Physiol. Plantarum* (in the press). SIEGEL, S. M., ROSEN, L. A., and RENWICK, G., *ibid., 15,* 304 (1962).
4. KIESS, C. C., and LASSOVZSKY, K., *The Known Physical Characteristics of the Moon and Planets,* Publ. No. *ARDC-TR*-58–41 (*ASTIA* Doc. No. *AD* 115–617) (Air Research and Development Command, Andrews Air Force Base, Washington, 1958).
5. DE VAUCOULEURS, G., *Physics of the Planet Mars* (Faber and Faber, London, 1953).
6. SIEGEL, S. M., ROSEN, L. A., and GIUMARRO, C., *Proc. U.S. Nat. Acad. Sci., 48,* 725 (1962).
7. LONG, C. (edit.), *Biochemists Handbook,* 1029 (Van Nostrand, Princeton, 1961).
8. SCHMIDT, K., and ALLEE, W. C., *Ecological Animal Geography* (Wiley, New York, 1949).

Index